Reader Series
in Library and Information Science

Published *Readers* in the series are:

Reader in Library Administration. 1969.
Paul Wasserman and Mary Lee Bundy.

Reader in Research Methods for Librarianship. 1970.
Mary Lee Bundy and Paul Wasserman.

Reader in the Academic Library. 1970.
Michael M. Reynolds.

Reader in Library Services and the Computer. 1971.
Louis Kaplan.

Reader in American Library History, 1971.
Michael H. Harris.

Reader in Classification and Descriptive Cataloging. 1972.
Ann. F. Painter.

Reader in Technical Services. 1972.
Edmond L. Applebaum.

Reader in Medical Librarianship. 1973.
Winifred Sewell

Reader in Medical Librarianship

edited by

Winifred Sewell

1973

Library of Congress Catalog Card Number: 72-86634
ISBN: 0-910972-27-3

Published by NCR/Microcard Editions,
901 26th Street, N.W.
Washington, D.C. 20037

Printed in the United States of America

Foreword

Unlike many other academic disciplines, librarianship has not yet begun to exploit the contributions of the several disciplines toward the study of its own issues. Yet the literature abounds with material germane to its concerns. Too frequently the task of identifying, correlating, and bringing together material from innumerable sources is burdensome, time consuming or simply impossible. For a field whose stock in trade is organizing knowledge, it is clear that the job of synthesizing the most essential contributions from the elusive sources in which they are contained is overdue. This then is the rationale for the series, *Readers in Library and Information Science*.

The *Readers in Library and Information Science* will include books concerned with various broad aspects of the field's interests. Each volume will be prepared by a recognized student of the topic covered, and the content will embrace material from the many different sources from the traditional literature of librarianship as well as from outside the field in which the most salient contributions have appeared. The objectives of the series will be to bring together in convenient form the key elements required for a current and comprehensive view of the subject matter. In this way it is hoped that the core of knowledge, essential as the intellectual basis for study and understanding, will be drawn into focus and thereby contribute to the furtherance of professional education and professional practice in the field.

Paul Wasserman
Series Editor

Contents

III

ORGANIZATION OF A MEDICAL LIBRARY FOR SERVICE

Collection of Materials

Organization of Materials

Retrieval of Materials

IV

TYPES OF MEDICAL LIBRARY

Hospital Libraries

Medical School Libraries

V

MEDICAL LIBRARY NETWORKS

National Library of Medicine Support and Regional Medical Libraries

Regional Medical Programs

Introduction

Each kind of librarianship partakes of the general elements of librarianship, and each has a flavor all its own. This book is intended to present the flavor and philosophy of medical librarianship to the student or novice. If it gives a new perspective to some practicing librarians or administrators in health science organizations, so much the better.

If it were ever possible to think of medical libraries in isolation, it is so no longer. One must conceive of them as part of a medical system, and indeed as part of a system that goes beyond the narrow confines of medicine as practiced by a single physician for a single patient. It extends into the health sciences as represented by dentists, pharmacists, nurses, veterinarians, medical technologists, medical associates and dozens of others, some not yet possessing a clear identity. It includes research, education and practice. In addition to the clinical sciences, the system involves the preclinical ones and preventive medicine and public health. Increasingly, socioeconomic considerations have moved into the mainstream of medicine.

People in the United States have become concerned with the cost of illness and the deficiencies of our health record in comparison with that of other countries. From the point of view of the nation, we have come to regard health as a national resource, and from that of the individual, we have designated it a right. If it is a national resource, then information on health should be communicated as efficiently as possible throughout the nation by whatever networks are necessary. If health is a right, we need to reexamine the right of the layman to health information and the role of the library in transmitting it.

It was recognition of health as a national resource in the mid-1960 Report of the President's Commission on Heart Disease, Cancer and Stroke (deBakey Report) which led to two pieces of legislation. The National Library of Medicine, through the Medical Library Assistance Act, was enabled to distribute funds for advances in technology and research in medical information handling, education of medical librarians, scholarly compilations and translations, the improvement of medical library facilities and resources and the establishment of a network of regional medical libraries. The other legislation established Regional Medical Programs. In a grass-roots approach, these Programs have made money available for continuing education and support of medical care in which medical libraries have participated. Together, these programs have had a powerful influence on medical librarianship.

Even without these recent trends, there have always been elements in medicine which cause medical librarianship to differ from other kinds of librarianship. As an example, the individuality of the living organism leads to a great deal more redundancy in publication in the biological sciences than there is in the physical sciences. The lack of precision in biology has also led it to rely much more heavily on the use of statistics in its publications than is necessary with the physical sciences. Vocabularies of information systems in medicine are dependent upon terminology which is defined descriptively rather than quantitatively.

In addition, as Dr. Orr points out (page 65): "Large organized programs of research are the exception and the technical report, which plays so important a role in engineering and in areas of the physical sciences that are oriented toward technical development, is a relatively unimportant channel for biomedical communication. Biomedical research, moreover, is conducted mainly in academic institutions and is rooted in individual intiative. For these reasons, new forms of communication and new types of services that serve other scientific communities effectively will not necessarily be appropriate to, or of comparable usefulness in, the biomedical sciences."

Besides participating in the medical system, the health sciences library is a part of a larger library system. Since this volume is addressed to librarians, it is assumed that they are well aware of all of the useful interfaces between health science libraries and research, special and public libraries.

Long before the President's Commission report, medical libraries were leaders in innovation. John Shaw Billings, the founder of what has become the National Library of Medicine, was an innovator *par excellence*. Work on MEDLARS (Medical Literature Analysis and Retrieval System), the pioneering effort in use of a computer for publication of a major index and for search of a major body of scientific literature, had its origins in a research project on problems of medical indexing including the possibility of using machine methods, conducted by Dr. Sanford Larkey at the Welch Medical Library in Baltimore in the late 1940's.[1] The availability of money to support research and development in the late 1970's made possible creation of tools and ideas in medical libraries which are useful to other parts of librarianship.

One may look at the health sciences library system from a number of points of view. We have chosen to start with the environment of which it is a part—the functions of education, practice and research in the health sciences and their dependence on communication and the library. Then we have turned to the medical librarian, as the key element in the library component of the system, and have presented his current characteristics and professional activities. Next we examine the anatomy and physiology of the medical library, the elements of its structure and function, particularly as they are influenced by the field of medicine. Turning from the microcosm within the individual medical library, we move to the various kinds of library that are most important in today's system. And finally, we review the total system as it is reflected in regional and national networks.

To select papers which fit into this framework was a problem, not because of the dearth of publication on the precise subjects of interest, but because of the number of excellent articles illustrating each point. We endeavored to find papers which were not only descriptive and instructive, but also presented issues and stimulated the student to think about them. In the last analysis, the choice was very personal, bringing in favorites which I have enjoyed reading and discussing with students.

Because of rapid change, many important early works are so outdated that we have chosen to use more recent papers which have built on them. The vast majority of the articles selected were published during 1969, 1970, 1971 and early 1972 (29 or 71%). Only five appeared before 1967. A quarter were published in 1971 or 1972 and half in 1970 or later.

To all of the publishers who have so generously allowed us to reprint from their publications, we are deeply grateful. To the authors who responded to our requests both cooperatively and enthusiastically go my thanks for making work on the *Reader* a pleasant experience. And finally, to the many people who have contributed to the field of medical librarianship through articles which I wished to include in this volume but could not, thank you for making the task so stimulating.

Cabin John, Maryland
April 10, 1972

Winifred Sewell

---

[1] The National Library of Medicine Index Mechanization Project, July 1, 1958–June 30, 1960; Council on Library Resources, Inc. Grant No. 28. (Washington, D.C., National Library of Medicine, 1961), pp. 1–7.

I

THE ENVIRONMENT OF MEDICAL LIBRARIES

To understand medical libraries today, one must first understand medicine and then the nature of biomedical communication. Both medicine and its modes of communication are changing as is apparent throughout this volume.

The rapid increase and change in knowledge with which the medical librarian must contend are in no way unique to the medical field, and perhaps some of the other characteristics of the biomedical discipline enumerated in this book cause problems for medical libraries that are little different from those in other kinds of library. But, taken together, the elements form a unique biomedical system which must be studied and understood if the biomedical librarian is to perform at his best.

Education, Practice and Research

Some aspects of the nature of medicine and its communication make its librarianship differ qualitatively from that of other disciplines. The facts that medicine is concerned with research, education, and practice in more or less equal proportions and that a single individual may perform two or even all three of these functions lead to a complexity in library service requests. The different functions require special kinds of collections and even varying availability of materials.

To reduce the manpower shortage, we need to find means of shortening the medical education process and of using people with various backgrounds and training in the health science professions. The librarian will be called on directly or indirectly to assist in the effort.

Increased emphasis on health care delivery brings with it a whole complex of different demands on the library system. Whereas the medical school library has been predominant in the past, libraries are now called for in every hospital, so that recorded knowledge can have direct impact on patient care.

Though research may be less in the forefront of the health care picture than it was ten years ago, medical libraries are still trying to achieve in their budgets increases proportional to the funds made available to other parts of the organizations they serve. Resources for education and health care delivery given to an institution without provision for library support can cause the same sort of imbalance in the future as did funds poured into academic research projects in the past.

Tomorrow's Medical Student

by Daniel H. Funkenstein

While Dr. Funkenstein looks primarily at the student, his discussion summarizes trends in medicine for the past sixty years and sets the stage for our thinking about its future and the needs of today's students who will be tomorrow's practitioners. Delivery of health care to all segments of the community will require an extension of library service.

Tomorrow's medical student must be viewed in the context of both yesterday's and today's students. In this analysis, the students now in medical school will be compared to those now in college who aspire to medical careers. One can go no further than this because we do not know what will come after them.

During the 20th century, medicine has gone through four eras, and in each of them the principal role of the physician has been distinctly different.

THE GENERAL PRACTICE ERA 1910-1935

Modern medicine dates from the Flexner Report in 1910 which brought science and clinical research into the medical school. Preclinical science was taught in the first two years and, although not much was known, what was known was directly relevant to clinical medicine. The ideal physician was in the great tradition of Osler. He was a general practitioner, very much interested in science, in the personal and family components of the patient's illness, and not too concerned about whether the entire community was getting care. Although he did devote a certain amount of his time, without charge, to taking care of the poor, this was seen as a charity endeavor. During this era, the chief role of the physician was that of general practitioner and his social responsibility was defined as the art of medicine, meaning attention to the social, emotional, and family aspects of the individual patient's illness. The pragmatic use of science was included in this definition but was less

Objective	Generalized Education
Curriculum	All Students study same subjects; Science in first two years related to Clinical Medicine
Extracurricular	Sports, fraternities, dating
Faculty	PATIENT CARE and TEACHING; Research
Student-Characteristics	Student-Clinician
Student-Faculty Relationship	Master-apprentice; Junior Colleague
Role Model	Clinician in Osler Tradition
Summer	Vacation; Work in Hospital
Family Background	Professional or affluent
POSTGRADUATE EDUCATION	Internship: Rotating, then practice 1910–1935 Residency: Specialized 1935–1959

SOURCE: Reprinted from *Potential Educational Services from a National Biomedical Communications Network* edited by Cheves McC. Smythe, pp. 50–62. Report of a Conference held February 25-26, 1969, National Library of Medicine, Bethesda, Maryland. Sponsored by the Council of Academic Societies of the Association of American Medical Colleges under Contract No. NLM 69-8 with the National Institutes of Health, Department of Health, Education, and Welfare, National Library of Medicine.

important than the art of medicine. The characteristics of this period are diagrammed on page 7.

THE SPECIALIZED PRACTICE ERA 1935–1959

In the late thirties, medicine began to change. More scientific information became available as the result of astute clinical observation and research, largely at the bedside and in the operating room. Certain doctors began to develop great skill in certain aspects of patient care, and it became obvious that no one individual could know enough to be a highly competent physician. Thus began the rise of specialization. The boards for the certification of specialists were founded, residencies in specialties became the order of the day, and the decline of the general practitioner began. The era of clinical specialization resulted in improved technical aspects of diagnosis and treatment, but the increased emphasis on knowledge resulted in less attention to the art of medicine. Then, too, most patients with complicated problems were referred by general practitioners to specialists who referred them back to the referring physician who continued to practice the art of medicine. The role of the physician changed to that of clinical specialist, and the social responsibility of the physician was defined as a high degree of competence in his chosen specialty. The characteristics of this era are diagrammed below:

COMPETENCE — Specialization with increased skills based on clinical experience and clinical research

Pragmatic Use of Science

Art of Medicine
prevention by biological techniques

ROLE MODEL:
Clinical Specialist

SOCIAL RESPONSIBILITY:
Competence in a specialty

THE SCIENTIFIC-TECHNOLOGICAL ERA 1959–1970

In 1948, medical schools, society, and the government decided that in order to solve many medical problems, research in the sciences underlying medicine must be increased. This resulted in the founding of the National Institutes of Health, the availability of foundation funds for research, and the campaigns to raise funds for medical research by societies such as the March of Dimes and the Heart Fund. Vast sums were expended for research in medical schools, and with the discovery of DNA in 1953, rapid advances began in molecular biology. It is naive to think that this change was due to the availability of government funds alone. It was related to the convergence of many forces that can only be understood in the term that the "time was ripe" for this development. Although clinical medicine benefitted from this research, the more spectacular advances were made in the laboratory sciences unrelated to clinical medicine. This was justified on the basis of promising great advances in "curing" diseases in the future. The reaction to the launching of Sputnik in 1958 caused an acceleration of the research trend and many opportunities became available for students at all levels to do research. The increased research in the basic sciences became not only a part of the medical school but also a part of the hospitals affiliated with the medical schools. The basic sciences became more basic and were being increasingly taught in other parts of the university. The preclinical sciences were no longer preclinical. Graduate schools in the same universities as the medical schools also pursued this type of research, whereas in the previous era, all medical research was confined to the medical school and its hospitals.

In background, the students came from professional and educated people. After internship they went on to a residency and many to a postdoctoral fellowship. By 1965 about 50 percent of the interns in the United States had such plans.

As a consequence of these changes, much of the science taught in the first two years of medical school bore little relevance to clinical medicine. It was now necessary to become a scientist and to do research to become a good physician. The attitudes, methods of approach, and new knowledge of the scientist improved the diagnosis and treatment of disease. The role of the physician was that of the academician who spent 30 percent of his time with hospitalized patients often with rare diseases and 70 percent of his time in basic research with little interest in the art of medicine or the community.

The social responsibility of the physician was to be a scientist doing research. The characteristics of this era are summarized in the following.

Objective	Highly Specialized Scientist: RESEARCH, Patient Care; teaching ACADEMIC MEDICINE
Curriculum	1. All students study same curriculum 2. Research in free time 3. Division of first two years into basic sciences with little relevance to medicine taught by basic sciences faculty 4. Preclinical sciences relevant to medicine taught by clinical faculty 5. Omission of some areas of preclinical sciences relevant to medicine
Faculty	RESEARCH: Consultation; teaching
Student-Characteristics	Student-Scientist
Student-Faculty Relationships	Distant except on research project; proselytizing; Dean of Students and Psychiatrists
Summers	Research
Role Model	Physician-Scientist in Academic Medicine 30% time with patients; 70% research
Family Background	Professional, educated, affluent, and middle class
POSTGRADUATE EDUCATION	Internship: Straight Residency: Specialized Postdoctoral Research in Basic Sciences

THE COMMUNITY ERA 1970–

The dawning of the community medicine era is now here and is the result of the convergence of many forces. There is a tremendous concern for the community and for the delivery of medical care. Other forces include demands by students for more attention to the admission of minority group members and the delivery of medical care to all segments of society; the demands by the community for more, better, and different health services; the government of financing of health care by the Medicare and Medicaid programs; and the changing emphasis by foundations away from research in natural sciences to medical education and the delivery of health care. The administration of most medical schools is concerned with trying to get the delivery of more medical care by various ways, but most of the faculty is still involved in the scientific research area, and patient care is concentrated in the hospital. The curriculum is becoming less specialized in most medical schools. Sixty are changing, and 40 more are said to be ready to change. Extracurricular activities are not sports but working in slums and settlement houses. The students are rejecting the medical academician as a role model. A large number also reject the practitioners in the community because of their conception of his lack of concern for giving care to all segments of society. The features of this era are summarized on page 10.

TODAY'S MEDICAL STUDENTS

The impressions to be described are based on data gathered from a large group of medical applicants to and men admitted to medical schools at such universities as Harvard, Vanderbilt, Colorado, and the University of Michigan. The years mentioned refer to the expected date of medical school graduation for the cohorts described.

Among the changes from the late 1950s to the class of 1971 are almost total absence of premedical concentration in college, a large increase in biology majors, a very large increase in chemistry majors, a few physical scientists such as engineers and physicists and mathematicians, and not so many students in the humanities. The students

Objective	*Administration*	Delivery of medical care
	Faculty	Scientific research; patient care concentrated in hospital
	Students	Delivery of Medical Care; Student Health Organization; Student AMA
Curriculum	Multitracked; specialization in medical school	
Extracurricular	Working in slums; settlement houses, politics	
Faculty	RESEARCH: Consultation, teaching	
Student-Characteristics	Marked Diversity with common core of interests in patients and delivery of care in community at large	
Role Model	Rejection of medical school professors and community practitioners. Generation Gap	
Summer Activities	Summer projects in slums; hospital work	
Family Background	Educated and affluent. Plans for Disadvantaged	
POSTGRADUATE TRAINING	Internship: Straight: Eliminated?	
	Residency: Shortened due to specialized medical education	
	Payment for services rendered	
	Programs for delivery of care	

who have been coming to medical schools recently are highly specialized individuals.

Of the class that entered in 1958, about 5 percent had had graduate courses in the sciences but ten years later, toward the end of the scientific era, almost 25 percent of the students admitted to medical school had studied science at the graduate level. The conclusion that is about to be described that entering medical students' interest in science is waning is derived from such background data as these. In addition there is the political fact that the draft of graduate students in sciences has come about, the lack of any increase in science funds, and the change in emphasis by the foundations and the government toward funds from scientific research to the areas of health care and of education.

The aspirations of applicants to medical school have changed. A tremendous number now seek a career in practice in the community. A study of a pool of about 1,500 applicants to Harvard, most of whom are now in medical school, shows that in ten years there has been a shift from a majority pointing to academic medicine to less than 5 percent recently. One gathers the same impressions from students in colleges all over the country. Even the students with Ph.D.s and recent recipients of other degrees who come to medical school want now to practice in the community. The physics Ph.D. and the molecular biologists are coming in large numbers to medical schools or to urban studies and city planning. Their hope is not to apply their science to biological research. There is a marked decrease at Harvard, MIT, Yale, and Princeton in graduate school applicants in the sciences for next year. In biochemistry, for example, the application rate is about half of the previous levels. Conversely, there is a 2,000 percent increase in applicants for urban studies and city planning at MIT. Applicants for the study of economics have doubled as is true of government. The emphasis is again on the community.

Some deplore this shift of attitude. The natural sciences are facing difficult times. Dr. Weisner of MIT thinks the changes are good. On the other hand, there are enormous problems in the society. The attraction of these issues for the best minds of our time should be seen as a salutary change and a source of optimism.

It should be noted that psychology is not prominent among the areas of concentration for the large number of medical school applicants who have majored in the social and behavioral sciences.

CHANGING AREAS OF MAJOR INTERESTS

The results of areas of interest tests are also changing. When students are asked to indicate primary interests in either people and service, science, or human behavior, most will check only one major interest. In the class entering Harvard in 1958 interest in people and service was high and in science low. Five years later this had reversed, with interest in science dominant. In other words, the students were responsive to the changed environment of the medical school in the scientific era. This incidence of attitude has persisted until very recently, when interest in science began to wane rapidly, interest in people and service to increase slowly, and interest in human behavior to soar.

There is another change in today's students. In past years their interests were relatively pure or narrowly focused. Those who were interested in science were interested in science, or those who cared about people and service cared only about people and service. Today, however, we find students who combine science with an interest in human behavior or combine being a scientist with being a person who wants to work with people.

The increased interest in human behavior is not in psychiatry. The number of students prepared in psychology or psychiatry had increased in the sixties, but there is a dramatic fall in these interests in the students now entering medical school. As sociology, social psychology, anthropology, economics, and government are all thought to be more relevant to the practice of medicine in the community, these areas have become attractive. Psychiatry is not included.

In the future there will be greater diversity among students. They will come from all segments of society, and all medical schools are making a large effort to find such students now—not only blacks but from all those backgrounds which have become conspicuous by their absence.

In preparation for the study of medicine, there will be increased interest in the social and behavioral sciences, economics, sociology, and cultural anthroplogy. There will be decreased interest in biological and physical sciences not directly relevant to clinical problems. There will be a marked shift in biology in college, and the balance between molecular biology, organ systems, ecology, and ethology, will change. Note that the Ford Foundation is now going to put a very large sum into chairs in ethology in colleges. At Harvard there has been almost nothing in biology but molecular biology, but now courses in ethology, ecology, and organ systems control are being introduced.

In terms of career plans, there will be increased numbers in family practice. This will continue to be the internist and the pediatrician rather than the new family physician, but these specialists will become more concerned with the role of public health than the typical bedside clinician of today. In our school last year, the 29 students in the first-year class who have indicated a career interest in public health indicate that greater numbers will seek careers in this long-neglected field. There will also be increased numbers interested in medical administration. A large number of students now indicate a desire to manage the hospitals in which they find many faults. There will be increased use of paramedical and allied health personnel. The decreasing interest in scientific research has been mentioned.

The community orientation will involve the delivery of medical care to all segments of society, emphasis on prevention, and much more concern with politics.

Relations with the medical school faculty and administration will be marked by representation on committees evaluating the teaching and actions of the faculty and administration. Teaching will improve as a result, as will counseling and guidance. Closer student-faculty relations can be expected but in quite different roles with rejection of the *in loco parentis* concept.

As for intellectual characteristics, the prediction that there will be less emphasis on scientific attitude and emphasis on action before reasoned analysis is based on what is being seen in students in college and in freshmen medical students. Responses to hypothetical questions stress action rather than an analysis of the causes of what is happening or the gathering of facts on which to base an action program. The requirement of analysis of a problem is rejected as researching an issue to death. The word "passion" is constantly used and a passion for change will frequently be based on the trial and error method. (It will be a great challenge to clinicians to change this viewpoint when these students get into the clinical years.) There will be less interest in research and less interest in basic sciences not directly relevant to clinical problems, and the sciences—biological, physical, social, and behavioral—will be used more pragmatically. Students would like to get through school and out into the world more quickly. There is a tremendous increase in the interest in and familiarity with the use of computers, TV, and movies. Students are suggesting that these can be used as learning tools and applied to the expansion of medical schools.

Revision of the medical care system so that access to care is based on need rather than on finances and little interest in fees for service with preference for prepayment plans, salaried positions, and less interest in material things for themselves—all mark economic attitudes. Whether these will change when their responsibilities increase remains to be seen.

Increased concern for the emotional, social, and family aspects of care is striking. This is epitomized by the heated criticisms of patient management in the teaching hospitals' outpatient departments. The criticisms are not accompanied by solutions.

High on any list of liabilities of this new breed of students is the propensity for action before reasoned analysis. The lack of interest in the scientific aspect of medicine carries over to lack of interest in the scientific aspects of community programs. It is hard to get cooperation with the public health people and others already at work in these areas of their concern. Research and the basic sciences are seen as irrelevant. However, only a very small percentage, about 2 percent, feel that our established institutions, whether medical or otherwise, will never work and that their ends justify their tactics. This small percentage is supported by a much larger number than anyone thinks, and this is a grave danger in many, many areas.

DEMANDS

The medical students are demanding (a) increased admission of minority group students, (b) improvement in teaching, learning, and facilitation of their personal development, (c) attention to the emotional, social, and family aspects in the care of the individual patient, (d) delivery of medical care to all segments of society without regard to finances, (e) attention to and consultation with the community about the preventive aspects of medicine through social action involving housing, education, and employment, and (f) a voice in their own educations and the policies of the medical schools. About 90 percent of the many medical students to whom such questions have been put come out with answers like these. The students agree with this kind of program, and it should not be confused with the issues raised by those activists who would be destructive. Recognition that we must produce more physicians and we must do something about the medical care is imperative. Otherwise, the scientific part of our establishment is apt to topple down. The faculty is still in the scientific and technological era, but the students are not. The shift in attitude from seniors to the sophomores is impressive, but the real split comes with the freshmen and the students coming in. The foundations are identifying with this last group. They are putting their money into the delivery of care and into medical education to try and produce more physicians. The government is still split but moving toward concern with distribution of care. These divergent goals produce tremendous tension in any social system.

To save the scientific and research part of medicine, better ways to deliver medical care must be found. The students have ideas to which attention must and will be paid. Many of these students are going to go into the community for a while, and they are going to try to solve these particular problems. That this is another pendulum swing, like the swing away from the clinicians to science in the fifties and sixties (which was a great gain), does not minimize its significance and the fact that it must be dealt with. The scientific aspect of medicine cannot be abandoned and our students, in their great surge to change things, cannot be allowed to lose out on becoming very competent and very scientific physicians.

ABOUT THE AUTHOR—Dr. Daniel H. Funkenstein is Director, Program for Research in Medical Education, Department of Psychiatry, Assistant Professor of Psychiatry, and Consultant on Studies in Medical Education, Harvard Medical School. His M.D. is from Tulane University and he interned in Cincinnatti General Hospital. He also served as Surgery Intern and Resident at Barnes Hospital in St. Louis. He has been Director of Psychiatry at the Massachusetts Mental Health Center and a Consultant at the Brockton Veterans Administration Hospital.

Among his professional assignments is that of Executive Secretary, Dean's Subcommittee on Neuropsychiatry, Boston Veterans Administration Program. He is a member of the American Psychiatric Association, the American Psychosomatic Society and the American Psychoanalytic Association.

Higher Education and the Nation's Health, Policies for Medical and Dental Education, A Special Report and Recommendations

by The Carnegie Commission on Higher Education

This paper is the summary of a more detailed report which it introduced. The manpower shortage to which it is addressed is likely to bring about changes in education and function of many health professionals with consequent revision of demands on health science libraries. The role of the health science librarian will be affected whether or not all the reforms here recommended are carried out.

1. MAJOR THEMES

"Life . . . and the Pursuit of Happiness"

Americans deserve and can afford better health care. We have the highest standard of living, but not the highest standard of life—as measured by infant mortality and average life expectancy. A number of countries surpass us. In fact, in comparison with other nations, we are losing. Better health care is clearly a high national priority.

The Four Components of Better Health Care

To improve health care requires:

- More and better health manpower
- More and better health care facilities
- Better financing arrangements for the health care of the population
- Better planning for health manpower and health care delivery

This report is concerned with more and better health manpower, particularly at the level of doctors and dentists. The Commission believes that the provision of highly skilled health manpower is a special responsibility of higher education. The adequacy of health care facilities, however, is the responsibility, not of universities and colleges, but of federal, state, and local health authorities. As to the financing of individual care, the report assumes that as the result of public and private efforts, some form of health insurance will be available to all American citizens within this decade. Planning is partly a responsibility of higher education, particularly the planning for health personnel, but mostly of public agencies.

All four components of better health care mentioned above must be carefully developed in order to yield maximum benefits. This report is primarily concerned with only one major aspect of these components—the contributions of university health science centers. Most health care personnel are trained outside these centers, and we recommend that the total spectrum of health care personnel be reviewed by a National Health Manpower Commission.

A Serious Manpower Shortage

The United States today faces only one serious manpower shortage, and that is in health care personnel. This shortage can become even more acute as health insurance expands, leading to even more unmet needs and greater cost inflation, unless corrective action is taken now. It takes a long lead time to get more doctors and dentists.

SOURCE: Reprinted from The Carnegie Commission on Higher Education, *Higher Education and the Nation's Health, Policies for Medical and Dental Education, A Special Report and Recommendations* (New York: McGraw-Hill Book Company, October 1970), "1. Major Themes," pp. 1-11, by permission of The Carnegie Commission on Higher Education.

Higher Education and Health

Higher education, as it trains the most skilled health personnel, has a great responsibility for the welfare of the nation. What colleges of agriculture once did for a rural society can now be done for an urban society by the health science centers—and that is to improve the quality of life for nearly all people in their areas.

The Carnegie Commission is giving special attention to medical and dental education because of their high importance to national welfare, their greatly increased complexity, and their heavy burden of costs. We have elsewhere identified the greatest priorities for higher education in the 1970s as being: (1) to provide greater equality of educational opportunity for all our youth, (2) to undertake reform and innovation, and (3) to provide more health care personnel. All three of these priorities are involved in this report. We know of no single area in all of higher education where more constructive action can be taken now than in medical and dental education.

A Propitious Time to Act

This is a most favorable period for new and improved endeavors:

- The public has a great concern for health care.
- Existing medical and dental schools are expanding, and new ones are being built; and a period of growth can also be a period of change and improvement.
- The students of today are highly motivated to encourage and support constructive change.
- The medical and dental schools have a number of remarkably able leaders.
- The professional associations are open to new ideas and are anxious to find better ways to provide better health care—to their great credit and to the nation's great advantage.

As a consequence, medical and dental education are undergoing more constructive self-examination than they have since the Flexner report of 1910[1]—and more self-examination is going on than in any other field of higher education. The second great transformation of medical education and research is now underway, and the United States, once again, will greatly benefit.

The Goals

We see these as major objectives:

- To provide more health care personnel of the right kinds
- To achieve a better geographic distribution of personnel and educational facilities, particularly for the sake of the central city and rural areas.
- To ensure more equality of opportunity for women and members of minority groups
- To provide more appropriate training for the work actually to be performed and, in doing so, to respond to the constructive suggestions of students
- To relate health care education more effectively to health care delivery
- To bring about a more equitable distribution of the financial burden between the federal government and the states, and among the several states
- To limit costs to the greatest extent possible

We shall make recommendations toward achieving each of these goals. To the extent that they are achieved, inflation will be slowed and, at the same time, health care will be improved.

The Flexner Model and New Models

The Flexner model, based on Johns Hopkins, Harvard, and, before them, German medical education, called for emphasis on biological research. Science was to be at the base of medical education. The Flexner model has been the sole fully accepted model in the United States since 1910. Some schools have fulfilled its promise brilliantly; others have been pale imitations; but all have tried to follow it. It has led to great strides forward in the quality of research and the quality of individual medical practitioners. The Flexner, or *research* model, however, looked inward to science in the medical school itself. It is a self-contained approach. Consequently, it has two weaknesses in modern times: (1) it largely ignores health care delivery outside the medical school and its own hospital, and (2) it sets science in the medical school apart from science on the general campus with resulting duplication of effort. This second weakness is now being highlighted by the extension of medical concerns beyond science into economics, sociology, engineering, and many other fields. Medical schools have had their own departments of biochemistry, but to add their own departments of economics and sociology and engineering would accentuate the problem of duplication of faculty and equipment. Also, the better economists would rather be in a department of economics on a general campus than separated from their colleagues in a department of medical economics: members of other disciplines would have similar preferences. The self-contained Flexner model thus leads to expensive duplication and can lead to some loss in quality.

Two new models are arising: (1) the *health care delivery* model, where the medical school, in addition to training, does research in health care delivery, advises local hospitals and health authorities, works with community colleges and comprehensive colleges on the training of allied health personnel, carries on continuing education for health personnel, and generally orients itself to external service; and (2) the *integrated science* model, where most or all of the basic science (and social science) instruction is carried on within the main campus (or other general campuses) and not duplicated in the medical school, which provides mainly clinical instruction. In this model (as in England), the medical school may be, essentially, a teaching hospital; but this is not necessary—it may, rather, carry on all its "Flexner" functions except the traditional first one or two years of science education.

Mixtures are of course possible and are occurring among these "pure" types. The research and health care delivery models may be combined, as is being done at Harvard and Johns Hopkins; the research and integrated science models may be combined, as is being proposed at Michigan and for the new Harvard-MIT endeavor; and the health care delivery and integrated science models may be combined, as at the new medical schools of the University of Illinois. All three, of course, could also be combined.

We believe that the new interests in health care delivery and in the integration of science and other disciplinary efforts are wise. The simple Flexner research model is no longer adequate as the sole model. A few schools, and many parts of schools, will, and should stay with the Flexner model, but we believe that the nation will be better served as many schools move in different directions. A diversity of models and mixtures of models is now desirable. Not only can the developing and new schools experiment; but as existing schools expand, they can direct their expansion in new directions so that there can be diversity *within* schools—for example, the next group of 40 additional students admitted might be asked to take their science on the main campus of the parent university. The "cluster-college" approach of changing and diversifying—rather than just duplicating on a larger scale—when expanding a general campus can be undertaken also in a health science center.

Pacesetter schools, such as those noted above, are moving toward health care delivery, or the integration of science, or both. We support these directions of movement. The nation has a sufficiency of the pure research model type of school. New developments should be toward greater integration with social needs, or toward greater integration with the general campus, or both.

More Doctors and Dentists

We see a need for expanding the number of places for training doctors during this next decade by 50 percent, and of dentists by 20 percent. Many of these new places should be filled by women and members of minority groups.

More Allied Health Personnel

The current ratio of all health care personnel to doctors is about 10 to 1; in the long run we see this ratio rising substantially. We particularly favor expanded training of medical associates who can work under the general supervision of doctors and expanded training of medical assistants who can work under the doctors' specific directions. We regard as especially promising the Medex program of training medical corpsmen with military experience to become doctors's assistants, and we note that as many as 3,000 a year might be trained with an all-out effort.[2,3] We believe such an all-out effort is unlikely, however, and we estimate that by the end of this decade about 3,500 associates and assistants may be trained each year. The public, of course, will need to be willing to accept the services of these associates and assistants, as they do in some other countries, and we believe they will. We similarly suggest the training of dental associates and dental assistants.

MAP 1 ***University health science centers and Carnegie Commission goals for new university health science centers by 1980, by state***

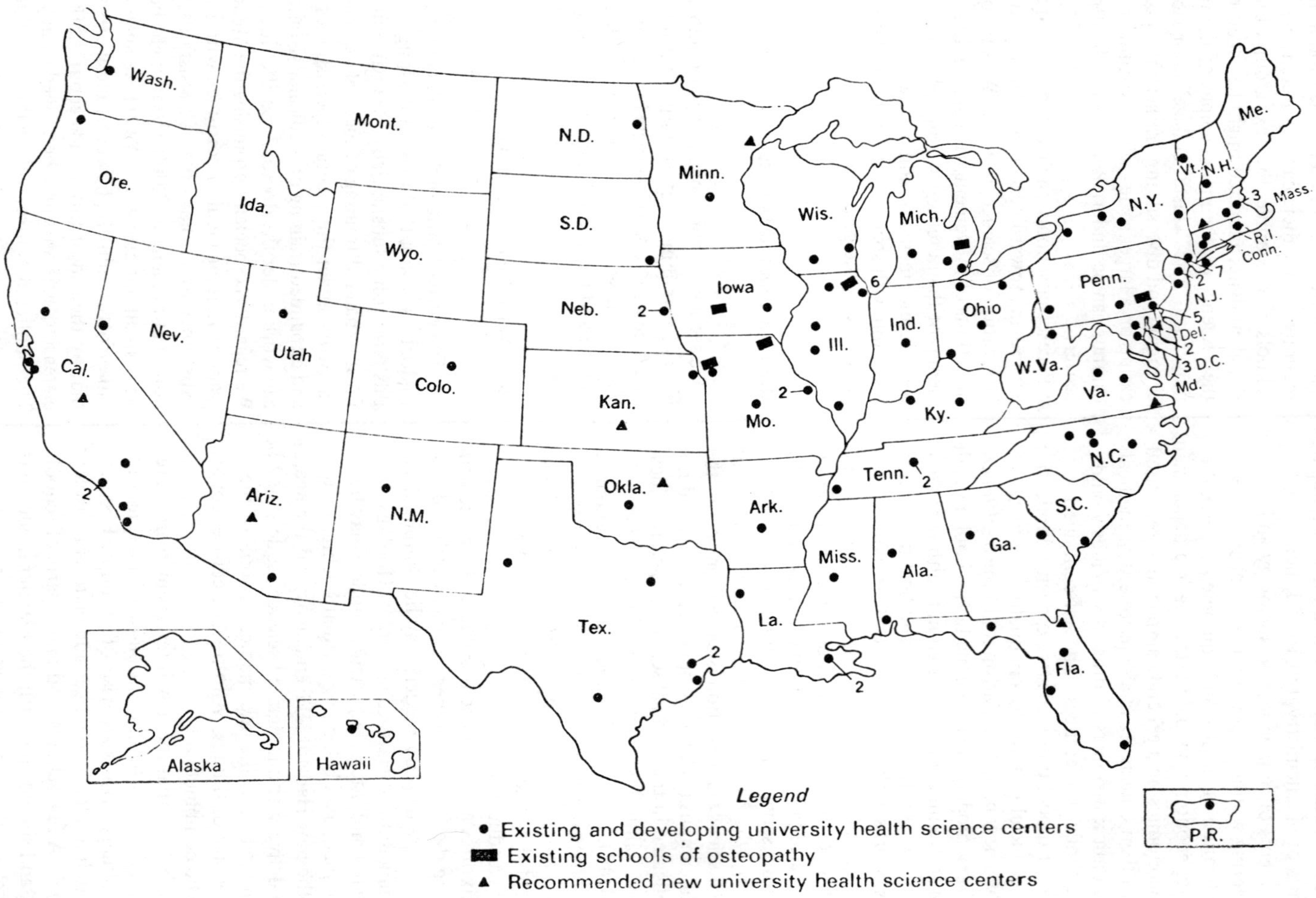

Legend

- ● Existing and developing university health science centers
- ▬ Existing schools of osteopathy
- ▲ Recommended new university health science centers

MAP 2 ***Existing area health education centers and suggested area health education centers by 1980, by state***

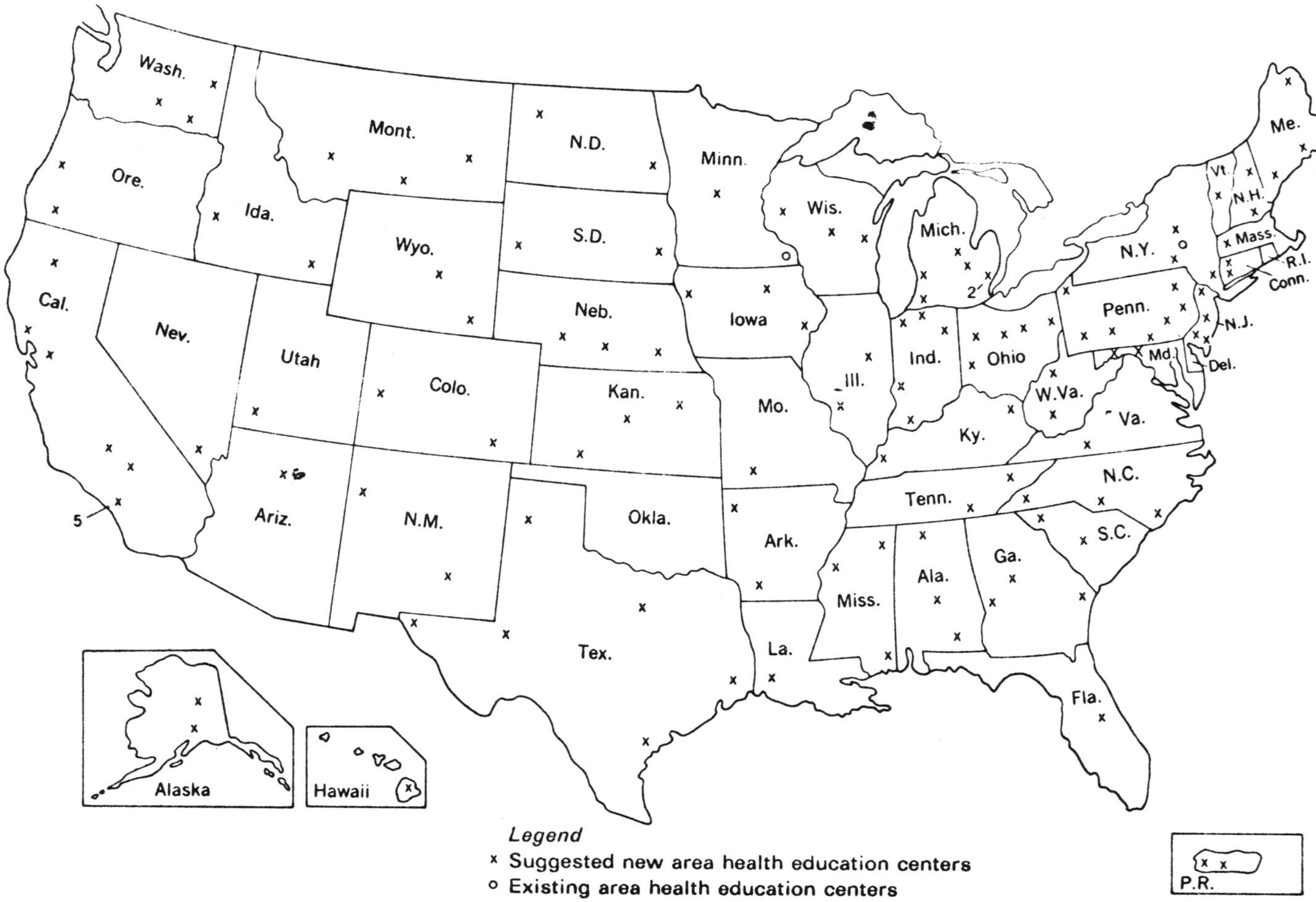

Legend
× Suggested new area health education centers
○ Existing area health education centers

Colorado, Duke, and Washington are among the universities now giving leadership in these directions.

Most of the allied health personnel will be trained in comprehensive colleges and community colleges, and their roles in this area will greatly expand. Allied health personnel can be trained more quickly and less expensively than doctors and dentists, and their availability will make possible the better use of the time and skill of doctors and dentists. Primary emphasis should be placed on increasing the supply of allied health personnel.

To Serve all the People Everywhere

We believe in the geographic dispersion of health training centers, as our recommendations will make clear. The Flexner model school could be located anywhere, for research results are easily transported. The *health care delivery* model needs to be located where the people live.

New Health Science Centers

Twenty-seven health science centers are now being started around the United States. It is said that seventy more are being considered. We see a need for nine more (see Map 1) to give adequate regional coverage.

Area Health Education Centers

We recommend 126 area health education centers to serve localities without a health science center (see Map 2). Each of these centers would be at a local hospital. The centers' educational programs would be administered by university health science centers. They would train medical residents and M.D. and D.D.S. candidates on a rotational basis; they would carry on continuing education for local doctors, dentists, and other health care personnel; they would advise with local health authorities and hospitals; they would assist community colleges and comprehensive colleges in training allied health personnel; and, in other ways, they would help improve health care in their areas. We consider this development of basic importance. It would put most of the local advantages of a health science center into many localities which do not warrant a full-scale center. This proposal would put essential health health services within one hour of driving time for over 95 percent of all Americans and within this same amount of time for all health care personnel. Much of the nation would be served by a higher level of expertise than is now locally available.

Reforms

We favor:

- Shortening the time it takes to become a practicing medical doctor from eight years after the B.A. to six years.
- Providing an extra mobility point or decision-making point for both the student and the school by creating a degree between the A.B. and the M.D. It would normally be awarded after students satisfy the general science requirements. It might be called a Master of Philosophy in Human Biology, or a Bachelor of Medicine, or a Master of Science in Human Biology. The student could decide at that point whether to go on to the M.D., move in the direction of the Ph.D., or take employment as a teacher or a medical assistant or associate (perhaps after some additional practical training). At this point, the school would also be in a good position to advise the prospective M.D. candidate and to judge his quality.
- Improving the curriculum by tying more closely together basic science and clinical instruction—they now too often stand as unrelated worlds. Improvement could also be achieved by tying clinical instruction to work with "gardenvariety" as well as "exotic" patients; by creating several paths, rather than one, for students depending on their prior background and their special interests—for example, a psychiatrist needs less basic science than a person intending to become a research scientist; and by having the students help determine the curriculum. Case Western Reserve recently has given notable leadership in curricular innovation.
- Improving the residency by giving the young doctor a wider variety of experience and more of it under skilled supervision.
- Creating a National Health Service Corps.

- Providing an Educational Opportunity Bank for medical and dental students.
- Improving the planning of health manpower.

Sharing the Financial Burdens

We recommend:

- That the federal government meet more of the costs of medical and dental education. It already supports most of the costs of medical research. Doctors can and do move from state to state, and some states are reluctant to educate M.D.'s for practice elsewhere.
- That the states support private medical and dental schools.
- That the levels of support among states be more nearly equalized. Some states exploit the investment other states make in medical education.
- That both the federal government and the states seek reforms and improvements as they expend their funds.

Cutting Costs

The expanded health manpower and external service programs we recommend will cost substantial sums of money, but total expenditures should be held to the lowest reasonable levels. Costs could be reduced by:

- Reducing from four to three the years it takes to get an M.D. degree. This change alone, if adopted by all medical schools, would increase the number of student places available by one-third, without further construction costs and with little further operating costs. It would also result in student support savings and will get students into practice sooner. Dartmouth is developing a program designed to meet some of these objectives.
- Reducing from four to three the years it takes to fulfill residency requirements. This, too, will save costs and get doctors into practice earlier.
- Combining science work on the campus and in the medical school, thus reducing duplication.
- Reducing the ratio of faculty to students, which is particularly high in medical education.
- Entering two classes a year and thus making better use of laboratory facilities and teaching personnel.
- Teaching during the summer period.
- Holding federal research expenditures steady as a percentage of GNP after a period of spectacular rise.
- Greatly increasing the number of allied health personnel and thus raising the productivity of doctors and dentists.
- Raising the minimum size of a medical class to 100 and thus obtaining economies of scale.
- Using outside hospitals for clinical training rather than, or in addition to, subsidizing a "university hospital."

Expenditures of medical schools have gone up twice as fast in the past decade as expenditures in higher education generally, yet the number of students in medical schools has risen only half as fast as in the rest of higher education. It is high time to look more carefully at costs.

The nation has a good opportunity to improve the health care of its citizens. By its contribution to that improvement, higher education has a great opportunity to become more useful to society.

NOTES

[1]Flexner, A., *Medical Education in the United States and Canada*, A report to The Carnegie Foundation for the Advancement of Teaching, Bulletin no. 4, (Boston: D. B. Updike, The Merrymount Press, 1910).

[2]Sanazaro, P. J., *The R & D Approach to Health Manpower in the 1970's*, paper presented at the Conference on Physician Support Personnel, American Medical Association, Chicago, March 19, 1970.

[3]Fenderson, D. A., *Manpower for a System of Health Care*, paper presented at the Rural Health Conference, Brookings, South Dakota, May 2, 1970.

ABOUT THE AUTHORS The Carnegie Commission on Higher Education consists of the following: Eric Ashby, The Master, Clare College, Cambridge, England; Ralph M. Besse, Chairman of the Board, The Cleveland Electric Illuminating Company; Joseph P. Cosand, President, The Junior College District of St. Louis; William Friday, President, University of North Carolina; The Honorable Patricia Roberts

Harris, Partner, Strasser, Spiegelberg, Fried, Frank, and Kampelman, Attorneys, Washington, D.C.; David D. Henry, President, University of Illinois; Theodore M. Hersburgh, C.S.C., President, University of Notre Dame; Stanley J. Heywood, President, Eastern Montana College; Carl Kaysen, Director, Institute for Advanced Study at Princeton; Kenneth Keniston, Professor of Psychology, School of Medicine, Yale University; Katharine E. McBride, President, Bryn Mawr College; James A. Perkins, Chairman and Director, Center for Educational Enquiry; Clifton W. Phalen, Chairman of the Executive Committee, Marine Midland Banks, Inc.; Nathan M. Pusey, President, Harvard University; David Riesman, Professor of Social Sciences, Harvard University; The Honorable William W. Scranton; Norton Simon; Kenneth Tollett, Professor of Law, Texas Southern University; and Clark Kerr, Chairman. It received assistance from many sources, including its Advisory Committee: Dr. Mark S. Blumberg, former Director of Health Planning, University of California; Dr. Robert Tschirgi, Professor of Neurosciences, School of Medicine, University of California, San Diego; Dr. Julius H. Comroe, Director, Cardiovascular Research Institute, University of California, San Francisco; Dr. Robert Glaser, Vice-President for Medical Affairs and Dean, School of Medicine, Stanford University; Dr. Clifford Grobstein, Vice-Chancellor for Health Sciences and Dean, School of Medicine, University of California, San Diego; Dr. David A. Hamburg, Executive Head, Department of Psychiatry, School of Medicine, Stanford University; Dr. Phillip R. Lee, Chancellor, University of California, San Francisco; and Dr. James A. Shannon, Professor and Special Assistant to the President, The Rockefeller University.

Medical Research, Some Aspects That Warrant Public Understanding

by James A. Shannon

Though a great deal of effort has been put into medical research in recent years, the dollar amounts are low in relation to overall health expenditures or cost of illness. There are still many basic questions as to the nature of disease and its prevention or amelioration which will ultimately be answered from studies of quite fundamental nature, at molecular and cellular levels. The needs here expressed put into perspective the changes in manpower, education and health care delivery described in the earlier papers, and indicate further requirements for the medical library.

PROPOSITIONS

Too frequently the conversation of scientists is limited to exchanges with other scientists, rarely with the people whom they serve and who are to benefit in a direct fashion. In consequence, the advances of science, their application to relevant areas of technology and the effect of these upon society is filtered through the news media in the form of small, discrete capsules of information.

Actually, science reporting is done quite well, but at a substantial disadvantage to the scientists, and to the public understanding of the work that is reported. The media, perforce, present science in a fragmented fashion, as a series of "little spectaculars." The thread of scientific continuity is generally lost, and the tedious but essential building of a science base that must precede a dramatic observation is too often obscured. Also, the drama of the presentation, which necessarily emphasizes the positive nature of a scientific advance, too frequently leads to unsupported speculation on its meaning and too great anticipation of immediate practical benefit.

In medicine this is particularly unfortunate. The common sense of the public is overlooked. People have been exposed to too many little science spectaculars, the early expectations of which have not fully proved out. In consequence, some have become frustrated and then disbelieving of the net worth of the science enterprise and disenchanted with the power of science. There is a tendency to downgrade the many and broad advances that have been made in medicine and at times to view scientific activities with some cynicism, considering much of the activity to be for the self-fulfillment of the scientist rather than for the benefit of society.

I will consider some aspects of medical research in terms of several general propositions that will be acceptable to most in principle, if not in detail.

The first principle states that medical research and its associated technologies are generally benign in their intent. They are broadly directed toward the development of knowledge and its application in purposeful ways to limit the social and economic burdens of disease and to foster the maintenance of health.

The second states that medical research is not an isolatable function. Rather, it is best viewed as one of a triad of interactive professional activities in research, in professional education and in the delivery of health services.

The third states that in the selection of program emphasis within the medical research field (that is,

SOURCE: Reprinted from James A. Shannon, "Medical Research: Some Aspects that Warrant Public Understanding," *New England Journal of Medicine*, 284 (Jan. 14, 1971), pp. 75-80, by permission of the publisher and the author.

The substance of this article was presented as a Lowell Lecture, sponsored by the Lowell Institute and Boston University Medical Center, and presented at Boston, Mass., January 13, 1970.

the development of priorities), two sets of considerations are important. The first is internal to science and relates to the assessment of the scientific opportunities available and the likely significance of alternative courses of action for the solution of medical problems. The second is social in nature and involves the comparative assessment of alternative courses in relation to societal needs and their satisfaction.

SCOPE AND NATURE OF MEDICAL RESEARCH

Few will quarrel with the belief that medical research has been highly productive in recent decades, but there are those who hold that with such pressing problems in the health-care field, program emphasis should now be limited to the production of physicians and related health personnel and the development of more rational health-care delivery systems, even if this must be at the expense of ongoing research. Some of these would also hold that present medical research is too often exotic and impractical in nature and lacks relevance to the obvious needs of society.

There is indeed a shortage both of physicians and of ancillary health personnel. That of physicians is due in part to a too low absolute number and, in part, to their inequitable distribution. Furthermore, the lead time required for an increase in physician production is long, and the forces that determine their distribution difficult to modify. Still, both these problems are amenable to direct action, and such action should be taken. Meanwhile, it must not be forgotten that medicine is a science-based profession and separation of physician education from a live science base would directly contribute to the development of mediocre physicians with a high rate of obsolescence. The transfer of physicians now involved in medical research to the health-care area, or the transfer of support funds from research to service programs, as has been proposed by some, would have little effect on either the physician shortage or deficiencies in service. Deficiencies in our present systems for the delivery of health-care services can only be resolved by appropriate direct actions.

Medical research is not competitive with such direct-action programs. Quite the contrary: a broad base of medical research is essential for a sound education program and for the production of new faculty, if physician production is to be substantially expanded. It also makes very direct and critical contributions to the quality and the effectiveness of health care.

But medical research cannot be discussed in the abstract, or its net worth explored as a generalization. One must have solid information on the research accomplishments to date, some perception of the major problems and some estimate of their likely solution. Furthermore, any consideration of research must be made with an understanding of the social and economic burden of disease. Unfortunately, the burden of our ignorance is not subject to precise quantification, but an economic indicator of its importance may be the $63,000,000,000 that the nation spent last year to support all health activities. This is somewhat more than 6.0 per cent of the Gross National Product and as a discrete activity was only exceeded in cost to the nation by our defense expenditures.

A listing of the positive advances in our knowledge will find at its head the wonder drugs of the forties and fifties that have made mock of the seriousness of many infectious diseases—beginning with the sulfonamides of the late thirties, penicillin in the mid-forties and, later, a large number of antimicrobial substances of a natural or synthetic origin. The new viral vaccines are equally remarkable. Beginning with the poliovaccines of the mid-fifties, these now include new modern vaccines for smallpox and wholly novel preparations for measles, mumps and rubella.

Paralleling these advances has been the progressive increase in our understanding of the nature of many diseases, and of the organs and organ systems that are involved. Such advances have led to more definitive diagnosis and more rational management, even though the latter may not be such as to lead to prevention or cure. Representative of this group is the modern management of acute coronary disease. The latter type of advance has been made possible in part by the explosive development of a number of potent new drugs largely developed during the period from 1945 to 1965. These include the many effective drugs useful in the management of hypertension and other cardiovascular disease, diabetes and the allergies. Then there are more effective analgesics and anesthetics and drugs that modify mood.

There are also the advances that are derived from a broader understanding of organ physiology coupled with intelligent therapy and the development of extraordinary surgical technics and skills. These have led to wholly new fields of surgical achievement. One can call particular attention to vascular, open-heart and pulmonary surgery and, to a lesser extent, the news-catching advances in organ transplantation.

All these and many other areas of dramatic progress are quite easy to understand since the immediate benefit is clearly apparent. There are other advances of a more complex nature less easily understood. First in order of importance I would place our progressive development of a molecular base for our understanding of genetics. The prospect of a full comprehension of the information systems of the cell opens wide vistas of increased medical capability. These extend from considerations that relate to the normal processes of human growth and development, through the area of genetically based disease susceptibility, to the exciting, or horrendous, potentials of genetic manipulation, the purpose of which could be to modify the behavioral or biologic characteristics of offspring. Less exciting perhaps but equally important in a practical sense is the beginning understanding of the fundamental biochemistry of the body, aberrations of which result in serious diseases such as atherosclerosis and its attendant manifestations in heart attack and stroke.

Then, there are the striking advances of modern virology. It is not visionary to hold that a further clarification of the intimate inter-reactions of viruses and cells will most probably clarify the role of viruses in the causation of cancer, and some of the devastating diseases of the central nervous system such as multiple sclerosis and Gehrig disease. Advances in associated fields are highlighted by our increased understanding of fundamental immunology. Upon this depends the development of routinely successful organ transplantation and a beginning understanding of autoimmune diseases. Among the likely examples of the latter are rheumatoid arthritis, rheumatic fever, glomerulonephritis and some of the fatal so-called collagen diseases.

What is included in such an abridged listing is largely a matter of taste, but the listing, however abridged, conveys a sense of rapid advance on a very broad front in terms of specific accomplishment. The advances are solid, the overall achievements remarkable, and the future for further advance creditably bright.

But everyone is well aware through bitter experience of a personal nature of the devastation that still accompanies the unsolved problems of medicine. Let me list some of these areas of ignorance and in some cases give an indication of their consequences.

Approximately 1,000,000 people die each year from diseases of the cardiovascular system. Such a gross figure is less important than an appreciation that the toll of disability and death from these diseases too frequently begins in the early forties and increases rapidly thereafter.

The second leading cause of death is cancer, not one, but many related diseases, each characterized by the unrestrained growth of a ravaging group of cells. These include the leukemias of our youth, cancer of the cervix, the uterus, and breast beginning in the child-bearing years, and cancer of the lung, prostate and gastrointestinal tract occurring as interruptions of well-being during the more mature years.

Then, not causing death, but producing profound social disruption to families and high cost to society, are the many conditions leading to mental retardation. Causation here is known to be due to genetic defects, to disturbance in fetal growth due to nutritional disturbances, to chemicals (such as drugs), to viral infections (such as rubella), to immunologic antagonisms between mother and child, to trauma to the infant during birth, and to social and nutritional deprivation during the early months and years of development. Probable causes can only be assigned to about half these intellectual cripples. Importantly, these known and unknown causes result in tragic human wastage that involves as much as 2.0 to 3.0 per cent of our population.

Finally, it would be grossly remiss of me not to mention the puzzling vascular problems of the aging diabetic person leading to heart attack, renal failure and blindness. Also, there are the other great disablers: the chronic neurologic diseases; the arthritides; the chronic disorder of the lungs and kidneys and the neuromuscular system; and disability due to mental illness.

One may well ask with some frustration how is it that we have experienced what, on the one hand, appear to be such striking advances and, on the other, such broad continuing deficiencies of knowledge, such ignorance concerning so many of the major ills that still beset us. The important chronic illnesses, for example, have common characteristics in relation to the balance of our knowledge and our ignorance. In no case are we too certain of the fundamental causation of the disease. In no case are we too clear about the biologic circumstances that foster progression or regression of the disease, and in most cases, we have far too little knowledge of the factors controlling the operations of the cellular and organ systems involved.

Yet an extraordinary amount of information has been accumulated on each of the major diseases falling into this category and on the operation of the systems involved. Furthermore, there are sound working hypotheses that now serve as a basis for the extension of our knowledge of both the nature of the disease and, ultimately, its prevention, or its amelioration. Indeed, in each case, much information has been developed that now permits the more intelligent management of the disease, if not its prevention, as contrasted with the situation some 10 years ago. Importantly too, it is these diseases that occupy the majority of the attention of the medical scientists today.

But, unfortunately, this assault on ignorance is not now amenable to the strategy of direct confrontation. For there is no doubt that we are dealing with derangements of essential systems that are fundamental to the normal operation of vital biochemical systems, cells, organs and organ systems—indeed fundamental to intelligent life itself. In some cases, we are dealing with fundamental departures from the "normal" of the information systems contained within our cell groupings, which, though compatible with what appears to be normal growth and development, nonetheless contain the directive information that ultimately takes over under as yet ill defined circumstances and dominates the economy of the organism as a whole in later production of serious disease. Such changes may be quite subtle, so as to cause only a change in personality, a moderate change in fat metabolism, or a moderate impairment in intellectual development. In other cases, the changes can well unloose a raging cancerous growth or produce a susceptibility to a number of equally devastating diseases.

Definitive answers will ultimately be achieved in each of these major medical problem areas, but this will only be derived from studies of quite fundamental nature, many at molecular and cellular levels, rather than at the level of organs and organ systems. Such studies will involve the molecular biologists, the fundamentally oriented virologist and his counterpart in immunology and the probing inquiries of the epidemiologist in association with the basically oriented clinician.

Equally important will be the results of those who are ingeniously developing new animal models, the more rapidly to pursue a lead uncovered by either the clinician studying the disease in man or the biologist operating at a more fundamental level. The clinician using the recently acquired powerful tools of science is of critical importance. His studies must be both probing and fundamental in his inquiry into disease mechanisms and highly applied in his use of new knowledge to the actual disease situation. The hallmark of this generation of physician scientist is hardly the white coat and the stethoscope of the twenties and thirties. Rather, it is the array of powerful instruments that support and extend the observations of his probing mind.

I suppose that I may be accused of overkill in my emphasis on the fundamental nature of the work that must be undertaken if we are to solve our large medical problems, and the likelihood that penetrating insights into their solution will only emerge at such a basic level. There is, however, too little public understanding of the complexity of the biologic problems posed by disease and too little understanding of the motivation of the scientists who work at such a level. Too frequently one encounters the simplistic view that if only these scientists would undertake more practical problems, problems with a more understandable end in view, we would be assured of more rapid progress toward the goals we all desire.

I emphasize the fact that the application of new knowledge to the specific circumstances of disease is now both extensive and rapid. It is in these areas, above all others, that the university medical center operates most effectively. It is a superbly designed, though I must say poorly supported, switching center between the fundamental and applied areas of science. In such a situation, and given adequate support, applied research increases or decreases in response to opportunity rather than any other factor in the environment.

The credibility of these views is derived from a consideration of the continuing productivity of past and current activities. But, importantly, the definitive solution of our major medical problems will not be from research with short-range objectives although striking progress should be observable in the middle-range future (that is, five to 10 years). Such a view emphasizes the need for the development of clearly defined middle-range and long-range goals and the modification of support programs, from the standpoint of both the level of support and the support mechanisms utilized, to facilitate the achievement of the goals selected for emphasis.

SOCIAL CONCERN AND SOCIAL ACTION

The resolution of many serious medical problems in the recent past is directly attributable to a broad program of biomedical research. This was made possible by the provision of adequate federal funds for the support of research itself, for the development of a substantial body of competent scientists, and for the participation of scientific and educational institutions in the program.

But it is now quite clear that a point of program

development in medicine has been reached where the effective continuation of research requires not only an increase in the federal support of research itself, but also more realistic support for the parallel educational and service functions. But recent constraints on federal expenditures have resulted in inadequate provision for each of these three coupled functions. The substantive support of a number of areas of medical research has been sharply curtailed. The support of medical education, though accepted as a direct federal obligation, has not been financed adequately. The delivery of medical services continues to leave much to be desired, and needful study of innovative remedies is lacking. Finally, the physical plant for these enterprises is grossly deficient.

In such a situation, society at large must make judgments on whether the constraints of federal spending in these areas are in the best interests of the nation. The average citizen is acutely conscious of the combination of high cost and broad deficiencies in the delivery of medical services. He is only generally aware of equally acute problems in the educational and research areas and lacks general information on the coupled nature of research, education and service. His base of understanding of these problems must be broadened, and he should be encouraged to use his increased knowledge in an effective fashion.

Fortunately, the public's interest in medical affairs is now more than passive. This is particularly evident in the activities of two types of citizen groups: the well established voluntary health agencies and consumer groups. Traditionally, each voluntary health agency has accepted a general responsibility for public education, for the support of some research and for the delivery of a limited array of specialized services, each of these in the area of particular interest to the agency. The large number of such agencies and citizen participation in them is a peculiarly American phenomenon. Consumer groups are also numerous, but except for a few, they have largely limited their efforts to the health-service area and most frequently to particular local deficiencies. National consumer groups are of relatively recent origin, and their full impact is yet to be felt.

It is important to appreciate the social and political power of well organized citizen groups. For example, the voluntary health agencies were in the forefront of the forces that produced the general social and political climate so essential for the growth of medical research programs in this country. In consequence, it was possible to develop the biomedical sciences to an extent that the United States now has no peer in the scope and excellence of its medical research activities. But, looking to a future, a simple continuation of the activities of the past will not satisfy the nation's needs. We are entering a period of reshaping of our broad national priorities. In addition, it will no longer be profitable for each health-oriented group to limit its concern and support to its own limited objective.

Although an agency and its membership may profitably express intimate concern with the consequences of ignorance in relation to a category of disease (such as heart disease, cancer, mental retardation and mental illness) or a single medical function (such as service) each agency must also develop a more sophisticated understanding of the broader needs of society. Only in this way can we obtain a balanced program in medicine consisting of highly productive research, an adequate educational system and competent medical services that are reasonably distributed. This view emphasizes the conviction that unless each of these general medical activities is carried out in a satisfactory manner, it is unlikely that the special desires of any special group will be satisfied.

The average citizen, one may suspect, does not perceive that he has an important social role in securing the continuing productivity of biomedical research. Traditionally, the leadership of the voluntary agencies has been well aware of its influence, but even this group has not made effective use of its broad membership base.[1] As for the membership itself, this is just beginning to appreciate that the major supporter of medical science is the federal establishment and that the primary patron is the private citizen.[2] In such a situation properly mobilized groups of private citizens can have a profound influence on the course of action taken by their officials in the Congress and Executive branches of the federal establishment.

But too few people now have the information that permits them to behave in a responsible fashion both as patrons of science and as proponents for the evolution of sound research policies for the nation. As intelligent patrons, the people must have a better conception of the scale of the federal support programs and a conviction that the research effort is reasonably deployed. Both these ends are achievable.

Let us consider how the expenditures for medical research can be made more understandable. Medicine, for example, can be viewed as a large science-based industry that requires an evolving science base for effective operation. In this view, comparison can be made between medicine and private industry. Science-based industries have found it not only expedient but essential to expend substantially more than 10 per cent of their total operational costs for research and development. In the more innovative segments of the pharmaceutical and electronic industries a company may expend as high as 20 per cent; in the aircraft and aerospace industries the percentage may be even higher. But medicine, including industrial research and development, will spend less than 5 per cent of the total national cost of health activities for research and development. Such a comparison provides no simple justification of any given level of biomedical research support, but it does suggest that the national expenditure is low rather than excessive.

Another example can be derived from a comparison of the federal support of biomedical research and for research and development for space activities. The latter area, NASA (National Aeronautics and Space Administration), will expend approximately $4,000,000,000 this year [1971] on space exploration, and the Department of Defense will spend up to an additional $2,000,000,000 on the development of defense applications of space technology. One may ask, in terms of very broad social purpose, which is the more important: the federal expenditure of $1,500,000,000 for health research or something in the order of $6,000,000,000 for space. The public's answer to such a question, if followed by social action, will affect our national priorities.

These general considerations are important in comparing the reasonableness of very large research and development expenditures made for quite different social purposes. But research expenditures become more explicitly meaningful when they are related to the burden of specific categories of disease. The following examples are interesting to examine.

Mental Health

Half the public hospital beds are occupied by the mentally ill at a cost of $1,400,000,000 annually, and all mental-health services cost the nation approximately $4,000,000,000. In such circumstances, the annual national expenditure of approximately $140,000,000 for mental-health research does not seem exorbitant, provided the opportunity for progress is real, as it is. This sum includes research on mental health in the conventional sense, and on drug addiction, chronic alcoholism, juvenile delinquency, suicide prevention and some aspects of mental retardation. It also includes studies of community and hospital arrangements for more effective delivery of mental-health services.

Such a comparison suggests that the limitation on support of research in the mental-health area should depend more upon the availability of fruitful research opportunities and competent scientists than upon general national economic considerations.

Dental Sciences

Research in the dental sciences presents an analogous situation. The cost of dental services is somewhat in excess of $3,000,000,000 annually, and the support of dental research in the past has been substantially less than $30,000,000 annually.

Cardiovascular Disease

As mentioned earlier, crude mortality due to cardiovascular disease is approximately 1,000,000 per year, and approximately 30,000,000 people have some degree of cardiovascular disability. The nation expends approximately $200,000,000 a year on research and development into these diseases. A valid question is clearly evident. Provided the research program is sound, can the nation afford to limit the expenditure in research and development into these disabling diseases to as little as an average of $1 per person per year? It is important to note that the primary objectives of many such studies are not the simple reduction of mortality. Rather, they are directed toward the prevention or, at least the deferral to a later age, of the ravages of these diseases. Such a goal is certainly within the realm of possibility.

This latter approach can be extended to a consideration of the aggregate national expenditures for biomedical research as against the nation's population base of 200,000,000. In such a situation, the question is posed: "Can the nation afford to expend as much as $10 per person per year to lessen the social and economic burden of disease and improve the quality of living?" Or, alternatively, "Can the nation afford to limit this expenditure to as little as an average of $10 per year per person?" Actually, if one only considers the federal expenditures for biomedical research directly concerned with the health of the nation, the figure is substantially less, perhaps as low as $7 per person per year.[3]

It is truly difficult to balance death and disability against abundant health, and to derive constants that provide the right dimensions of dollars that should be available to support the medical-research enterprise. The examples considered are illustrative of some meaningful ways to view the support of research in a comparative context, accepting the view that such comparisons are necessarily imprecise. Nonetheless, it is quite clear that when research expenditures are viewed against economic or social indexes that have meaning, the current levels of research expenditures are modest.

Judgments on the quality of research and the reasonableness of its distribution are not easily made. In fact, they are impossible to make by the individual nonscientist with the type of information generally available. On the other hand, there is broad participation of nonfederal professionals and consumers in the general judgments on social need and scientific opportunity that characterize all levels of the technical decision-making processes in the civilian-oriented biomedical research agencies of the federal establishment. These circumstances should give the interested person a feeling of substantial security that the quality of the federally supported research is generally high, and the allocation of resources is generally sound. Furthermore, the intimate interaction that now obtains between the voluntary health agencies and well informed citizens on the one hand and the Congressional committees and the executive agencies on the other is further assurance that the expenditures in support of research are in the best interest of the people.

Medical research has been highly productive in the past and with reasonable support will be so in the future. However, although much advance is to be expected looking to short-range objectives, the definitive solutions of the major disease are accomplishments that must be looked for in the middle-range (five to 10 years) and long-range future.

The public must obtain a broader understanding of medical research and its intimate relation to education and the delivery of health services. The effective support of research is wholly dependent upon such public understanding. Both the voluntary health agencies and nationally oriented consumer groups have a special and an essential part to play in such an informational program.

NOTES

[1] The national voluntary health agencies with their local chapters now involve as many as 10,000,000 people.

[2] The federal expenditure for biomedical research directly applicable to the nation's health is about $1,500,000,000.

[3] These are very broad general figures to indicate relative orders of magnitude. For more precise estimates see Health Activities: Federal Expenditures and Public Purposes, Committee on Government Operations, United States Senate, June 1970 (U.S. Government Printing Office 43-8601).

ABOUT THE AUTHOR—Dr. James A. Shannon was associated with the National Institutes of Health for nearly 20 years and was its Director from 1955 through 1968. Since his retirement he has been Special Adviser to the President of the National Academy of Science and Professor and Special Assistant to the President, The Rockefeller University. After obtaining an A.B. from Holy Cross College, Massachusetts, and an M.D. and Ph.D. from New York University, he was on the staff of the N.Y.U. College of Medicine, advancing to Associate Professor. He was also Director of Research Service, N.Y.U. Medical Division, Goldwater Memorial Hospital. Before going to the National Heart Institute, he was Director of the Squibb Institute for Medical Research for three years.

Dr. Shannon has held a variety of important and honorary appointments. He is a Member of the Board on Medicine of the National Academy of Science, has served on its Subcommittee on Shock, and was an Executive Committee Member-at-large and P.H.S. Representative, as well as the Chairman of the Panel on Malaria of the Division of Medical Sciences. He was a Member of the President's Science Advisory Committee and of the Federal Council on Science and Technology, and he has been an adviser to the World Health Organization, Pan American Health Organization, and Agency for International Development. He served on the U.S. National Committee of the International Union of Physiological Sciences. Among the awards he has received are the Presidential Medal for Merit, the Rockefeller Public Service Award, the Presidential Distinguished Federal Civilian Service Award and the John Phillips Memorial Award of the American College of Physicians.

Structure and Function of Medical Communication

A basic reason for differences in the environment of the health sciences is that it is focused on the nature of the living process (Dr. Orr, page 165). To understand that process, man relies on his observation of the relationships he finds in nature—scientific classification—and names the phenomena, using those relationships.

To communicate his understanding, man has been talking with his peers and writing to them over the centuries. The periodical evolved naturally from his letter writing and continues to be a dynamic means of reporting new information. Since its inception, there have been conflicts between the need for high standards and that for rapid dissemination and interaction.

The librarian must match his library classifications to scientific ones, his subject headings to the scientist's vocabulary and his selection and handling of periodicals to the scientist's communication needs and patterns.

Principles of Classification Illustrated by the Problem of Virus Classification

by N. W. Pirie

The history and theory of scientific classification are used as a backdrop for consideration of the classification of viruses. While our knowledge of viruses has increased since this paper was written, the principles of scientific classification do not change. For the medical librarian, they offer an interesting contrast to the practical library classifications with which he is familiar and they may form a basis for his understanding of the scientific approach to biomedicine.

Languages, as soon as they get beyond the primitive stage of giving every object an individual name, establish systems of classification. Categories of varying degrees of generality are recognized and nature is constrained to comply with them; men are differentiated from women, people from animals, animals from plants, the living from the nonliving, and so on. Much of philosophy is a wrangle about the goodness of fit between phenomena and language; and even when we have quoted and digested Bacon, Hobbes, Goethe, Buffon, Blake, and others, we still find that thought is controlled by the words we think with and thus by the categories laid down by those who made our languages.

Primitive distinctions are concerned with practical matters such as medicine, magic, and agriculture; to a person interested in milk, a cow and a nanny-goat have more in common than a cow and a bull. Thus English has different words for most of the permutations of sex and age in cattle but lacks a word, in the singular, for the species as a whole. Languages that are even more primitive carry subdivision further. In some African languages, for example, color in cattle is stated by different nouns rather than by adjectives, and in the New Hebrides each grade of intersexuality in pigs has its own name.[1] Alongside this extensive system of labeling there is generally a group of names for categories, such as *bush, weed,* and *drug.* These represent a form of classification, but it is classification in terms of the use to which we put the object. This is obviously the important thing to the practical man; it is scientists who think that classification should delve deeper and deal with the intrinsic properties of the things classified.

Labeling is an essential prelude to classification. In biology, the relevant aspect of labeling is the recognition of a species; this has caused, and still causes, much difficulty. Buffon's scepticism is well known. A passage from his essay on the ass may be quoted:[2]

> . . .but we should not forget that these families are our own works, that we have made them for the ease of our memories, that if we cannot comprehend the real relations of all beings, it is ourselves, not nature that is in fault, who knows not these pretended families; and, in fact, contains only individuals.
>
> An individual is a separate detached being, and has nothing in common with other beings, excepting that it resembles, or rather differs from them. All similar individuals which exist on the earth, are considered as composing the species of those individuals. Notwithstanding, it is neither the number nor collection of similar individuals which form the species, but the constant succession and renewing of these individuals which constitute them; for, a being which existed for ever would not be a species.

Many others have maintained a similar disbelief. Blake, for example, remarked:[3]

SOURCE: Reprinted from N. W. Pirie, "Principles of Classification Illustrated by the Problem of Virus Classification," *Perspectives in Biology and Medicine*, 5 (Summer 1962), pp. 446–472, by permission of the publisher and the author.

> For Art & Science cannot exist but in minutely organised Particulars
> And not in generalizing Demonstrations of the Rational Power.

The point will be generally conceded. Nevertheless it is abundantly obvious to even casual observation that the individual organisms we see do not form a continuum but can be so nearly universally grouped into species that special attention is given in text books to those instances where the standard criteria for a species prove equivocal. The reasons for the brief persistence of intermediate forms are obscure and need not delay us here, but throughout most of biology it is nearly as easy to recognize a species, in spite of variability, as it is to recognize a letter of the alphabet in spite of the enterprise of typographers. What is more, in species that are gregarious or in which there is sexual congress, lower organisms recognize a species too; it is probable that they rely on "minutely organised Particulars" in doing this rather than on "generalizing Demonstrations."

Having attached labels to the species, we can consider the essence of the problem. If only an index is needed, the labels can be arranged alphabetically. The comprehensive systems of virus "classification" do little more than this, and their limitations have been amply and cogently discussed[4,5] If something better is to be produced, more attention must be paid to the intrinsic properties of viruses, but examples from other branches of biology show how easy it is to be misled by the obvious and salient features of the group being classified. Thus animals could be divided into those living in water or on land, those usually naked or hairy, those with horns and without, the retromingent and promingent, and so on. The possibilities of idiosyncratic classification are endless, and each would have a specialist band of devotees such as, to take in order the examples cited, war-time food-controllers, parasitologists, taxidermists, and catheter manufacturers. We classify on the basis of a point of view and with an end in view and, so long as the classification meets these needs, it is valid. The search for Order, or Design, in Nature supplies the stimulus to look for something better than this—for the attempt to construct *the* classification of a group and not just *a* classification. When that is done the things classified must be studied in more detail; so many of their attributes must be considered before the lines of classification are drawn that there is little prospect of new knowledge compelling a rearrangement. But it is observation and not logic that ultimately shows which of the systems are idiosyncratic. In this article several examples will be mentioned where confusion has been, or could be, caused by using only one quality, even when that quality is dramatic, as a complete criterion for designing a scientifically rather than a practically useful grouping. The implication is that the same troubles would arise were similar attempts made in virus classification.

Etymologically, the word species means "what can be seen," and all early classification depended on differences between organisms that were apparent to the unaided eye without even looking inside the organism. Buffon's article on the American opossums is amazing; he fusses away about the distribution of claws on their hind toes as a feature distinguishing opossums from all other animals (this was before Australian fauna had reached laboratories) and attaches little importance to the peculiarities of their urino-genital structure, although he was aware of some of them. Linnaeus attached more importance, in animals at any rate, to internal structure. He used, for example, similarities in skull structure to define relationships; but embryology and biochemistry had not then developed far enough to be woven into the system. Gilbert White probably introduced the first non-structural quality into accepted classification when he distinguished the chiff-chaff from the the willow warbler because of its different song. This is important for our theme, for it gave an activity as much importance in classification as a structure.

The agents causing infectious disease were vigorously and, within the technical limitations of the time, intelligently discussed in the period from Fracastoro[6] to Bradley;[7] then came the doldrums that preceded Pasteur. Linnaeus and his pupils, e.g., Nyander,[8] put several of these agents among the *Acarids* although they must have realized that their knowledge was inadequate for attempting any classification at all. But the urge to do something with every known entity is strong; the agents of disease were therefore shoved in at a point where they would be least objectionable. This casual treatment is odd because Linnaeus was a professor of medicine and wrote extensively on medical themes.

Since the time of Pasteur, so much knowledge has been won about the larger microorganisms that systems of classification are justified; but the Linnean urge still operates, and many people try to include viruses in their systems. Partial justification for the tendency to carry reverence for

Linnaeus so far as to copy his bad habits comes from the use of the word "taxonomy," which carries the connotation of getting men into line in an army—it matters little how unlike they are so long as the result is tidy. If the science had been called diatithetics, from διατίθημι, which can carry the connotation of arranging goods as in a shop, we would be constrained to be more careful. The point would be brought out that the primary object of classification is use; it should be a rational system for helping us to find the entities classified afterwards and should not merely be a means of getting them out of the way.

Linnaeus was entitled to assume that people knew what plants and animals were; all he had to do was arrange them. But virus research is not a subject like Botany or Zoology; instead, it is like Agriculture in that it gets its unity from our directed interest and not necessarily from an intrinsic uniformity in the subject material. Attempts to group all the viruses together may therefore be as ill-conceived as would be an agriculturist's attempt to relate potatoes and eggs because of their comparable size, shape, edibility, and role in the perpetuation of the species. In justification for this point of view, three possible ways in which viruses appeared, or are still appearing, may be mentioned.

(*a*) They can be the extreme form of degeneration of microorganisms so that, from merely being able to multiply in a host, they have become totally parasitic and dependent on the host's synthetic systems.

(*b*) They can arise in a cell when, as a result of an aberration in metabolism, it produces a structure robust enough to withstand normal scavenging processes, and able to act as a model for further synthesis.

(*c*) They can be structures with qualities similar to those needed in possibility *b* but coming into the cell from outside—from another species, for example.

Of these three, possibilities *a* and *c* are probably the most generally accepted. The possibility that anything similar to the viruses we now study was a stage in the evolution of more elaborate organisms, though often touted, need not be taken seriously. The viruses that are now being studied demand so much from an environment before they can multiply in it that they are improbable components of the pro-biotic world. It is, of course, possible that there are still-undiscovered viruslike forms with simpler requirements and that these are stages in biopoesis.

The group we are attempting to classify is therefore uncertain and so is the concept of a species in it. Mayr's dictum[9] is that "the most objective property of species is perhaps the gap between different species. It is the place where gene exchange is interrupted." This is admirable in the context in which he used it. But it does not apply here because a virus can introduce genetic material into its host and this, in principle, permits a degree of hybridization unknown in the metabionta. By hindsight, this compatibility is not altogether surprising, for the simpler a structure becomes, the more likely becomes an accidental congruity.

A brief summary of the last two paragraphs is that there is no reason to think that viruses are related, as plants and animals are generally held to be, by an evolutionary sequence. Many taxonomists maintain that evolution is not a fundamental part of their science, and they have abundant historical justification for their point of view. Ray, Tournefort, Linnaeus, and de Candolle preceded Darwin and believed, unlike some of their contemporaries, in the fixity of species. By an odd reversal of the usual present-day outlook, they would probably have argued that if species were not fixed, there would be little point in attempting classification at all; that is to say, they did not see, to use again Mayr's phrase, that the gap between different species is the fundamental thing. It is difficult now to understand the motives of the early classifiers and what made them think their systems had any real validity. In so far as it had any logical basis, their work was an attempt at deductive theopsychology; Nature ought to make sense because the Creator was sensible. But their work shows clearly that valid classification is possible before its logical foundations are assured.

Two other objections are often raised against the idea that a valid classificatory scheme is essentially the same thing as an evolutionary tree. The fossil record is so incomplete, especially for plants, that the supposed evolutionary sequence is often arbitrary and is, in many places, deduced from present-day classification rather than vice versa. Furthermore, some groups of organisms are thought to have a polyphyletic origin. Both arguments depend on ignorance, which time will presumably dispel. Most of us think that, unless a classification is intended for practical use only, it should make phylogenetic sense, and that if the members of groups such as the angiosperms or teleosts have come to resemble each other by convergent evolution, the grouping is unsatisfactory and the group will be sorted out when knowledge increases. The unique position of Linnean classification depends on this: though the family tree may not be known, we assume that each species among the metabionta evolved in only one way. We cannot make this assumption about viruses. An appeal to phylogeny is not, therefore, helpful now nor is it likely to become so in the foreseeable future. The essential taxonomic prop seems to be missing. We may go on to discuss the merits and limitations of the various types of evidence on which a system of virus classification may ultimately rest.

I. QUALITIES USEFUL IN VIRUS CLASSIFICATION

The number of qualities needed to classify the members of a group depends on the size of the group. When each quality is simply present or absent, n of them are needed for the unequivocal labeling of 2^n species. When the quality offers several mutually exclusive possibilities, as with color, a smaller and not necessarily predictable number will be needed. For classification two to three times as many qualities would be needed, depending on the precise degree of subdivision that is proposed. About ten independent pieces of information would therefore be needed concerning each of the 200–500 viruses before they could even be unequivocally labelled, and twenty or more for their classification. This illustrates clearly one reason why classification is easier when organisms are visible and complex rather than invisible and simple; more can be found out about them. As much information is gained by a glance at a flower as by a year's work with a virus. Successful classification depends on the use of much more than the theoretical, minimum amount of information. All the properties of viruses should therefore be used in their classification, for success probably depends as much on the number of different directions from which evidence is coming as on anything else.

A. Morphological Classification

It is obvious that chaos would be introduced into plant and animal classification if size and external shape were regarded as very important; these properties have assumed importance in virus classification because the particles have often been referred to as molecules, and that disguises their commonly pleomorphic character. This loose phraseology raises few difficulties with the smaller, more-or-less spherical, viruses. X-ray evidence shows that those viruses that can be crystallized have constant diameters; electron micrography or ultracentrifugation allows viruses to be arranged at present into perhaps ten size categories with the probability of greater refinement in the future. The crystal form complements electron-micrographic evidence about particle shape but has so far shown little rationality; thus many unrelated viruses crystallize, as spheres might reasonably be expected to do, in rhombic dodecahedra, whereas preparations of serologically related members of the tobacco necrosis group of viruses crystallize in surprisingly diverse manners.[10]

Tobacco mosaic virus (TMV), and other elongated viruses, have not so far been crystallized, but X-ray evidence on dried orientated preparations suggests that they have constant cross sections. The particle lengths, in spite of reiterated claims for constancy,[11,12] are variable,[13] and Johnson[14] claimed that the mode, with TMV, depends on the host plant. This point needs fuller study by modern and more refined technique. It may be that variability is caused by destruction or aggregation in the host or during preparation for electron micrography, but, until it has been controlled, proposals[15] that viruses should be classified by length measurements, in spite of their attractive simplicity, should be treated skeptically.

The fundamental reason why size and external shape will probably not play a large part in a scheme for classifying the smaller viruses is that they do not offer enough qualities when studied by present-day methods. One rod or sphere is very like another, and even the word "sphere" is often used loosely to include all solids whose dimensions are approximately equal—e.g., cubes and cylinders with height equal to the diameter. This is a matter of technique, and it should soon be possible to say with certainty whether the subunits are so arranged that the final structure has the facets of a dodecahedron or icosahedron. With the larger viruses, such as vaccinia and some bacterial viruses, external shape is already a valuable guide to classification because there are more qualitative differences to be used.

B. Chemical Classification

As a prelude to any attempt to use chemical methods of classification, the success of these methods in the domain of pure chemistry deserves attention. As always, the initial problem was labeling, and it was to this that such writers as John Locke[16] directed attention.

> From what has been said, 'tis evident, that Men make sorts of Things. For it being different Essences alone, that make different Species, 'tis plain, that they who make those abstract Ideas, which are the nominal Essences, do thereby make the Species, or Sort. Should there be a Body found, having all the other Qualities of Gold, except Malleableness, 'twould, no doubt, be made a question whether it were Gold or no; i.e. whether it were of that Species. This oould be determined only by that abstract Idea, to which every one annexed the name Gold: so that it would be true Gold to him, and belong to that Species, who included not Malleableness in his nominal Essence, signified by the Sound Gold; and on the other side, it would not be true Gold, or of that Species to him, who included Malleableness in his specifick Idea. And who, I pray, is it, that makes these divers Species, even under one and the same name, but Men that make two different abstract Ideas, consisting not exactly of the same collection of Qualities? . . .
>
> I do not deny, but Nature, in the constant production of particular Beings, makes them not always new and various, but very much alike and of kin one to another: But I think it is nevertheless true, that the boundaries of the Species, whereby Men sort them, are made by Men; since the Essences of the Species, distinguished by different Names, are, as has been proved, of Man's making, and seldom adequate to the internal Nature of the Things they are taken from. So that we may truly say, such a manner of sorting of Things, is the Workmanship of Men.

With the development of a satisfactory conception of the nature of an element, various pieces of classification could start–e.g., Döbereiner's Triads, which grouped the then-known halogens and the alkaline earth metals. Newland's "Law of Octaves" was a major success, but it was not quite complete enough to win general acceptance. That had to wait for the genius of Mendeleev with the Periodic Table, which gives a unique and unequivocal classification that was, in the end, strengthened by the apparent anomalies (e.g., the inversions of A & K, Co & Ni, Te & I). Nearly a hundred years earlier, Bergman [17] had tried to classify salts along Linnean lines. It is easy now to see why he failed and Mendeleev succeeded. First, Mendeleev tackled the simpler problem of the elements, and he had much more information to help expose bad bits of classification. Secondly, Mendeleev relied on atomic mass, and this, as we now know, is closely connected with the actual architecture of the atom. But the third reason is the most relevant. We now classify salts interchangeably by grouping under the metals or under the acids and see that it is just convenience that makes us use the former arrangement predominantly. Bergman, and some would-be virus classifiers, did not realize that the sequence of words in a Linnean classification is not arbitrary but vital[18,19] and that the Linnean appearance of such names as sodium chloride or ferrous sulfate is spurious.

The elements, therefore, can be classified unequivocally and the salts arbitrarily. As molecular complexity increases, chemical classification becomes chaotic. One fact makes it, of necessity, more straightforward than the classification of organisms or viruses–a molecule must contain an integral number of atoms. This means that the difference in mass between molecules, equivalent to the gap between species, has a minimum size and this, for the small molecules with which most of chemistry is concerned, is a significant proportion of the whole. The classification of some groups of molecules–the saturated fatty acids, for example–is straightforward; they are arranged in order of size, though it is sometimes useful to split them into two series according to whether they have an odd or even number of carbon atoms. Problems arise when there are substituent groups because the same structure can be considered from different points of view. This is well illustrated by the early controversy over the stereochemical naming of threonine. It was called threonine because of its relationship with threonic acid; naturally occurring threonine has the orientation of the threonic acid that, because of its derivation through the sugar series from D glyceraldehyde, is called D. But this orientation is that of the amino acids found in proteins, and in them it is called L. There is no satisfactory solution; the molecule can equally logically be regarded as having two separate derivations, but it is arbitrarily called L because it is more often handled by those interested in proteins and amino acids than by those interested in sugars.

The sugars illustrate another aspect of the problem. The first volume of that monument to chemical logic, *Beilsteins Handbuch der Organischen Chemie*, treated glucose and similar sugars as straight-chain polyhydroxy compounds. Fifteen years later (1933) volume 17 appeared, and it was then known that sugars are usually six-membered heterocycles containing one oxygen atom and so should be dealt with in that volume. At the right place there was a note to this effect promising treatment in the *Ergänzungswerk*. But when this appeared, logic admitted defeat, and a special volume on carbohydrates, considered as an arbitrary group in their own right, was announced, and it was published in 1938. Chemical classification is clearly not in such a happy state that it can be accepted as axiomatic that increasing knowledge of the chemistry of viruses will lead automatically to their classification. It is, however, probable that this increasing knowledge will help, as it has in the classification of other groups. We may go on to consider the extent of this probable help.

Aristotle, knowing neither *Chironomus* and the root nodules of legumes, nor those antarctic fish with no red corpuscles, used the presence of hemoglobin as the criterion for membership of a group that is more or less the same as our vertebrates. It would have seemed logical, ninety years ago, to say that, if an organism contained cellulose, it was not an animal. Then cellulose was found in tunicates; but they have so many other biochemical peculiarities that they are recognized as universal exceptions, and cellulose remained a useful criterion for a plant. Now it is known as a component of aging tissue even in man[20] and so loses all value. Similarly, the use of hydroxyapatite in bonelike structures is not limited to the vertebrates but appears in *Polytoma* and *Polytomella*.[21] The systematic study of the occurrence of essential oils, alkaloids, raphide crystals, and other substances of generally unknown function is often called biochemical taxonomy. It would be better to call it analytical taxonomy, and it has not so far proved helpful.[22] Even at the species level, elementary analysis can be misleading. Thus, Carlisle[23] finds that some individuals of *Molgula manhattenensis* contain niobium instead of the vanadium that most individuals of this species contain.

Simple analyses are therefore not likely to be useful. The smaller viruses, such as TMV, are not known to contain anything besides protein, ribonucleic acid, iron,[24,25] possibly calcium,[19] and a base related to spermidine (Markham, unpublished). The large viruses generally contain lipids, and ribonucleic acid (RNA) is replaced by deoxyribonucleic acid (DNA). These chemical criteria have been used[26] as the basis for a classification, but obviously they do not allow even enough permutations for labeling. At one time, persistent efforts were made to correlate the presence of RNA or DNA with the ability of a virus to infect plants, animals, or bacteria. This correlation seemed groundless *a priori*,[27] and it has gradually been demolished as more analyses have been published on carefully made virus preparations; its last remnant disappeared with the discovery of a small bacterial virus containing RNA.[28]

Although the simple presence or absence of such components as RNA, DNA, and lipids is not sufficient for a classification, any classification must recognize the role that these components appear to play in synthetic processes; one would question any arrangement that grouped an RNA and a DNA virus together. In this connection it is pleasant to see the increasing interest now being taken in lipids, for they too have considerable capacities for showing specificity. Almost the only point on which geneticists have remained unanimous during the past twenty-five years is that, whatever else a gene is made of (at the beginning of the period, protein, and now more fashionably, DNA) it is never made of lipid; estimates of the weight of a gene traditionally start from defatted gametes One should remember, before dismissing the heretical suggestion that lipids may carry specificity, or "information," that only ten years ago it was generally believed that nucleic acids were too simple to fill that role.

The detailed structure of a macromolecule is very relevant to the classification of structures in the virus size range because here chemical structure plays the role of morphology in metabionts.

Before the study of chemical structure can be usefully undertaken, it is essential to explore the range of variation within what is being regarded as one species, for we cannot assume that the environment—that is to say, the synthetic preconceptions of the host—is unimportant. This is well understood by taxonomists working with other material. Many hundreds of specimens from as diverse a set of environments as possible are compared to see which features are plastic and which invariable, and a new species is not accepted until it can be shown that all the examples of it have properties falling outside the range of normal variation of any other species. Nothing of this sort has been attempted on a comprehensive scale for any virus, and the evidence that the same chemical entity is made, regardless of the conditions of multiplication, is ludicrously inadequate. The baseless assumption seems generally to be made that entities carrying the same name must, of necessity, be invariable.

The steps that should be taken to establish even such a simple point as the constancy of amino acid or nucleotide composition are obvious and have already been set out,[13] but they are so often disregarded that they may be stated again.

> To get the maximum value out of the labor expended on amino acid determinations it is important that the analyst should publish more information because there are several different types of probable error. Some variations in values for the same quantity depend on the errors of weighing, colorimetry, the uniformity with which the basic reactions proceed, and so on. These can be in part predicted and they can be measured by doing an adequate series of determinations on one homogeneous bulk sample of the material being analyzed. The extent to which different preparations of what should be the same material differ from one another is an entirely different question. This is measured by seeing whether the values got in a series of determinations on one preparation differ consistently from those got on another. The recognition of differences between preparations of different types, e.g. different strains, is an extension of this, and a difference is only significant when preparations of one type differ from those of another to a greater extent than preparations of the same type differ among themselves. With viruses, to make sure that any apparent differences are real, it would be necessary to use preparations from plants grown under a wide and varied range of conditions. To do all this would be very laborious, but I contend that, unless the analyses are reported as thoroughly as that, they are hardly worth doing at all, and significance cannot be given to them by simply grouping all the different sources of error together as a mean deviation.

Those detailed studies that have been made show that what is apparently the same virus can have significantly different properties when coming from different environments. Thus, Johnson[14] found shorter particles in exudates from pepper than from other plants infected with TMV, Bawden[20] described a strain of TMV that had a different amino acid composition and physical and serological properties according to the host on which it was grown, and it is claimed[30] that preparations from different hosts have different infectivities. Clearly a virus may have only a limited capacity to impose its own pattern on the host; it may be built up from what is readily available, somewhat as a caddis worm makes its case out of whatever it can find on the bottom of a stream. The reasons for expecting this *a priori* have already been discussed.[31,32]

We should not overrate the amount of control that has to be exerted during synthesis. Molecules have their own ways of fitting together, as crystallization shows clearly. The rather tedious, step-by-step, processes used by the synthetic chemist when making a large peptide can be sidestepped as Fox[33] has shown, by simply heating a mixture of amino acids together. You do not in this way get a prearranged structure, but each particular mixture behaves regularly. It is unlikely that, out of the 10^{100} or so possible isomers of an average protein, only one would be suitable for a given job–the organism probably puts up with what it can get easily and is content to do those things for which the catalysts are easily available. One is reminded of the stories of Apelles failing to paint the froth on a dog's jaws and getting it when he threw his sponge at the painting in fury; or Rossini noticing that an ink blot, made carelessly on a musical passage already written, improved it.

A rational classification, based on chemical information, must depend on detailed knowledge of molecular structure, and this will not be quickly gained; sperm whale myoglobin is at the moment the only protein for which a plausible morphology has been proposed.[34] We know the amino acid sequences–or, parts of them–for other proteins, but this is only half of the problem. As Haldane[35] has wisely pointed out, the word "macromolecule" has been extended to cover what ought to be called megamolecules, for *μαχρόσ* means long and *μέγασ* big. The relevant molecules may well be long chains with a certain amount of cross linking but, as with cats-cradles or any other structure made from the convolutions of thread, specificity depends on the precise morphology–called in this case topology. The prerequisite for a chemically based classification of viruses would be three-dimensional models of the arrangement of the amino acids, nucleotides, and other components in preparations of different viruses from different environments, and enough experience to know which differences are significant.

The attempt to classify in terms of macromolecular morphology will act as a powerful stimulus to attempts at the structural classification of molecules that have hitherto been classified functionally. A beginning has already been made, and certain similarities appear among the hemoglobins and between enzymes that share a name though coming from different sources. The recognition that enzymes and other proteins, from the same source, may be heterogeneous[36,37] is a further important step toward differentiating the essential from the variable parts of a structure. The biological advantages that may depend on this heterogeneity have been discussed in general,[38] and specifically with the lactic dehydrogenases.[39] Variation among the p-aminobenzoate-metabolizing enzyme in different pneumococcus mutants[40] is a particularly interesting example because it was studied by measuring differences in the response to different analogues to the substrate. These presumably reflect differences in the surface configuration of the enzymes. Until the nature of this tolerated variation has been fully analyzed, we will not, to use an animal analogy, be able to distinguish the essential characteristics of a species from mere variations in color or hair length.

Discussion of issues such as these is sometimes condemned as being philosophical. It is none the worse for that. We all have a philosophy—it is the code of expectation that leads us to decide whether a new phenomenon is natural or surprising—the important thing is to find out what our philosophy is as a first step to deciding whether we intend to go on adhering to it. An essentially metaphysical approach to viruses is apparently more widespread than a chemical approach; it underlies the suggestion, made from time to time in medical journals, that TMV is the cause of the increased incidence of lung cancer among smokers. This presupposes[41] that viruses are in some way special, and share what Duns Scotus called a *hiccity*, Kant a *noumena*, and we would now call a characteristic functional group, so that there is a general virus quality that could be abstracted or considered separately from the other aspects of the particle. It is because there is no hint of evidence for this that such an attitude may be condemned as metaphysical; if it depends on anything, it depends on the alchemical doctrine of signatures, *similia similibus curantur*, modified to read, "like effects will be produced by like causes." This is repeatedly contradicted by the facts of biochemistry. Different organisms often use entirely different substances to bring about the same physiological effect—e.g., the tapetum can be made of riboflavin, guanine, zinc cysteine, cholesterol derivatives, or parallel fibers,[42] and nitrogen is fixed in different ways by plants in the many genera possessing this faculty.[43] It is unlikely, therefore, that virus classification will depend either on any feature that is not part of normal biochemistry, or on any one type of feature. This is not a labyrinth from which we will escape by following a single clue.

C. Serological Classification

Amino acid, or nucleotide, analysis is a precise method for determining the number of pieces in a structure; serological comparisons are a rough method for finding out something about their arrangement. A serological reaction is evidence that the antigen being tested has some chemical resemblance to the antigen used to make the antibody; it has, therefore, the same bearing on taxonomy as any other type of chemical analysis. When a sufficiently unusual chemical combination is found, the evidence for a relationship is strong, but serological evidence alone does not tell us how unusual the structure is and, when an extensive range of materials is studied, taxonomically absurd cross-reactions are often found. Thus, many unrelated species share the Forssman antigens, and structures that appear in some pneumococcal polysaccharides also appear in plant gums. This lack of rigid species specificity is to be expected from Landsteiner's work showing that quite small molecules, if suitably attached to proteins, can act as specific antigenic determinants. It is a great pity that, with natural antigens, the actual structures responsible for each facet of antigenicity are not known. If the conclusion of a serological comparison were that two viruses were related because they shared, to take a reasonable example, a certain tetrapeptide, the cogency of the argument would be assessed more accurately than it is now when hidden under the glamorous phrase "they share a common antigen." The permutations of amino acid sequences would be thought of and estimates would be made of the probability of congruence by accident.

In spite of enthusiastic advocacy,[44–46] serology has not, so far, played an important part in the classification of animals or plants. There are several reasons for this. Serological tests, though admirably objective, are for that very reason limited and undiscriminatory; until recently[47] they lacked the qualitative subtlety that experts in the art of classification have come to expect and relish. Furthermore, the metabionta offer abundant other traits that can be used in classification; and organ specificity complicates the picture. But the main obstacle, for plants at any rate, was personal. The most comprehensive attempt at serological classification, the "Königsberg Stammbaum," appeared as a vast group of papers culminating in a patented master-chart; this restricted comprehension and reproduction. It was then vigorously, though probably unfairly,[cf. 46] attacked and has never regained serious attention. In virus classification the position is different. There is a shortage of other traits for use in classification, and those who work with viruses often have a medical or bacteriological background that gives them familiarity with, and confidence in, serological techniques.

Serological studies are, in principle, better adapted for showing that two viruses are not related than for showing that they are. Thus, if two viruses react satisfactorily with their homologous antisera, but fail to react with the heterologous serum, it would be unreasonable to maintain that the viruses were related closely. For the reasons already given, cross-reactions are more difficult to interpret. Nevertheless, it is unquestionable that serological resemblances are more common among viruses that, for other reasons, seem to form members of one group, than among viruses as a whole. This has led to the establishment of some groups of related virus species, or, as Bawden[4] prefers to put it, strains; but these groups, or genera, remain unrelated to one another in higher stages of classification such as families. Valid conclusions can probably only be drawn when the homologous and heterologous reactions take place at comparable dilutions. When one reaction is 1 to 10 thousand times as powerful as the other,[48] several alternative explanations of the cross-reaction are possible even when the reaction does not appear to be unspecific.

D. Biochemical Classification

The essential difference between biochemistry and chemistry is that the former is concerned with the manner in which substances act in vivo rather than with their composition and structure. Biochemistry is therefore getting nearer to the essence of our problem for, by definition, viruses cause changes in the host. The presence of the same substance or mechanism in two organisms is valid evidence of a relationship only when alternative substances or mechanisms exist. To take an analogy from human affairs: a certain pattern painted on pots, or a certain written symbol for a letter, if used by two groups of people, suggests strongly that they have had contact because these things are arbitrary. But the use of the wheel or the basic process of weaving is not evidence for contact because there seems to be only one way of solving certain problems. The uniformity of biochemistry constantly poses this problem: do two different organisms use the same mechanism or substance because they are related or because there is only one efficient way of doing the job and this has arisen independently from time to time in different phyla? There has been considerable illogicality about biological thought on these matters. Uniformity is often used as evidence for common descent by people who, in discussing the origins of life, assume that this is intimately bound up with the origins of proteins and nucleic acids. To them, life without proteins is unthinkable; this means that they are assuming that there is only one way of doing certain things. If this is so, if enzymes have to be made of protein, biochemical uniformity becomes an uncertain guide either to evolution or classification.

The biochemical classification of viruses would depend essentially on grouping them according to the processes used in the synthesis of their components, and in the assembly of the components into finished virus particles. It is conceivable, though no doubt improbable, that the components exist normally in the uninfected host and the incoming infective particle has only to act as a "crystal focus" to promote an anomalous aggregation; the host would then suffer from the sequestration of essential metabolites.[49] If we discount this possibility, and postpone discussion of the evidence that can be got from a study of host enzymes and reactions to a later section, all that remains to be considered here is the evidence for enzyme-like participation by the virus in its own multiplication.

As we move from the autotropic microorganisms through the saprophytes, we can arrange a sequence of increasing biochemical inadequacy so that the further along the sequence we move, the more components a culture medium must have. Early in the succession we reach a region where the nature of the components is unknown and crude extracts have to be used. Further along, extracts fail and we get obligate parasites such as the rust funguses and plasmodium. The general assumption is that this type of obligate parasitism is a consequence of our ignorance; the organism needs something that is rather unstable and so is not present in the extracts we make. Or it may need coenzymes at the high concentration in which they exist in certain regions of the host cell and cannot make use of them when they are diluted as in extracts. The host is not just a bag of substrates; it has its own internal geography. With increasing knowledge, and care in making extracts, the missing components should be found and the group of obligate parasites will shrink. These obligate parasites, though in some ways inadequate, contain many enzymes. Several of the larger viruses—e.g., influenza and T_2—carry enzymes that appear to help them to penetrate the host cell wall; it is therefore reasonable to accept them as genuine virus components. The small plant viruses that have been thoroughly studied cannot infect an undamaged plant; their enzyme activity is feeble, and, with TMV at any rate, it is reasonable to assume,[26] that it is a consequence of secondary absorption from the environment.

These issues were discussed at length at a symposium held in 1952. Bawden and Pirie[50] argued that a virus did not use its host simply as a culture medium supplying inert molecules for the virus to build into copies of itself with the help of its own enzymes; instead, they saw no reason to assume that a virus had any capacity other than the ability to misdirect the synthetic mechanisms of the host. This point of view, rephrased in modern jargon in the form "the virus carries information into the cell" is now widely accepted. The apparent absence of enzymes from many viruses may mean only that the correct substrates for the virus's synthetic actions have not been tested, but, if the absence is real, attempts to grow viruses on media containing only substrates and coenzymes are bound to fail. Some part of the integrated synthetic system—for example, microsomes and mitochondria or their fragments—would be needed. According to this outlook, the biochemical distinction between viruses and other microorganisms is that the viruses need the organized machinery of the cell whereas the others need its products only, and it is essentially an accident that this distinction is so closely correlated with size. When examined carefully, the distinction is not quite so clear cut as it first appears. It is easy enough to distinguish between an enzyme and its substrate; an enzyme does a job and is then ready to do it again, whereas the substrate is changed. But a coenzyme is also, at the end of the cycle, ready to do the job again. The distinction between an enzyme and a coenzyme seems to depend on size, and the logical basis of our attempted new definition of a virus is not much better than that of the old. When two substances are working together in a cycle, the larger is the enzyme and the smaller the coenzyme; but each acts on the other, and neither can be looked on as the more dynamic.

The study of enzyme reactions is therefore still a problematic or even improbable approach to the classification of viruses. This is not unexpected when we consider the small part it plays in the classification of other groups. It plays a significant part when bacteria are "put through the sugars," for then an enzyme survey is being made; it would be better if the results were expressed more precisely and stated what acid or gas was being produced and at what rate.[19] The appearance of new enzymes by adaptation is a source of trouble and so is the loss of enzymes by certain strains. Occasionally, however, the claim is made that a particular enzyme is invariably associated with a distinct part of a classificatory scheme; thus ornithine transaminase[51] appears to be present in all organisms except blue-green algae and gram-negative bacteria.

Work on either the chemical or biochemical properties of viruses is generally limited to a study of the minimum structure needed for infectivity; it is assumed that anything that can be stripped away without loss of infectivity is simply a contaminant—in the chemical sense of the term. There is no reason to accept this assumption, and many examples have been given[32,52-54] of separable components that normally accompany viruses in the initial extracts and of changes brought about during purification. In those articles this Procrustean attitude toward the process of "purification" was likened to processes such as the cutting off of the ears and tail from a rabbit, because these excrescences were not necessary for its survival. It may be, therefore, that what we are trying to classify is the *écorché* rather than the organism. In the present context a better simile would be that the attempt to classify viruses from a study of the minimum and most highly refined phase of their existence is like trying to classify animals by a study of sperm and ova. At the present time, chemical and morphological studies would produce only a patchy and uncertain system, but it is generally agreed that the specifications for the complete organism are contained in the structure of these rudimentary stages in the developmental cycle. A hyperbiochemistry should be able to read in the structure of a gamete the form of the completed organism. Ignorance is not the only factor that keeps this from being done, or even from being an immediate probability. Superficially the same form can be attained in unrelated complete organisms by convergent evolution, and similar characters can appear in unrelated species by the action of different genes.[55] Nevertheless, it is reasonable to assume that there is some stability in the controlling chemical structures. This expectation depends on the same principles that underlie much conventional morphological classification. A useful structure depends on the integrated action of many different parts so that, to get another structure that will act in the same way, rather than a monstrosity, several simultaneous and radical changes would have to occur. This is unlikely. We therefore find the basic plan of an organ such as a foot persisting from the amphibia on through two hundred million years and appearing in perhaps a million species. When morphological stability of this degree is possible, it is reasonable to think that there will be corresponding, though unknown, stability in the basic plan of the specifications. The complexity of the genetic structure of plants and animals makes this hyperbiochemistry remote and, though interesting, it would not be particularly useful at present. The viruses are simpler, and their classification along these lines is likely to come earlier than that of the gametes.

E. Classification by the Capacities and Reactions of the Host

Having considered the intrinsic properties of viruses—composition, morphology, structure, and activities in vitro—that could be used in classification, we come to the property by which the category "virus" is defined: its relationship to a host. A few aspects of this relationship can be dismissed quickly. Unrelated viruses in unrelated hosts share certain common attributes, as Bradley[7] recognized when he compared the transmission of striping, in plants grafted with a bud from a striped plant, to the transmission of an animal disease. By a lucky accident, he chose smallpox as the example and so compared two viruses with one another. If we accept the general principles of plant and animal classification, infections follow no obvious phyletic rules; the same virus can cause disease in monocotyledons and dicotyledons, or plants and insects.[56,57] Bacteria can infect both vertebrates and plants, but viruses are not known to do this; it would be possible to erect only a limited classification on that exclusion. Furthermore, susceptibility to infection is not a completely clear-cut property of a host. It is bedevilled by latency or symptomless carriage; by mild and short-lived infections; by infections that can be demonstrated only in bizarre circumstances—for example, the insect virus[58] that manifests itself only in high concentrations of CO_2; by viruses that multiply only in the presence of another virus;[59] and by effects of the physiological state of the host on its susceptibility. Variations in temperature or light intensity before or after attempted infection can alter by a factor of ten or even a hundred the apparent susceptibility of a host plant. Such extreme dependence on physiology has been less often demonstrated in animal or bacterial hosts, partly because it has been less often looked for and partly because these hosts are themselves less tolerant of physiological change. But in animal tissue cultures, where temperature and pH can be controlled, equally dramatic effects are found.[60]

More intimate aspects of the host may, however, in time, play a part in classification; we may be concerned less with what the virus multiplies *in* and more with it multiplies *on*. Viruses, by definition, are obligate parasites, and the reason for this, by general consent, is that they use the organized enzyme systems of the host. These systems are now being studied in vitro actively, and progress is being made on the separation of intracellular particles bearing specific activities so that differences in the activity of preparations consisting predominantly of microsomes, mitochondria, chloroplasts, etc., are well known.[61,62] As this knowledge increases, it should become possible to determine the type of particle associated with the multiplication of each virus, and the existing categories of intracellular particle will no doubt undergo further subdivision. This knowledge will be the basis of a rational biochemical classification. Its validity obviously depends on a pure assumption: that particles concerned with the same type of action will prove to be recognizably similar throughout an extensive group of hosts. This assumption may well be challenged, but it is an extension into an intermediate size range of the well-established homology of organs, on the one hand, and, on the other hand, of the use of the same basic biochemical mechanisms by almost all the organisms that have been studied. A crude analogy for such a system would be the differentiation of the categories *coin*, *key*, and *corkscrew* because they get a characteristic reaction from slot machines, locks, and bottles, respectively, although all are of comparable size and made of metal. The rationale behind this type of biochemical classification is that the multiplication of viruses is limited to certain hosts, not only by the difficulty of getting into the host cell, but also by the absence from some cells of systems whose normal metabolism can be so modified by the invading virus as to lead to the production of more virus.

This aspect of the biochemistry of viruses can be studied in many ways. Ultimately it should be possible to isolate parts of the metabolic hierarchy of the host cell able to synthesize their appropriate viruses in vitro. As a first step, however, it should be possible to inhibit the multiplication of some viruses by relatively specific inhibitors. This will not necessarily be a step toward the chemotherapy of virus infection, for the inhibited system was presumably useful in the normal cell so that its inhibition would be as lethal as the infection;

but inhibition of multiplication by the same substance will be as good a unifying feature between viruses as any now in use.

A more indirect approach would be to follow the early manifestations of virus infection. There is already a suggestive lead in the tenfold increase in the respiration of tobacco leaves that occurs within an hour of infection,[63] although this was not found with *Nicotiana glutinosa*.[64] This phenomenon needs confirmation and detailed study, with isotopically labelled substrates, of the type of respiration that is being stimulated. The preferential use of one substrate would show which enzyme systems were affected in the first stage of virus multiplication.

The idea that two viruses are likely to be related if they use the same part(s) of the metabolic machinery of the host is clearly an extension of the idea that they are related if they interfere with one another's multiplication. Interference by related strains is a well-known phenomenon, but it is by no means invariably a trustworthy guide to relationship. For example, Bawden and Kassanis[65] presented a strong case for regarding tobacco veinal necrosis virus as a strain of potato virus Y although infection of three different hosts with it gave no protection against Y. Difficulties also arise because protection, when it exists, is not always reciprocal. Thus severe etch virus protects against Y and hyoscyamus virus 3,[66] but established infection with these two viruses does not protect against severe etch. To get round these difficulties it has been suggested that two viruses can be considered unrelated when simultaneous infection is more severe than infection by either alone. This raises the old problem of what is meant by "severity." For the whole host a generalized infection seems more severe than a localized one but it is less so for the cells in the infected locale. In the limit, a virus that killed the cell it first invaded suddenly enough would probably never be recognized at all; it would disappear in the tiny necrotic spot left by the dead cell.[67]

If the conclusions in the last two paragraphs are valid and the metabolic systems used for virus synthesis have been diverted from some other activity, light may be thrown on the nature of this normal activity by a study of the morphology of the virus particle. This mutual relationship between studies on normal and perverted hosts has proved fruitful in many other aspects of research; somewhat on the principle that Herodotus attributes to the Persians of making up their minds on all important issues when drunk and then, when sober again reviewing the conclusion come to. There are two extreme cases. The subunits of the particle may come together without the active intervention of the host, by a process analogous to crystallization, so that the final form may give more information about the surface properties of the subunits than about the system that made them. This appears to be the state of affairs with TMV and perhaps also with very regular particles such as tomato bushy stunt and poliomyelitis viruses. At the other extreme come large bacterial viruses, such as T_2, with an elaborate morphology. The obvious interpretation of the structure is that it is an aberration of some structure in the normal host. The question is: what? The choice is wide and need not be restricted to structures of a similar size; a change in size may be one feature of the aberration. There are many instances–insect salivary gland chromosomes, for example–of ill-defined environmental influences causing great enlargement of a structure, and diminutions are also known. The chromosome structure may indeed be more than an analogy–especially for viruses that contain DNA. This possibility was foreshadowed in Muller's suggestion that a virus was a free gene and the lemma to it[52] that the only essential difference between a gene and a virus was that the former remained anchored whereas the latter must become detached and move around in the cell. Many other cell components, flagella, plastids, mitochondria, etc., have intricate structures that are presumably built in response to instructions stored in the normal cell and that could act as partial models for virus synthesis. All this is pure speculation. But it seems to arise logically when we get away from the conception of a virus as an independent entity growing in a passive host and look on it instead as an aberration of normal metabolism. Speculation along these lines can be justified because it gives a motive for more persistent effort to extend the host range of viruses. A difference in the form of the same virus when grown on different hosts should help in identifying the structure of which the virus is a caricature.

II. CONCLUSION

The first essential step in classification is esthetic–a synoptic survey of the domain to be classified to see which are the essential and useful features in it. The second is logical–using the criterion chosen, to see if it leads anywhere to obvious nonsense. The third is the scientific step—to see, if the criterion seems to work, why it works. And *why*, a generally misleading word, is legitimate here because it is a comment on a process going on in a human head. These principles apply to every type of classification. They apply particularly well when we are classifying the products of human ingenuity because we are then aware of all the components and possibilities. This was recognized by Wilkins[68] when he tackled even such an unruly tangle as language and managed, with reasonable success, to devise a universal symbolic language based on a set of classifiable relations between classifiable symbols. But when we are not sure that we are aware of all the components and possibilities or when, as with viruses, we are sure that we are not, the possibility remains open that new knowledge will invalidate what had seemed to be tidy piece of classification.

Linnean classification of plants and animals was based predominantly on morphology; but it is outstandingly successful, and the large additions to knowledge about plants and animals that have come recently from work on their biochemistry and serology have not necessitated any serious changes. This should surprise those taxonomists who think of their art, as Linnaeus did, as the arrangement of a set of independent objects unrelated to one another by descent or in any similar way. But taxonomists, if one may consider their own taxonomy, are often somewhat rigid in their outlook and slow to make use of new relevant phenomena. Those who regard a satisfactory piece of classification as a summary of the probable phylogenetic relations of the organisms classified are not surprised, because to them it is inconceivable that new knowledge should conflict with a correctly based piece of phylogeny. Obviously it may correct erroneous phylogeny. Nothing is known about the evolution of viruses; it is even unlikley that most of them have an evolution in the conventional sense. This will introduce an arbitrary element into virus classification, but even an arbitrary arrangement depends on the existence of enough information to put detail into a synoptic view. The prerequisite for virus classification is more information about viruses.

A survey of the traditional types of information—external morphology, chemical composition, host reaction, etc.—shows that, if used alone, they would lead to curious pieces of classification among the larger organisms and bacteria; it can be assumed that they would apply even less well among viruses. We need, as a supplement, the infant science of macro- or megamolecular morphology. Some principles of classification will have to be introduced for large molecules in any event, and their development will be speeded up if an insistent demand comes from those interested in viruses. Other biologists might join in too, for a rational classification of large molecules would be as useful a guide in all other branches of biology as morphology is today, and successful classification depends on the presence of many different lines of evidence.

If we had enough independent pieces of information, confidence could be put in mechanized classification[69-71] in which every fact that is admitted as relevant has equal weight; but the amount of information needed in such a system is enormous. This approach to the problem depends, to use communication-engineering terminology, on great "redundancy." When information is scanty, either because of the undeveloped state of the subject or because of the intrinsic simplicity of the things being classified, it is inevitable that alternative arrangements of equal apparent validity will be possible. This will cause trouble because biologists are so accustomed to thinking that classification is at fault when the same organism is claimed as a member of two different families that they tend to overlook the fact that chemistry can operate successfully without laying down emphatic rules to settle, for example, whether glucuronic acid is to be thought of among the sugars or the acids.

When there is enough information, useful and agreed classification can precede the recognition of the principles that make it valid. Thus mammals had been grouped together before their presumed evolutionary relationship validated the grouping, regardless of shape and size and whether they walked, swam, or flew, and this was done at a time when any resemblances between them were thought of as a whim on the part of a creator. The grouping depends on the morphological arrangements that about half the members of each species make for coping with milk secretion. The unifying feature is not milk secretion itself—pigeons and some sharks can manage that and make use of similar biochemical mechanisms for it—but on the integration of capacity and structure in a manner not found outside the group.

From our knowledge of viruses, no unifying principle emerges with a comparable impact on our experience or imagination. This can mean two things: that we do not know enough about them and there is a genuine unifying principle somewhere; or that there is no unifying principle and we have slipped into the error of trying to group together entities united only by their ability to misdirect synthetic systems in the host. The first I have stigmatized as, at the moment, a metaphysical approach, though it is conceivably correct; the second, if correct, is the explanation of the difficulties taxonomists have got into hitherto when handling viruses. These are the fault of the viruses rather than the taxonomists, but taxonomists are at fault for not recognizing this.

NOTES

[1] J. R. Baker. Man and animals in the New Hebrides. London: G. Routledge, 1929.
[2] G. L. L. De Buffon. J. S. Barr (trans.). Natural history, 5, 187. London: H. D. Symonds, 1807.
[3] W. Blake. Jersusalem, III, 55, 1820 (quoted from Nonesuch Edition, ed. G. Keynes, London, 1941).
[4] F. C. Bawden. Chronica Botanica. U.S.A. 1950.
[5] C. H. Andrewes. H. Gen. Microbiol., 12:358, 1955.
[6] H. Fracastoro. De contagione et contagiosis morbis et curatione. Venice: 1546.
[7] R. Bradley. A general treatise of husbandry and gardening. London: W. Mears, 1721.
[8] J. Nyander. Exanthemata viva. Uppsala: L. M. Hojer, 1757.
[9] E. Mayr. *Ann. N. Y. Acad. Sci.*, 56:391, 1953.
[10] F. C. Bawden and N. W. Pirie. Brit. J. Exp. Path., 23:314, 1942.
[11] H. Boedtker and N. S. Simmons. J. Amer. Chem. Soc., 80:2550, 1958.
[12] C. E. Hall. J. Amer. Chem. Soc., 80:2556, 1958.
[13] N. W. Pirie. Advance Virus Res., 4:159, 1957.
[14] J. Johnson. Phytopath., 41:78, 1951.
[15] J. Brandes and C. Wetter. Virology, 8:99, 1959.
[16] J. Locke. An essay concerning humane understanding, bk. 3, chap. 6, para. 35, 37, 4th ed. London: Awnsham and John Churchill, and Samuel Manship, 1700.
[17] T. O. Bergman. Nova Acta Soc. Sci. Upsal., 4:63, 1784.
[18] N. W. Pirie. Brit. J. Philosophy Sci., 2:269, 1952.
[19] ______. J. Gen. Microbiol., 12:382, 1955.
[20] D. A. Hall, P. F. Lloyd, and H. Saxl. Nature, 181:470, 1958.
[21] F. G. E. Pautard. Biochim. Biophys. Acta, 28:514, 1958.
[22] R. D. Gibbs. J. Linnean Soc. (Lond.), Botany, 56:49,1958.
[23] D. B. Carlisle. Nature, 181:933, 1958.
[24] H. S. Loring and R. S. Waritz. Science, 125:646, 1957.
[25] H. S. Loring, S. Al-Rawi, and Y. Fuminoto. J. Biol. Chem., 233:1415, 1958.
[26] P. D. Cooper. Nature, 190:302, 1961.
[27] N. W. Pirie. *In*: R. Prakken (ed.), Conference on chromosomes. Netherlands: Zwolle Willink, 1956.
[28] T. Loeb and N. D. Zinder, Proc. Nat. Acad. Sci. U.S.A., 47:282, 1961.
[29] F. C. Bawden. J. Gen Microbiol., 18:715, 1958.
[30] R. C. Lindner, H. C. Kirkpatrick, and T. W. Weeks. Phytopath., 51:15, 1961.
[31] N. W. Pirie. Nature, 166:495, 1950.
[32] N. W. Pirie. *In*: G. E. W. Wolstenholme and E. C. P. Millar (eds.), The nature of viruses. Ciba Foundation Symp., 1957.
[33] S. W. Fox and K. Harada. J. Amer. Chem. Soc., 82:3745, 1960.
[34] J. C. Kendrew, H. C. Watson, B. E. Strandberg, R. E. Dickerson, D. C. Phillips, and V. C. Shore. Nature, 190: 666, 1961.
[35] J. B. S. Haldane. *In*: Vergleichend biochemische Fragen. 6 Colloquium der Ges. f. physiol. Chem. Berlin: Springer, 1956.
[36] J. R. Colvin, D. B. Smith, and W. H. Cook. Chem. Rev., 54:687, 1954.
[37] J. C. Perrone, L. V. Disitzer, and A. Lachan. Nature, 184:1225, 1959.
[38] C. L. Markert and F. Moller. Proc. Nat. Acad. Sci. U.S.A., 45:753, 1959.
[39] N. O. Kaplan, M. M. Ciotti, M. Hamolsky, and R. E. Bieber, Science, 131:392, 1960.
[40] R. D. Hotchkiss and A. H. Evans. Fed. Proc. 19:912, 1960.
[41] N. W. Pirie. Lancet, pp. 707 and 978, 1960.
[42] ____. Nature, 191:708, 1961.
[43] G. Bond. Symp. Soc. Exp. Biol., 13:59, 1959.
[44] G. H. F. Nuttall. Blood immunity and blood relationship. Cambridge: Cambridge University Press, 1904.
[45] A. Boyden. Sigma Xi Quarterly, 24:152, 1936.
[46] K. S. Chester. Quart. Rev. Biol., 12:19, 165, and 294, 1937.
[47] P. G. H. Gell, J. G. Hawkes, and S. T. C. Wright. Proc. Roy. Soc. [Biol.], 151:364, 1960.
[48] R. Berks. Virology, 12:311, 1960.
[49] N. W. Pirie. *In*: J. Needham and D. E. Green (eds.), Perspectives in biochemistry. Cambridge: Cambridge University Press, 1937.

[50] F. C. Bawden and N. W. Pirie. Symp. Soc. Gen. Microbiol., 2:21, 1953.
[51] W. I. Scher and H. J. Vogel. Proc. Nat. Acad. Sci. U.S.A., 43:796, 1957.
[52] N. W. Pirie. Cold Spring Harbor Symp. Quant. Biol., 11:184, 1946.
[53] ——. Exp. Cell Res., 1 (Suppl.):184, 1949.
[54] ——. *In*: Interaction of virus and cells, p. 11. 6th International Congress of Microbiology. Rome: Istituto Superiore di Sanità, 1953.
[55] S. C. Harland. Biol. Rev., 11:83, 1936.
[56] D. D. Jensen. Virology, 8:164, 1959.
[57] M. Watson and R. C. Sinha. Virology, 8:139, 1959.
[58] Ph. L'Heritier. Heredity, 2:325, 1948.
[59] B. Kassanis and H. L. Nixon. J. Gen. Microbiol., 25:459, 1961.
[60] A. Lwoff and M. Lwoff, Ann. Inst. Pasteur. (Par.), 98:173, 1960.
[61] W. S. Pierpoint. Biochem. J., 75:504, 1960.
[62] ——. *Ibid.*, p. 511.
[63] P. C. Owen. Ann. Appl. Biol., 43:114, 1955.
[64] ——. *Ibid.*, 46:198, 1958.
[65] F. C. Bawden and B. Kassanis. Ann. Appl. Biol., 38:402, 1951.
[66] ——. *Ibid.*, 28:107, 1941.
[67] F. C. Bawden and N. W. Pirie. Ann. Rev. Plant Physiol., 3:171, 1952.
[68] J. Wilkins. An essay towards a real character, and a philosophical language. London: Royal Society, 1668.
[69] D. J. Rogers and T. T. Tanimoto. Science, 132:1115, 1960.
[70] P. H. A. Sneath. J. Gen. Microbiol., 17:184, 1957.
[71] ——. *Ibid.*, p. 201.

ABOUT THE AUTHOR–Norman Wingate Pirie is Head of the Biochemistry Department at Rothamsted Experimental Station, Harpenden, Hertfordshire, Great Britain. He was educated at Emmanuel College, Cambridge and was Demonstrator in the Biochemical Laboratory at Cambridge for several years before going to Rothamsted as Virus Physiologist.

He is a Fellow of the Royal Society and a Member of the British Broadcasting Company Science Consultative Group. His publications include such varied subjects as the origins of life, the need for greatly extended research on food production and contraception, biochemical engineering, the separation and properties of macromolecules and viruses. In his listing in *Who's Who*, he describes his recreation as "politics."

Medical Literature: The Campus without Tumult

by Franz J. Ingelfinger

Dr. Ingelfinger uses the analogy of the journal as a "campus" where its readers are educated by the faculty, consisting of the editor, or "dean," the editorial board and the authors. From this perspective, he finds reasons to be dissatisfied with several parts of the journal publication system and suggests some ways of improving it.

About 3 years ago, when I was privileged to succeed Dr. Joseph Garland as editor of the *New England Journal of Medicine*, some doubts were raised concerning the wisdom of a move from a professor's to an editor's chair. The doubters, being professors of medicine themselves, held that the duties of a full-time medical editor were not as rewarding as those of a professorial personage. But they were wrong, I hope. Indeed, in my well-rationalized imagination, I had become a dean, and a dean not only of the campus of the usual medical school, but of the unseen campus of a mighty multiversity to which right now 120,000 students pay tuition. The amount of this tuition, I admit, is a scandalous pittance. In addition, before anyone objects that a medical school deanship these days hardly warrants the word "promotion," let me emphasize the unique advantages of my deanship. Whatever happens to me, it is quite unlikely that my rambunctious students will break down my doors, smoke my cigars, deposit dejecta in the corners of my office, and—on top of it all—throw me physically downstairs.

The comparison of the general medical journal with a medical school is not farfetched. For the primary purpose of the *New England Journal of Medicine*, as an example, is certainly educational, and, like the medical school, the *Journal* has a pedagogic philosophy and a curriculum. It also has its teachers (the authors), its students (the readers), as well as its dean. Its campus, although invisible, is nonetheless real.

As is true of most educational institutions, the faculty generates problems for the dean, but it is really not appropriate to speak of my faculty as a homogeneous body. It actually consists of three factions. In the first place, I have an editorial board which is in essence an executive committee of senior faculty—its members advise, find fault, and are permitted to make unsubstantiated assertions. The biggest portion of the faculty is made up of younger people who really do the work. They are the authors who are kind enough to send their manuscripts for possible publication. A third group is intermediate and overlaps the other two: it is the cohort of reviewers—an elite group of experts comprising both old and young faculty, usually anonymous but very powerful—the Green Berets, as it were, of medical literature.

In a sense, then, this is not a lecture. Rather it is a faculty meeting. Admittedly it is not a meeting of the dean and his faculty, but a faculty that like the migrant scholars of earlier times exercises its talents in many schools. It is a meeting at which the dean, as usual, will harangue and cajole the faculty with the hope that it will see things his way.

As we enter the 1970's the tangible university is characterized by an affect that values an aggressive exploration of change. By contrast, the invisible campus of the learned and educational medical literature appears quite inert—some are unkind enough to maintain that brain death has already set in. The type of literature I have in mind includes not only general medical journals such as the *New England Journal of Medicine, JAMA, The Lancet,* and the *British Medical Journal*, but also publications for the internist—*Annals of Internal*

SOURCE: Reprinted from Franz J. Ingelfinger, "Medical Literature: the Campus without Tumult," *Science*, 169 (Aug. 28, 1970), pp. 831-837, by permission of the publisher and the author. Paper presented at the 15th Annual Meeting of the Western Association of Physicians at Carmel, California, Jan. 28, 1970.

Medicine and the *American Journal of Medicine*, for example—as well as pediatric and some surgical serials. This group of periodicals must have an immense student body: one or more of them must be seen by every physician who looks at the medical literature—which excludes of course that group of doctors whose horizons of postgraduate education are defined by *Medical Economics*. Yet this vast student body appears content with general medical journals that differ little in orientation, format, or style from their predecessors 10, 25, 50, or even 100 years ago.

Editors and their advisers are of course uncomfortably aware that their publication should adapt to changing times. Something, the editors know, should be done about it. The simplest thing to do is to put on a new cover and to change the page size. A common ploy to symbolize progressiveness when a new editor takes over, is to alter typeface and layout drastically. Such exercises at redecorating a publication's appearance are like playing at curriculum reform. The dean may call what used to be third-year outpatient department, "dynamic interaction for community health," but a visit to the place shows that it is essentially the same old department.

The character of the multiversity of educational medical literature may thus be faulted for complacent acceptance of traditional practices, for preoccupation with trivia of design, and for an apparent indifference to more fundamental issues. Yet this lack of tumult does not indicate an absence of issues. They do exist. Indeed, they are well recognized by individual editors, contributors, and readers. Evolution of individual beliefs into party platforms, however, is difficult for obvious reasons. Medical journals are exposed to no activist society of authors, no organized constituency of readers. Even editors have made little effort, at least until the last few years, to examine mutual concerns, and public discussions among those who produce and those who consume the medical literature are all too infrequent.

For today's agenda, I should like to select three issues that are not shaking the campus of medical literature overtly but are responsible for some incipient tremors. These three are (i) reconciliation of faculty and student goals, (ii) relations between medical literature and medical journalism, and (iii) the promotion of social issues.

As is true of many similar periodicals, the *New England Journal of Medicine* is divided into sections such as Original Articles, Special Articles, and Medical Progress. It is in the category of Original Articles that the conflicting goals of authors and readers (that is, faculty and students) are most painfully evident. When articles are submitted for publication in this section, authors not infrequently engage in a stratagem that clearly derives from one of Aesop's case reports. "Dear Sir," the covering letter says, "Enclosed please find a report of a study which we of course could have published in our specialty journal; but the importance of the subject is such that it requires wide dissemination, and for this reason we have selected your journal, as it is known to have a large and varied readership." The implicit flattery may influence the susceptible editor, but its impact on the hard-headed reviewer will be lost, if only for the reason that he never sees the covering letter.

The point I wish to make about these articles is this—although they are submitted in the express hope that they will reach a varied readership, their style of presentation as a rule could not be more effectively designed to defeat this very purpose. Authors who write Original Articles really do not have a varied readership in mind. To the contrary, they use concepts, language, symbolism, and methodologic descriptions that will attract and impress the coexpert. The reasons for this are obvious. Acceptability of the article for publication will be judged first by reviewers who are specialists, and then by similarly qualified and hypercritical readers. If the peer specialist happens to be a department chief or a man otherwise influential in the reaches of academic medicine, so much the better for the young author's status and his chances for advancement. On the other hand, a fine review, or an interpretative and educational presentation of already published material, is no more rewarding academically than is the good teacher vis-à-vis the good researcher. Will a young and productive author then be motivated to write in the style sanctified by the powerful research establishment—and certainly a good style for peer communication—or will he write to educate? My complaint is an old one; the primary objective of the medical faculty is not necessarily education.

The reaction of many readers is well known: too much esoterica, or—to quote from a recent letter—"Indeed it would be a worthwhile experience if they (that is, investigators) spent some time outside the academy with 'gutsy' everyday medicine. Perhaps then they would appreciate the plight of the practitioner trying to dispense a high level of medicine. In following journals, he is flooded with exotic diseases, tons of theory and detailed reports of little interest except to ultraspecialists. The practitioner clamors for more definitive studies on practical problems (for example, postmyocardial infarction and anticoagulation, the value of cardiac resuscitation, cardiac shock, definition and treatment of urinary tract infections and specific 'antibiotic' therapy). But the trained medical scientist responds to this need by reporting another new rare chromosomal abnormality." I call this the reaction of "many readers." The trouble is that I do not know how many. If any constituency suffers from having a silent majority, it is that of medical journals. It is part of the inertness of the campuses that these journals comprise. Yet editors must secretly share the reactions of their epistolarian readers. Outside my own "little Luxembourg" of gastroenterologic expertise, I find many articles in the *New England Journal of Medicine* hard going.

What can be done to respond to the needs of both authors and readers? Perhaps nothing—perhaps their goals are irreconcilable, and the *New England Journal of Medicine* and others like it should abandon the printing of original articles. This is what the former editor of *The Lancet*, Sir Theodore Fox, had in mind when he suggested that medical journals should either fish or cut bait. (I am paraphrasing, of course, for no literary Englishman would ever stoop to such vernacular.) Sir Theodore proposed two types of journals: medical records that would record new observations, experiments, and techniques; and journals, which he called medical newspapers, that would inform, interpret, criticize, and stimulate, all with the purpose of advancing medical practice.[1] A great idea, but one that apparently has not influenced a single general medical journal—not the *Annals of Internal Medicine*, not the *New England Journal of Medicine*, nor even *The Lancet* itself. Somehow these journals not only publish but actually feature—in their very first section—reports of relatively new and original clinical studies.

At this point I should very much like to explain why this is so. I should like to overwhelm you with reasons why the general medical journal continues to publish original articles. In an apologia in *The Lancet*[2] I tried to explain, "The original article has an appeal quite different from that of the comprehensive survey. Perhaps it is the appeal of the first offering as opposed to the secondhand. The reader is more involved, his appetite is less dulled by the flavour of predigestion, and his self-esteem is sustained by the fact that his cerebral exposure to the new is direct, not through a dialysing membrane. Or perhaps editors just *think* that their readers, in response to original articles, are more involved, more piquantly fed, and more intellectually flattered."

That does not have the ring of compelling logic, does it? As a matter of fact, I have nothing better to offer now. The explanation why the *New England Journal of Medicine* continues to publish original articles is based, I suppose, on the most persuasive of human motivations, intuitive belief. Without such original articles, editors of general medical journals seem convinced, our printed efforts would become nonviable, gutless shells.

The editor, thus driven by supernatural inspiration on one hand and the pragmatic needs of his readership on the other, seeks reconciliation. Ninety-five percent of our acceptance letters are conditional—some contributors call them threatening—"We will publish if you will reduce length by half, eliminate five of the ten tables, and clarify your rationale." Usually the authors agree—if reluctantly. I suppose if the investigator, his assistants, his technicians, and his human subjects have labored and suffered for 2 or 3 years—all with the support of a hefty $200,000 grant from the NIH that must be justified—it is understandable why he presents his major message in the abstract, in the tables, in the figures, and several times in the text. There is no good reason, however, why repetition and tables presenting the tedious detail of raw data should not be eliminated. Science does not suffer, for satisfactory means exist to make such tables available to the few who need them.

A few journals—*The Lancet* for example—engage in considerable editorial rewriting to make their wares educationally more effective, but the necessary personnel and talent are scarce.

A device favored by the *New England Journal of Medicine* is to make the editorial serve educational purposes. Many of our editorials are therefore in a sense transitional essays intended to make the meaning of an original article in the same issue clearer to the nonexpert. The editorial should elaborate on the rationale, should put the report into context and, most of all, should indicate how the principal finding or conclusion may directly or indirectly affect patient care. Some editorialists whom we invite, you may be surprised to learn, balk at this. They think that they will demean themselves and lose face if they do not discuss the forefront of knowledge. Men with such attitudes obviously do not belong on the faculty of a general medical journal. Fortunately most of those who are on our editorial-writing faculty—possibly by a process of gradual attrition—cooperate with the dean. Did you by any chance see the editorial

"Rubbish in the Red Cell"[3] in one of last fall's issues of the *Journal?* In this editorial a young and sophisticated investigator in the field of erythrocyte metabolism made it possible for someone like me to see Howell-Jolly bodies, Cabot rings, Pappenheimer bodies, and Heinz bodies, not as mere eponymic monstrosities, but as meaningful defects in the red cell.

Popular belief to the contrary, physician authors with considerable literary talent do exist and, given the opportunity, these men could break out of the exoskeleton that so rigidly determines the shape of scientific medical communication. What would happen, however, if some latter-day Oliver Wendell Holmes or William Osler submitted a manuscript written in his characteristic style? "Revise!" Or some copy editor would unerringly excise all stigmas of individuality. Yet, at least in some areas of medicine, a presentation can be both enticingly educational and scientifically sincere. Whenever I look at the reserve book collection in Harvard Medical School's Countway Library I am impressed that one of the most popular authors, with the largest number of titles on the shelves, is not a physician. It is Mr. Berton Roucché, who writes principally for the *New Yorker*. Yet he has also written urbane and sophisticated detective stories, which in addition happen to be classics of epidemiology. "The 11 Blue Men" is well known, but my own favorite is "The Alerting of Mr. Pomerantz," the story of how the vector of Kew Garden fever, or rickettsialpox, was tracked down.

Wouldn't it be great if some article in the *Journal*, a Medical Progress article describing the components of complement perhaps, were written in the Roucché style? Imagination sweeps me further. Perhaps we could have a socially oriented article dealing with marital infidelity, with case reports written by John Updike. Or Vice President Agnew might contribute a psychonalysis of the effete snob.

But enough of such chimeras. More realistic solutions are possible. In particular I have in mind the type of presentation practiced by *Scientific American*. By careful writing and editing, and by skilled use of diagrammatic illustrations, this publication manages to make archeology attractive to the allergist, and cosmology comprehensible to the conservationist. Why do not medical journals take advantage of the same techniques? As a matter of fact, one journal—*Hospital Practice*—does. It happens to be distributed free of charge, but in this instance a throw-away is for keeping.

During 1970, the *New England Journal of Medicine* will experiment with the same technique. Starting this summer the *Journal's* department now known as "Physiology for Physicians" will have a new subeditor and also a revamped title—"Physiology in Medicine"—a nice example of the face-lifting that is pathognomonic of editor-changing. More important, the new subeditor and I have agreed that we should try the *Scientific American* approach. That we can successfully imitate the style is of course far from certain, but at least the attempt will be made.

Another method to make science more palatable to the medical profession is that of the medical news media, which present simplified but souped-up accounts of the latest in diagnosis and treatment, frequently offered in the same breezy monosyllabic style used by the tabloids in reporting a multi-murder or the latest in scandalous behavior. Here is an example. The *New England Journal of Medicine* is publishing an article entitled "Sequential Atrio-Ventricular Pacing in Heart Block Complicating Acute Myocardial Infarction." When essentially the same thing appeared in *Medical World News*, what do you think the headline was?—"One-Two Punch for Heart Block".[4] Medical news accounts presented in this style are unquestionably eye-catching and entertaining, and they do serve an alerting and informing function. They are relatively up-to-date, and the professional writer is very much in evidence. That such accounts are widely read and appreciated is unquestionable. Doctors, like anybody else, want capsule news, and they want to read it quickly. Indeed, I understand that a recent series on speed reading in *Modern Medicine* elicited over 30,000 reprint requests.

In contrast to these attractive features of what may be called medical journalism are the characteristics of what may be identified as medical literature—laborious presentation, delayed publication, and a ballast of technical detail. Editors of medical literature desire to be scholarly; they would like to exemplify the truth of the statement that what is needed is not faster reading, but better writing that is worth reading slowly. These goals are not always attained, and one may ask whether for general educational purposes the style of medical journalism is not preferable to that of medical literature.

The major difference, if superficialities are discounted, that separates medical journalism from medical literature is the selection of content. News media feature material that is spectacular, novel, and controversial. Although they pride themselves on reporting accurately, there is no assurance that what they report is accurate in the first place. Speculation is not clearly differentiated from well-documented conclusions, and the unwary reader may get the wrong idea. Thus, a furor has followed an article in *Medical World News* that cited some highly tentative suggestions that cat viruses might infect man to induce leukemia.[5] It has led to a variety of modifying or contradictory statements. Here is one released by the Massachusetts Society for the Prevention of Cruelty to Animals: "The front-page story (in a local newspaper) was based on a sensational and inaccurate *Medical World News* report of highly technical papers presented at a recent international symposium on leukemia. Implications in *Medical World News* went far beyond the evidence in these papers.

Cat owners are strongly urged not to panic."

Although I have been differentiating some of the features of medical journalism and medical literature, their territories overlap to a considerable extent. Under the protective label of "preliminary communication," an unsubstantiated concept may find its way into the medical literature with relative rapidity. A superb interpretative essay of impeccable science may be the product of medical journalism. Some outstanding purveyors of medical literature, such as *The Lancet*, downgrade the importance of review by peers. An account in a medical news medium sometimes is so complete that subsequent publication of the same material in the medical literature provides no additional information of importance.

The overlapping interests of medical literature and medical journalism bring me to a second major point—the relation between the standard medical journals and the medical news media. If in this respect the campus of medical literature is sensing a few tremors, I may receive a share of the blame, or part of the credit, whichever way you look at it. Here is what the world's most senior medical editor, M. Fishbein, had to say about it: "After 1925, the medical profession became aware of the great public interest in medical progress. Representatives of the press were invited to attend medical meetings; abstracts of manuscripts, and even complete papers, were sent to news media; and members of the press began to be invited to interview speakers who had important messages even before they read their papers to the assemblage. The sunny horizon that appeared with this trend is now suddenly somewhat beclouded. Editorials appearing in the *New England Journal of Medicine* and in the *American Journal of Obstetrics and Gynecology* demand a total halt to this procedure".[6]

This comment, salted, one might say, by the exaggeration that marks the authoritative, was caused by two editorials. One was called "Prepublication of Portions of Medical Articles",[7] the other was entitled "Definition of 'Sole Contribution' ".[8] Essentially these editorials maintained that articles submitted as "original" had to be original—in other words, not published previously. That two editors who do not even know each other should independently feel obliged to print almost simultaneously such a hoary self-evident fact would suggest that something was increasingly wrong. It was and it still is.

The nub of the problem, the fault responsible for the tremors, is the publication by medical news media of scientific articles in such complete conceptual and documental form that subsequent publication of the same material in the medical literature merely serves archival, bibliographic, and narrow technical purposes. This practice expresses itself in several forms, which are objectionable to varying degrees.

The expression that I find most offensive is the publication in a medical news medium of an article that has already been accepted for publication in the *New England Journal of Medicine*. After an article is selected for publication in that journal—and I might point out that in view of the *Journal's* 15 percent rate of acceptance a very important criterion in the selection is that the article has not been published previously—there is an interval ranging from 2 to 6 months before the date of publication. The average interval is 4 months; it could be 3. During this time the author makes revisions, the editing process goes on, a 7-week printing process takes place, and uncertain delays occur because the backlog of manuscripts awaiting publication cannot be controlled precisely.

Imagine the editor's consternation when during this interval the essence of the article, including the most important figures and numerical data, appears in some other publication—perhaps a standard radiologic journal, or in *Hospital Practice*, or *Science*, or in *Medical World News*, or *Medical Tribune*, or *JAMA*'s Medical News section. If the article appears in the standard medical literature, it may be surmised that the author has engaged in a little hanky-panky. If it appears in the medical news media the responsible mechanisms vary. The author may have been guilty of at least some complicity if he has given a public presentation and has, in addition, made his more complete manuscript, including figures and data, available to be used as desired by inquiring reporters. Or he may be quite blameless if a public speech he has made has merely been transcribed by one of the listeners. Or he may even be an unknowing and unwilling victim of the public relations office of a medical meeting that has made the manuscript available, without his explicit permission, to any reporter who wants to see it—a practice that some professional societies not only permit but encourage, but that warrants, I submit, vigorous extirpation.

Whatever the mechanism that accounts for prior publication elsewhere of an article that has already been accepted by the *Journal*, the end result is the same: the *Journal's* rights, and sometimes those of the author, have been ignored, and one of the criteria used in selecting the article in the first place, has been vitiated. Dr. Fishbein sees no harm in this. He is pleased to remove medical literature from the busy desk and store it on the dusty shelf. The editor of *Medical Tribune*, Mr. F. Silber, likewise sees no harm if his paper gives extensive coverage to an article that is scheduled for publication in the *Journal*. In fact, he sees the practice as mutually beneficial and deplores remarks such as I am making as generating unwarranted competition between medical literature and medical journalism.[9] This assertion is best examined in the light of copyright laws, devised for the purpose of protecting printed material from unethical competition. According to these laws, a medical news medium, or any other publication for that matter, if it quotes text verbatim or reproduces figures from an article that has already appeared in the *New England Journal of Medicine*, must give due credit, and indeed such credit is usually given. Yet when the chronology is reversed, when a medical newspaper or magazine publishes the same material and the same figures from one of the *Journal's* articles just before the *Journal's* publication date, Mr. Silber would argue that this is not competitive. I agree—it is much worse.

The situation is far more complex when a medical news medium presents material that has not yet been offered for publication to the medical literature. Ethical considerations are not at stake under such circumstances, for editors and their advisers can take into account the extent of prior publication when they evaluate any corresponding article that is subsequently submitted. If certain figures have been published, they have at least the opportunity of asking for different ones. In general, the *Journal's* attitude would be influenced in a negative way if the principal ideas of an article, as well as its crucial data and most important figures had already appeared in a medical news medium—just as the effect would be negative if the identical items had been published by a paradigm of staid medical literature.

There has also been an effort to convince science writers that the attitude of the *Journal* and that of *Obstetrics and Gynecology* is a regressive attempt to interfere with a free dissemination of the news. If science writers had come and talked to me about it, I could have tried to reassure them that the meager paragraphs usually devoted to reporting a scientific observation in a lay news medium never come near qualifying as prior publication in my mind. If on that most rare occasion when a medical scientific report is so important that it is covered extensively by *The New York Times*, then probably the *Journal* is happy to publish the second or third report of that same event. Indeed, a few paragraphs in any publication, including *Medical World News* and *Medical Tribune*, do not concern me. Such reporting of the news is perfectly proper in any medium.

There are of course other, rather ticklish points that agitate the issue. It has been argued that those who make scientific presentations at meetings should thereafter edit and amplify a reporter's account of this presentation to ensure accuracy and comprehensibility. It has also been pointed out that medical news reports are usually not cited in scientific bibliographies, but the practice in this regard is inconstant.

When territory is in dispute, it is always hard to draw a sharp boundary, and the more precise a boundary, the greater the opportunity for unhappy repercussions. I believe, however, that it is time for medical literature and medical journalism to reach some understanding.

It should be accepted, first of all, that material that has already been accepted for publication in the medical literature will be handled in a circumspect and restricted manner by medical news media. In particular, direct quotations, specific data, and figures contained in the manuscript should not be used. At the other extreme, summary statements consisting of two or three paragraphs will not be considered objectionable, particularly if the statements are in the reporter's own words, or if material is quoted from a published abstract.

When an account that has appeared to some extent in a medical news medium is then submitted in more elaborate form to a standard medical journal, decision must be based on individual considerations. In general, however, reporters should not ask for, nor should authors offer, excerpts from the text or the specific figures that they eventually hope to submit to the medical literature.

A modus operandi somewhat along these lines has already been accepted by one of the major medical newspapers. Others, I hope, will follow suit. The issue, however, will not be settled by editors, nor will it be clarified by angry or supercilious editorials. It is you, the faculty (the writers) and the student body (the readers), who will decide upon what is desirable and what is proper in this controversial area. My reasons, as far as the *New England Journal of Medicine* is concerned, are certainly selfish, but authors, readers, and editors face a much larger issue: whether extensive and unrestrained prior publication of medical articles in medical news media will in the long run benefit our ultimate objectives, that is, better medical science and the proper care of patients. What will be the effect on these objectives if reports of medical research and study are more and more emphasized in news media, uncritically selected and without the benefit of peer review, with the old medical literature types existing as mere microfiches of themselves in some archival repository? If this picture does not alarm you, let me mention briefly a closely analogous problem: namely, that of priority. If A and B discover something simultaneously but independently, and A's findings are reported first and extensively in a medical news journal, and B's at a later date in the *New England Journal of Medicine*, B would make the *Index Medicus*, but the big splash, noted by all, would be made by A.

Let us not, as Art Buchwald says, be over-communicated. Let us insist that policies of pure laissez faire have no place in our complex society, and that all who put the word of medicine on paper—whether litterateurs or journalists—must for the common good recognize and observe certain rules of conduct.

The *New England Journal of Medicine*, you may have noted, likes to present contradictory views—with the conviction, I guess, that no one can be entirely wrong. The *Journal's* editor reflects his publication's ambivalence, a sort of journalistic expression of that aphorism about ontogeny and phylogeny. For now I want to pay tribute to the medical news media. If it were not for their efforts, the medical profession would be even more ignorant than it is about anything encompassed by the word social—and I didn't say socialistic. We owe a great deal to medical journalism for telling us about economics, ethics, and politics, both national and medical. In this area, by contrast, the medical literature has been woefully deficient. In this area, the difference between the tumult of the tangible campus and placidity of medical literature's invisible campus is most obvious. Does the American medical literature in its overall orientation have its *Ramparts* or its *New Republic?* A silly question. Medical journals don't even have a *Saturday Review*.

In saying this, I am aware that medical student journals, particularly those started by Student Health Organization groups, exist. I am aware of such publications as *Health-Pac*, but these are for the most part parochial and hence restricted in their influence. There are also some rightist publications. One of these is a throwaway called *Private Practice*, which complains about the makeup of the American Medical Association. Why? Because association policies and actions are dominated by educators and researchers. By and large, however, the medical literature in terms of its general attitude and readiness for innovation, consists of just so many *Saturday Evening Post's*.

Admittedly, this is an exaggeration. Nevertheless, look at any standard medical journal—90 to 100 percent of its contents are directed to the science of medicine or its practical application. Articles on the interaction of medicine with its social milieu are very much in the minority. And in specialty journals, except those devoted to the specialty of making money, such articles are practically nonexistent.

As a result many physicians do not understand what the federal government is doing in the field of health. I am not talking about sympathetic understanding; I am talking about simple comprehension. In spite of its fabulous success, the purposes and activities of the National Institutes of Health are little known by physicians except those academically engaged. The purpose and nature of the manifold agencies, task forces, committees—their administrative organization and their specific missions—are complete mysteries to many. Do you know, for example, what the initials HSMHA stand for, or MAAC, or HIBAC? In fact, I've forgotten what they stand for, although I do remember that they represent important administrative and advisory bodies. Necessarily the practicing medical profession knows about the practical details that pertain to the collection of fees under Medicare and Medicaid, but philosophical questions about how the health dollar should be spent are little appreciated.

The dominance of habit is an obvious reason for this state of affairs. The original objective of any trade journal was to promote performance of that trade. Philosophical questions of how that trade meshed with other trades to attain broad humanitarian goals did not appear vital. In fact, it is only recently that society has become aware of itself? that many people, not just a few philosophers or politicians, have become socially conscious. It is thus not surprising that the professional literature of an ultraconservative profession is among the last to respond to changing times.

Another reason for this state of ignorance is that there is no general and unbiased source of information. Doctors, like other citizens, may read about the activities of the Department of Health, Education, and Welfare in the daily press. Fuller coverage, as I have acknowledged, may be found in some of the medical news journals. These, however, usually are descriptions of what was done, not an interpretation of the problems that are being attacked, nor a reasoned explanation of why a certain federal action took place in the field of health. If a more elaborate account does find its way into the standard literature, its purpose is apt to be promotional rather than informational. A functionary in the government, if he has the time and interest to write an article, will usually closely adhere to the party line, that is, his account glows with praise for the federal agency that employs him. The converse obtains when the American Medical Association engages someone to describe a federal activity.

In short, right now, we have no group of authors who have the time, interest, and competence to explain in an analytical manner to the average physician, by means of the standard medical literature, the doings in Washington. No wonder the medical profession distrusts political efforts in the field of medicine. No wonder the doctor fails to get responsibly involved when his literature does not inform him of the variety of problems and alternatives.

In other areas, a faculty interested in the sociopolitical aspects of medical practice does exist, but its output is inferior, at least it seems so to an editor accustomed to general medical trade writing in which concepts are supported by data and an attempt is made at originality and rigorous objectivity. Outstanding vices of this faculty are undisciplined repetition and speculation, endorsement of proposals and schemes without a shred of evaluative evidence, and extrapolation of generalizations from anecdotes. Anyone who reads the literature related to health problems in the United States is well aware that this country's record in infant mortality is relatively poor, that in some regions malnutrition prevails, and that in certain rural and urban areas the unavailability of medical care is critical. Yet the *Journal* continues to receive manuscript after manuscript that reports these points ad infinitum. Perhaps some people feel that truths, like falsehoods, have to be iterated over and over before people will believe them. One writer on prepaid comprehensive health provision even had the gall to send to the *Journal* a manuscript that not only repeated the ideas of another article of his that we had already printed, but actually contained paragraphs that word for word were the same. Authors on social topics must learn that their passion for a cause does not give them license to dispense with originality.

Another characteristic of this new and not yet mature faculty in social medicine is its tendency to submit plans for correcting a certain deficiency but without any evaluation of the feasibility or success of that plan. Time after time we find that we must reject articles that consist of enthusiastically presented but totally untried suggestions. In other instances some attempt at evaluation is made, but the evidence is pitifully inadequate. Recently, for example, we had a manuscript in which the authors found that a patient population that was under regular surveillance by a health team required fewer laboratory tests and x-rays than a control population that visited outpatient or emergency facilities on an ad hoc basis. So far so good, but what do you think the conclusion was? It is cheaper to provide planned-surveillance-type medical care than that which is conventionally available at present. This is a startling deduction, but it was reached by simply ignoring the costs necessary to support the surveillance team and its facilities. Even a noneconomist like me can detect some weakness in this balance of accounts.

The tendency of the social medical literature to analyze on the basis of what happens in a single or a few instances is of course a methodologic problem. Quantitative measurement is difficult and intuitive deductions are correspondingly encouraged. Thus the weakness of the faculty in this respect is not personal; it reflects the underdeveloped state of the discipline.

Even reviewers in this general area are soft. They are so emotionally committed to the social goal that they may recommend acceptance of a grossly inferior article merely because it endorses a desirable objective. "I know, I know," said an otherwise skeptical professor of community medicine when I remonstrated with him for recommending a dreadful manuscript, "But the art needs help–you've got to make allowances."

Perhaps general medical journals should engage the services, as science does, of a cadre of reporters whose duty it would be to analyze the social environment of medicine for those who practice medicine.

Last fall M. J. Halberstam maintained that his type of solo practice was just great, that doctors should stick to doctoring and that it was not their business to cure political or social ills.[10] That doctors should be excused or excluded from the duties and privileges of citizenship is strange argument, but in any case it is irrelevant to the principal reason why physicians must become better acquainted, through the medical literature and other means, with the sociopolitical problems of medicine. One of those endlessly repeated but yet true statements about which I complained earlier is that we are confronted by a "massive crisis" in health care and that "we will have a breakdown in our medical system which could have consequences affecting millions of people throughout the country" (the words are President Nixon's). A physician, like any other citizen, may or may not want to become involved in problems of war, poverty, or school integration. But he must know, if only for his own sake and welfare, how well in the opinion of society he is doing his job. He should have some ideas about the systems that are available for improving his performance, and it is to his advantage to be cognizant not only of the systems that he could voluntarily adopt, but those that he might be forced to accept.

Probably the greatest potential influence on this university's adaptability, its sensitivity to changing needs, is its student body. On the whole the student body (the readership) of the medical literature has been a passive entity that has influenced *Journal* policy but indirectly through its subscriptions. A major problem, I recognize, is that the readership has no means of formulating its thoughts as a body and then communicating them to the editor. Furthermore, I do not wish to give the impression that I am recommending guidance of medical journal policy by a majority vote of the readership. I do wish, however, that the invisible campus of medical literature were wired with a better feedback system involving all of us, for all of us are readers, most of us are writers, and many of us are editors or reviewers.

NOTES

1 T. Fox, *Crisis in Communication: The Functions and Future of Medical Journals* (Oxford Univ. Press, London, 1965).

2 F. J. Ingelfinger, *Lancet* 1968-II, 766 (1968).

3 D. G. Nathan, *N. Engl. J. Med.* 281, 558 (1969).

4 "One-two punch for heart block," *Med. World News* 10, 38 (4 July 1969).

5 "Track of the cat at leukemia scene," *Ibid.* 10, 13 (17 October 1969).

6 M. Fishbein, *Ibid.* 10, 44 (28 November 1969).

7 S. L. Israel, *Obstet. Gynecol.* 34, 469 (1969).

8 Editorial, *N. Engl. J. Med.* 281, 676 (1969).

9 Editorial, *Med. Tribune* 10, 19, Section 2 (16 October 1969).

10 M. J. Halberstam. "The MD should not try to cure society," *The New York Times Magazine* (9 November 1969), p. 32.

ABOUT THE AUTHOR–Editor of the *New England Journal of Medicine* for the past five years, Dr. Franz J. Ingelfinger has been on the faculty of the Boston University School of Medicine since 1940, his latest position being Clinical Professor of Medicine. He received an A.B. from Yale and an M.D. from Harvard. He is a Diplomate (gastroenterology) of the American Board of Internal Medicine, and has served on the staff of a number of Boston hospitals.

Dr. Ingelfinger is a Past President of the American Gastroenterological Association, a Fellow of the American College of Physicians, and a member of many other professional societies. Among his other editorial assignments are that of Editor of the Gastroenterology Section of the *Yearbook of Medicine* from 1953 to 1969 and Chairmanship of the Editorial Board of *Gastroenterology* from 1964 to 1968. He has served as a consultant to the National Institute of Arthritis and Metabolic Diseases, the National Institutes of Health, the Medical Research and Development Command of the U.S. Army, the Surgeon General of the U.S.A.F., and the Armed Forces Epidemiological Board. His interest in libraries and continuing education are evident from the fact that he was a Trustee of the Boston Medical Library for many years, a member of the Biomedical Communications Study Section of the Public Health Service, an Advisor to the National Library of Medicine, and Director of the Post-Graduate Medical Institute of Boston.

Death of an Experiment

by David Green

Information Exchange Groups (I.E.G.'s) are a means of rapid communication between scientists in an informal, but structured, manner. The communications distributed are a little like the letters among scientists which in the last half of the seventeenth century became the first periodicals. Dr. Green describes how the I.E.G.'s were discontinued. The student should study this paper in conjunction with that of Dr. Ingelfinger to understand the issues involved in the transition from informal to formal communication among scientists.

In 1961, Errett C. Albritton of the National Institutes of Health, Division of Research Grants, conceived and initiated a remarkable experiment in communication among scientists. The experiment took place in the biomedical sciences, but the idea on which Dr. Albritton's experiment was based is one which is relevant to many technical areas—indeed, any area where rapid communication is important. This is the first of two reasons why the story of this experiment should be told. But the second reason may be of even greater significance: A few months ago, the experiment came to an abrupt and puzzling end. How this came about, and why, shall be the other component of this narration.

If this experiment in communication were only of interest to biomedical scientists, there would be little point in giving an extended account. But I believe it no exaggeration to say that Dr. Albritton's idea represents one of the most revolutionary innovations in the history of science communication.

The plan and strategy of the experiment was simple. A sharply focused field of inquiry was selected as the umbrella for a particular group of scientists. For example, I was a member of a group whose subject matter was electron transfer and oxidative phosphorylation. A group chairman was selected whose essential mandate was to ensure that every active worker in the field should become a member, and that communication between members should be maximized. The only qualification for membership was evidence that the applicant was an active worker in the field. Membership was open to workers from any country of the world. Of the 725 members of my group, 329 were resident outside the U.S., with 32 different countries represented.

Our group was set up in early 1961. Because it was the first group to be established, it carried the name IEG No. 1. By 1966 six additional IEG's had been established and were functioning smoothly. During those five years, the number of participating investigators increased from a few dozen to several thousands. The success of the experiment was rapid and profound. But at the point when the value and the validity of the idea had been established—and when plans were being formulated for both the long-term structure of existing groups and the expansion of the concept to other groups, the editors of five biomedical journals met and agreed to refuse publication of any manuscript previously circulated via IEG. This unaccountable decision turned out to be lethal to the IEG. In late 1966 all seven IEG programs were terminated. (It was my pleasure to serve as chairman of my group—IEG No. 1—and hence I can hardly consider myself a neutral commentator, but I shall strive here to give more than a one-sided account of l'affaire IEG.)

The rise and fall of the Information Exchange Groups has much to tell us about how important decisions affecting the scientific community are made, about the confusion existing between what

SOURCE: Reprinted from David Green, "Death of an Experiment," *International Science and Technology*, number 65 (May 1967), pp. 82–84, 86, 88. Copy written by and reprinted with the permission of *Science and Technology*, May 1967 issue, and the author.

is good for science and what is good for the journals, about the crises faced by scientific journals generally, and about the unwillingness of some editors to face up to the obvious facts that the journals can satisfy only a diminishing part of the needs of the scientific disciplines in respect to communication of information.

Let us look more closely at the mechanics of the idea. The office of the IEG in Washington undertook to transmit any communication submitted by a member to all listed members of his particular group, with group members abroad receiving their communications via air mail. (Many scientists from Eastern Europe–including the U.S.S.R., Poland, Czechoslovakia, East Germany–were among the most enthusiastic members. Just before the termination, our group had considered the admission of an investigator from mainland China; the approval for his admission had been given by the State Department.) The time elapsed, from receipt of a communication in Washington to its transmission via the mails, could be a matter of days or weeks. In the early days, IEG communications were circulated within a week of the time of receipt.

A communication could be anything a member chose to submit: a copy of a paper he had submitted for publication, a comment on another communication, a long paper or a short paper, a request for information, a review article, a protest against some indignity, even a sounding off about something or other. You name it and there was bound to be a communication answering such a description. No censorship of any kind was exercised, but one notable limitation was imposed. At the discretion of the chairman, communications containing slanderous statements of a personal nature could be returned for revision. Wherever possible, efforts were made to induce authors to withdraw defamatory remarks, but when a deadlock was reached the contributor's right to speak his piece was never denied.

Officially, IEG Memoranda (as the communications were called) were treated as personal communications; they could not be mentioned in the established literature, other than as personal communications. However, all members agreed to honor and acknowledge the sources of information even though the memorandum referred to had no status in the established literature. What some critics believed would be the principal roadblock to the growth of IEG (the priority of discovery problem) turned out to be of minimal importance: in general, there was the most scrupulous observance of the code of honor in recognizing priority of discovery or acknowledging a concept that had made its debut through IEG.

The first two years of our group were rather lean: only 27 Memoranda were submitted. Then the floodgates opened and there was a torrent that steadily increased in volume with the passage of years and the augmentation of membership. Nearly 800 communications were distributed to members of our group throughout the period of its lifetime. It was thus possible to know on a current basis what every active worker in the field in all parts of the world was accomplishing. At least 90% of the important papers in my field were being processed through IEG No. 1 before the group was terminated. This meant that every IEG member received quickly information relevant to his field–at least six months sooner than would be the case if he waited to read it in his professional journal. Through the IEG's the "exotic" journals were monitored for the membership. The days of library hunting were over for workers in the seven fields.

Workers in foreign countries acknowledged that our IEG made it possible–for the first time–to be on an equal basis with their American colleagues with respect to the updating of information, since the major part of the research in our field–the field of electron transfer and oxidative phosphorylation–originates in American laboratories. The end of IEG meant the return to scientific isolation of a large number of investigators in laboratories outside the U.S.

In the early days, many believed that the IEG's would be outlets for a flood of rubbish. This flood never materialized. When a communication is to be scrutinized by 700 or more experts, only a fool would risk presenting an inferior article or a potboiler. The quality of the communications was certainly no worse than the quality of articles found in the published literature, and this despite the absence of reviewing or editorial selection.

The IEG reestablished debate and dialogue among scientists. It was possible to criticize outworn theories, inadequate experiments and conclusions–in fact, anything that drew the wrath of a member. This type of dialogue has virtually disappeared from the scientific journals. No one argues a point in a journal if it takes a year from the time of submission of a manuscript to the time of publication. Moreover, journal editors frown on controversy. It is this ban on controversy that explains why certain untenable theories have become canonized for decades in the literature befor they could be rooted out.

One of the most satisfying features was the time saved by knowing who was doing what and where. Before a manuscript by *X* was submitted to, or was published in, one of the journals, *Y* might come along and show *X* to be wrong. One did not have to wait years to correct a mistake or argue a point. This could now be done in days or weeks. Occasionally, an SOS was sent out by a member for information on an obscure point. Within the month the required information would come through. Such were some of the dividends of the IEG.

How much did the experiment cost? It is estimated that the 1966 cost for the printing and distribution of memoranda for *all seven* IEGs came to a total of $416,000. The cost of IEG No. 1, relative to the total expenditure required to support the salary and research expenses of each of the 725 members, was $1 for every $73 of research cost. This ratio is based on an estimate of $10,000 as the assumed mean cost of supporting one scientist for one year anywhere in the world, and $100,000 as the known cost of supporting IEG No. 1 for one year. When viewed in proper perspective, the annual cost—$140 per member—was miniscule, relative to the dividends received by the members and the total cost of supporting their research.

Not all seven IEG's were unqualified successes. It soon became apparent to Dr. Albritton that the choice of the right umbrella to hold an IEG together was critical; without this, the IEG lacked unity and *esprit de corps*, and the membership was indifferent and apathetic. But at least five of the seven groups were highly successful and the formula for setting up other successful groups had been thoroughly worked out by the end of 1966.

During the first four years of the IEG experiment, no major criticism was openly aired. Many editors of scientific journals were members of one or another IEG and their advice and counsel in respect to the day-to-day problems of IEG were sought and received. There was no publicized evidence that any journal editors were opposed to the operation. There seemed to be general agreement that it would fill a need for rapid communication that could not be satisfied by the journals and that the journals would continue to be the final arbiters of the form in which communications would become part of the archival literature.

But this absence of criticism was deceptive. In a meeting in Vienna, in the early fall of 1966, the executive editors of five biochemical journals decided to reject the publication of any article that had been distributed previously through IEG. James Shannon, director of the National Institutes of Health, was informed of this impending move by way of a letter from the chairman of the group of editors. Federal-funding agencies are traditionally sensitive—and properly so—to the charge of interfering in the making of policy by scientific societies, and although the action of the editors must have seemed almost incredible to NIH, it was accepted as representing the will of the societies. In retrospect, it was not the failure, but rather the overwhelming success of the experiment, which finally spelled its doom.

Some basic questions have to be raised to see l'affaire IEG in proper perspective. What is the aim of science? Quite apart from the quest for truth, which is the framework within which scientists operate, the aim of science reduces to the solution of outstanding problems. Anything which leads to, or accelerates, the solution of problems is in the best scientific interest. Conversely, anything which obstructs or slows down the process is not in the best scientific interest. This is, in fact, the yardstick by which the U.S. government, through its funding agencies, decides how and where to spend its money on science. By this yardstick, there can be no question that IEG had an important place among the devices and tactics calculated to facilitate scientific progress. By intensifying and accelerating communication among scientists, IEG was rendering a notable service to science. In my view, its strangulation was a disservice to science.

The journals are the servants of the scientific community, charged with the responsibility of sifting from the mass of manuscripts the few which add significantly to our knowledge. Moreover, the journals play a critical role in maintaining the standards of scientific research. But the journals, by reason of their rigidity and formalism, cannot embrace the entire scientific effort; nor should the journals serve as the exclusive arbiters of this effort. As science progresses and expands, each journal will be able to deal with a steadily decreasing proportion of the scientific effort.

This leads to the thesis that we have lost sight of some important facts; decisions made by apprehensive editors are not necessarily in the best interest of science. The crisis of the journals antedates IEG. If anything, this same crisis will be intensified by its demise. IEG was a step in the direction of solving the problem of the information explosion. Surely the journals, wedded as they are to inherently slow publication processes, cannot cope with the problem alone.

The setting of scientific policy is the responsibility of the professional societies. In the society with which I am affiliated, the American Society of Biological Chemists, there is a special publication committee (elected by the membership) entrusted with the responsibility for making all policy decisions with respect to the administration of the society's journal. What does the record show with respect to the operation of the constitutional safeguards? The policy decision pertaining to the abolition of the IEG was not made by the publication committee. The decision was made by the group of editors. The tentative decisions of the editors at the Vienna meeting were made known to James Shannon *before* the members of the publication committee had an opportunity to evaluate them. No one considered it necessary to inform or consult the membership of the various professional societies represented by some of the editors. Incredible as it may seem, an issue of transcending importance to science was decided by 5 editors. Two of these men were answerable only to their publishers and were, therefore, without direct responsibility to the scientific community; the others in the group, although answerable to some society, chose to participate in the lethal action without either consulting or informing the membership. An ironic twist was that the American scientists learned what was going on behind the scenes by reading an announcement in *Nature*, the English weekly journal. The editors of *Nature* spilled the beans prematurely. It became apparent to the American scientists that in a matter of profound importance to them and to science, their wishes had neither a forum for expression nor a spokesman.

Much has been written in the columns of *Nature* during the past few months about the iniquities of the IEG. It was touching to learn, for example, of the concern of the anonymous editor of *Nature* for the high cost of IEG to the National Institutes of Health. Whoever was responsible for these unsigned editorials has had little or no accurate information about the realities of the IEG. Insulting jibes such as "pamphlets galore" were among the tactics used to discredit the IEG without even an attempt being made to describe its workings objectively. One must assume the *Nature* author was fearful lest IEG impair the position which *Nature* has assumed as a medium of rapid communication in science. One cannot criticize the editors for their zeal in protecting what they considered to be their journals' best interests. They would be expected to show such zeal. But, just as it would be folly to ask the railroads to make policy for the trucking industry, so it would be unwise to expect that editors can act completely judicially and rationally in matters in which they are already committed and compromised by their very positions.

Science recently published a full, official statement of the position of the editors with respect to IEG. In their statement, the editors acknowledge the value of the IEG, recognize its contribution to the problem of communication, and praise many of its innovations. In fact, this statement is probably the most powerful defense of IEG yet written.

The editors' essential action—to ban the circulation of material intended for publication—could only have one end result, namely the emasculation of IEG. What is there to communicate other than the material which is destined for eventual publication? To restrict the IEG to material that is not destined for publication would have the effect of turning it into a debating society of marginal interest to scientists. The NIH clearly interpreted this decision of the editors to ban distribution of papers through IEG as a fatal restriction; no granting agency would be interested in supporting communication in such attenuated form.

What are the reasons given by the editors to justify the ban on IEG? Dual publication, copyright infringement, and the danger of misunderstanding are the trio of stated reasons.

Dual publication, in the sense used by the editors, is a daily practice in science. At the annual meetings, at international meetings, at symposia, the same material that was or is to be published is reiterated again and again. There are in fact journals like *Science, Nature* and *Biochemical and Biophysical Research Communications* which specialize in the preview of work to be published more fully later on. The spectre of dual publication can hardly be taken seriously even if we equate the distribution of preprints among members of an IEG with dual publication (an equation which few scientists would accept). Actually, there is only one form of publication that has significance to the scientist—publication in a professional journal. Everything else is merely communication.

Infringement of copyright is an even less convincing reason. The laws of copyright apply *after* publication of an article, *not before*. In any event, what has copyright to do with the dissemination of scientific information at the primary level? The results of science are in the public domain.

The possibility of misunderstandings and confusion arising from the transition of a manuscript from the form published in the journals is set forth as yet another reason for the ban on IEG. There are only two known instances, among several thousand memoranda distributed by IEG, in which any confusion could have arisen. Can the journals point to a better record?

It is my opinion that the stated reasons are not the real reason. Rather, the stated reasons merely hide the fact that the editors were apprehensive that the status and prestige of the journals would be downgraded if another agency (IEG) were distributing to its members, from 6 months to a year earlier than the journals, the very papers which would eventually appear in the journals, though not necessarily in the same final form.

The editors of the classical journals have vented on IEG their dissatisfaction with the present status of their journals. It is common knowledge that few scientists rush to read the journals. The exciting developments are well publicized long before they reach the stage of publication in the established journals. This is not the fault of IEG. This state of affairs antedated IEG and it will continue, whether IEG continues or not.

There is basically no conflict of interest between the IEG and the established journals. Each can serve an important function in the scientific process. There are two stages in the discovery of new concepts and the experimental verification of hypotheses. The first is an explosive, chaotic phase, characterized by rapid changes in direction and excited controversy. It is hard to distinguish fact from conjecture at this first stage, so IEG and the media for rapid publication are the logical forums of expression here. Indeed, censorship and publication restrictions can be fatal during this transitional stage in scientific development. When the dust has settled and the unassailable facts have to be set forth in their definitive form, then and only then is it the appropriate time for the application of the winnowing and sifting process by the journal editors and the reviewing apparatus. For the journals to attempt to encompass these two phases in scientific development is folly; to discourage the first phase is a disservice to science.

In the best interests of science, the question of the IEG should be reopened and the appraisal made by scientists of stature, appointed by each of the professional societies and perhaps by the AAAS. These people should be neither IEG partisans nor editors of journals. The decision has to be made in the framework of what is best for science. Only a decision arrived at properly, without bias and prior commitment, will be acceptable to the scientific community, whatever the decision turns out to be.

As a final comment, one should pay tribute to Errett Albritton who conceived the concept of IEG and masterminded this massive experiment. In addition, the willingness of the National Institutes of Health to undertake such a bold and far reaching experiment is one of the many tokens of the imaginative policy of the director, James Shannon. The pity is that the efforts of these men and their collaborators should be nullified in such an unconsidered and offhand way.

ABOUT THE AUTHOR—Dr. David Ezra Green has been Professor of Enzyme Chemistry and Codirector of the Institute for Enzyme Research, University of Wisconsin, since 1948. His undergraduate and master's work was done at Washington Square College, after which he received a Ph.D. from Cambridge University. He continued work at Cambridge as a Research Supervisor and Research Fellow until he went to Harvard in 1940. Between 1941 and 1948, he was first Associate in Biochemistry and then Assistant Professor of Biochemistry and Director of the Enzyme Chemistry Laboratory at Columbia University College of Physicians and Surgeons.

His leadership of the Information Exchange Group on electron transfer and oxidative phosphorylation evolved naturally from his research interests. Discoveries with which he and his group are associated include: mechanisms by which fatty acids are oxidized and synthesized in the animal body; mechanisms by which sugar is oxidized to carbon dioxide and water in the animal body; the discovery of metalloflavoproteins; and a theory of organized enzyme systems. He has published and edited a variety of books and journal articles, among them the following: *Mechanisms of Biological Oxidation* (1940); *Molecular Insights into the Living Process* (1967); and *Energy and the Mitochondrion* (1970).

The Biomedical Scientist's Use of Recorded Information

Biomedical libraries and information services provide a link between one scientist as transmitter and another as user of information. To facilitate the biomedical scientist's access to the recorded information, the librarian must understand the environment of medical communication and its structure and function already discussed. He must also study current patterns of the medical scientist's use of libraries and information centers and look at possible future designs of health science information centers.

This section contains recommendations based on a detailed study of current patters in handling biomedical research information as well as a description of an information center, a representative library use study, and a design for a future center.

Communication Problems in Biomedical Research: Report of a Study. Introduction, Statement of Basic Considerations, Conclusions and Recommendations

As explained in Dr. Cannan's introduction, an extensive study of communication among working scientists in the biomedical area was carried out in 1963. The summary published here highlights the more detailed reports that were published in Federation Proceedings.[1] *Many of the objectives stated in this document have now been accomplished; others have been tried and abandoned; but there remain many suggestions that merit serious consideration. The total work is still the most complete study of biomedical research communication that has been carried out.*

It has been aptly said that new scientific knowledge is increasing much more rapidly than any other product of society. Many scientists have expressed their belief that the present problems of communication within the scientific community are critically different from those of the past. Because this outpouring of information results directly from the great expansion of research that has been instigated and financially supported by society, it is not surprising that society also has begun to be concerned. Specifically, the question is being asked whether the new knowledge is being transferred as expeditiously as it might be to those in a position to use it in the public interest.

Pressures for action to improve communication in science are developing in both the legislative and the executive arms of government. For some time, the Senate Committee on Government Operations has been probing and exhorting. Meanwhile, the Federal Council on Science and Technology has been working to improve the exchange of scientific information among the many government agencies involved in research, and the Office of Science Information Services of the National Science Foundation has been encouraging the systematic study of problems in communication and the search for more efficient methods of processing scientific information, as well as promoting cooperation among all activities, both private and governmental, that handle scientific information. The President's Science Advisory Committee initiated two broad studies that led to reports containing specific recommendations for action.[2] Although these studies attempted to cover science as a whole, their general recommendations were influenced primarily by conditions in the physical sciences and associated technological fields. The Public Health Service issued a report dealing directly with the biomedical sciences and the health professions.[3]

Initiative, however, has not by any means been confined to the agencies of government. Within many quarters of the scientific community there has been a parallel increase in concern and activity. Sessions devoted to the problems of scientific communication,[4] committees to seek solutions, and society action programs have become common.

As an extension of these and other efforts to assess and strengthen the information resources of science, the Director of the National Institutes of Health, in October, 1962, invited the Chairman of the Division of Medical Sciences, National Academy of Sciences–National Research Council, to organize and conduct "a broad examination and assessment of the problem of communication among working scientists in the biomedical area." Subsequent conversations indicated that the Director was thinking of an intensive study that would develop, in the space of a few months, some basic considerations that would be helpful in shaping national policies with respect to improving the biomedical communication complex, i.e., the aggregate of all information activities serving bio-

SOURCE: Reprinted from "Communication Problems in Biomedical Research: Report of a Study," *Federation Proceedings*, 23 (Sept.-Oct., 1964), pp. 1119-1132, by permission of the publisher.

medical research. It was therefore agreed that the proposed study should have limited objectives. First, it should be confined to "scientist-to-scientist" communication, recognizing that better communication between working scientists and professional practitioners and between scientists and the public are urgent social needs worthy of separate study. Second, the study should survey the broad potentialities and implications of modern information technology, rather than attempt to evaluate specific applications in information processing that are already being actively investigated by other competent groups. And third, the importance of encouraging the flow of biomedical information across national, linguistic, and cultural boundaries should be acknowledged, but emphasis should be placed on the problems and needs of the generators and users of biomedical information in the United States, and on actions relating to the American biomedical community.

If anything more than a superficial survey were to be made within the imposed time limit, it was evident that the Division would need the help of organizations already knowledgeable in the field of biomedical communication. Accordingly, the cooperation of the Federation of American Societies for Experimental Biology (FASEB) and the Institute for Advancement of Medical Communication (IAMC) was sought and has been given without reserve. The Office of Documentation of the Academy–Research Council has also been most helpful. Dr. Richard H. Orr, Director of IAMC, accepted responsibility for the design and conduct of the project and for the assembly of a small group of expert consultants to undertake special studies on a part-time basis. An outline of a program was quickly developed and the study was formally launched on January 1, 1963, with a target date of the end of October, 1963, for completion of the report.

Shortly after the staff work began, an Advisory Committee was appointed under the able chairmanship of Dr. Maurice B. Visscher. The members were selected to be broadly representative of the biomedical field and on the basis of an avowed interest in questions of scientific communication. The function of the Committee was to guide the staff studies, to review the results, and, on the basis of these and of the opinions and judgment of its members, to develop a statement of principles, conclusions, and recommendations.

Within the limitations of time and of staff, the study was designed to achieve the following objectives: 1) to survey the existing complex of information services, and to consider the degree to which it constituted a coherent, functional system (including not only such formal channels of communication as meetings, journals, indexes, abstracts, and reviews, but also informal, person-to-person communication); 2) to analyze past and current studies of scientific communication in terms of their pertinence to the biomedical field; 3) to collect data on the biomedical information services and the communication habits and prejudices of biomedical scientists, and to collate views on ways of improving the existing biomedical communication complex; and 4) to identify basic principles and derive conclusions, as guidelines for private and governmental agencies responsible for promoting biomedical communication, distinguishing between actions that may appropriately be taken forthwith and those that require further study or testing on a pilot scale.

The findings were summarized in a brief report, supplemented by a compilation of staff working papers, and formally submitted to the Director of the National Institutes of Health. The report is published here with only minor revisions of form. Those who have worked on the project hope that it will be of interest to those engaged in biomedical research and to the specialists in communication who seek to serve biomedical research.

R. Keith Cannan, Director

Division of Medical Sciences, National Academy of Sciences–National Research Council, Washington, D.C.

STATEMENT OF BASIC CONSIDERATIONS

A. Nature of the Problem

1. The Problem is Real and Concerns Both the Public and the Scientific Community

Communication in science, as in most human affairs, has always been and always will be a problem. The past two decades, however, have witnessed changes that aggravate this chronic problem of science. Not only has the output of new scientific information increased, but also the horizons of the traditional scientific disciplines and the ways in which research is conducted and administered have changed profoundly. These developments have combined to impose on the national resources for scientific communication severe stresses that are both quantitative and qualitative.

Most scientists today acknowledge that the communication problem is real and important, but relatively few feel that the situation is so critical as to call for crash programs or precipitate massive innovations. The general demand is for continuing intensive study and experimentation; and the scientific community has, accordingly, approached the problem conservatively by expanding established forms of communication and by evolving and testing new forms.

Today, however, scientific communication is no longer the concern of scientists alone. It is a problem in the public domain. Now that society has adopted research as an important instrument of national policy, the scientific community must accept the obligation to satisfy the public that the massive social investment in research is being soundly managed. Some of those responsible to the public for the nurture and surveillance of the research effort have become fearful that the social returns on the investment are being delayed by inadequate communication of the results of research to potential users. This concern has also been voiced by individual scientists in all fields.

The community of science must examine critically its ability to continue to manage and improve its own communications. Unless the scientific community shows more concern for this problem, it is likely to lose some of its traditional control over the forms of its communication.

2. The Problem is International, but National and Regional Initiative Will Speed Progress

Because science is not constrained by national or cultural boundaries, scientific communication must be international in its scope, and free exchange across geographic and language barriers must be encouraged in all practicable ways. The promotion of cooperation and innovation at the international level, however, is a slow and deliberate process. Progress can be accelerated if functional national and regional scientific organizations will put their own houses in order and take the initiative for international action.

3. The Problem is Science-wide, but the Realities of the Present Organization of Science and its Communications by Disciplinary Groups Need be Considered for Effective Action Toward Improvement

An ideal system of communication would embrace all of science. Science is largely organized and managed, however, by disciplines and in disciplinary groupings, not only professionally and institutionally, but also with respect to sources of support. Inevitably, these disciplinary groups have developed channels of communication to meet their own particular needs. To make the most of the communication resources they have developed, and to prevent disruption of their communications, the disciplinary groups must play an active role in the development of the new and expanded services required to handle the growing volume of scientific information.

4. The Biomedical Community is a Functional Disciplinary Grouping Appropriate for Initiating Action to Increase the Efficiency of its Communication Channels

The life sciences constitute a rational segment of science and, within the life sciences, the biomedical sciences are a coherent group identifiable by their own professional and institutional organizations, by common conceptual foundations, and by particular obligations to the health and medical services of society. Like other disciplinary groupings, the biomedical community has evolved its own communication channels. It is appropriate that this community assume the initiative in designing and implementing the changes required to serve its special communication needs. Although it seems best, for practical reasons, to approach the problems of scientific communication at the biomedical and national levels, it is of the utmost importance that means should be developed to improve interdisciplinary and international coordination of these partial efforts so that the intellectual unity of science may be sustained.

B. Nature of Scientific Communication

1. The Functions of Communication Services are Broader Than Mere Transmission of the Results of Research

It is sometimes implied that the primary need for good communication services is to ensure that the final product of research shall be expeditiously incorporated into the body of current scientific knowledge. This is a narrow view. Scientific communication fertilizes research at all stages in its conception, development, and fulfillment. The kinds of communication services that the scientist requires change with the progress of his investigation.

2. Scientific Communication is an Intellectual, not a Mechanical, Process

The problem of improving scientific communication should not be conceived as chiefly one of finding more efficient means of switching "facts" from points of origin to points of use. The problem is much more complex and elusive than this. Intrinsically, scientific communication is an intellectual interaction between individual minds. It is personal and intimate. It has an evanescent quality and is loaded with value judgments. Conceptual scientific communication in particular requires a degree of resonance between sender and receiver that cannot be ensured by efficient switching devices. Any service that is to aid this process should be so designed as to accommodate these subjective attributes of the process.

3. The Complex of Activities Contributing to Scientific Communication is Only Partly Formalized

Studies of the scientific communication complex and efforts toward its improvement have tended to concentrate on the formalized channels and tools of written communication, such as journals, bibliographies, abstracts, and reviews. Recently, the formalized oral communication represented by the structured part of meetings has received some attention. The working scientist, however, does not depend on these formal channels alone. Much of his essential communication, whether oral or written, is informal and is achieved through impromptu exchanges on a person-to-person basis by conversation and correspondence. In the operation of the communication complex and in the design of communication services or "systems," these informal means of exchanging information should be given due weight.

4. The Need is for Better Rather Than More Information

The power of science grows by the continuous reordering of knowledge in the light of new information and concepts, rather than by mere accretion of "facts." The mounting output of biomedical information calls for a more rigorous winnowing of the wheat from the chaff—a more severe control of quality—and for greater emphasis on viewing new information in the perspective of the old. Such control and critical evaluation should be exercised at all stages of the communication chain, from generator to user. Only biomedical scientists can perform these vital functions of science.

5. Communication Requirements Vary With the Individual Scientist, His Role, His Field, His Project, and His Environment; This Variety Must Be Accommodated by the Complex of Information Services

A scientist may play many roles in the biomedical scene. At one time or another, he may be investigator, practitioner, teacher, evaluator, administrator, or manager. What information he requires and how he wants it will vary with his role as well as with the field of his inquiry, the nature of his problem, the progress of his investigation, and the intellectual environment in which he is working. An effective biomedical information complex must be comprehensive and flexible enough to respond to the changing requirements of the individual scientist and to accommodate the wide variety of biomedical investigations and investigators without imposing on all the patterns peculiar to any one. An information service that attempts to be all things at all times to all scientists is likely to be satisfactory to none.

6. Modes of Communication and Types of Information Service Useful in the Physical Sciences Are not Necessarily Appropriate for Biomedical Research

The range of functions that the biomedical communication complex is called upon to perform is much the same as that in any other area of science. The environment of biomedical research, however, is distinctive in many respects. The fact that biomedical investigation is focused on the nature of living processes imposes unique restraints upon experimental approaches and unique levels of complexity on the ways investigators organize their thoughts and vocabularies and pursue their studies. Large organized programs of research are the exception and the technical report, which plays so important a role in engineering and in areas of the physical sciences that are oriented toward technical development, is a relatively unimportant channel for biomedical communication. Biomedical research, moreover, is conducted mainly in academic institutions and is rooted in individual initiative. For these reasons, new forms of communication and new types of services that serve other scientific communities effectively will not necessarily be appropriate to, or of comparable usefulness in, the biomedical sciences.

C. Design and Management

1. The Biomedical Community Should Retain Responsibility for Managing its Communication Complex

In the past, the community of biomedical scientists has been largely responsible for evolving and managing its own information services. This is natural inasmuch as the biomedical investigator is the primary generator, evaluator, and user of the information generated by the biomedical research effort. The vast expansion and the professionalization of this effort in recent years has greatly magnified the task of processing documents and information but has not created any critically new situation that justifies relieving biomedical scientists of this responsibility.

2. Today's Communication Problem Requires New Relationships Between Biomedical Scientists and Professional Information Processors in Their Information Services

The traditional handlers of scientific information— editors, librarians, and publishers—have been recently reinforced by new types of information processors between generators and users—documentalists, computer engineers, information system designers, audiovisual experts, document analysts, and other kinds of specialists. Despite the efforts of the most able processors of both the traditional and the newer types, however, the communication complex cannot function efficiently without the active and educated participation of the generators and consumers of the information. The mounting loads and demands on this complex can be met only by intimate cooperation among generators, processors, and consumers. Those who process biomedical information must be integrated into the biomedical fellowship.

3. Tomorrow's Communication System Should be Developed From the Present Complex by Judicious Introduction of Innovations

It is sound policy to build upon the communication complex that now exists and has been proven by experience. Major innovations should be incorporated only after they have been tested for acceptability, efficiency, and compatibility with other components of the complex.

4. Effective Coordination is Necessary to Transform the Present Complex into a System That can Perform as Required at Reasonable Cost

An ideal system for biomedical communication would provide any scientist with the information he needs, when and where he needs it, and in the forms best suited for his use. The existing complex of services comprises many interdependent organizations, activities, media, and languages that must be integrated into a coherent system if these requirements are to be approximated. At present, mechanisms for effective coordination are poorly developed. Both the over-all performance of the complex and its efficiency in terms of returns for expenditure of manpower and money suffer. Better coordination is necessary to ensure complementarity and compatibility between journals, abstracting services, and libraries, as well as among libraries and among abstracting services. The argument for coordination is not, however, an argument for a monolithic master plan. There is need for flexibility and plurality in information services. There is a place for some redundancy and for some services that repackage information to serve particular groups and individuals.

5. A Comprehensive Communication System Requires Services for Information Processing as Well as Document Processing

A comprehensive biomedical communication system must include not only document processing—the systematic distribution, storing, and cataloguing of documents so that they reach those likely to be interested and may be retrieved readily on demand—but also the collection, evaluation, digestion, synthesis, dissemination, and retrieval of items of information selected from documents and other sources. This information processing begins where the processing of documents leaves off and requires a different type of processor. Compendia, critical tables, and review articles represent traditional types of information processing. These are and will continue to be of great value to science. These forms do not, however, completely meet today's needs for specific information on demand. Recently a number of services have been established that provide users, on a continuing or demand basis, with items of information in a narrowly defined field. These services have come to be known as Specialized Information Centers. Those services that also undertake to provide expert evaluation of the quality, validity, and significance of the information proffered qualify as Specialized Information Evaluation Centers of the type recommended in the Weinberg report.

6. Authors and Editors Must Participate to Make Document and Information Processing More Efficient

Efficiency in processing documents and information for ready retrieval and use requires close cooperation between the generators of information and those who carry out the processing operations. Authors and editors must accept a responsibility for presenting new material in forms that facilitate indexing, abstracting, evaluation, and synthesis.

7. Modern Technology Should Be Exploited With Full Appreciation of its Promise and Problems

Modern information technology, including intellectual techniques as well as mechanical and electronic equipment, by saving time and manpower, can contribute significantly to making better services possible. Mechanization of clerical operations can greatly expedite storage and retrieval of documents. Every effort should be made to exploit these new techniques in biomedical communication. Future technological developments hold the promise of automating completely some types of information services, including operations now considered to be intellectual as contrasted with mechanical but it should be recognized that the transition from partial mechanization to complete automation may carry the danger of reducing the flexibility previously provided by men in the processing chain. Efficient mechanization and automation will require a greater degree of coordination and compatibility of services than now exists.

8. Local Biomedical Libraries Are Logical Channels for Access to Total Resources for Document and Information Processing

Services are more readily adaptable to individual needs and are more fully used if they are in immediate contact with the scientist. A coordinated network of strong local libraries and information services, linked to the large national and regional libraries and to other centralized information services, will provide the channels through which a scientist can tap national resources yet retain the advantages of dealing by personal contact with a local service.

D. Support: Funds, Research, and Manpower

1. The Biomedical Community Previously Exercised Control of its Communication Complex by Holding the "Purse Strings"; Ways Must Be Found to Preserve Control as Public Subsidy Increases

In the past, biomedical information services have not, in the main, been a public charge. This is a healthy tradition that should be maintained as far as possible because it provides the best assurance that the biomedical community will continue to control its own communications. With the great expansion of scientific information in recent years, however, it has proved impossible to maintain some of the essential communication services and to meet some of the demands for new and improved services on the same basis as in the past. The sponsors of research have found it necessary to subsidize many services performed by private organizations and to establish and operate themselves a number of new services, some of which are intended primarily to serve their own managerial needs. The necessity for research sponsors to support communication services will probably increase as biomedical literature and the size and complexity of the biomedical research effort continue to grow. In this situation, it is essential that new mechanisms be developed to preserve control by scientists and ensure that elements of the complex do not become autonomous and poorly related to the community functions they are intended to serve.

2. Research on Scientific Communication Can Speed the Total Biomedical Effort; It Should Be Generously Supported and Recognized as a Scientific Endeavor in its Own Right

Research on the means and processes of communication can make a very significant contribution to the national biomedical effort. Generous support is warranted, both for investigations and pilot projects that seek to exploit advanced information technology for biomedical communication services and for basic inquiry into the functions served by communication processes. Equally important for bringing the best talent to bear on the problems of biomedical communication is the recognition of communication research as an endeavor in the same scientific tradition as the more traditional lines of research.

3. Mounting Demands for Trained Personnel to Provide Services and Conduct Research in Communication Require Recruiting and Training Programs Best Based in Adacemic Institutions

There presently exists a shortage of trained personnel to man existing biomedical communication services. Any large effort to improve and diversify these services will intensify the demand. A sustained effort in recruitment and in the provision of a variety of training programs is required. There is need to recruit personnel whose major experience has been in biomedical investigation or instruction and to train them in the techniques of handling documents and information. There is need, also, to acclimatize librarians, documentalists, and other types of specialists in information handling to the concepts and practices of biomedical investigation. Both types of training are best provided in an academic atmosphere where education is associated with research in communication. Graduate schools for the biomedical sciences, with their local communication services and their university environment, can supply this atmosphere but will probably need to be subsidized if they are to develop the needed facilities.

Although the required numbers of personnel are smaller, recruiting and training programs for research in communication are equally critical. The ideal atmosphere for these programs is also the biomedical graduate school.

CONCLUSIONS AND RECOMMENDATIONS

A. Responsibilities of the Biomedical Community

In the catalogue of Basic Considerations that has been presented above, repeated emphasis is laid on the principle that the biomedical community must continue to play an active role in the conduct and management of its communications if the quality and usefulness of the scientific record is to be maintained. These responsibilities should be accepted not only as an obligation to science and to society, but also as a challenge to scholarship. A large segment of the biomedical community does accept this obligation and challenge. Many others, however, are reluctant to serve as teachers, editors, referees, critics, or evaluators of the literature in the fear that these responsibilities will be a burdensome distraction from their own investigations.

1. Community Action

There is a need to diffuse more widely among scientists an appreciation of the principle that the nurturing of good communications is an intrinsic and rewarding part of the advancement of knowledge, a hallmark of scholarship, and a stimulus to creativity. A need exists also to extend greater academic recognition and prestige to those scientists who willingly contribute thought and effort to the improvement of scientific communication and to the members of those professional groups that operate information services for the benefit of scientists. Participation in the communication process should be more widely spread over the expanding biomedical community so that the burden on individual scientists will not be onerous and the fellowship of science will be enriched.

2. Individual Action

Much can be done by individual scientists to improve the existing channels of communication and prepare for the introduction of new types of information services.

a. In their role as instructors, scientists should place more emphasis on training their graduate students in oral communication and the use of visual aids, in the writing of original papers, in editing and abstracting, and in the preparation of critical reviews and bibliographies. There is need also to train students more adequately in the use of libraries and of other information services and to encourage them to explore the potentialities of modern information technology. All these activities should be introduced to students as intrinsic elements in the life of a mature investigator. Instructors should be alert to identify the occasional student who evinces an unusual interest in problems of communication and should encourage him to pursue these problems as worthy intellectual endeavors.

b. In their role as investigators, scientists should seek to cultivate a closer fellowship with the staffs of the institutional libraries that serve them so that a spirit of mutual participation in research by the generators, users, and processors of information may be cultivated. Libraries will be encouraged thereby to seek to improve and diversify their services in ways that will be most responsive to the needs of individual investigators.

c. As members of faculties, scientists can promote the importance of local scientific communication services at the administrative levels of their institutions and can press for more adequate support of institutional library services.

d. As members of national advisory groups, scientists have the opportunity to encourage sponsors of research to promote the study of problems in communication and to explore the potentialities of new proposals.

e. As members of editorial boards, scientists should also seek to improve coordination, to maintain high standards of quality, to accelerate publication, and to reduce costs. They should cooperate with the Conference of Biological Editors and with other private and governmental organizations in seeking these ends.

B. Facilities and Services

The following conclusions and recommendations pertain to improvements and innovations in information services and facilities.

1. Meeting Announcement Services

The Library of Congress, the Department of Health, Education, and Welfare, and other governmental and private agencies provide information on forthcoming meetings of interest to biomedical scientists in addition to the meeting notices printed in many professional journals. *Science* and the *Journal of the American Medical Association* publish particularly extensive lists of future meetings. International meetings are covered by the Council for International Organizations of Medical Sciences. These announcement services are steadily improving but do not cover all meetings.

A national clearinghouse of information on biomedical meetings should be established in an appropriate institution such as the National Referral Center for Science and Technology of the Library of Congress. Those who sponsor or support meetings should ensure that the organizers of these meetings inform the clearinghouse of plans and programs.

a. Open meetings. The proposed clearinghouse would provide any meeting announcement service with information on open meetings to supplement that from their own sources and would also, on request, provide organizers of prospective meetings with information on possible conflicts or duplication.

b. Closed meetings. Attendance at many biomedical meetings is limited to invited participants. Support for many of these closed meetings is sought from funding agencies, which, if they are to program effectively and to avoid undesirable duplication, should have means of learning whether related meetings have recently been held or are under consideration. The proposed clearinghouse would provide this information.

2. *Translation Services* (see also sections B.8.*b*. and *c*.)

a. National translation clearinghouse. Although the past few years have seen the development of several private and governmental centers that maintain lists of existing translations of scientific documents and provide copies of translations on request or inform potential users about where these translations may be obtained, the completeness, speed, and ease of use of the service provided by these centers leave much to be desired.

The Public Health Service (PHS) should assume leadership to ensure that an effective national clearinghouse is developed for the biomedical community by working with the National Science Foundation (NSF) to improve one of the existing clearinghouses. To avoid the expense of paying for translations that have already been made elsewhere, biomedical libraries and information services should be able to learn quickly from such a clearinghouse, by mail or faster means, whether a desired translation is available elsewhere.

b. Local translation coordination centers. All libraries of institutions conducting biomedical research should act as local translation "coordination" centers to which biomedical scientists could turn first when they need translations. Libraries should be organized to perform the following functions in response to a request: find a translated abstract; determine whether any of the institution's staff have the required language and subject-matter proficiencies; arrange for partial translations by local staff; search lists of translations that have been made elsewhere and, if the desired translation is available, obtain a copy; contract with commercial services for translations that cannot be accomplished by local staff, that are not listed as available, or that are urgently needed; and register any translations made or ordered locally with the national translation clearinghouse.

3. *Audiovisual Services* (see also sections B.10.*a*. and *b*.)

For biomedical information recorded in audiovisual form, the National Audiovisual Facility of the Communicable Disease Center of the PHS should be developed to the point where it is analogous to the National Library of Medicine (NLM) as a central resource for such records and a compiler of "tools" for their retrieval.

4. *Specialized Information Evaluation Centers or Services*

The term "specialized information evaluation center" (SIEC), or "service" if decentralized, should be used to designate a service available to scientists on a national or international basis that performs one or both of the following functions for a field of research and development: evaluation of the quality, reliability, or validity of information; and synthesis of information extracted from a number of documents or other sources. Providing this type of service requires the participation of scientists who are themselves actively engaged in research in the given field.

By this definition a number of existing services qualify as specialized information evaluation centers (or services), for example, the *Handbooks of Biological Data* complied under the auspices of the Federation of American Societies for Experimental Biology, the American Physiological Society's continuing series of *Handbooks of Physiology*, and periodicals devoted to critical reviews, as well as less conventional services, such as the Psychopharmacology Service Center of the National Institute for Mental Health (NIMH). Existing services of this nature should be supported and strengthened once their quality and utility have been established.

Currently there is considerable enthusiasm for establishing new centers to handle unpublished and published information in active biomedical research areas and to provide service that emphasizes currency, speed and responsiveness to inquiries by individual scientists. The value of this type of SIEC, when properly conceived and organized, has been established for certain areas of engineering and the physical sciences. However, since such centers are expensive in terms of both money and research manpower, and since biomedical research has distinctive characteristics, this concept of service should be adopted with caution in the biomedical field pending the outcome of pilot projects. Agencies funding biomedical research should support by contract a limited number of carefully selected pilot projects for a 3- to 5-year period, with built-in provisions for objective evaluation. Special attention should be given to ensuring that such centers utilize to the optimum the services of existing document processing services, such as the Medical Literature Analysis and Retrieval System of NLM (MEDLARS), rather than duplicate their work.

Although not designed specifically to evaluate

this concept of information service, experience with the National Clearinghouse for Mental Health Information now being developed by NIMH, and the National Clearinghouse for Drug Information planned by the PHS, will also provide information useful in assessing the promise and problem of SIEC's in biomedicine.

5. *Specialized Information Centers*

This term is currently used very loosely; at one extreme it is used as equivalent to SIEC, at the other it denotes a collection of documents specialized for a particular area of research and organized to provide rather conventional library services to scientists on a national or regional basis. Several hundred services in the United States have been identified, to which this term in the broad sense might be applied. Currently the National Science Foundation is encouraging the development of objective methods for evaluating the quality and utility of the variety of services offered by such centers. Although there are undoubtedly areas of biomedical research that could profit from the services of centers that attempt to collect all available information in a given area (published and unpublished) and that organize documents so that they may be retrieved in highly sophisticated ways, in general the greatest promise seems to be in centers that process information rather than documents and that make possible true information retrieval, by providing scientists with the specific items of information they want rather than referring to documents that may contain the desired information. This type of service may consist of publishing a "tool" that assists such information retrieval, e.g., the *Index-Handbook of Cardiovascular Agents*, or of answering specific inquiries, e.g., the *Cancer Chemotherapy National Service Center of the National Cancer Institute.*

Like SIEC's, this type of center is expensive in money and scientific manpower. Although scientists actively engaged in research may not be necessary for this type of information processing, a high level of scientific competence is required. Support for existing and new centers of this type should be governed by the same consideration as for SIEC's.

6. *Local Biomedical Libraries*

The libraries of academic and research institutions represent a vital component of the biomedical communication complex. This component has, however, deteriorated progressively from lack of support while the demands on it have steadily mounted. If institutional biomedical libraries are to function as local information service centers through which the scientist can tap the total national resources for document and information retrieval, and if scientists are to obtain the documents they learn about through the more efficient reference retrieval services that are being rapidly developed, strengthening this key component of the complex must have the highest priority.

An effective program to repair the damage resulting from years of neglect, and to transform biomedical libraries into modern information service centers, will require substantial financial support as well as efforts to train personnel, to develop new and improved types of services, to establish standards of service, and to elevate the status of libraries in the academic environment. (see sections B.2.*a*., C.4, D.2.*a*., and E.1.) For the short term, this support should be in the form of direct grants-in-aid to academic libraries in amounts sufficient to enable each to improve substantially and rapidly the quality and scope of its services and to enable all to meet certain minimal standards of service. This aid should supplement, not replace, regular institutional support. For the long term, means must be found to ensure that these libraries are adequately and continuously supported so that they may provide a high level of services to biomedical scientists. This may require the routine allocation to library services of a set percentage of research funds received by biomedical institutions.

7. *Interlibrary Loan Services*

The load on the interlibrary loan network of the biomedical information complex has been increasing steadily and promises to mount sharply with the imminent advent of new and improved reference retrieval services. The capacity of this network is seriously strained at present and is grossly inadequate to meet the loads of the next few years. Pending the results of a special study (see sec. C.4.*b*.) of ways to improve this network and the establishment of effective monitoring of the traffic in this network, immediate steps should be taken to provide short-term support for this network by subsidizing the interlibrary loan services of academic and other nonprofit institutions.

8. The National Library of Medicine

As the central resource for the network of biomedical libraries and information services, and as the major indexing service in the biomedical field, NLM is the hub of the entire document retrieval component of the biomedical communication complex. NLM is to be congratulated on the careful planning that has gone into the MEDLARS program and into increasing the coverage, currency, and quality of *Index Medicus*. The biomedical community and all agencies concerned with biomedical communication should give NLM full support in its efforts to improve its services, which are indispensable to the effectiveness of the present complex and to its future development.

NLM is at present considering many plans for new types of bibliographic services. The following represent endeavors worthy of special attention:

a. It is essential for the biomedical sciences to have a single, master bibliographic tool that is truly comprehensive and sensitively reflects the changing scope of biomedical research. NLM should be encouraged to broaden the coverage of *Index Medicus* and MEDLARS to encompass the total output of U.S. biomedical research, beginning with that supported by National Institutes of Health (NIH) and other governmental agencies, regardless of whether the form of publication is a journal article, book, technical report, or other type of document, and irrespective of whether the document is covered by another indexing service. Indexing performed by other services could be accepted if compatible with MEDLARS and suitable for the biomedical community.

b. NLM, in consultation with the National Federation of Science Abstracting and Indexing Services, should be encouraged to seek out gaps and deficiencies in the abstracting coverage of biomedical literature and to assume leadership in seeking to close these gaps and correct any deficiencies (see section B.9., C.3., F.2.) Particular effort should be made to ensure that all substantive foreign literature is being abstracted with reasonable promptness. The current NLM program to improve abstracting coverage of Russian literature as well as that in other languages commanded by few American scientists is an excellent step in this direction. Eventually, it may be desirable to include for each biomedical document stored in the MEDLARS system either an abstract or information on where abstracts of the document may be found.

c. NLM currently supports the publication, in widely circulated journals, of translations of Russian articles carefully selected by editorial referees. This program is an excellent way of introducing to the U.S. biomedical community relatively unfamiliar and neglected segments of the foreign literature. NLM should be encouraged to extend this concept to other foreign-language material that is also unfamiliar to American scientists.

d. NLM should utilize the full resources of the Federal Library System (the Library of Congress, National Agricultural Library, etc.) and endeavor to fill, in this way, requests by libraries for biomedical documents not held by NLM.

e. Although, in the MEDLARS program, the terminology of requests for subject searches will be used as a guide for revising and updating the subject headings used for indexing and producing *Index Medicus*, NLM should be encouraged in its efforts to establish continuing mechanisms whereby the community of research workers can participate directly in developing new subject headings and revising outmoded terminology.

f. NLM should ensure that the biomedical community and its libraries are aware of recent changes in the policy of the Defense Documentation Center (formerly the Armed Services Technical Information Agency, ASTIA) that make available to all grantees and contractors of the PHS the center's services for searching the technical report literature and supplying copies of reports.

g. Depository for unpublished documents. There is a growing need for a mechanism whereby voluminous tables and other details too lengthy to include in published papers can be made available to the relatively few who need this type of material. Pilot trials of new forms of publication, in which copies of documents are furnished on request (e.g., see sec. B.10.*c*.), also require a similar mechanism. Therefore, NLM should examine the question of a proper depository for such "unpublished" documents that would deliver the documents rapidly and inexpensively, and should decide whether the biomedical field should use the present depository service provided by the Library of Congress or establish one elsewhere.

9. Specialized Abstracting and Indexing Services

Aside from the broad, inclusive abstracting and indexing coverage recommended in sections B.8.*a* and *b*., the most pressing need is for a special study to develop standards for abstracting and indexing services (see sec. C.3.) and for a program to continuously monitor biomedical abstracting and indexing (see sec. F.2.). In the meantime, support of conventional types of abstracting and indexing services by agencies funding research should be limited to relatively narrow fields where a special need can be convincingly demonstrated. Any such specialized services should make maximal use of the output of the major broad services and should be supported by short-term contracts. Continuing support should be dependent upon objective and systematic evaluation of the quality and utility of the service.

10. Pilot Trials of Nonconventional Types of Services

The evidence accumulated in other fields of science and from studies of scientists' information habits and requirements is adequate to justify carefully designed and selected pilot trials of several nonconventional types of information services. Agencies funding biomedical research should support by contract, for limited periods, such pilot trials to test the feasibility, value, and acceptability to the biomedical community of these types of services, and to assess their compatibility with existing conventional services. These pilot trials might include: *a*: making available quickly, on request, informal records (in the form of documents or audiovisual materials) of oral reports given at meetings; *b*: using telephone, radio, television, and motion pictures to bring the benefits of active or passive participation in meetings to a broader segment of the United States and international biomedical community; *c*: publishing, by established journals, of abbreviated versions of papers, the full texts of which are supplied on demand in full-size or microform copies and are processed by abstracting and indexing services; *d*: using advanced techniques in the publication of established biomedical journals, e.g., computer composition, phototypesetting, microform editions, author composition, and methods for obtaining continuous "feedback" from readers; *e*: screening computer tapes that list new documents, such as the magnetic tapes produced in the MEDLARS program, to provide individual biomedical scientists with a current awareness service specially tailored to their interests, habits, and preferences; and *f*: providing thesauri of current terminology in major areas of biomedical research suitable for use by authors and editors in choosing indexing terms to be published with journal articles or supplied to appropriate abstracting and indexing services. Such thesauri should be compatible with and complement those of the major, broad indexing services, such as *Index Medicus* and *Chemical Abstracts*.

C. Special Studies Needed for Policy Decisions

It is recommended that further study of the areas outlined in this section be undertaken before certain policy decisions are made regarding support of information services. Other investigations of a more general nature are recommended in section D.

1. Prepublication Channels of Information

a. Meetings, conferences, and symposia. The contemporary biomedical scene is characterized by a heavy calendar of meetings varying widely in purpose, form, and size. Some follow traditional patterns of scientific assemblies while others take forms improvised to cope with the expanding population of biomedical scientists and the changing horizons of the disciplines. The sponsors of research are being increasingly called upon to support meetings of all sorts and varieties and are embarrassed by the lack of criteria by which wise decisions may be made. In the absence of an agreed set of principles, there is danger that choices may be made on the basis of the uncoordinated decisions of many independent advisory groups or simply on a policy of "first come, first served."

There is need for a deliberate study leading to the development of an acceptable set of criteria to guide those responsible for programming and funding the national biomedical research effort. The study should include a survey of current practices in the organization and conduct of meetings, of the extent to which duplication occurs and is justified, of the purposes served by different types of assemblies, and of the views of the biomedical community on the informational functions of various types of meetings. Consideration should also be given to the question of how the products of meetings should be placed in the printed record. The study should be under the direction of a representative group of biomedical scientists in consultation with officers of organizations experienced in the planning of meetings and with representatives of research funding agencies.

International congresses and international meetings of more limited scope provide unique channels for formal and informal oral communication between American scientists and those in foreign countries. Judicious support of these assemblies by funding agencies is fully justified by the substantial contribution that they make to the advancement of biomedical knowledge and to the encouragement of international cooperation in research. International biomedical meetings are, however, increasing rapidly in number and in variety of sponsorship and subject matter. Such international bodies as World Health Organization, International Council of Scientific Unions, and Council for International Organizations of Medical Sciences should be encouraged to intensify their endeavors to improve the quality of international meetings, to experiment in new forms, and to minimize undesirable duplication.

Requests for the support of the organizational costs of international meetings and for travel funds for participants continue to mount. The investment of U.S. funds is already substantial and could become disproportionate to the scientific returns if wise discrimination is not exercised in alloting funds. The efforts of funding agencies to develop criteria for administering the funds available to support international communication should, therefore, be endorsed by the scientific community.

b. Directories and registries of ongoing research. Some agencies (e.g., National Aeronautics and Space Administration and Atomic Energy Commission) have extensive services to inform individual participants in their research programs of the existence of other contemporary work related to their own. Recently, NIH began publishing an annual subject index of all its extramural grants. A service with more comprehensive coverage is offered by the Science Information Exchange (SIE). This organization seeks to maintain as complete a registry of all ongoing research as possible and a file of summaries of all active research projects. SIE is prepared to make searches of this file for responsible scientific organizations and individual scientists. It is to be commended for the services it provides and should be encouraged to increase its coverage, particularly with respect to intramural research in government institutions and to projects that are not included in the program of major granting agencies.

These kinds of services are available to those responsible for the administration of funding programs and those who direct mission-oriented programs. They are also helpful to those who wish to explore current trends in the national research effort. As yet, however, there is little evidence bearing on the extent to which working scientists use services such as SIE or the *NIH Research Grants Index*, or on the potential value of these services for the conduct of research. A study of these questions would be helpful in guiding policy with respect to modifying or expanding these kinds of services.

2. *Publications*

a. Page charges. The expanding output of original papers, coupled with the increasing costs of publication, has forced up subscription rates of many journals close to or beyond the point of diminishing returns. Journals that are unable to command large advertising revenues or do not receive some other form of subsidy are threatened with insolvency or restrictions on the volume of material they can publish. A form of support coming into increasing use is the page charge. Insofar as funding agencies accept these charges as part of the costs of research, they are obviously providing an indirect subsidy to the journals that use this device.

The problem is not simply an economic one. If the practice of page charges is not to be abused, funding agencies must develop criteria for determining whether the charges of a particular journal will be accepted. The costs of an indiscriminate policy will be high and difficult to assess, and such a policy will tend to encourage uneconomic practices and to perpetuate journals that have outlived their usefulness. A policy of discrimination, on the other hand, will have the effect of withdrawing from the biomedical community a measure of control over its channels of primary communication.

There is urgent need to study the question of page charges before this device becomes a generally accepted practice in the biomedical field. The study should examine in depth the anticipated effects on the standards of primary publication in the biomedical field of this and other forms of subsidy.

b. Economics of publishing separates. From time to time it is suggested that the user of biomedical information would be better served if he received only those articles that interested him rather than bound issues containing all articles accepted by journals in his field. The usual proposal is that a journal circulate to its subscribers a list of titles of accepted articles. Separates of all articles would be printed and distributed to libraries while individual subscribers would be entitled to receive the particular articles they selected from the list of titles.

As a preliminary to any pilot trial of this form of publication, it is recommended that a study of costs be undertaken. It should be possible from the unit costs of the various operations involved to derive a formula that would predict costs in defined situations to the user, the publisher, and those who would have to process the documents, e.g., librarians, and abstracting-indexing services.

3. Abstracting and Indexing Services

The development of consistent policies for support of abstracting and indexing services is hampered by lack of approved standards and criteria. As a basis for the development of standards, a careful study should be undertaken of duplication, promptness, accuracy, compatibility, and users' needs. Any proposed standards should be reviewed by representative groups of biomedical scientists and operators of abstracting and indexing services.

4. Library Services

a. Standards. It is increasingly evident that institutional libraries will require additional public support if they are to meet the needs of the expanding research activities of their institutions (see sec. B.6.). Subsidy is, however, justified only if acceptable standards of service are met.

The present standards for service by institutional libraries vary widely and are not defined in terms of the needs of the user. A study is needed to establish minimal standards and optimal goals for the operation of the various services that local libraries offer. These standards will provide valuable guides in developing a long-term program for the support of biomedical libraries.

b. Interlibrary loan system. The present informal system of interlibrary loans is perilously close to breakdown. Short-term measures to preserve this vital service are recommended in section B.7. Several plans have been suggested for the long term: 1) a new centralized system might be developed around the National Library of Medicine, which would undertake to meet all demands for interlibrary loans of biomedical documents throughout the nation; 2) regional loan centers might be established to serve restricted areas; or 3) local biomedical libraries might be so strengthened as to become self-sufficient. Each of these proposals would involve large commitments in funds. A systematic study of present and future needs and of the relative advantages of these and other alternatives is required before a course of action is chosen.

D. Research and Development

Systematic research and development in scientific communication is relatively new. The biomedical sciences can profit from lessons learned in the physical sciences, where research and development in scientific communication first became a major endeavor. Although activity in this new field has recently expanded rapidly, the promise that such research offers for increasing the effectiveness of the entire scientific effort has only begun to be realized. Up to now concentration on the problems of storing and retrieving documents and information and of mechanical translation has led to relative neglect of large areas equally fruitful for study. A balanced, long-term program of research, including behavioral studies and new conceptual approaches to communication, as well as exploitation of mechanical and electronic devices, is required for major improvements in biomedical communication.

1. Specific Research Projects

A number of specific studies and projects have been recommended elsewhere in this report. Here attention is called to broad areas that have special promise for research and development.

a. Meetings: improvement of the design and conduct of meetings of all types;

b. Journals: assessment of quality control by refereeing and other means, publication habits of authors, foreign distribution of U.S. biomedical publications;

c. Linguistics: languages for facilitating man-machine exchanges, spoken languages to facilitate international communication;

d. Microforms: applications to publishing and document storage, studies of acceptability and economy;

e. Media other than the printed word: uses of film, video tape, computer tape, sound recordings, and other nonprint media in biomedical communication;

f. Behavioral studies: habits and prejudices of biomedical scientists as generators, evaluators, and users of information; relation of creativity to use of information resources; and

g. Potentialities of future technologic developments: probable implications and impact of practical associative electronic memory banks, machine translation, and high-speed character readers and telefacsimile transmission upon biomedical communication.

2. *Centers for Research and Development*

SIC's and SIEC's, although functioning primarily as national services, must maintain active programs to develop their services if they are to maintain quality and efficiency and meet the demands of increasingly sophisticated scientist-users. Two other types of centers, however, are also needed in the biomedical community to provide appropriate environments for developing the entire spectrum of document and information processing services, to exploit the potential of audiovisual media, to improve methods of oral communication, and to conduct research on the fundamental processes of biomedical communication.

a. Centers for development of local document and information processing services. Local Development Centers associated with enterprising biomedical libraries should be established as "grass-roots laboratories" for assessing, with a local population of users, the utility of conventional types of library services and for testing new ways to supply scientists with the documents and items of information they need. This kind of practical development must be conducted in the realistic setting of an institution engaged in biomedical research, inasmuch as success can be determined only by continuous, intensive feedback from actual users of the services proffered. Academic institutions are particularly good settings for such centers, because the development program could be a cooperative endeavor of the library, the departments active in biomedical research, and other parts of the university, e.g., an engineering or library school.

Proposals for establishing these centers should be judged competitively, with no prior decision as to how many centers should be established. As particular centers prove outstandingly productive, they should be encouraged to expand their programs. Where the associated library provides regional as well as local services, a Regional Development Center can evolve.

b. Centers for broad research in biomedical communication. In addition to the library-centered development programs described above, there is an urgent need for research centers where all the processes of biomedical communication can be studied at a broad conceptual level and all communication media and techniques can be explored. This type of center should be established as a Department of Biomedical Communication within a graduate biomedical school. Its primary function would not be to act as the development arm of the school's library or of other local communication service activities, such as photographic and illustration services, but rather to provide a combination of teaching and broad research, like any of the usual departments of biomedical schools.

Each of the three types of research and development programs described as appropriate for SIC's and SIEC's, for Local and Regional Development Centers, and for Departments of Biomedical Communication can, when conducted separately, make a significant contribution. Some academic institutions, however, offer opportunities for establishing more than one type of program. A single school might have research and development programs associated with a SIC that serves an international population of scientists, with its local library, and with a Department of Biomedical Communication. Such a combination would be synergistic and constitute a major resource for research, for training specialists in information services, and for preparing scientists for careers in communication research. Only when the kinds of centers for research and development recommended in this report have been established in universities and have begun to provide intellectual leadership will the full contribution of communication research to the biomedical effort be realized.

E. Training

A major obstacle to expansion and improvement of information services for the biomedical community, and of research and development in biomedical communication, is the lack of qualified personnel, which is already critical.

1. Training for Biomedical Information Services

Information services require numerous types of personnel with a variety of skills, knowledge, and experience; and programs for training such personnel must be correspondingly varied. Knowledge of the subject matter of the biomedical sciences, competence in foreign languages, understanding of the functions of communication media and of the principles of processing documents and information—all these are required in greater or lesser degree for the different types of positions to be filled. The special training needs of photographers, illustrators, manuscript editors, and experts in telecommunication should also be considered.

The various types of research centers proposed in section D. offer favorable environments for training personnel for biomedical information services. Other settings in which valuable training can be secured are library and engineering schools, indexing and abstracting services, and SIC's and SIEC's. Establishing and conducting training programs will, in many cases, require financial support for teachers and trainees and for other operating costs. The experience of the National Science Foundation in evaluating proposals for training programs should be drawn upon by other sponsors of programs.

2. Training for Research in Biomedical Communication

Diversity in the backgrounds of candidates for careers in communication research is desirable. The main qualification would seem to be a strong motivation for research, supported by graduate training in some scientific field or substantive experience in a scientific information service. A doctoral degree in medicine or in a biomedical science is desirable but not essential. The National Institutes of Health are to be commended for recognizing the importance of this type of training and for sponsoring pilot programs.

For graduate training of the type and quality required to prepare candidates for investigative careers in biomedical communication, an academic environment is especially important.

F. Coordination of the Biomedical Information Complex

One of the main purposes of the study summarized in this Report was to delineate more clearly how each type of service in the biomedical communication complex contributes to the dissemination of information and to the exchange of ideas and experience. In general, each service came into being because some group of biomedical scientists identified a need and sought to fill it. It is natural, therefore, that more thought and effort have gone into the nurturing of the individual services than into the task of integrating them into a functional coherent system.

1. Journals

The editorial boards of journals have a responsibility to monitor the efficiency with which their journals are fulfilling their intended purposes. This they do with varying degrees of diligence in respect of such ponderables as rejection rates, backlog, speed of publication, circulation, and costs. Less thought is given to coordinating the policies of a particular journal with those of others in respect of subject coverage, duplication, uniformity in terminology and citations, and possible savings in printing and publishing overhead that might result from group action.

The establishment of the Conference of Biological Editors in 1956 reflected a realization of the need for a larger measure of coordination in the management of the journal literature. This organization serves as a forum for the exchange of experience and proposals. The efforts of the Conference and of other professional associations, such as the American Medical Writers' Association and the Association of Dental Editors, in which biomedical editors also meet to share their experience and develop common approaches, are to be commended.

NSF has pioneered in collecting data that may be used to monitor the general state of journal publication for science as a whole and to detect where serious problems exist. To promote coordination of effort among biomedical journals and of policies for supporting journal publication, objective data on trends and on adequacy of publication outlets for the various fields of research are essential. The PHS should encourage an appropriate organization to undertake the development and maintenance of a continuing monitoring program to collect data on journal backlogs, speed of publication, costs, circulation, numbers of articles and pages per issue, births and deaths of journals, and other objective indices.

2. Abstracting and Indexing

Formation of the National Federation of Science Abstracting and Indexing Services was stimulated by NSF to promote coordination of effort, to correct gaps in coverage, and to improve the general quality of the services. This organization now encompasses 20 of the major U.S. abstracting and indexing services, both governmental and private. A certain amount of work sharing has been achieved, and a start has been made toward developing an entity with which a group desiring abstracting coverage for a narrow field can negotiate for a "package" service that draws upon the abstracts produced by two or more members of the Federation. The perennial value of this organization has only begun to be realized.

The biomedical field is fortunate in having a single indexing service (*Index Medicus*) that provides relatively fast and uniform coverage for most of the substantive literature; however, in respect of abstracting coverage, the situation is less satisfactory. Although many services exist, their combined coverage has significant gaps and quality and promptness are uneven. To promote coordination of effort among abstracting services and of policies for supporting abstracting services, it is essential to have the same kind of over-all picture of trends and adequacy as for journal publication. The PHS should, therefore, encourage an appropriate organization to develop and maintain a similar monitoring program for continuously collecting data on gaps and overlapping in the coverage of biomedical literature, on growth in the number of services and of documents processed, unit processing costs, currency, and other objective indices.

3. Over-all Coordination

The Weinberg report[5] recommended that, for each area of mission-oriented research, a single agency within the Federal Government be made the "delegated agent" for information in that area, with responsibility for "supporting and otherwise carrying out information activities," and that "each agency should establish a highly placed focal point of responsibility for information activities that is part of the research and development arm, not of some administrative arm, of the agency." It will not be simple to implement these recommendations in the biomedical field, but some means must be developed to ensure that government policies regarding biomedical information services are coordinated effectively and are sensitive to the needs of the biomedical community.

The total biomedical communication complex with its government and private components comprises a chain of processes in the reordering and refinement of information. There must be a continuous effort to fashion the operation of these phases so that they will be as complementary to and compatible with each other and with the communication services of contiguous scientific disciplines as possible. This is a task that only the biomedical community can execute intelligently.

It is recommended that an appropriate scientific organization that commands the respect and support of biomedical scientists be encouraged to establish a representative deliberative body to maintain surveillance over the whole field of biomedical communication. A forum would thereby be provided in which the views of the academic, industrial, professional, and governmental contributors to the national biomedical effort in research could be ventilated and examined; resources, needs, and opportunities could be evaluated; and emergent problems could be identified and analyzed. Such a group should not have operational responsibilities, but should be available for advice on planning and programming.

NOTES

[1] *Federation Proceedings*, 23 (Sept.–Oct. and Nov.–Dec., 1964), pp. 1117–1176 and 1297–1331.

[2] Task Force to the President's Special Assistant for Science and Technology (James H. Crawford, Jr., chmn). *Scientific Technological Communication in the Government*, April 1962.

President's Science Advisory Committee. *Science, Government, and Information: the Responsibilities of the Technical Community and the Government in the Transfer of Information*. A Report. Washington, D.C.: The White House, January 10, 1963.

[3] Public Health Service. Report of Surgeon General's Conference on Health Communications, Nov. 5–8, 1962. Dept. of Health, Education, and Welfare, Feb. 1963.

[4] One example in the biomedical field is the symposium, Biomedical Information, held by the Federation of American Societies for Experimental Biology in April 1963. *Federation Proc.* 22: 973, 1963.

[5] President's Science Advisory Committee. *Science, Government, and Information: the Responsibilities of the Technical Community and the Government in the Transfer of Information*. A Report. Washington, D.C.: The White House, January 10, 1963.

ABOUT THE AUTHORS–The total investigation of which this paper is a summary was designed and directed by Richard H. Orr, M.D., Director of the Institute for the Advancement of Medical Communication. Dr. Orr completed a B.S. at the University of Chicago before receiving an M.D. in 1950 from the University of Southern California. He worked as a Research Fellow in endocrinology and adrenal physiology at the University of California Medical Center, San Francisco, and as Medical Director of Grune & Stratton, before organizing the Institute. During 1971–1972 he has been working at Aslib on a Fellowship from the British Office of Scientific and Technical Information.

Since the inception of the Institute, Dr. Orr has functioned as a physician studying the process of communication of biomedical information. He has served on editorial boards and as an editor of a number of journals, including *Metabolism, New York State Journal of Medicine* and *Methods of Information in Medicine*. He is an Honorary Director of the Council on Medical Television and a past President of the American Medical Writer's Association. A recent profile by Claire K. Schultz appears in *Information* 4: 56–60, January-February 1972.

Dr. R. Keith Cannan, who wrote the introduction, was Chairman of the Division of Medical Sciences of the National Research Council. Prior to that he had been Professor of Chemistry at New York University. His B.S., M.S. and D.S. are from the University of London, where he was an Assistant in Biochemistry and a Lecturer. He had a Rockefeller fellowship for travel in the U.S. during 1924 and 1925. Since retirement as Chairman of the Division of Medical Sciences, he has been Special Assistant to the President of the National Academy of Sciences.

Academic Information Centers[1]

by Lois F. Lunin

The information center, in whatever setting, is an instrument in biomedical communication with which the medical library must be fully coordinated. Mrs. Lunin summarizes experiences in 67 academic information analysis centers, and discusses the functions and organization of the Information Center for Hearing, Speech, and Disorders of Human Communication. Effects of the university on the center and the center's unifying influence within a part of the university are considered, with resulting recommendations for administering medical information centers.

INTRODUCTION AND DEFINITIONS

"The Academic Information Center" is a challenging subject for many reasons. Little has been written about such information centers and little has been speculated about their future. Are they different from other information centers in terms of collections, activities, organization, personnel? If so, in what way? What is their position within a university? What are their special problems? What are their special contributions?

Let's first define some terms so that we're all referring to the same base.

Once upon a time before the days of grants and contracts and multi-universities, a *university* was defined[2] as "a body of persons gathered at a particular place for the disseminating and assimilating of information in advanced fields of study."[3] This definition is now considered archaic; a university today is defined as "an institution of higher learning providing facilities for teaching and research and authorized to grant academic degrees." While the emphasis in definition of a university has shifted from a body of persons handling knowledge to an institution providing facilities and granting degrees, the archaic definition of a university now well describes the modern academic information center. The information center housed in a university can be said to have reached its logical and natural home, where it does exactly what universities started out to do centuries ago.

Universities arose in the twelfth and thirteenth centuries in response to growing demands in the professions of law, theology, and medicine, and to increasing knowledge.[4] They have been in the information handling business for a long time. Their purpose is to gather, store, transmit, and add to knowledge of every kind. They provide a pool of experts who may be called upon for advice or direct service. In contrast, the purpose of an information center is to gather, store, transmit, and add to knowledge of a *specific* kind. An information center might be thought of as a college within the modern university. Its users are its students; its faculty is the body of experts who may be called upon for advice or direct service. It is the "visible" college to whom seekers of information in a specific area can turn for expert opinion, guidance, and a variety of materials for education and research.

The definition for *information center* might be an amalgamation of Simpson and Flanagan's[5] and COSATI's[6] definitions for information analysis centers: organizations, usually mission-oriented, accomplishing in-depth acquisition, storage, retrieval, analysis, and synthesis, and critical and substantive reviews of a subject area pertinent to the mission.

A *scientist* is defined as an individual with advanced training in a field of study who is currently actively engaged in that field for some or all of his time either in laboratory research, seeing patients, or teaching, but with emphasis on investigation. He has considerable experience and is engaged in

SOURCE: Reprinted from Lois F. Lunin, "Academic Information Centers," *American Documentation,* 20 (Jan. 1969), pp. 39–49, by permission of the publisher and author.

activities that keep him skilled in his field of training. His main endeavors are creative efforts in his scientific discipline. When reported, the results of his efforts appear in scientific journals. He is distinguished from those with the same training who spend all of their time in administration.

A *state-of-the-art paper* is defined as a review paper synthesizing what is currently known on a subject. It provides information on present status, identifies important research projects, describes research trends, points out problem areas, and outlines research or education and training needs. While it generally has a short useful lifespan, this life does not necessarily have to be briefer than that of a textbook or chapter within a textbook.

An *academic information center* is an information center housed in a university, staffed by people some of whom hold academic appointments and all of whom are subject to the rules and regulations of the university, *and* it prepares state-of-the-art reports.

ACADEMIC INFORMATION CENTERS

History and Present Number of Academic Information Centers

During the period 1817 to 1899, 28 information services were formed in the United States by universities, government, industry, and associations[7]. (The source material grouped universities with nonprofit groups and associations.) From 1900 to 1939, 111 more information services were started, some of which were located at universities.

By 1961, 52 information services were listed as being located in colleges and universities. In contrast, 114 information services were housed outside the university in industry, government, or association. Since 1961 the number in universities has risen to 67.[8]

Comparison of University and Nonuniversity Environments

Some general differences exist among universities, industry, and government that might influence an information center. Table 1 shows the three types of organizations according to location, orientation, personnel, facilities, products, funding, and flexibility. The major differences between a university and the other organizations are the stress on education, the large number of experts in many different subject areas, the large number of facilities, the dissemination of the products through scholarly publications, and the amount of flexibility.

Let's examine these aspects. First, *location.* A university is located usually in one geographic location. Physically, the people and facilities are in one place. Industry, if decentralized, can have several divisions in different locations. Government agencies can be regional or located throughout the continental United States.

Next, *orientation*. The main purpose of a university is education (to conserve, transmit, analyze, and advance learning). The emphasis is on education with a broad background of knowledge to prepare the individual to be useful to the university and to society. In contrast, industry is profit-oriented. There may be emphasis on training to perform a mission-oriented task, but only rarely is broad education provided for the benefit of the individual and society in general. The government has a service orientation.

Third, *personnel*. The university consists primarily of students (pre- and post-doctoral), educators, and researchers. There is free contact with people from all over who are available for consultation. A university is filled with faculty members from many disciplines and professions and skills. Industry has no real students and educators but it does have researchers. Government has no students and faculty but it does have researchers.

Fourth, *facilities.* By its very nature, a university has a large body of experts, large libraries, and computing centers. Industry has a narrower group of experts, libraries which are more restricted in content, and perhaps computing centers. Government has some experts and large libraries and computing centers. Both industry and government often look to the university to obtain the guidance of experts through consulting relationships.

Fifth, *products.* The products of a university are available to the world freely and openly. Industry's information products such as technical reports are often restricted to internal use because of the profit motive. Some of the government's products are available to the world and some are available only to those with the appropriate need-to-know or the appropriate ability-to-steal.

Sixth, *funding.* At one time there was a difference in source of funds for each but now this is hard to generalize. To some extent, government funds support university and industry. To some

TABLE 1

COMPARISON OF UNIVERSITY, INDUSTRY, AND GOVERNMENT

Aspect	University	Industry	Government
1. Location	Usually located in one geographic location. Physically people and facilities are in one place.	If decentalized, can have several divisions in different locations.	Can be regional or continental U.S.
2. Orientation	Education (conserve, transmit, analyze, disseminate), advance learning; emphasis on education with broad background so individual is useful to university and society.	Profit. Training programs available to develop skills to make individual more useful to organization. Such programs may be restricted.	Service.
3. Personnel	Students (pre- and post-doctoral), educators, researchers. Free contact with people all over who are available for consultation.	No students. Researchers.	No students. Researchers.
4. Facilities	Experts, large libraries, computing centers.	Narrower group of experts, more restricted libraries.	Some experts, large libraries.
5. Products	Available to world.	Usually restricted to internal use but can include patents and publications written for profit motives.	Some.
6. Funding	At one time there would have been a difference in source of funds. This is hard to generalize now. Government funds to some extent support university and industry. Industry funds to some extent support university and government.		
7. Flexibility	Most.	Some.	Some.

extent, industry funds support university and government.

Last, *flexibility*. Of the three, a university has the most flexibility and freedom. It is committed to education and the advancement of knowledge.

With this background in mind, the academic information center will be examined to see how it compares with its cousins in industry and government.

Activities, Personnel, and Organization

Activities

Briefly, the types of activities and services performed by the information services at universities are much the same as those performed outside the university setting. They include:

1. identification, location, collection
2. preparation of thesauri, indexes, abstracts, extracts
3. storage of data, information, documents
4. retrieval of data, information, documents
5. lending of documents
6. compilation of data, information, bibliographies
7. performance of literature searches
8. evaluation of data and/or literature input
9. development of state-of-the art papers and critical reviews
10. issuance of ad hoc and/or serial publications such as newsletters, journals
11. research on communication and information
12. contractual arrangements for products and services.

Personnel and Organization

When they provide staff information, information services located at universities list among their staff administrators, information specialists, computer specialists, scientists, and clerical staff. Only the scientists will be discussed in this paper: the roles of the other groups have been described in a number of papers and do not seem to vary with environment. More important, what appears to be different in the university information center seems to be the role played by the scientist.

The now-classic Weinberg Report[16] prescribed in general terms the role of the scientific personnel in information centers:

> We believe the specialized information center . . . must be led by professional working scientists and engineers who maintain the closest contact with their technical professions and who, by being near the data, can make new syntheses that are denied those who do not have all the data at their fingertips. Information centers ought to be set up where science and technology flourish. (p. 3)
>
> Science can ultimately cope with the information expansion only if enough of its most gifted practitioners will compact, review, and interpret the literature both for their own use and for the benefit of more specialized scientists. (p. 14)

It is generally agreed, whether for academic or nonacademic centers, that when a major objective of the center is to provide technical assistance, the staff should be composed heavily of scientists (around 50 per cent) supported by information specialists.[7,17,18] Although it is generally agreed in the literature that the staff should be composed in part of scientists, no detailed information was found about the organization of information centers presently located at universities. For example, do scientists in the information centers have academic rank and duties? Is the information service an integral part of the university?

In an effort to obtain some of this information, a brief letter (Fig. 1) was sent to 66 academic information centers listed in the directories mentioned earlier. Table 2 tabulates the results.

Fifty replies from information centers were received. Many more people responded to the questionnaire than the totals indicate: some services no longer exist; some have been combined with others. The questionnaire replies indicated that 34 information centers are an integral part of their universities and 10 are not. Thirty-eight said that the scientists associated with the information service hold academic rank in the university; six said they do not. Forty-two stated that members of the information service do research and publish original articles in the professional literature; three said they do not. Twenty-eight sponsor meetings, symposia, or seminars in the subject area covered by the information service and 16 do not.

What do these figures indicate? For one thing, most information services located at universities are an integral part of these universities. Next, most scientists associated with an information service located at a university hold academic rank. Third, indications are that these scientists are

THE JOHNS HOPKINS UNIVERSITY

Please address reply to:
INFORMATION CENTER FOR HEARING, SPEECH, & DISORDERS OF HUMAN COMMUNICATION
310 Harriet Lane Home
The Johns Hopkins Medical Institutions
Baltimore, Maryland 21205
TELEPHONE: 955-3390

Dear Sir:

For a paper I am preparing on The Academic Information Center, I would like to obtain answers to the following questions. I would greatly appreciate it if you would answer these questions and return this questionnaire in the enclosed self-addressed stamped envelope.

Please circle the appropriate answer:

1. Is your Information Service an integral part of your university (a recognized unit of the university subject to university policy)?
   Yes No

2. Do the scientists associated with the Information Service hold academic rank in the university?
   Yes No

3. Do members of the staff of your Information Service do research and publish original articles in the professional literature (journals, books) of your subject area?
   Yes No

4. Does your Information Service sponsor meetings, symposia, or seminars in the subject area covered by the Information Service? if you sponsor any of these, please answer yes.
   Yes No

Number of scientists on staff: Full time ______ Part time ______

Please sign your name ________________________________

and title ________________________________

Thank you very much for your assistance.

Sincerely yours,

Mrs. Lois F. Lunin
Program Director

LFL/wmr

FIGURE 1. Questionnaire

TABLE 2

SUMMARY OF INFORMATION FROM QUESTIONNAIRE

Number Sent	Number of Replies	Question 1		Question 2		Question 3		Question 4		Total Number of Scientists		Range of Number of Scientists	
		Yes	No	Yes	No	Yes	No	Yes	No	FT	PT	FT	PT
Non-NINDB 63*	46 (73% return)	30	10	34	6	38	3	25	15	369	1744	1-110	1/4-27
NINDB network 4	4 (100% return)	4		4		4		3	1	0-19	25	19	2-12
Total 67	50 (overall return 75%)	34	10	38	6	42	3	28	16	388	1769		

*Since the time of the initial survey, an additional 12 academic information centers have been located.

scientists by the definition established in the earlier part of this paper since they publish original articles in the professional literature. Finally, more information services located at universities sponsor meetings and seminars than do not, an indication, for one thing, that this is an accepted activity for an information service.

The size of the scientific staff varies. The number of full-time scientists on the staff ranged from 1 to 110; part-time, from one-fourth to 27. The average number of full-time scientists was 8, and the average number of scientists on the staff part-time was approximately 3.8.

Conclusions Regarding Location and Activities

Some conclusions are possible at this point. The first is that information centers have been located at universities for over half a century, perhaps longer. Thus, their location is not new.

The second conclusion is that the activities of information centers located at universities seem much the same as those in nonacademic settings. All appear to be engaged in the full spectrum of information-handling activities.

The third conclusion is that the university's traditional spirit of freedom and creative scholarship, its large number of eminent scientists and scholars in one geographic location and its extensive library holdings (both of which can be consulted frequently and easily), and its emphasis on the exploitation of information probably influences to a great extent the philosophy and policies of the information center.

SPECIFIC ACADEMIC INFORMATION CENTERS

A Look at Four Academic Information Centers

While little specific information is available about the interaction of most of the information centers and the universities that house them, specific operational data are available about a group recently established in four university medical centers.

Background

The National Institute of Neurological Diseases and Blindness (NINDB) held a conference in March 1963 on "Information Storage, Retrieval, and Exchange in the Neurological and Communication Sciences." The conference group recommended that the NINDB establish a group of specialized information centers to help cope with the information problems created by the rapidly increasing accumulation of published scientific journals and to test this concept as a way of meeting the information problems. These specialized information centers have become the Neurological Information Network which is the core of the program.

Establishment of the Centers

In the four years since that recommendation, four centers have been established. They are in the order of establishment: The Parkinson Information Center[19] at Columbia University; The Brain Information Service[20] at UCLA; The Information Center for Hearing, Speech, and Disorders of Human Communication[21] at The Johns Hopkins University; and the Vision Information Center[22] at Harvard.

Their mission is to collect, identify, index, store, and retrieve documents and other information items concerned with their defined fields, and to evaluate, distill, and otherwise utilize, repackage, and disseminate the information contained in the documents.

Organization

Each of these centers is organized somewhat differently. The Parkinson Information Center has 32 scientists on its staff, 22 of whom are intramural scientists and 10 of whom are extramural. They represent neurology, neurosurgery, neurochemistry, neuroanatomy, neuropharmacology, neurophysiology, neuropathology, and epidemiology. Their documentation staff consists of 11 people, 5 of whom are part-time and 6 of whom are full-time. This does not include clerical personnel. The Brain Information Service has 16 people, mostly documentary rather than scientific. The Information Center for Hearing, Speech, and Disorders of Human Communication has 12 scientists and 8 information specialists in addition to clerical personnel. Little information is available at present on the Vision Information Center, since it is still in its initial phase.

According to a plan developed at NINDB, each of these four specialized centers provides documentation for its total area but carries out information analysis in only a small, well-defined segment of the area of documentation. With full development, each documentation center will support several "information analysis satellites" in sub-areas of its field. While the network of major documentation services will be a stable structure, the information analysis groups will be expected to fluctuate according to need in subjects, number, and locations.[23]

These centers have already worked cooperatively with the National Library of Medicine, a Task Force of the National Academy of Sciences–National Research Council, and other centers and clearinghouses of the government or associations that are pertinent to their subject area.

Technical Requirements

The technical requirements of these information centers in a university are much the same as in industry or government. The centers need a well-supplied library; computing facilities if there is a computer-based storage and retrieval system; space to house the information center; and such office equipment as typewriters, desks, chairs, reproduction machine, files, and the like.

Each of these NINDB information centers uses a library (or libraries) that is a well-established unit in the university medical center. The Parkinson Information Center uses the Columbia University College of Physicians and Surgeons Medical Library. The Brain Information Service uses the UCLA Biomedical Library; the Vision Information Center uses the Countway Library of Medicine at Harvard; and the Information Center for Hearing, Speech, and Disorders of Human Communication uses the Welch Medical Library of The Johns Hopkins University. Each information center uses its university's computing center or a division of that center. The policies and procedures for the use of these libraries and computing centers have had to be established.

Information Center for Hearing, Speech, and Disorders of Human Communication

The activities of this information center comprise all aspects of information handling. We identify, locate, collect, analyze, store, retrieve, do literature searches by computer for material on magnetic tape and manually for material not on magnetic tape, maintain a current awareness service, and undertake special projects such as the preparation of programmed texts, translations, index-handbooks, and state-of-the-art reports. We plan to sponsor seminars and workshops.

Administratively, our organization consists of three main areas: Executive Committee, Information Science, and Scientific Advisory Committee.

Executive Committee

The Executive Committee consists of the Director, Codirector, Program Director, and Scientific Director. The Director is an M.D. who is Professor of Laryngology and Otology in the School of

Medicine and head of that division in both the medical school and hospital. The Codirector is the Director and Librarian of the Welch Medical Library. The Program Director, an instructor in the School of Medicine, coordinates the units in the Information Science area. The Scientific Director, an associate professor in the School of Medicine, coordinates the Scientific Advisory Committee (Fig. 2). The Executive Committee is concerned with the general philosophy of the Information Center. It formulates policy, makes all decisions on employment of professional personnel and development of staff, determines relations with the Welch Medical Library, and generates ideas for Information Center activities.

The Information Science area presently contains four active units: Collect, Analysis and Process, Literature Search, and Edit. More units are planned for activation.

Information Science

The *Collection Unit* is responsible for identifying and locating sources of information and for acquiring information from the published literature and from the technical report literature. This section is also responsible for maintaining a manual current awareness service until such time as an SDI system is operational or a weekly publication is prepared.

The *Analysis and Process Unit* is responsible for indexing and storing the documents included in the system and for phrasing the search requests for information from the magnetic tape files. This section is also responsible for preparing and maintaining the vocabulary control. All programs for computer storage, search, print, and editorial check have been prepared in this unit using the Information Package[24] available from The Johns Hopkins University Computing Center.

The *Literature Search Unit* is responsible for answering questions that require searches beyond the magnetic tape master file of the retrieval system. Such activity involves retrospective searches and the subsequent preparation of bibliographies, abstracts, and literature reports.

The *Edit Unit* is responsible for editing all reports and assisting in the preparation of material for the seminars that the Center will sponsor.

The *Program Unit* when developed will be responsible for using the MEDLARS tapes, for writing conversion programs to use tapes prepared for other systems, and to develop any new programs desired. At present there are no programmers on our staff although we have an operational computer-based retrieval system.

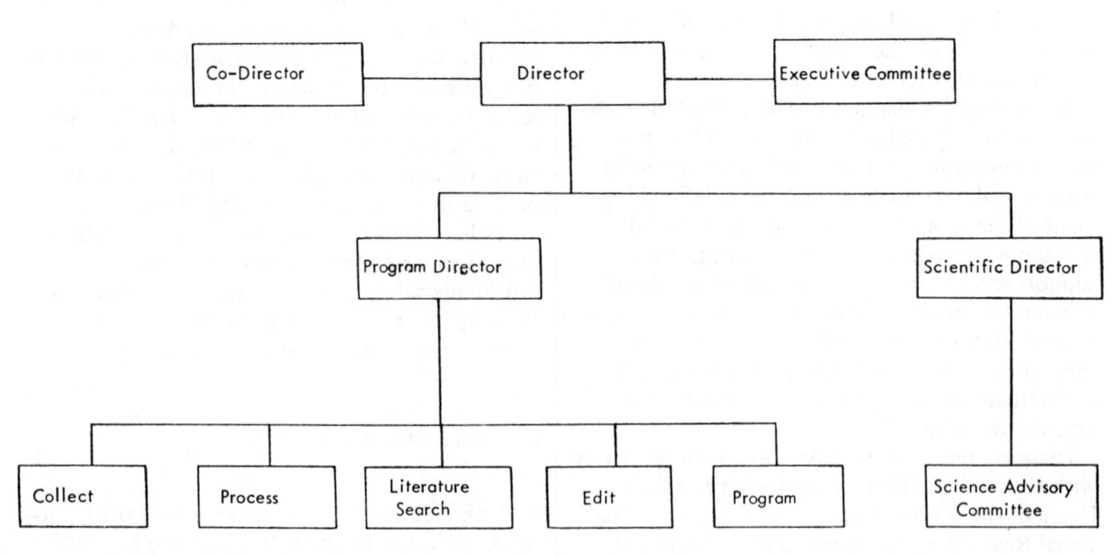

FIGURE 2. Organization of the Information Center for Hearing, Speech and Disorders of Human Communication

Scientific Advisory Committee

The Scientific Advisory Committee consists of the scientists and clinicians associated with the Information Center who provide scientific judgment and assistance in the area of their expertise whenever required, for example, in defining the scope of our field, in the indexing of certain documents, in the selection and arrangement of terms during the preparation of the thesaurus, and in the checking of certain literature searches. They will also be responsible for the preparation and conduct of the seminars. They are coordinated by a Scientific Director who is committed to spend 40% of his time in the Information Center and who presides at monthly Scientific Advisory Committee meetings. The 10 scientists each give 10% of their time to the Center but not at fixed times.

TWO AREAS FOR FURTHER DEFINITION

Scientific Activities in Academic Information Centers

In spite of its rich and stimulating environment, an information center in a university has certain problems relating to that environment. One has to do with the scientists; another has to do with the administration within the university.

It has been apparent in our Information Center that the scientist needs an image of himself, and he needs a well-defined scope of activities in relation to his work within the Center. This situation exists partly because we are a new enterprise in our university. There are no precedents to follow. We have to carve out our identities and roles. Presently the scientists answer questions when we call them, but sometimes the questions keep coming in one area and never in others, with the result that the men representing these untapped areas are never contacted.

The participating scientists meet once a month for 2 hours to discuss such subjects as the function of the Scientific Advisory Committee, projects for adoption by the Information Center, the clarification of criteria for a Directory, subjects useful for seminars, and facilities of the university such as the university press that are available for use by the Center. The evaluation of papers going into the retrieval system has also been discussed. The scientists in our Information Center are strongly opposed to evaluating papers, although this activity has been one of the functions proposed in many papers for scientists in information analysis centers.

Information Analysis

As stated by NINDB, information analysis is

> . . . a job for the established, experienced professional in the field and is not a job for graduate students or residents. Without strong participation of competent scientists, it is doubtful that an information analysis center can succeed. A professional scientist or researcher working in information analysis should spend at least 10 percent, but no more than 50 percent, of his time on it, and he should continue to work actively in his field . . . . Experience has shown that it is usually cyclic, a period of research and a period of information analysis. The latter has been found to have considerable spin off as it acts to stimulate and recharge the scientist's interest, as well as give him new ideas.[25]

Simpson[26] offered an analogy which is both descriptive of the information situation and a solution to part of the information problem.

> . . . if we have a seven-foot shelf of information pertaining to some scientific subject, and if we are looking for research gaps or if we are looking for knowledge as to what we have done already in order to find our research gaps, then we could condense this . . . , using knowledgeable scientists and engineers under an effective system, and provide the customer with something he can digest.
>
> . . . it is equivalent to going to a physician. You are going to him for an opinion and he bases his opinion on whatever information he has, plus experience. (p. 54)

The NINDB Centers have such scientific expertise. They have physicians and scientists on their staff whose word other physicians can accept.

Kelsey[27] once stated that most basic scientists are distrustful of other people's judgments and evaluations on principle. This distrust of other people's judgments is an important point and one that perhaps can be directly related to the level of training and experience of the scientists in an information center. It may well be the key to acceptance of such centers by peer scientists.

Preparation of State-of-the-Art Reviews

It has been said that the state-of-the-art review has a civilizing effect on the literature. In the past and present, such syntheses have often been written for textbooks. Perhaps the textbooks of tomorrow will be state-of-the-art reports, with information centers having both the authority to commission such a report wherever a need is apparent or suspected and also the prestige to entice as contributors people who can make significant contributions.

State-of-the-art reviews are useful for students, teachers, and researchers. The review integrates results, each of which has been accepted as a part of the literature but all of which have not been synthesized for science because of the profusion of papers or lack of incentive for interpretation of all those papers by experts. Such reviews have other than educational uses. They are of value to the decision makers at the governmental level who program education and research activities.

The NINDB Centers are required by contract to prepare one state-of-the-art review each year. Writing such a review is consistent with the usual activity of a scientist and, except for the problem of timing (it is due at the end of the academic vacation), this causes no real difficulty.

The University's Role

The University has a role in the development and growth of an information center. The administration must support the Information Center morally and intellectually. It must be aware of the objectives of the Information Center and approve the Center's activities. It must allow some of its faculty to commit a percentage of time to the Information Center. It should offer all the rights and privileges and benefits of the university to members of the Information Center.

There must be financial support. If there is government funding, as there is in our Information Center, the Center has two fathers and thus twice the administrative headaches and paperwork. If there is government funding, it is also essential to determine that the university and sponsor are not incompatible in philosophy. If the government funding runs out, what then? Does the university have a responsibility for trying to absorb the personnel, or at least the information specialists?

As in any organization where a new unit is established, such management procedures as reporting patterns, channels of communication, and lines of authority must be established. The relationship with the administration must be clarified on all university policies and procedures such as construction of facilities, equipment orders, and charges for computing time.

The Information Center as a Unifying Force Within a University

The university, as Weinberg points out in "Reflections on Big Science,"[28] is discipline-oriented. Its viewpoint is the sum of viewpoints of the separate disciplines that constitute it. New problems, new techniques, and fresh approaches to old problems lead to new disciplines. An information center can play a role in encouraging and supporting such a rearrangement when there are justified indications of the value of such reorganization. It is possible that an information center might exert a unifying effect on a field of education or research within a university where such a unity does not presently exist. In a university medical school such unity is implied where a categorical research institute exists. But in a univeristy that has no research institute in a particular area and where the research activity exists as many separate islands of investigation, the information center having the subject as part of its scope can stimulate discussion and bring together information and scientists to help them deal with problems as a whole rather than as unrelated parts of the whole.

The Information Center for Hearing, Speech, and Disorders of Human Communication has demonstrated such a unifying influence in an area of research in The Johns Hopkins Medical Institutions.[29] It has brought together all individuals who are working on aspects of communication disorders, regardless of their departments. While the combinative force exerted by the Information Center is till too fresh to know the full value and meaning of this action, the activity merits continued observation.

RECOMMENDATIONS FOR ADMINISTERING AN ACADEMIC INFORMATION CENTER

Some practical suggestions on the establishment and management of an academic information center are offered here. These recommendations are made in the form of a list. They are based on experience in a new and developing Information Center in an area where none existed before and where each procedure and responsibility has had to be carved out either from principle or arrived at by hindsight.

General Suggestions

1. University authorities should fully understand the declared objective of the Information Center.
2. If it is appropriate because of the interdisciplinary nature of the subject covered, the Information Center should be accepted as an interdisciplinary entity within the university.
3. The Information Center should be housed in a university building on the campus close to the library, computing center, and scientists.
4. It should have the amount of space necessary for the proper conduct of its activities.
5. It should be able to use the other facilities of the university as appropriate.
6. It should have administrative support.
7. It should have adequate financial security for the present and if possible for the future.
8. It should hold joint meetings with the scientists in the physical area of the Information Center as often as necessary.
9. It should teach information science within the university.
10. Its participating scientists should have a clearly defined role.
11. It should offer salaries competitive with information centers outside the university.
12. It should have adequate visibility (publicity).

Suggestions for Scientists in an Information Center

1. They should help work out areas of scope for the Information Center and work out procedures for information problems as necessary.
2. They should review as necessary any questions that come into the Information Center and the answers prepared for the users. Each scientist on its staff should be "on call" to the Information Center.
3. They should help select documents that are reasonable and suitable to translate.
4. They should help define the role of the Information Center regarding needs in specific areas. For example, they should analyze questions quarterly that come to the Information Center to determine the needs of the users.
5. They should periodically ask for a search on subjects of interest to them, look at the indexing, compare this with how they would have indexed the articles to indicate any possible deficiencies in analysis.
6. They should hold workshops to standardize test procedures, to generate plans for collaborative research activity, to plan training programs, and to standardize data-handling operations.
7. They should explore new areas of activity for an Information Center such as computer-aided instruction.
8. They should hold joint meetings with information specialists to explore better means of communicating information.
9. A medical student, intern, or resident should be able to include some service in an Information Center as well as in a hospital because it will significantly advance his knowledge of his specialty.
10. The Information Center should be allowed a visiting scientist for a period of six months to a year to use the facilities of the Center and to work on a subject approved by a national study section.
11. The scientists should write the state-of-the-art reviews prepared by the Information Center.
12. The scientists should constantly search for fresh and more effective ways to advance and integrate knowledge.

THE INFORMATION FRONTIER IN THE UNIVERSITY

By definition, a university consists of faculty members from many disciplines who possess pieces of knowledge and skills in many subjects. By implication, the university has characteristically been operating at the information frontier. An Information Center located at a university is in the midst of a richness of minds and materials. It should harvest from all these areas. It should take advantage of its location by using all the resources available. Charles Odegaard,[30] president of the University of Washington, pleaded the need for a medical school to turn its flirtation with the university to a full-blown romance. An Information Center should also have a full romance with the university of which it is a part: it should draw from all the treasure in a university whether it be the traditional medical science, engineering, administration, social work, nursing, or the social sciences.

Twentieth-century man, especially the twentieth-century physician, has been characterized as knowing more and more about less and less. The information center with its charter to gather and synthesize can be one medium to counteract this limitation. It can provide man with knowledge about more and more. The academic information center can expect to be a dynamic textbook constantly responsive to and interactive with its users. The sections of the text already come in an unending flow from the world's researchers. The staff of the information center continually analyze, summarize, and interpret these contributions. At any one point in time the collective text represents the best thinking of the best minds on that subject.

Information can be considered a disease as well as a useful product of civilization. To make today's large amount of information optimally useful calls for the participation of a large number of scholars, scientists, and information scientists to handle it wisely and well. The cost of such a living system is time and money. The alternative is progression to chaos.[31]

NOTES

[1] This work was supported by the Information Center for Hearing, Speech, and Disorders of Human Communication. This Information Center, a part of the Neurological Information Network of the National Institute of Neurological Diseases and Blindness, is supported under contract number PH 43–65–23.

[2] Gove, P. B. (Ed. in Chief), *Webster's Third New International Dictionary,* G. & C. Merriam Company, Springfield, Massachusetts, 1967.

[3] Mrs. Lunin notes that the word "information" which appeared in the second edition of Webster was changed to "knowledge" in the third edition.

[4] Bridgewater, W., and S. Kurtz, (Eds.), *The Columbia Encyclopedia,* Columbia University Press, New York, 1963.

[5] Simpson, G. S., Jr., and C. Flanagan, Information Centers and Services, *in* Carlos A. Cuadra, (Ed.), *Annual Review of Information Science and Technology,* Vol. 1, American Documentation Institute, Interscience Publishers, New York, 1966.

[6] COSATI Panel #6 on Information Analysis Centers, *Preliminary Directory of Federally Supported Information Analysis Centers,* 1967. (Now available as Directory of Federally Supported Information Analysis Centers, April 1968, Sponsored by Panel #6, Information Analysis and Data Centers, Committee on Scientific and Technical Information. The Clearinghouse for Federal, Scientific and Technical Information, $3.00.)

[7] Panning, L. J., B. A. Frautschi, W. H. Veazie, Jr., A. P. Lecher, and G. S. Simpson, Jr., *Survey and Analysis of Specialized Science Information Services in the United States,* Final Report to the National Science Foundation, Battelle Memorial Institute, Columbus, Ohio, September 1962.

[8] According to information in the directories used for this report (6, 9-15) many more information services are located at universities than have been included here. From the point of view of this paper, there are two problems with the source materials which should be mentioned: one is the possible omission of a university's name in the directories from which the information was obtained. Several of the information services listed were located at universities but the name of the university was not used as a part of the title or address. The other assailable information concerns statements regarding the state-of-the-art reports. Some services may have stated that they prepare such reports because they thought it was fashionable to do so, or intended to do so, and not because they actually produced them.

Unfortunately for the purpose of this paper, information was not given in most directories on organization or type of staff so that it was impossible to determine whether there were sceintists on the staff of the information service, whether the state-of-the-art reports were prepared by those scientists, and whether the information service was an integral part of the university or was merely housed in the university.

[9] *Specialized Science Information Services in the United States: A Directory of Selected Specialized Information Services in the Physical and Biological Sciences,* prepared by Battelle Memorial Institute, National Science Foundation, Washington, D. C., November, 1961.

[10] Hoshovsky, A. G., and M. R. Eades, *R & D Information Directory–Government Technical Offices and Centers, Arlington, Va.,* Office of Aerospace Research, AD 612-513, June 15, 1966.

[11] *Directory of Selected Specialized Information Services* (CONF. 651 131), Ad-Hoc Forum of Scientific and Technical Information Analysis Center Managers, Directors, and Professional Analysts, sponsored by Battelle Memorial Institute and Oak Ridge National Laboratory, 1965.

[12] Information Research Center, *Directors of Specialized Information Centers and Services*, Battelle Memorial Institute, Columbus, Ohio, March 16, 1967.

[13] National Referral Center for Science and Technology, *A Directory of Information Resources in the United States: Physical Sciences, Biological Sciences, Engineering,* Washington, D. C., January, 1965.

[14] National Referral Center for Science and Technology, *A Directory of Information Resources in the United States: Social Sciences,* Washington, D. C., October, 1965.

[15] National Referral Center for Science and Technology, *A Directory of Information Resources in the United States: Federal Government,* Washington, D. C., June, 1967.

[16] The President's Science Advisory Committee, *Science, Government, and Information. The Responsibilities of the Technical Community and the Government in the Transfer of Information,* The White House, Washington, D. C., January 10, 1963.

[17] Jenny, A., 2nd, *Toward a Psychological Operations Information and Analysis Center,* Human Sciences Research, Inc., McLean, Va., January, 1966.

[18] USPHS Proposes 22 "Communications" Plans: Electronics Research, Drug Data Exchange and 50 Information "Evaluation" Centers . . ., *Drug Research Reports,* November 14, 1962.

[19] Categorical diseases of the nervous system. This center has subsequently been discontinued.

[20] Neuroscience items not related to categorical diseases.

[21] Hearing, language, speech, and disorders of human communication.

[22] Vision and diseases of the eye. This center has subsequently been discontinued.

[23] *Annual Progress Report, NINDB Neurological Information Network,* National Institute of Neurological Diseases and Blindness, Public Health Service, U.S. Department of Health, Education, and Welfare, Bethesda, Md., October, 1966.

[24] Programs and complete description of the Information Processing System may be obtained by request from Dr. R. H. Shepard, Computing Center, Medical Division, The Johns Hopkins University School of Medicine.

[25] Bering, E. A., Jr., The Neurological Information Network of the National Institute of Neurological Diseases and Blindness, *Bulletin of the Medical Library Association,* 55 (2): 135-140 (April, 1967).

[26] Simpson, G. S. Jr., Scientific Information Centers in the United States, *American Documentation,* 13(1): 43-57 (January 1962).

[27] Kelsey, E. F., Government Responsibility for Science Information, Federation Proceedings, 22(4):975-979 (July-August 1963).

[28] Weinberg, A. M., *Reflections on Big Science*, The M.I.T. Press, Cambridge, Mass., 1967, p. 45.

[29] Mrs. Lunin is indebted to Dr. John E. Bordley for this observation.

[30] Odegaard, C. E.: A Description of the Role of the University in Modern Society Together with Encouragement to the Medical School to Turn Its Flirtation with the University into a Full Blown Romance, *California Medicine*, 106:337-345 (May 1967).

[31] Mrs. Lunin acknowledges several people and organizations for assistance and advice: Miss Barbara Frautschi, Director, Information Research Center, Battelle Memorial Institute; Dr. Joseph Caponio, Scientific and Technical Communications Officer, NINDB; the National Referral Center for Science and Technology; and the 66 people who so kindly and promptly answered the questionnaire.

ABOUT THE AUTHOR—Mrs. Lois F. Lunin is Co-Director and Program Director, Information Center for Hearing, Speech, and Disorders of Human Communication, The Johns Hopkins Medical Institutions. Other appointments she holds at Johns Hopkins are: Instructor in Public Health Administration, Division of Communicative Sciences, School of Hygiene and Public Health, and Instructor, Division of Laryngology and Otology, Department of Surgery, School of Medicine. She has an A.B. in Psychology from Radcliffe College and an M.S. in Information Science from Drexel Institute of Technology.

She is a Member of the Editorial Board of *The Johns Hopkins Medical Journal* and a Member of the American National Standards Institute, Sectional Committee Z-39, Subcommittee 9, Terminology.

The Use of Biomedical Literature at the National Lending Library for Science and Technology

by D. N. Wood and C. A. Bower

Though this paper reports experience in Great Britain at its National Lending Library, it is pertinent because the users of this single institution represent a high proportion of all biomedical scientists in the country and hence a broad spectrum of various kinds of use. It is relatively recent, having been carried out in February 1969, and covers both borrowing patterns, and sources of information on the materials borrowed. Fifty per cent of the requests in medicine were for literature less than 3½ years old, and in biology for literature less than 5¾ years old. The majority of issues loaned (87.8 percent) were English language periodicals.

INTRODUCTION

The National Lending Library for Science and Technology (NLL) is the principal source of scientific and technical (including medical) inter-library loans in the United Kingdom. Despite the fact that the demand on its total resources is somewhat biased towards technology,[1] the use of the library appears to reflect fairly accurately the national demand for, and hence the use of, literature within particular subject fields. Subject oriented studies of the loan demand at the NLL can therefore produce useful and generally applicable use data regarding the date, title, language and subject of scientific literature. This data could be of benefit to library administrators engaged in building up or weeding subject collections, and this paper presents the results of the latest study undertaken at the library.

In view of the 50 per cent increase in demand on the library over the last two years the investigation was planned as a follow up to the study of medical literature undertaken in 1967.[2] Furthermore, because of the overlap between medicine and biology it was decided to broaden the scope of the study to include biological literature.

As well as enabling the characteristics of the borrowed literature to be studied, the investigation was used to provide information on the sources used for references to biomedical literature.

METHOD

Between 25 and 30 percent of all the issues from the NLL are biomedical, and over 5,000 items in this field are requested each week. During nine days in February, 1969, every other biomedical periodical issued from the library was intercepted at the point of despatch and the subject of the required article, language, date of publication and library shelfmark were encoded on to questionnaires which were then despatched with the literature. In each case the requester was asked to supply details of the source of the reference and to return the questionnaire in the stamped addressed envelope which had been provided. As many details as possible were also recorded for unsatisfied requests, but the satisfaction rate at the library is so high (88.5 per cent) that only 439 such questionnaires were despatched. The replies to these questionnaires have been excluded from the analysis and will not be discussed. Their absence does not affect the conclusions drawn.

During the survey period 3,330 questionnaires relating to supplied items were despatched. Two

SOURCE: Reprinted from D. N. Wood and C. A. Bower, "The Use of Biomedical Periodical Literature at the National Lending Library for Science and Technology," *Methods of Information in Medicine*, 9 (Jan. 1970), pp. 46–53, by permission of the publisher and the authors.

months were allowed for their return by which time 2,218 (66.6 per cent) had been received. The information on the completed questionnaires was transferred to IBM 80 column punched cards for analysis.

RESULTS

1. The Literature Used

(a) Range of Titles Requested and Frequency of Use

During the survey a total of 1,084 periodical titles were borrowed. 622 were requested for the biological articles they contained, 540 for their medical content and 131 were classed either as general (i.e. they covered more than one of the specified subject categories) or, because the article itself was not specified, were unable to be classified at all. The majority of titles were used very infrequently; 666 for instance were borrowed only once each, and 183 twice. A few titles, on the other hand, were used comparatively often, the *Annals of the New York Academy of Sciences* being borrowed twenty times. A full tabulation indicating the range of titles used and the frequency with which they were requested is presented in Table 1. The pattern is virtually the same if the medical and biological literature are considered separately. This is illustrated in Figure 1 where, for purposes of comparison, similar results obtained from the 1967 survey of medical literature are also shown.

A list of the most frequently used titles is presented in Table 2. It is of interest that all the

TABLE 1:

FREQUENCY OF USE PER TITLE

No. of requests per title	No. of titles
1	666
2	183
3	87
4	48
5	31
6	26
7	11
8	11
9	10
10	1
11	–
12	2
13	2
14	2
15	1
16	1
17	–
18	–
19	1
20	1

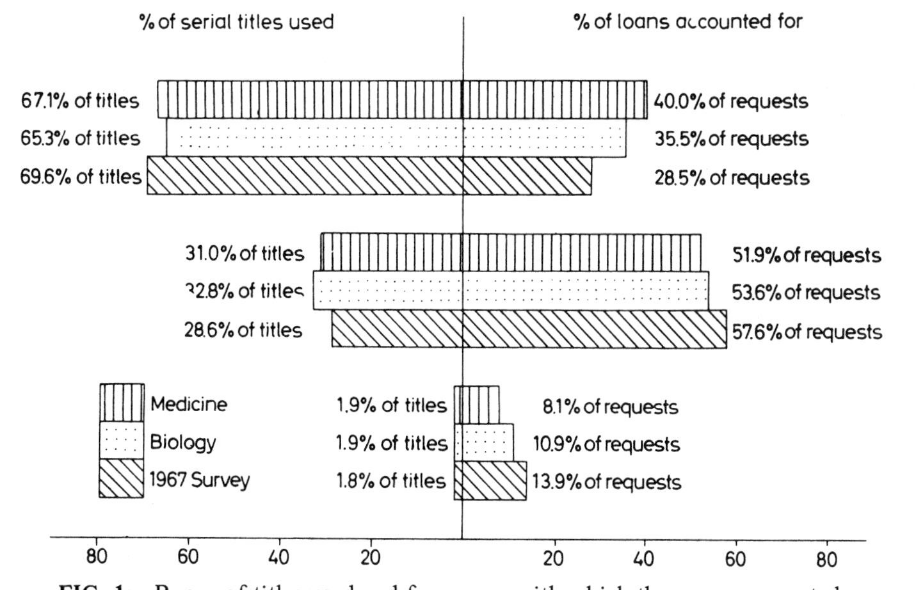

FIG. 1: Range of titles used and frequency with which they were requested

TABLE 2:

MOST USED SERIAL TITLES

Rank	No. of Times Used	Title
1	20	Annals–New York Academy of Sciences
2	19	Science (New York and Washington)
3	16	Journal of Biological Chemistry
4	15	Proceedings–National Academy of Sciences of the United States of America
5	14	American Journal of Physiology
	14	Journal of Bacteriology
7	13	British Medical Journal
	13	New England Journal of Medicine
	13	Proceedings–Society for Experimental Biology and Medicine
10	12	Anatomical Record
11	10	Biological Reviews–Cambridge Philosophical Society
	10	Journal of Physiology
13	9	Archives of Biochemistry and Biophysics
	9	Cancer Research
	9	Federation Proceedings–Federation of American Societies for Experimental Biology
	9	Journal–American Medical Association
	9	Journal of Biochemistry (Tokyo)
	9	Journal of Clinical Investigation
	9	Journal of Investigative Dermatology
	9	Journal of Neurochemistry
	9	Journal of Pharmacology and Experimental Therapeutics
	9	Lancet
	9	Nature (London)

medical titles listed also appear, although not in the same order, in the list of heaviest used titles published as part of the results of the 1967 survey. Two notable omissions from the list are *American Journal of Obstetrics and Gynecology* and *Circulation Research* which, in the previous survey, were ranked first and ninth respectively. The absence of the former must be explained as being atypical since a subsequent check of use has revealed an average weekly loan demand of about twelve. If this had occurred during the survey, the journal would have been among the ten most used titles.

(b) Distribution of Requests by Subject

As each item of literature was issued the subject of the requested article was recorded. Where the article was not specified on the loan request form the journal as a whole was, where possible, classified. However, the contents were often so diverse that it was impossible to place the journal in any single class, and for such cases a »not known« category was created. The classification was based on the UDC system,[3] although a few modifications were made. For instance, certain subjects such as farm management were omitted from classes 631.4-639.18 and dentistry was removed from class 616 and treated separately.

The subject breakdown is presented in Table 3. Slightly more biological than medical literature was borrowed, and the biggest single category was general biology which accounted for almost 25 per cent of the total issues. In the medical field the distribution of requests was broadly similar to that discovered in the 1967 survey and in a survey conducted at the Yale Medical Library.[4] The most heavily used medical literature was that in classes 615 and 616.

(c) Distribution of Requests by Language

From the language analysis of the 2,218 loans which is presented in Table 4, it will be noted that in both biology and medicine very little use was made of non-English language material. Of the latter, literature published in German and French was not surprisingly the most frequently requested. Between them English, French and German publications accounted for 95.4 per cent of all issues. This pattern of use shows no significant variation from one subject class to another and is very similar to that revealed by the previous NLL study. Compared with American studies,[2,5,6] these results suggest that British workers in the biomedical field rely much less on non-English language publications than do their transatlantic counterparts.

(d) Distribution of Requests by Date

The distribution of the publication dates of the periodicals borrowed is shown in Table 5 and Figure 2. The most obvious thing to emerge from a study of this data is the difference in decay rates of biological and medical literature. The latter is »alive« for a significantly shorter period, the »half-life« being $3\frac{1}{2}$ years compared with $5\frac{3}{4}$ years

TABLE 3:
SUBJECT DISTRIBUTION OF THE REQUESTS

Field	UDC class	Subject	No. of requests	% of field requests	% of total requests
Biology	56	Palaeontology	8	0.7	0.4
	571/2	Anthropobiology/anthropology	7	0.6	0.3
	574–579	General biology (genetics, evolution, microbiology, bacteriology, parasitology, general properties of life, biological techniques)	555	48.4	25.0
	581	General botany	118	10.3	5.3
	582	Systematic botany	10	0.9	0.5
	591	General zoology	288	25.1	13.0
	592–599	Systematic zoology	28	2.4	1.3
	631.4–639.18	Agriculture/plant husbandry and breeding/forestry/animal husbandry/stockbreeding (excluding farm management, equipment and animal produce)	119	10.4	5.4
	639.2–639.6	Fisheries	13	1.1	0.6
	All classes		1,146	99.9	51.7
Medicine	611/2	Anatomy/physiology	126	13.8	5.7
	613/4	Health/preventive medicine	78	8.6	3.5
	615	Pharmacy/pharmacology and therapeutics/toxicology	332	36.4	15.0
	616	Disease/pathology and medicine (but excluding dentistry)	274	30.0	12.4
	617	Surgery	29	3.2	1.3
	618	Gynaecology/obstetrics	17	1.9	0.8
	619	Comparative pathology/veterinary medicine	47	5.2	2.1
	–	Dentistry	9	1.0	0.4
	All classes		912	100.1	41.1
General	–		8		0.4
Not known	–		152		6.9
Total			2,218		100.1

TABLE 4:
LANGUAGE DISTRIBUTION OF THE REQUESTS

Language	Biology		Medicine		Total (inc. General and Not known)	
	No. of requests	% of requests	No. of requests	% of requests	No. of requests	% of requests
English	1,029	89.8	786	86.2	1,948	87.8
French	31	2.7	38	4.2	72	3.2
German	40	3.5	46	5.0	96	4.3
Cyrillic	13	1.1	9	1.0	22	1.0
Italian	4	0.3	10	1.1	16	0.7
Japanese	11	1.0	7	0.8	21	0.9
Other	13	1.1	11	1.2	26	1.2
Not known	5	0.4	5	0.5	17	0.8
Total	1,146	99.9	912	100.0	2,218	99.9

TABLE 5:

DATE DISTRIBUTION OF THE REQUESTS

	Biology			Medicine			Total inc. General and Not known		
Date	No. of requests	% of requests	Cumulative %	No. of requests	% of requests	Cumulative %	No. of requests	% of requests	Cumulative %
1969	13	1.1	1.1	10	1.1	1.1	27	1.2	1.2
1968	174	15.3	16.4	187	20.6	21.7	407	18.5	19.7
1967	101	8.9	25.3	126	13.9	35.6	246	11.2	30.9
1966	81	7.1	32.4	98	10.8	46.4	188	8.5	39.4
1965	88	7.7	40.1	57	6.3	52.7	147	6.7	46.1
1960–64	273	23.9	64.0	210	23.1	75.8	519	23.5	69.6
1955–59	153	13.5	77.5	91	10.0	85.8	257	11.7	81.3
1950–54	81	7.1	84.6	55	6.1	91.9	144	6.5	87.8
1940–49	82	7.2	91.8	41	4.5	96.4	137	6.2	94.0
1930–39	62	5.4	97.2	24	2.6	99.0	88	4.0	98.0
Up to 29	32	2.8	100.0	8	0.9	99.9	45	2.0	100.0
Total	1,140	100.0		907	99.9		2,205	100.0	

for biological literature. In both fields however, the literature in most demand was that published in the year prior to the survey, i.e. 1968.

If individual subjects are considered separately a wide range of »half-lives« is detectable. Pharmaceutical literature on the one hand has a »half-life« of only $2\frac{1}{2}$ years whilst that for general botany is 8 years. Further details of »half-lives« are presented in Table 6. The date distribution of requests in different subject fields is further illustrated by the data in Table 7 where the percentages of requests for material published in 1965 or later are compared with the percentages for pre-1965 literature.

TABLE 6:

»HALF-LIVES« OF THE MOST REQUESTED SUBJECTS

Subject	Half-life
General Biology	4.5 years
General Botany	8.0 years
General Zoology	6.5 years
Agriculture	6.0 years
Pharmacy	2.5 years
Anatomy/Physiology	5.0 years
Disease/Pathology	3.5 years
Health/Preventive Medicine	3.5 years

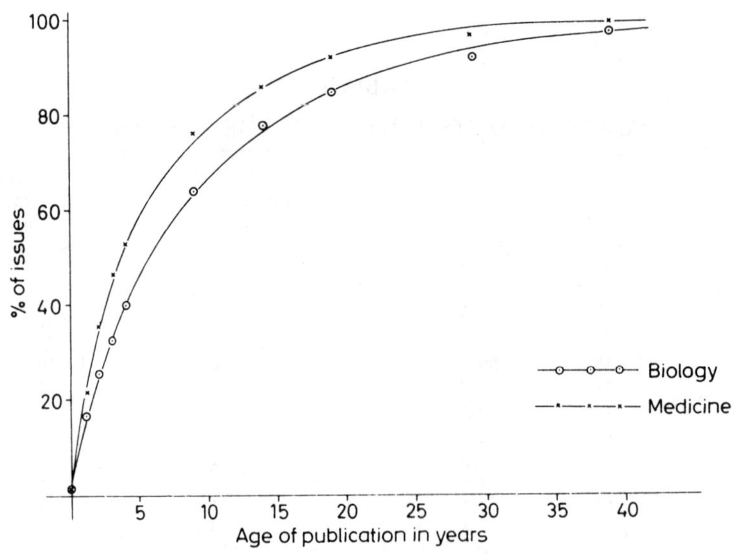

FIG. 2: Distribution of requests by date of publication

TABLE 7:
DATE DISTRIBUTION OF REQUESTS BY SUBJECT

Subject	% of requests for 1965 or later material	% of requests for pre-1965 material
All medicine	52.7	47.3
All biology	39.8	60.2
General biology	47.7	52.3
General botany	33.3	66.7
General zoology	33.0	67.0
Agriculture	36.1	63.9
Anatomy/Physiology	43.2	56.8
Health/Preventive Medicine	43.6	56.4
Pharmacy/Pharmacology	63.9	36.1
Disease/Pathology	50.9	49.1
All requests	46.0	54.0

The date distribution figures for medical literature confirm the findings of the 1967 survey, and agree with the results obtained during surveys at the National Library of Medicine,[6] at Yale[4] and among medical libraries in the New York area.[5]

2. Sources of References

(a) General

During the survey period the recipients of biomedical literature were asked to indicate, by ticking one of a list of possible sources, the source from which the reference had been obtained. The results are presented in Table 8.

The principal sources of references to biomedical literature are other periodical articles followed by abstracting and indexing journals, non-periodical publications and personal recommendations, in that order. These four sources were, between them, responsible for 90.8 per cent of all the references. If biology and medicine are considered separately the same situation pertains although users of medical literature rely more on abstracting and indexing journals than do biologists.

The use made of mechanised information retrieval systems is very low. Only 2.0 per cent of the biological references and only 4.6 per cent of the medical references came from these sources.

TABLE 8:
SOURCES OF BIBLIOGRAPHICAL INFORMATION

Source	Biology		Medicine		Biology and Medicine Combined	
	No. of requests	% of requests	No. of requests	% of requests	No. of requests	% of requests
Abstracting or indexing publication	272	23.7	280	30.7	552	26.8
Ringdoc	3	0.3	5	0.5	8	0.4
MEDLARS	6	0.5	26	2.9	32	1.6
CBAC	2	0.2	3	0.3	5	0.2
Other computerised information retrieval service	12	1.0	8	0.9	20	1.0
Periodical article	476	41.5	334	36.6	810	39.4
Non-periodical publication	212	18.5	123	13.5	335	16.3
Private or library index	36	3.1	51	5.6	87	4.2
Personal recommendation	106	9.2	71	7.8	177	8.6
Other	20	1.7	11	1.2	31	1.5
Not stated	1	0.1	0	0.0	1	0.0
All sources	1,146	99.8	912	100.0	2,058	100.0

The latter figure shows only a small increase on the corresponding figure of 3.9 per cent obtained in the 1967 survey. At that time mechanised information retrieval services in the UK were still in their infancy and it might have been expected that as they became better established they would play an increasingly important role in information retrieval. This they do not seem to be doing.

A breakdown of reference sources by subject reveals that although in almost all cases periodical articles are the principal sources of references, workers in different fields vary in the extent to which they use other sources. General biologists, anatomists, physiologists and pathologists exhibit the same characteristics as the sample as a whole. Botanists, zoologists and workers in health and preventive medicine, however, make comparatively little use of abstracting and indexing journals and rely more on non-periodical publications. Students of agriculture and pharmacy on the other hand make more than average use of abstracting journals, and in the case of pharmacists these sources are the principal means of locating references.

Two other parameters, date and language, have also been considered in relation to the use made of different sources of references.

The most significant variations in the relative importance of the sources occur when the dates of the references are considered. This is illustrated in Figure 3 where the percentages of references obtained from the four principal sources are plotted against the year of publication of the documents referred to. The figure refers to biomedical literature as a whole but the pattern is virtually identical if medical and biological literature are considered separately. It can be seen from Figure 3 that for literature published in 1968/69, 57.3 per cent of the references were obtained from abstracting and indexing publications. Citations in periodical articles on the other hand provided only 15.6 per cent of these recent references. Abstracting and indexing journals although providing proportionately fewer references, remain the principal source of 1967 references, but for 1966 material periodicals were equally productive. References to journals published before 1966 were derived principally from articles in other periodicals, whilst abstracting journals gradually decline in importance. For pre-1950 material for instance, only 4.4 per cent of the references came from abstracting publications. Non-periodical publications are seen to be useful principally as a guide to older material. These sources furnished only 0.8 per cent of the 1968/69 references but for pre-1950 they provided 35.3 per cent of the references.

The use made of the different sources of references is a function not only of the date of the literature referred to but also of the language of the literature. This is particularly true when the relative use made of periodical articles and abstracting journals is considered. References to English language material are obtained principally from periodical articles. Just over 40 per cent of the references came from these sources compared

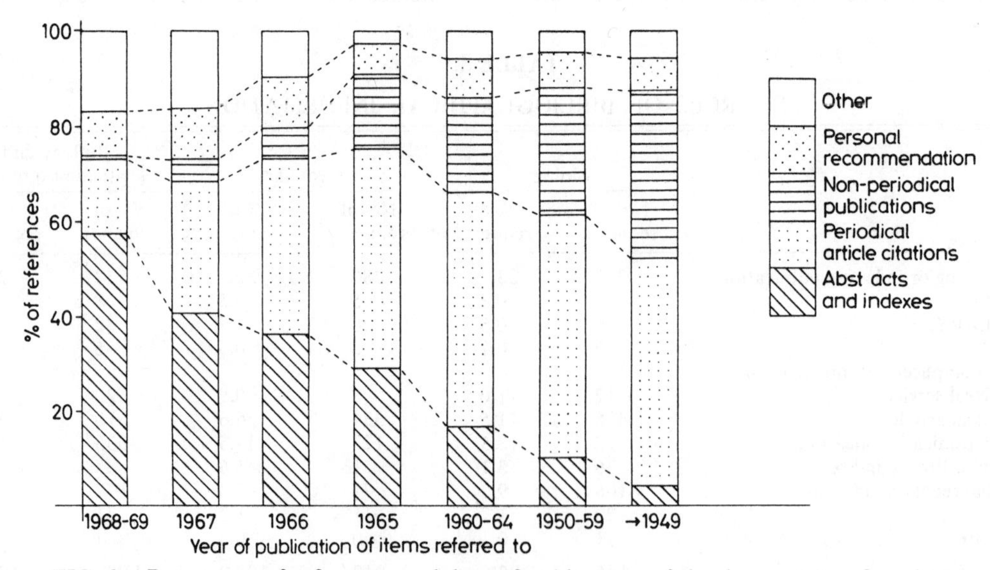

FIG. 3: Percentage of references and date of publication of the documents referred to

with 24.4 per cent from abstracting journals. However, because few English speaking authors read or cite foreign language literature (even though it may be useful), the main sources of references to this literature are not periodical articles. Only 29.2 per cent came from these sources whereas 45.5 per cent of the references came from abstracting and indexing journals. This situation is even more marked if medical literature is considered separately. 54.5 per cent of the references to foreign language medical articles came from abstracting journals and only 21.5 per cent from periodical articles. The corresponding figures for English language articles are 27.0 per cent and 39.2 per cent.

(b) Abstracting and indexing journals

References to 552 of the biomedical articles borrowed from the library during the survey period were obtained from abstracting and indexing publications. The relative use of the latter is shown in Table 9.

Altogether 92 different abstracting and indexing journals were used as sources of references. Leaving aside those listed in Table 9 they range from *British Research and Development Reports* and *Tropical Diseases Bulletin* to *Gas Chromatography Abstracts* and *Wild Life Review*.

The results of the survey suggest that the most useful guide to the literature in the biomedical field is *Index Medicus*. The position of prominence occupied by this journal is largely due to the very significant contribution which it makes to the retrieval of medical information. Over 36.8 per cent of the medical references obtained from abstracting journals came from *Index Medicus*, a figure which bears out the findings of the 1967 survey where the comparable figure was 34.6 per cent. The second most productive source of references in the medical field is apparently *Current Contents*.

In the field of biology no single abstracting journal stands out as the most frequently used guide to the literature. *Biological Abstracts* which one might have expected to furnish the bulk of the references in fact only provided 14.0 per cent. It is interesting to note that as a source of biological information *Current Contents* was used more than *Biological Abstracts*. Bearing in mind that the former is a guide to current literature and that the »half-life« of biological literature is considerably longer than in most other scientific fields this is rather surprising and suggests that biologists are, for one reason or another, somewhat disenchanted with *Biological Abstracts*.

Chemical Abstracts, in view of its broad data base, is useful to some extent in most subject fields and the present survey confirms that both biologists and medical workers find it of value. In the medical field it is the principal abstracting journal for pharmaceutical and pharmacological information, and in the biological field it is used mainly by biochemists.

The low use made of some abstracting journals, particularly those with a reasonably broad coverage of the literature is worthy of comment. Three such journals are *Excerpta Medica*, *International*

TABLE 9:

THE MAIN ABSTRACTING AND INDEXING PUBLICATIONS USED AS SOURCES OF REFERENCES

Source of reference (as listed in the questionnaire)	% of Biological Articles	% of Medical Articles	% of Biological and Medical Articles Combined
Index Medicus	8.1	36.8	22.6
Current Contents	19.5	13.9	17.1
Chemical Abstracts	12.9	8.2	10.2
Biological Abstracts	14.0	3.2	8.1
Index Veterinarius	3.3	3.9	3.4
Bulletin of the Royal Postgraduate Medical School	1.1	4.6	3.2
Nutrition Abstracts	2.9	0.7	2.0
Review of Applied Mycology	4.1	0.0	2.0
Zoological Record	3.3	0.4	1.7
Excerpta Medica	1.1	2.1	1.5
International Abstracts of Biological Sciences	0.0	0.0	0.0
Others	29.4	25.0	27.5

Abstracts of Biological Sciences, and *Zoological Record*. The fragmentation into individual subject sections is probably one reason why *Excerpta Medica* is used infrequently, since such an arrangement deters workers from carrying out a lengthy search for information on interdisciplinary subjects. *International Abstracts of Biological Sciences* is superficially a potentially useful guide to the literature, but its very selective coverage and the fact that the references duplicate those to be found in *Biological Abstracts* or *Index Medicus*, would seem to make it a somewhat unnecessary publication on the bibliographical scene. *Zoological Record* probably suffers from little use because of the time delays involved in its production; the latest issues refer to literature published in 1966.

The use of the various abstracting and indexing services varies considerably with the age of the information being retrieved. *Current Contents* is used principally as a source of recent references, 90.2 per cent of the references being to material published within the fourteen months prior to the survey. As a means of keeping up to date the usefulness of this publication is further indicated by the fact that it provided the references to 21.6 per cent of all the 1968 biomedical literature borrowed from the NLL during the survey.

Index Medicus is primarily used for obtaining references to literature published in the last three years, whereas the MEDLARS service, because of the ease with which retrospective searching can be carried out, is used for locating the older literature.

A significant proportion of the references obtained from both *Biological Abstracts* and *Chemical Abstracts* is to literature published before 1965. The actual figures are 36.2 per cent for *Biological Abstracts* and 39.7 per cent for *Chemical Abstracts*. In the case of the former the figure is probably not surprising in view of the relatively long »half-life« of biological literature. The use of *Chemical Abstracts* for locating older literature however is undoubtedly due to the availability of good cumulative indexes which allow retrospective searching to be carried out relatively easily.

NOTES

[1]Vickery, B. C.: Indicators of the use of periodicals. J. Librarianship 1: 170–182, 1969.

[2]Wood, D. N. and Bower, C. A.: Survey of medical literature borrowed from the National Lending Library for Science and Technology. Bull. med. Libr. Ass. 57: 47–63, 1969.

[3]Universal Decimal Classification. (BS 1000 A: 1961), Abridged English Edition, 3rd ed. (British Standards Institution, London 1961).

[4]Stangl, P. and Kilgour, F. G.: Analysis of recorded biomedical book and journal use in the Yale Medical Library–I. Date and subject relations, II. Subject and user relations. Bull. med. Libr. Ass. 55: 290–300, 301–315, 1967.

[5]Ash, L. and Bruette, V. R.: Interlibrary request and loan transactions among medical libraries of the Greater New York Area. (New York, 1966).

[6]Kurth, W. H.: Survey of the interlibrary loan operation of the National Library of Medicine. (U.S. Department of Health, Education and Welfare, Washington, D. C., 1962).

ABOUT THE AUTHORS–Dr. D. N. Wood was educated at Nottingham and Leeds Universities. After receiving his doctorate in geology at Leeds, he became a Research Fellow in the Institute of African Geology. In 1962 he joined the United Kingdom National Lending Library for Science and Technology where he is Principal Scientific Officer with special responsibility for research. He is also in charge of the UK Government sponsored translation service.

Miss C. A. Bower was educated at Manchester University, gaining a degree in Mathematics. She joined the National Lending Library in 1963, and since 1966 has been responsible for the design, organization and analysis of surveys and use studies.

Design for a University Health Sciences Information Center

by James G. Miller

In order to fit pieces of the future together and to plan for it, one must have a dream. There have been many discussions of future use of libraries, computer facilities and audiovisual materials for specific purposes. Here is a detailed design for integration of all the techniques into a health sciences information center serving the needs of research, education, and practice. While the specifics will change, the pattern can provide persepctive for many years.

Information-processing is an essential and major part of the educational, clinical, research, and service activities of the health sciences—as it is of any scientific or educational activity. Indeed, what every major unit of a university does chiefly is to "process information." (This term is used broadly to include the obtaining of information by individuals from some source in their environment, their association of it with other previously learned information, their storing of it in their memories, their making decisions on the basis of it, their creating new concepts and ideas, and their expressing such information in oral, written, or other forms whereby it is transmitted to other individuals.)

The various modes of information-processing in university centers for the health sciences have not ordinarily been coordinated. The several media of communication, old and new—face-to-face contact in the teaching situation, academic administration, and hospital administration; printed matter, including programmed instructional material; educational radio and television; photography and other forms of illustration; and electronic data processing—can under many circumstances substitute for one another, and there can be important trade-offs among them. Rapid advances are being made in information-processing technologies, and it is important that modern higher education make serious efforts to evaluate objectively the relative advantages of the traditional methods and the new opportunities.

A health sciences information center (HSIC) would bring together in one building many sorts of university information-processing systems in order to facilitate the coordination of their common activities and the solution of the problems which they share. Such coordination would also make it easier to evaluate the relative advantages, disadvantages, and costs of the various information-processing media. A number of administrative problems must be resolved if HSIC is to bring together such an assortment of groups on any university campus. The university might also establish information centers to serve its other undergraduate and graduate colleges, amalgamating all its information-processing functions into a university-wide information center operating a single network within the university.

If the university is a member of the Interuniversity Communications Council (EDUCOM), it will probably have an "Intracom" committee which relates to that organization.[1] The purpose of the Intracom committees is to bring together professors from various parts of the university who are concerned with the educational processes and persons technically trained in all of the information-processing media. The director of HSIC might report to this Intracom committee.

The new technologies will in a few years enable faculty, staff, and students of health science centers to have more rapid, accurate, complete, and flexible access to information; and this can importantly improve many of their functions. A

SOURCE: Reprinted from J. G. Miller, "Design for a University Health Sciences Information Center," *Journal of Medical Education*, 42 (May, 1967), pp. 404–429, by permission of the publisher and the author.

university health science center needs a central nervous system with peripheral neurons running to it. We must plan now how to take advantage of such systems and improve their sophistication, while at the same time training people to develop and operate them.

NEEDS

For the past five hundred years most information-processing activities in colleges and universities have been carried out in classrooms or in the library. The major method of information storage has been the printed page. The rapid growth and change now occurring in most academic areas are making extraordinary demands on colleges' and universities' information-processing facilities, and traditional methods are no longer adequate. The literature in the health sciences is doubling at least every twenty years, as is true of scientific publications generally. The number of students in the health sciences increases every year. Moreover, these fields themselves are changing. Health science activities now take into account the complex interplay of personal, emotional, and environmental factors that affect an individual's health and well-being. The health sciences are evidencing new interests in such disciplines as psychology, anthropology, economics, sociology, biophysics, ecology, mathematics, electronics, communication science, systems science, and operations research.

All this is creating unprecedented overloads on students, faculty, and staff, and on the various facilities which they use, in particular the libraries. C. F. J. Overhage[2], who is working on the automation of the library of the Massachusetts Institute of Technology, has observed 3 sorts of crises now facing university libraries: the physical crisis produced by the sheer bulk of the material; the operational crisis arising from the time required to process each item and the resulting costs; and the intellectual crisis deriving from the enormously complicated structure of the total knowledge of our day which makes retrieval of a particular piece of information a slow and costly process. He views the library problem as a particular manifestation of a more general overloading of the channels of communication among scholars. This difficulty is more acute in the heavily endowed areas of science and technology such as the health sciences. The conventional transfer path from the source of a piece of scientific information to the user is now often so long and uncertain that the information has lost much of its value when it reaches him–if it reaches him at all.

Fortunately, at a time when these problems are becoming critical, new ways of coping with them are appearing. From interdisciplinary origins, communication science is emerging as a new discipline; and much research and study have been devoted to problems of information storage and retrieval. General systems theory offers a conceptual framework for the development and evaluation of information-processing systems. Quantitative measures of the cost and effectiveness of different methods of information-processing have been developed.

The new information-processing technologies are providing man with prostheses to aid him in information storage, retrieval, manipulation, and dissemination. Several of these show great promise for increasing the efficiency and significantly decreasing the costs of university activities. Some of them require further basic research. All demand careful evaluation before they can be put into effective operation side by side with older methods, many of which will retain their usefulness.

Each of these new techniques should be compared with more traditional methods in order to answer such questions as the following: Does it accelerate and improve scholarship by making access to information more rapid, more complete, and easier? Is it less costly in human effort or in money? Each of these techniques should be tried out in appropriate settings in the health science areas, but always with a research design which permits careful comparison of the method under study with other techniques, in order to assure that it is not adopted simply because it is new, but rather because it truly improves health science functions. The emphasis should always be on the humane goals of a university and on the people that make it up rather than on gadgets.

This article describes an ideal health science information center for a typical university. No such system exists in any university at present, though some aspects of it do. However, the techniques and the knowledge on which the concept is based do exist, and any university desiring to develop a center like the one described here could begin to do so immediately.

HSIC is designed to enable the university of which it is a part to make available the most advanced information-processing facilities to students, staff, faculty, and the broader community which it serves, and to provide intimate and efficient interaction between individual users and a large part of the total fund of biomedical knowledge.

Growth and change are not unique to the health sciences. A program similar to HSIC could be used in other university units, and HSIC could eventually become a subsystem of a university-wide information-processing system.

OBJECTIVES

In any information center storage of information is essential. In HSIC, however, emphasis is also placed on transmission and manipulation. The system described here would be the center of what Licklider[3] has called a "procognitive system." Ultimately, he asserts, the system should:

1. Organize and process information so that a user has immediate access to all facts, concepts, ideas, or other items of information relevant to his particular needs.
2. Handle a wide variety of inputs, including formal publications, informal notes and comments, and items derived from more than one source.
3. Reduce the difficulties now caused by the diversity of symbols, languages, jargons, and terminologies.
4. Essentially eliminate publication lag.
5. Make possible retrieval of all or nearly all existing information relevant to a search.
6. Respond immediately to a user's request, interact with him, and adjust to his level of sophistication.
7. Facilitate interaction of groups of coworkers with each other and with the system.
8. Permit users to deal with abstract concepts and relationships, or with substantive information, or with both at once.
9. Provide the user on demand with either the flexibility, legibility, portability, and convenience of the printed page or the dynamic quality and immediate responsiveness of the modified TV screen or cathode-ray tube and the light pen, which will be described in the following section.
10. Store information on the users' interests and needs for the purpose of formulating policies about acquisition and retention, taking the initiative to keep each user informed about new information which is in his field of interest.
11. Develop flexible working relationships with other systems such as research systems, governmental information-acquisition systems, and industrial application systems.
12. Standardize cataloging, indexing, and abstracting activities to make them most efficient and most valuable to users.
13. Record and process all bookkeeping, billing, receipts, and disbursements.
14. Provide special facilities (languages, computer programs, computer subroutines, processors, and displays) for use in making and in implementing decisions that affect system policies and rules.
15. Handle guidelines, strategies, tactics, and rules of thumb intended to expedite solution of information-processing problems.
16. Provide for continuing efforts to improve the organization of and easy access to the existing body of knowledge.

According to Overhage and Harman[2], the library of the future will be a large network of information transfer services, coordinated by a central staff, which will spread to all parts of the academic community and also be linked to sources and users far beyond the campus. HSIC is planned as a center for such a campus information transfer complex which would include all health science branch libraries; departmental, institute, and center libraries or reading collections; and hospital libraries. Ultimately, there would be terminals in the offices or laboratories of faculty and staff members and in carrels for students and other users. Overhage's diagrams of the center—modified by the author—appear as Figures 1 and 2.[4]

As a transfer center, HSIC would not deal with all health science information-processing activities, but would function as a station in one or more regional or national electronic networks for information-processing relevant to the health sciences. Such a network would include scholarly centers,

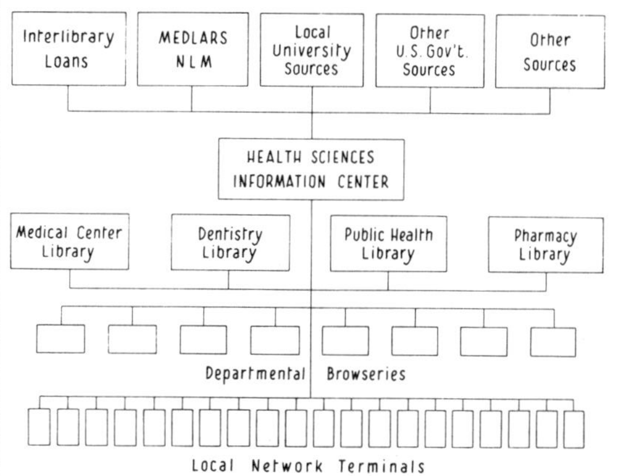

FIG. 1. The information transfer complex.

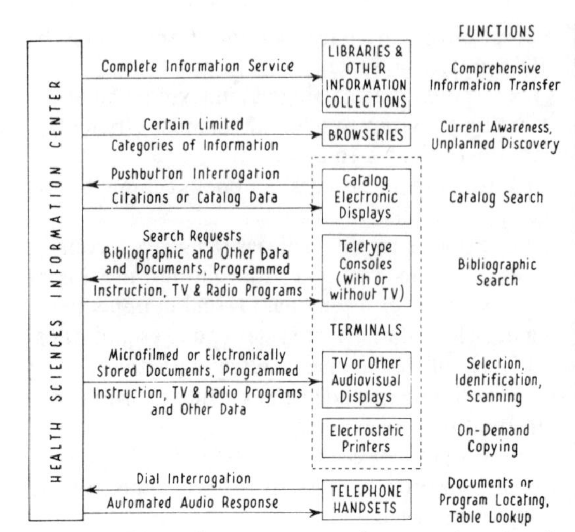

FIG. 2. The information transfer complex—levels of access.

hospitals, governmental agencies, industries, and various sorts of libraries. Its primary store of information might well be in the National Library of Medicine (NLM) in Washington. It would provide a means whereby, ultimately, catalog entries, bibliographic aids, complete texts of documents, television lectures, pictures, instructional computer programs and texts, other computer programs, and other information could be transferred electronically from one collection to another.

RECENT DEVELOPMENTS

A number of recent major technological advances make feasible the development of HSIC; they include the following:

1. The new generation of computers, such as the International Business Machine 360-67 or the General Electric 645, are capable of operating hundreds of remote terminals. HSIC would operate such a computer in the on-line, time-sharing mode, which in all probability will be widely adopted within the next few years.

2. Very large and increasingly less costly electronic information storage units are being designed. Computer memories are now available, 100 of which together are capable of storing electronically up to 100,000,000,000,000 (10^{14}) bits of information, which is of the order of magnitude of the information in the entire texts of all documents in the Library of Congress. Such memory is modular, with random access time to any bit of the order of a few milliseconds and between modules of the order of several seconds. Seven years ago the monthly rental for an electronic memory capable of storing 1,000,000 letters or figures (8,000,000 bits of information) was 533 dollars. Now it is 7 dollars. And in two years it may be about 5 cents.

3. Information stored anywhere in the United States can now be transmitted automatically, rapidly, and efficiently to any receiver in the country over the ordinary telephone network. Telefacsimile machines exist (but are not yet on the market) which are capable of receiving signals from computers over long-distance telephone lines and translating them into printed pages at a rate of about a page a second and at a cost of 1 or 2 cents a page (plus the line charges). This equipment can also reproduce pictures and diagrams clearly. It is possible that exchange of information among libraries or information centers with such apparatus will, in at least some cases, be cheaper than storing books and journals in libraries.

4. Photoreaders are now on the market which can read typed material directly into electronic storage, and it is reasonable to expect that within two or three years it will be possible to transfer printed material to electronic storage automatically and at very high rates of speed.

5. Computer programs are being written and constantly improved which will permit computers to abstract and index electronically stored documents; to translate information from one language to another; to notify users automatically of new information which fits their continually changing interest patterns; to "read" electronically stored documents and print out paragraphs or sentences in response to a wide range of queries; to scan documents over long-distance telephone wires; and to enable teachers to write computerized programmed instruction by using simple English even though they do not know machine language. Also centralized, automated library card catalogs which can be consulted from any remote terminal could be utilized.

6. Carrels are now being produced which contain an electric typewriter that can be attached to a computer, an audio output, and a modified television screen or cathode-ray tube on which the computer can display pages of books and serials requested via the typewriter or carry out programmed instruction much more sophisticated

than that done by teaching machines. It is also possible for a human being to signal the computer by pointing or drawing with a light pen on the face of the television screen. For example, he can point to that part of the display on the tube which is the correct answer to a multiple-choice question or which contains information on which he wishes the computer to carry out some logical or mathematical operation. Programs have been written to be used with such carrels which make it possible to draw graphic figures with a light pen on the face of the television screen and to store these figures in the memory of the computer. They can then, on demand, be retrieved from the memory and modified or recombined in different spatial arrangements.

An information center such as HSIC would not be created overnight, but would develop gradually over a number of years. The program outlined here assumes that traditional methods would be used at first and that after careful study some of these would later be replaced by new methods.

GENERAL LIBRARY FUNCTIONS

HSIC would make optimal use of 3 phases of technological development in the processing of information: Phase I—books and serials, Phase II—microform, and Phase III—electronic information-processing.

Phase I

HSIC would provide the following facilities and services:

Reader seating.—About two-thirds of the seats would be individual carrels and the remainder would be conventional table-and-chair seating. Group conference rooms would also be available. Gradually more and more of the traditional carrels would be automated for use with the microform and electronic information-processing activities.

Bibliographic and reference materials.—There should be a comprehensive collection of bibliographic and reference works located close to table seats and carrels.

Core collection of most-used books and journals.—Nearby there should be a relatively small but carefully chosen collection of the most-used biomedical books and journal files, mostly recent.

Users' advisory services.—Professional librarians should be stationed at the collections of bibliographic and reference tools and at the core collection. Their services include individualized help in locating materials, assistance in using bibliographic and reference tools, provision of "spot" information, verification of short lists of references, brief literature searches, preparation of short bibliographies, elementary editorial assistance, and the like. On-line access to appropriate computer memories available to the reference librarians should, as time passes, make such services increasingly effective and rapid.

These materials and services together would constitute a dynamic literature search laboratory in which users would move actively about, making literature searches with the help of the library staff. Users would be able to go there first to locate and—in a preliminary way—evaluate the books and journals they need, and then retire to suitable study areas to give their material extended and undisturbed attention.

Extensive historical and research collections.—The library's general collections of books and journals should be freely accessible on open shelves. A specially equipped rare book room would house high-priced or irreplaceable materials.

Lending services.—Circulation facilities, automated as soon as possible, would permit the majority of the publications to be borrowed for reading in carrels or outside HSIC, or to be lent to other libraries.

Bibliographic instruction.—Individual or group instruction in the nature of the literatures of the biomedical sciences, and in the proper use of the library's facilities and resources, should be provided to all primary library users, including students, faculty, and staff.

Interlibrary borrowing service.—This should be an important part of the library activity.

Copying service.—Subject only to accepted restrictions on duplicating copyrighted materials, any library user should be able within minutes to obtain free, or inexpensive, copies of articles and parts of books.

Special bibliographic and informational activities.—HSIC should assist users by preparing and making available checklists, catalogs, indexes, and other bibliographic aids and should carry on such other informational and promotional activities as appear desirable.

Phase II

Recently, there has been dramatic progress in microform technology. One of the most remarkable new developments is photochromic microimage introduced by the National Cash Register Company; for example, the 1,245 pages and 773,746 words of the entire Bible can be reproduced on a transparency about the size of an ordinary 35 mm slide. Using this technique, the 42,000,000 pieces on the 270 miles of shelving in the United States Library of Congress could be stored in 6 standard filing cabinets. The initial cost would be about $500 million; but subsequently, the cost of copies of the entire Library of Congress would be only about $1 million each.

If the WALNUT system, which is now operating in the Central Intelligence Agency, were to use photochromic microimage, it could easily store on microfilm the entire Library of Congress in one room of ordinary size. A computer could locate any page in this collection in a fraction of a second. This page could be rapidly enlarged to full size or scanned electronically and transmitted over telephone wires, coaxial cable, or microwave.

The quality of table microfilm readers has improved in recent years. It is also possible to read microform through a television camera and transmit it over coaxial cable to an ordinary television set, permitting electronic dissemination of such materials around the campus. As yet no satisfactory pocket version has been developed. Thus, at the moment, books and journals are definitely easier to carry around and read than is microform.

Despite advances in microform technology, its use would probably be relatively restricted in HSIC. Storing and retrieving large volumes of text electronically would provide much greater flexibility of information-processing. Electronic storage and data processing costs are decreasing markedly. Electronically stored information can be quickly disseminated over national or local networks. Also it can be manipulated by computers with increasing flexibility as more sophisticated computer programs become available for locating text, locating concepts, or answering questions from ordinary documents. The text can also become the base for programmed instruction. Access times to electronically stored materials are faster than to microform, so searches of the former are faster. It is not clear what the cost differential between microform and electronic storage will be in the next five years; and this, of course, will be a major factor in determining which technique is the most feasible.

Phase III

It is essential that a library have up-to-date, readily available information about the location of every publication in its collections. According to F. H. Wagman,[5] Director of the University of Michigan Libraries, with the traditional methods of cataloging, at the University of Michigan there could be as many as 16 separate cards describing a single book and stating where it is shelved, and these would be filed in different locations in 5 separate catalogs. There are constant demands on libraries to transfer large numbers of books from one collection to another. Volumes which are no longer useful must be removed from the central collections and put into storage. When a book is thus permanently located, all cards must be changed. When a book is circulated, this information is not entered in the card catalogs which are available to library users, but on a separate record. In outlining some of the dilemmas which face university libraries, Wagman[5] made the following comment:

> It would be impossible to estimate how many man-years of scholarly time have been wasted by people going in search of books which were not on the shelf where the library's catalogs said they were. . . . The clerical chore of sending people to the catalogs to make the location changes or to withdraw cards from books which should be removed from the collections permanently has become such a trial that we have been almost completely frustrated in our efforts to keep up with need. Obviously we need a system that would enable us to up-date the location of any given volume or to remove its location record easily and cheaply by performing one process. We need a system, also, whereby people, before they start on a quest for a given book in one of our many libraries, can ascertain with great precision in which library that book is located, if it really is on the shelf and available for use, or if it is removed from that location to some other for a period of time, and, in the latter case, when it is scheduled to be returned and available.

Scholars and researchers need rapid, easy access to all pertinent literature, especially journals, which in the natural and behavioral sciences are the backbone of research. Attempts to answer this need by creating branch libraries have proved to be unsatisfactory.

How can modern communications technologies

find practical ways to alleviate, if not solve, these problems? Recently, there have been many innovations in the automation of library management functions, including ordering, cataloging, circulation control, record-keeping on library activities, budgeting, and maintaining personnel records. Probably the most convenient and efficient way to perform these functions is on-line with a time-sharing computer. These functions are carried out most effienctly if they are combined in a single computer system.

The first step in automating a library system is to put the contents of the card catalog into computer storage. An alternative or additional procedure would be to depth-index the books and to integrate such indexes with the National Library of Medicine's MEDLARS citations. Keypunching the library cards by hand would be slow and expensive, but it is conceivable that they could be read into electronic storage by an optical character recognition device. The Philco general purpose print reader is one apparatus which reads with high accuracy and stores on magnetic tape a half-dozen typewriter typefaces at up to 1,500 characters a second. It cannot now read any printed material with better than 95 per cent accuracy but may be able to do so in the very near future. It can record all or any selected data in a document, and it can arrange these data in any sequence on the tape. It would cost about 10 cents to process a library card in this manner. Although the tape would require human editing because the print reader cannot distinguish among the different types of content on the card–subject, author, title–this procedure might still be cheaper than keypunching.

The card contents should be stored in the computer in a format compatible with the Library of Congress magnetic-tape edition of catalog cards which is soon to be issued. It might be desirable to add the medical subject headings of the MEDLARS system in order to make the catalog also compatible with the National Library of Medicine's bibliographical system. Indexing in depth would most likely be a cooperative project involving several libraries.

After the present library is cataloged in this way, each new title to be purchased would have its citation, cost, and publisher put into computer storage by an on-line typewriter or by reading in the Library of Congress card contents. The computer would print out the order form to send to the publisher or book dealer, then deduct automatically the necessary funds from the budget account to which the book is to be charged. It would also prepare a plastic book identification card. When a new title arrived, this card would be put in the book, which would be shelved; its shelf location would then be entered into the computer memory. The book would thus automatically be included in the active library catalog.

The computer could periodically print out a cumulative list of new titles for an accession announcement. As soon as the book was listed in the catalog, a user could type in its title and author at any remote terminal and the computer would type back its shelf location if it were in the library and, if not, when it was to be returned. If library policy permitted, it would also type the name, address, and phone number of whoever had charged it out. A program can be written to permit a single memory on the computer to contain this information, thus replacing the public catalog, the official catalog, the shelf list, branch library catalogs, branch library shelf lists, and any other such lists.

Each time a book was transferred elsewhere, the symbol indicating its location would be changed. Thus, the current location could be immediately known to anyone who has access to a terminal. The cost of changing catalog cards or reproducing frequent updated printouts showing which books have been moved and where they have been moved to would, of course, be eliminated by this procedure. To take out a book, the user would go to the proper shelf, get it, and take it to a charging terminal. He would insert the plastic book identification card and his own similar identification card. The computer then would automatically charge out the book and print out for the user a slip saying when it was due and whether it could be renewed. Later the computer would automatically print out and address overdue notices, if necessary. If could also, if desired, charge fines directly to users' accounts in the university business office. It could prepare statistics on who used the library, what categories of books they used, and how much each book was used. It could do accounting and budgeting. A similar system would carry out on-line processing of serials.

A few minutes after they were requested, copies of documents of up to 25 pages could be delivered by messenger to or near offices of users on the campus–who would be permitted to keep the material–or they could be transmitted by long-distance xerography or some other telefacsimile procedure, including closed-circuit television.

Such procedures would enable university

libraries to order only one copy of many journals which are now being subscribed to in duplicate and the money saved on subscriptions and storage space could be spent for facsimile transmitters and remote receivers.

SPECIAL INFORMATION STORAGE AND RETRIEVAL SERVICES

Bloomquist[6] has listed a number of specialized information storage and retrieval services which, he maintains, the library of a modern medical center should offer its users. Such services would be provided by HSIC. Some of Bloomquist's recommendations are presented below along with suggestions for implementing them:

1. Continuous bibliographic service. A reader wants to be kept up to date on the literature of a particular subject. The library undertakes the searching of current indexes and abstracting journals and new issues of the important journals in the subject field, as they appear. References to the articles or photocopies of the articles are provided for the reader as they are found.

HSIC might provide such a service by using MEDLARS magnetic tapes mailed out monthly from the National Library of Medicine. These would be searched on the computer each month and lists of citations which fell under subject headings of interest to participant users would be sent to them, along with forms on which to report what articles were read and how much those articles interested the reader. The University of California at Los Angeles has monitored an industrial contract for a program to be written which makes MEDLARS tapes IBM-compatible. With the IBM 360-67 such services could be programmed for on-line use at any terminal, and users could immediately get an up-to-date bibliography of any content area.

Under the direction of M. M. Flood of the University of Michigan[7-9], a computer program for developing and continually updating interest profiles of individual readers has been developed at the University of California at Berkeley. This system, called SASIDS (Stochastic Adaptive Sequential Information Dissemination System), has been pretested now for three years and appears to be working moderately well. On the basis of a participant's ratings of his interest in articles he has read, the computer chooses future articles for him. Some success has been achieved in using the ratings of one participant to predict the interest of other participants in a given article. This program could be implemented on-line by HSIC.

2. On-demand bibliographies. A reader needs a retrospective bibliography on a particular topic. The library undertakes the search using the appropriate bibliographic tools. The reader is provided with a copy of the bibliography.

Using a batch-processing computer and the MEDLARS or Institute for Scientific Information tapes, a library now can provide comprehensive or intensively selective on-demand bibliographies on any topic or combination of topics in a matter of hours. With the IBM 360-67 such bibliographies, and later abstracts, could be available through HSIC within seconds or minutes at any terminal.

3. Translation service. A reader needs information from an article written in a language he cannot read, or wishes to know if the article is pertinent. The library has on its staff persons who can undertake spot translations of a summary or a few paragraphs of text. Or if a formal, full translation is needed, the staff member can undertake it himself or can locate an appropriate translator.

HSIC should provide this service. Computer programs which can translate from one language to another now exist; but they are far from perfect. Undoubtedly, they will be improved in time and even now they might be of help in speeding human translating.

4. Audiovisual service. A reader needs a film or sound tape or recording dealing with a particular subject. The library can identify and locate, can buy or rent the item for him, and can provide the equipment to use it, the personnel to run the equipment, and perhaps the place to show or listen to the item. The library can also maintain an up-to-date collection of these items.

Such services should be provided by HSIC, which would also develop a large, organized, indexed, up-to-date collection of audiovisual aids.

5. Extension service. A reader in a place remote from the library (mainly rural areas) needs an item from the library's collections. The library is able to provide rapid delivery of the item or a photocopy of the item by mail (or

conceivably by one of the newer electronic devices . . .).

HSIC would attempt to meet statewide and perhaps regional needs for health science information.

6. Editorial service. The library maintains a service whereby all papers being submitted for publication pass through the library where the references are verified, the citations are checked for uniformity, and format, grammar, illustrations, etc. are checked before submission.

The HSIC reference staff would develop computer programs to check MEDLARS tapes and other such sources in order to verify and edit lists of references or bibliographies in manuscripts intended for publication by faculty and staff members of the health sciences colleges. This service could be requested from any terminal on-line to the IBM 360-67.

7. Literature assistance staff. The library is able to assign a competent staff member to any research group in the institution, as needed, to work on the literature end of any project. This could vary from full-time participation in a project to occasional consultation.

HSIC would provide these services. In addition, HSIC should be prepared to supply a consultant to serve temporarily as a bibliographic detective and advisor for any community groups (nurses, occupational therapists) who are engaging in research in the health sciences fields.

PROGRAMMED INSTRUCTION

Computerized programmed instruction courses are now being written and tested in such diverse areas as remedial reading, French, accounting, economics, psychology, physics, engineering, statistics, calculus, logic, medical diagnosis, nursing, computer programming, typing, and management decision-making. These programs differ not only in content, but also in approaches to the content. They can be used with all sorts of subject matter, including the writing of programmed instruction or information retrieval techniques. They promise to be as good as or better than standard modes of teaching, at least for some kinds of materials.

A single time-shared, on-line computer can monitor instruction of many students at remote terminals in many parts of the campus. The cost of such computerized instruction will not be exorbitant. Some estimate that it will soon be lowered to between 5 dollars and 1 dollar per student hour.

The computer presents a question to a student by typewriter, by projection of a picture, or on a television screen. He responds with a typewriter or by pointing with a light pencil to an answer on the television screen. The computer can interact with the student in a typed "conversation" in which both student and computer use ordinary, free English. It can pose a complex problem, provide information when the student asks for it, permit him to state the solution whenever he wishes, and deal with a wide range of answers. Like a tutor, it can respond favorably to good questions, rebuke premature conclusions, approve wise decisions, and question the grounds of inference.

The computer contains, conceals, and to some extent manages the teaching materials. The student never can peek at answers and he need not search around among pages to find the one he needs, as is necessary in some printed programmed instruction. A computerized system can supply, on request, various sorts of complex displays, such as the graph of a particular equation. It can check numerical data fed to it by the student and so give him immediate feedback as to the accuracy of his problem-solving procedure. It can analyze some linguistic constructions. A computer can generate in real time various exercises in arithmetic or logic, or randomize the order of presenting possible multiple-choice responses or select a few questions randomly from a larger pool so that each student's experience is different. It can also simulate laboratory experiments with projected still pictures and moving pictures so that the student can decide what manipulations to carry out and immediately learn what effects result. This way of learning laboratory work is certainly cheaper than conventional laboratory instruction, although its effectiveness as a teaching device has not yet been determined.

The computer can keep a play-by-play record of a student's responses. By making possible on-line revision of instructional materials, it permits the author to correct and revise his program with ease and speed. Furthermore, it can calculate a grade for the student while he is learning, thus eliminating the need for examinations. Most examinations are based on a small sampling of a student's knowledge, but a computer can base a grade on the complete record of the amount and rate of learning.

Computerized programmed instruction shares with printed programmed instruction certain other advantages over the lecture system. (*a*) The student can progress at his own speed. (*b*) He is continuously active during the learning process. (*c*) He learns at once whether he is right or wrong, and is rewarded if he is right. And (*d*) if he is wrong, he is immediately given further instructions or opportunity for the special kind of practice he needs to correct his own particular error. On the other hand, materials he already knows can be bypassed.

HSIC would cooperate with health sciences faculty members in carrying out a program to develop and test computerized programmed instruction courses.

AUDIOVISUAL PROGRAMS

Educational television, educational radio, health sciences illustration, health sciences photography, and health sciences museums are now being utilized by many health sciences centers. Closed-circuit television is used in classrooms, operating rooms, and interviewing rooms; and open-circuit television and radio broadcasts are also transmitted through commercial and educational stations and networks.

Many academic lectures are stored on television tape or film by universities and educational television stations. Lectures by the best instructors in any field could be available to all health sciences centers, either through a national television network or by exchange of films and tapes. This would also save much of the time that professors now spend on repetitive lecturing in standard courses.

Educational television and radio will not achieve maximal usefulness until an individual student can see or hear television or radio tapes whenever he wishes. Educational television should be available to a large number of student carrels, with provision for on-line control of many taped programs from each carrel. The equipment to make this possible is now commercially available.

The health sciences are advancing so rapidly that any professional person quickly loses contact with current thought unless he receives continuing education throughout his lifetime. Books and journals are centrally important to this process. Radio, television, and other techniques can also make continuing education programs produced anywhere in the nation available in professional persons' offices, hospitals, and homes, thus composing a nationwide "university without walls." Some liaison between the continuing educational activities of the health science colleges and HSIC is therefore indicated. Studios and other facilities for producing radio and television programs for continuing education would be provided. Medical illustration and photography activities in the health science areas would be integrated with the other forms of information processing in HSIC. Systematically storing and retrieving such audiovisual aids as drawings, photographs, stereopticon slides, film strips, movies, and microscope slides is difficult and rarely done. On-line computer techniques are easily adapted to this purpose.

Health sciences centers generally have collections of artifacts, old and current exhibits, training displays, and miscellaneous memorabilia. These would be stored and put on exhibit in a health sciences museum in HSIC.

AUTOMATED COGNITIVE AIDS

Man excels in setting goals, generating hypotheses, and selecting criteria—those aspects of problem-solving which involve laying down guidelines, choosing approaches, following intuition, exercising judgment, or making evaluations. Computers excel in executing explicit procedures. These 2 aspects of problem-solving are not easily separated. Nevertheless, recently there have been some remarkably productive interactions between a man and an on-line, time-sharing computer; Project MAC (*M*an *A*nd *C*omputer, *M*ultiple *A*ccess *C*omputer, *M*achine-*A*ided *C*ognition) at Massachusetts Institute of Technology is one example. The Project MAC computer contains hundreds of programs which operate as "thinking aids" to the scientists and scholars who use it. It can perform computations; solve problems; display data in curves, histograms, matrices, or tables; store, retrieve, combine, and manipulate line drawings such as mechanical drawings or electric circuit diagrams; administer psychological tests to patients; facilitate the editing of manuscripts; and do many other such cognitive functions at high speeds, thus adding an entirely new capability to scholarly thinking and scientific research. It seems reasonable to expect that on-line, time-shared, man-machine cooperation among the community of health scientists, including the sharing of programs and knowledge, can facilitate many of their scholarly and research activities.

A wide range of computerized aids to medical and dental diagnosis and prognosis have been developed at various centers around the country in the last six years. HSIC would carry out a program in this field which would include on-line computer assistance in: reading electrocardiograms and electroencephalograms; reading X-rays; relating laboratory findings to diagnosis; taking medical histories; evaluating differential diagnoses and prognoses; and determining, from hospital records, age, sex, race, and other factors related to the incidence of diseases. Since all these are specialized forms of problem-solving, they can be assisted by on-line cognitive aids similar to those described above.

ON-LINE RESEARCH LABORATORIES

New types of biological and behavioral experimental research will become possible with a large time-sharing, on-line computer with remote terminals. Some of this research involves computer monitoring of variables and calculation of data continuously as an experiment goes on. In general 3 kinds of data will be presented to the computer for analysis:

1. Electrophysiological signals in which important component frequencies may be as high as 2,000 to 4,000 cycles per second and which require analog-to-digital conversion rates of over 10,000 cycles per second to assure adequate following of wave forms. This class includes spike action potentials recorded from neural or muscle tissues.
2. Electrophysiological and other transduced signals in which the frequency components are very low, varying from 1 or 2 cycles per second to perhaps 50 cycles per second. This class includes such signals as the electrocardiogram, the psychogalvanic response, and the electroencephalogram, along with evoked potentials of various sorts.
3. Real-time behavioral experimentation with human beings which involves a specific, small permitted repertoire of discrete responses.

With computer techniques capable of processing these various classes of data sufficiently fast to calculate new input configurations contingent upon a pattern of previous outputs, it can be expected that current statistical methods and research strategies will be substantially altered. An experimenter can quickly determine from preliminary tests what range of some input variable elicits changes that interest him and then limit his intensive investigation to that significant range. The computer can also prepare and display to patients or subjects stimulus materials for a behavioral study which vary greatly in character and can easily be modified. Also the computer can analyze output data as soon as they are obtained and put them into the proper format for publication.

HSIC would be the central location from which on-line laboratory experiments could be monitored throughout the health science colleges. The IBM 360-67 will not, when in ordinary operation, be able dependably to give microsecond or millisecond access on demand. It would therefore be necessary to have a moderate-sized satellite computer such as a PDP-7, DDP-116, or an IBM 1800 in HSIC to carry out these functions. This satellite computer could act as a temporary information storage buffer, if necessary, transferring the information to the much larger storage of the IBM 360-67 when it was ready to accept it. It would also carry out many of the programmed functions itself, but refer complex computations to the IBM 360-67.

ACADEMIC MANAGEMENT FUNCTIONS

Computers are currently being used to improve industrial management. Similarly, many aspects of academic management could be carried out more efficiently if they were automated. Among these are new personnel actions and the maintenance of personnel records, purchasing, inventory, budgeting, student record-keeping, student registration, space allocation, and scheduling of classes and laboratory sections.

On-line, time-sharing computation can keep the records of all these processes continually updated, monitoring the lag times of each one. Errors can also be located by this method. Signatures for the approval of proposals, personnel actions, budget actions, purchases, and the like can be obtained by simply transferring the information from one on-line terminal to another. Information on the state of expenditures and of available funds, as well as budgetary planning, can be kept up to date and the annual harassment of budget-making time minimized. Costs of different activities can, on demand, be calculated by the computer. Confidential information can be sequestered in data-processing machines so that access to it can be gained only by authorized people.

The complex decision-making process of large human organizations is always less than optimal: there is often no clear-cut concept of goals or there may be disagreement about goals. Lack of understanding, lack of coordination, delay, and inadequate evaluation of relevant considerations are common. These shortcomings can often be alleviated by using the quantitative methods of operations research for planning. HSIC should take steps to make such techniques available for academic management.

Student counseling throughout the health sciences colleges should be carried out on the basis of updated records of the student's background, his previous courses, his grades, comments of his instructors, his health record, and other such materials. Frequently, these data are filed in different parts of the campus. An on-line system would make it possible for such records to remain current and consolidated, available on demand wherever they are needed on the campus. They would also constitute a data base for collecting any desired statistics on students.

Other possible uses of an on-line computer in management decision involve its ability to measure the flow of students, faculty, information, or materials in the center. From these data, plans can be made to remedy undesirable aspects of these flows. Planning for campus sites and buildings can be facilitated by use of the cathode-ray tube described earlier. A computer can be programmed to generate on such a tube perspective displays from a site plan and building dimension data, presenting various vistas of the proposed campus. Modifications of the plan can be made by drawing with a light pencil on the tube.

PATIENT-CARE FUNCTIONS

As has been noted, computers can give important assistance in many hospital functions: admission and management of patients, scheduling of outpatient visits, automatic recording of clinical data and clinical laboratory findings, hospital personnel actions, purchases, and budgeting, as well as research on all of these activities.

At the Massachusetts General Hospital (MGH), a system composed of many typewriter terminals on-line to a time-sharing computer is now functioning which carries out many of these procedures and is capable of performing them all. Following are examples of automated procedures so far developed there:

1. The computer proposes questions to the admitting officer, who asks them of a patient being admitted and then enters the responses into the computer memory by typewriter.
2. The computer has in its memory an instantly available record of every room and every bed in the hospital, including the type of room, the daily price of the room, and which beds are filled, among other things. Information can be updated or corrected as required.
3. Clinical laboratory reports can be stored in this system. A doctor decides what urine, blood, or other tests need to be done on a patient. This information is typed on the nearest terminal typewriter; it is immediately recorded in the clinical laboratory and the necessary laboratory analyses are made. The results of the tests are immediately available on request to every typewriter on-line in the system. The computer is programmed so that the laboratory information can be obtained in any way desired, whether it be a request for a complete listing of all results obtained in a single day or a compilation of the findings on repeated administration of a given test.
4. The system can be used for prescribing drugs. A physician may request pharamacological information about any drug. If he misspells the name of the compound, the computer will suggest to him the correct spelling. The computer will also tell him the route for administering the drug, the maximum single dose, the maximum daily dose, alternate proprietary names for the drug, and similar information. If he orders an improper dosage, the computer will immediately warn him and inform the pharmacy. On request the computer can also print out an updated list of all current medications for a given patient or tell the nurse all the drugs she is expected to administer to patients on her ward at a given time.
5. The computer can search through hospital records for medical research purposes and can formulate the data in any way desired. It can locate a given number of records showing any specific diagnostic condition, symptom, or sign, and then can analyze these data according to age, sex, duration of medication, clinical findings, or any other variables which interest the clinical

scientist. It can compute the significance of differences among various groups and present the data in charts or in other forms as desired or punch them on IBM cards, which can be used on larger computers for more extensive computations.

It is apparent that the MGH system can have salutary effects on the operations of that medical center. HSIC would carry out the developmental activities necessary to adapt such a system to its own university hospital.

Other examples of the host of possible uses of automated procedures as clinical aids include the following:

1. Physicians spend a significant part of their time leafing through records to find specific notes or records of laboratory findings. Much of this could be avoided if an on-line hospital record system were used. The data could be entered directly into the computer memory on an on-line basis and a physician could retrieve any part of the record he wanted within seconds. Computers could be used on-line for medical and dental history-taking and for recording physical examinations, if structured forms were used. In a few years it may well be possible for a physician to dictate into a microphone and have his words recorded directly in digital electronic storage.

2. Hospital records stored in computers become a data base for research on differential diagnoses and prognoses. At the Meyer Memorial Hospital in Buffalo, New York, for example, the computer analyzed the records of 220 white women and 208 Negro women, all aged seventy-six[10, 11]. It was found that the Negro women as a group had considerably lower blood urea nitrogen levels than the white women. A high level in a Negro patient of seventy-six, therefore, might be of greater significance than in a white woman of the same age, since it would represent greater deviation from the baseline.

3. Records of many patients might be analyzed by computer to see if they reveal new diagnostic categories or syndromes of signs, symptoms, and laboratory findings. The computer could provide all sorts of descriptive statistics about the patient population, including ranges of effectiveness of various old and new diagnostic and therapeutic procedures. A multitude of questions, such as whether or not there are seasonal variations in red cell counts and if these are more pronounced in particular categories of patients, could be answered in seconds in comparison to the time-consuming and laborious search of many individual patient records which conventional techniques require.

Some officials in the federal government are now giving some consideration to a national electronic network over which complete hospital records can be transmitted electronically from any health sciences center or hospital to any other one. If such a system is implemented, HSIC could be the network control center for the university hospital.

4. A computer simulation of a hospital could be undertaken. Various aspects of the system could be experimentally altered in the simulation on an on-line basis in order to determine what impact such changes would have on the overall system. Thus, for example, the effects of changing the hours of the outpatient department or rescheduling patient visits or adding a wing to a building could be evaluated, in terms of various measures of time utilization, cost, adequacy of service, and the like.

RESEARCH RELATED TO INFORMATION-PROCESSING

There should be a research emphasis in all the operations of HSIC. This would enable the medical center most effectively to utilize and contribute to developments in communication technologies. The research should be both basic and applied, but the primary emphasis should be on applied research. Investigations should be followed up with development and implementation of new techniques and applications, which should be integrated into HSIC's activities.

The hardware and software for information-processing are just beginning to be sophisticated enough to be of value in all fields of the health sciences. Yet much investigation is required before their usefulness becomes maximal. HSIC should undertake such research, making carefully controlled evaluations of new methods. A cost-effectiveness study would provide the basis upon which a decision about the permanent adoption of any new system would be made.

Basic Research

One part of the HSIC research program should be devoted to answering fundamental questions about the nature of living and mechanical systems and information-processing, including the learning process and the use of language. Finding such answers is prerequisite to making technical advances which have significant practical application.

General systems research.—Each of the man-machine systems which would be used in HSIC manifests certain basic characteristics. This is true of a computer programmed to control inputs through microelectrodes to a single cell in a neurophysical preparation; of a pacemaker in a heart; of a computer administering programmed instruction to a dental student; of a closed-circuit television system presenting a demonstration on tube-feeding to a nursing class; of a communication network for a school of public health; or of a national telephone system. The general systems principles, formal identities which apply to information-processing and other functions at all of these levels of systems, can be identified and quantitatively measured. Research in this area can provide the basis for determining the most effective applications of information-processing techniques to each situation. Such analysis can greatly improve overall understanding and planning of man-machine systems and can also underlie the design of computer simulations of such systems.

Natural language research.—Research on computerized retrieval of individual documents is well advanced, and such systems are in operation. No matter how advanced a document-retrieval system becomes, however, the user will ordinarily still have to scan or read through sizable amounts of irrelevant text. It would be better, of course, if he could have direct access to the material he wants without spending time searching for it. Computer programs can be written which will retrieve from any body of text all sentences or paragraphs that contain certain words or combinations of words. Thus, the user can quickly locate all specific references to the gall bladder, to bronchial asthma, or to Galen or Dorothea Dix, for example. However, retrieval of content from computer-scanned text in the form of completely worded answers to users' questions is beyond the present state of the art. To accomplish this, basic research is needed in linguistics and other fields which bear upon the problem. This research should also be of value in improving machine-aided language translation, which is still in an early stage of development.

Applied Research

The major HSIC investigatory functions should be applied research and development work with the goal of extending and increasing the efficiency and sophistication of the various information-processing services of the center. These activities would include research on many of the HSIC functions which have been described, including library management functions, special library storage and retrieval services, programmed instruction, educational radio and television, on-line research laboratories, and patient-care functions.

The following areas are considered in detail to provide examples of specific types of research projects that would be desirable:

Automated cognitive aids, including those for diagnosis and prognosis.—Project MAC at the Massachusetts Institute of Technology has clearly demonstrated that a large on-line computer with many time-sharing consoles spread throughout a university can be of great assistance in speeding and refining the thinking processes of students, faculty, and staff members in both pure and applied fields. Some of the competences developed in Project MAC might be used for a number of cognitive aids, which could have widespread application in the health sciences.

One of the most important cognitive functions in dental and medical schools is diagnosis. At New York University, Tulane University, George Washington University, and elsewhere, computers are being used with increasing effectiveness in a number of aspects of the diagnoses of patients, as was noted earlier. Some of the computer programs could be adapted for on-line use by HSIC. In addition, new programs for other such functions could be developed.

The cognitive processes whereby computers can perceive and translate patterns, recognizing the shape of a cell's nucleus as a mitotic figure, the shape of a handwritten letter, or the shape of a French sentence as being equivalent to a specific English sentence, need to be studied more thoroughly. Two approaches to machine-aided language translation—linguistic analysis programs and machine learning programs—need to be compared for accuracy. Pattern recognition has applications to diagnostic procedures and information storage technology; language translation, to information storage and retrieval. While computers can perform both of these kinds of functions to some degree, neither is done very well. Current research indicates that computer programs which recognize patterns may be quite similar to some which can translate languages. By simulating human cognitive processes, such programs could probably be improved. At the same time, HSIC scientists could learn more about human thinking processes and apply this knowledge to other automated information-processing activities.

Academic management functions—Putting the fundamental data on which to base academic management decisions into computers will not ordinarily be difficult, nor will keeping the material up to date. But devising programs that can provide administrators with the facts selected from these data, when they are wanted and in the most useful form, will take much work. The questions which will be asked will be many and varied. Rules for decision-making need to be clarified and made explicit. Careful thought must be devoted to the goals which are to be optimized in the decisions of academic administrators.

TRAINING

In addition to providing services to the community and doing research, HSIC should train personnel to carry out these new kinds of specialized communication services. A wide range of training would be required, including formal instruction in health sciences, behavioral sciences, computer science, library science, television and radio communications, photography, and medical illustration. Thus, the instruction would not be parochial—limited to one of the media—but interdisciplinary. The emphasis should be on information-processing as a total process, with the advancement of knowledge as its goal.

LOCATION, EQUIPMENT, AND ARRANGEMENT OF SPACE

The physical facilities of HSIC would, of course, depend to some extent on local circumstances. The plan outlined below is meant to be a guide rather than a prescription.

Ideally, all HSIC facilities should be in a single building, located close to the center of population of the university units which it would serve. The HSIC functions described here could be conveniently and efficiently houses in a building with a total of 12 stories, 3 underground and 9 above, as indicated in Figure 3. Sound-absorbent coverings should be used on the walls of corridors and other areas with high traffic flow.

Certain types of equipment would be found in multiple locations on different floors of HSIC. One such piece of equipment would be a typewriter-type remote computer terminal. Fundamentally, this is an electric typewriter capable of 2-way communication with an on-line computer over a telephone wire. It can also activate and be activated by another electric typewriter terminal over a telephone line. It may have an attachment which punches paper tape as the typewriter is used and which also reads such tape over the telephone line to the computer or to another terminal.

The second major type of equipment is the carrel, that is, a piece of equipment which provides a location for interacting with information. Almost certainly HSIC would have more than one kind of carrel. Probably the most common type used at first would be a simple desk with a book rack and a chair. This standard nonautomated carrel should be designed, however, so that it can accommodate automated equipment.

Careful thought must be given to the sort of automated carrels to be used in HSIC. An integrated carrel capable of all forms of information-processing would be desirable. The fundamental question is whether a single carrel can be designed for on-line computerized information retrieval, computerized programmed instruction, radio sound recordings, television, microform, and ordinary typing; or whether several kinds of carrels must be developed. This question will be answered by experimenting with various kinds of carrels. If an on-line typewriter is used to communicate with the computer and response is made by use of a typewriter or a light pen applied to a cathode ray display, the same equipment can be used for information storage and retrieval, for computerized programmed instruction, as a cognitive aid, for academic management and patient-care function, for sound recordings, and for television. Microform can also be read through television cameras, but it would be necessary to study whether or not the more expensive method of integrating this process into a multipurpose carrel is preferable to the less epxensive method of providing each carrel with a specialized microform reader.

Because automated carrels contain equipment which is noise-producing, they must be made soundproof. The ceiling of the booth should permit a user to lower from tracks on the ceiling his personal locker with books, microscope, microscope slides, writing materials, or other study aids. This unit would fit around the television tube and typewriter, turning the booth temporarily into his

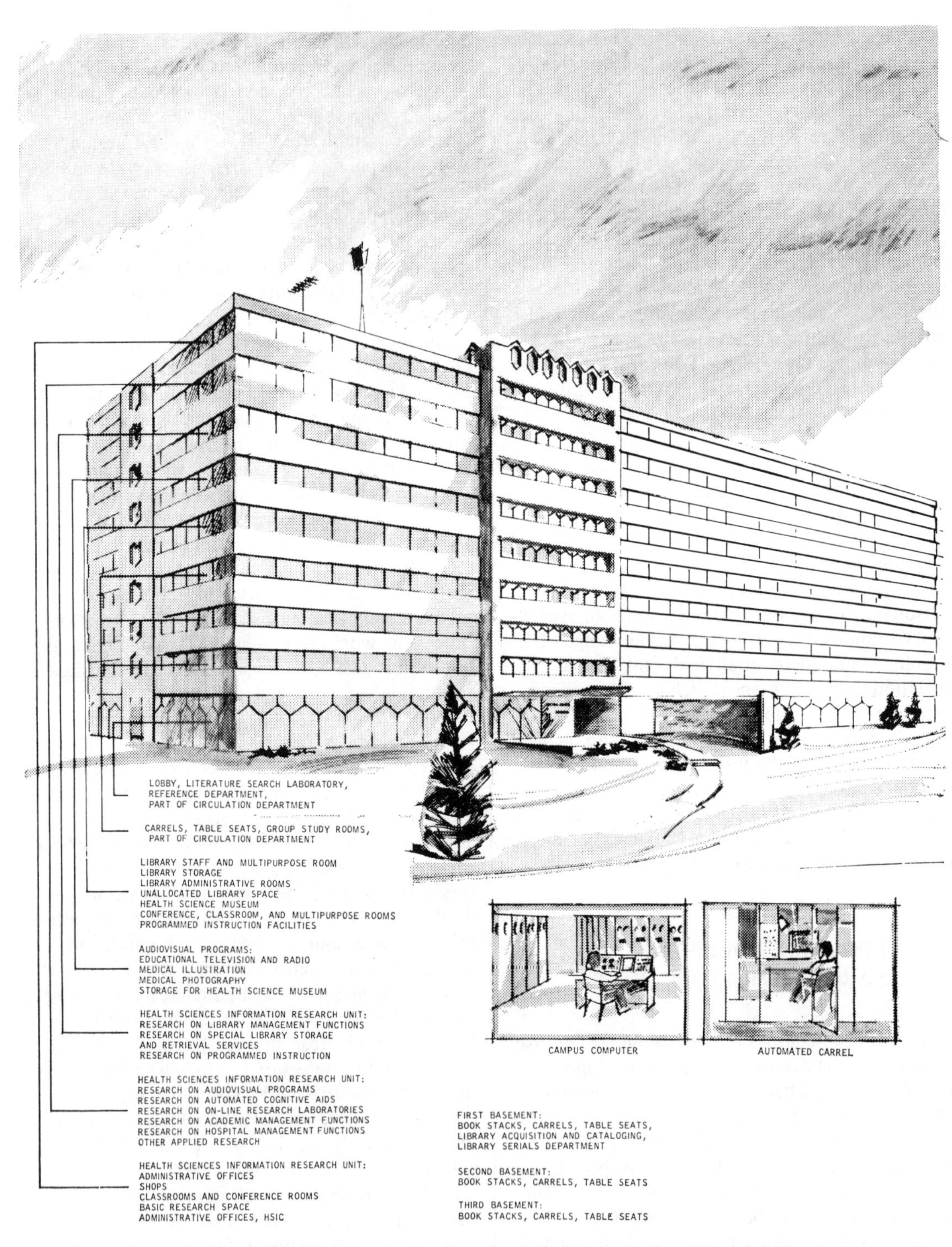

FIG. 3. One possible design for a health sciences information center.

private office. Nonautomated carrels would not need soundproofing unless they were used for typing.

Figure 3 shows a form of HSIC that could house as many as 1,500 carrels. Each floor would be 221 feet long and 100 feet wide, with about 22,100 square feet of gross space or 13,300 square feet of net space. This provides a total of about 265,000 square feet of gross space or about 160,000 square feet of net space. A possible floor-by-floor arrangement of such a building is outlined in the following sections of this article.

Third and Second Basements

The third and second basements would at first be used for open book stacks, nonautomated carrels (which could later be converted to automated carrels), and table seating. When HSIC opened, 80 per cent of the total library seating space would be used for carrels and the rest for tables and chairs. Later all of the space might be used for carrels. Each of these floors would be able to accommodate 50,000 or more volumes. At some future time, if a large collection of books and journals no longer appeared to be essential because of technological developments, the stacks might be progressively converted into space for carrels, subdivided into classrooms or used for some other purpose. The allotment of space on each of these floors would be as follows: book stacks, 6,650 sq. ft.; carrels, 5,320 sq. ft.; and table seats 1,330 sq. ft.

The building should be designed with partitions on all floors separating the access to the carrel space from the access to the book stacks so that it would be possible to lock the book stacks each night, but keep the carrel space open twenty-four hours a day. Where on-line, time-sharing computers have been used, it has been found that when confronted with delays because of overloads on the computer during the usual daytime hours of operation, users voluntarily adjust their schedules so that they can use the computer during the time when there is less load. This, of course, requires continuous twenty-four-hour access to the computer (or perhaps twenty-two-hour access since the computer is usually out of operation for two hours a day). Such scheduling increases utilization of the computer, and the building should be arranged so that this will be possible.

First Basement

Slightly over half of this floor (8,400 sq. ft. overall) would be similar to the stacks in the second and third basements. The rest of the floor would contain the following units:

Library acquisition and cataloging (1,200 sq. ft.).—This department would carry out document acquisition and catalog maintenance, using on-line, time-sharing, computerized techniques. New book lists would be published or stored in computer memory in a form that would make them retrievable from all campus on-line terminals.

Library serials (1,350 sq. ft.).—This section would represent an enlargement of the traditional serials activities of the health sciences libraries. It would contribute to the duplicate exchange program of the Medical Library Association. Its staff would also prepare for publication or put into on-line computer storage cumulative check lists and catalogs of serials.

Carrels (2,000 sq. ft.) and table seats (500 sq. ft.).—There would be 50 carrels and 80 table seats in this area. These facilities would be used primarily for information retrieval; but very likely, as the HSIC program expanded, all the other on-line information-processing functions could be carried out here.

Ground Floor

Lobby (2,000 sq. ft.).—A book-checking area would be located adjacent to an elevator, which would operate from the third basement to the fifth floor—the floors with books.

Information search laboratory (5,000 sq. ft.).—This would be a single large room, with bibliographical and reference materials in the center and the most frequently consulted books and journals, amounting to about 30,000 volumes, in alcoves along the walls. The use of these volumes would represent a high percentage of all consultation of documents in HSIC, and their close proximity would cut down user travel significantly. There would be perhaps 10 automated and 10 nonautomated carrels in the area and table seating for about 80 people.

Users' advisory service (1,200 sq. ft.).—This would be made up of 10 offices arranged in a square around a corridor leading from the information search laboratory. In these rooms users would consult librarians when they needed assistance in locating or processing information.

Reference department (3,100 sq. ft.).–This section would contain the offices of the personnel responsible for the activities going on in the information search laboratory, including operation of the users' advisory service. The reference department would provide bibliographical instruction and special bibliographical and informational activities such as current awareness service, information-searching in depth, editorial service, liaison service, and various regional or extension services. Its personnel would be responsible for standard xerographic reproduction in the building and eventually for the entire campus over coaxial cable or microwave, if the cost of such telefacsimile xerography transmission becomes reasonable. They would also operate a long-distance xerography receiver-transmitter to other libraries. In addition, they would answer the telephone, reply to mailed requests for information, and assemble collections of pamphlets, and would feed the HSIC's television cameras if remote viewing of books and journals should be attempted. Finally, they would care for the rare book room and its contents.

Circulation department (2,000 sq. ft.).–This department would assume responsibility for lending services, pick-up and delivery services, and interlibrary lending. It would undertake staffing of the public loan desks and exit control. Its staff would see that circulation regulations are correctly administered, keep in proper order all shelves and reading areas, and reshelve used materials except in the information search laboratory. Pick-up and delivery service for carrel users would also be carried out by them.

This department would occupy space on both the first and second floors. The first floor would contain offices for the department head and for the lending service supervisor; the main loan desk; a book-sorting area; and a shipping-receiving, pick-up and delivery station. Around the main loan desk would be perhaps 6 machines, each capable of accepting simultaneously 2 plastic cards–a book card and a user's identity card–automatically recording the information on these cards in the on-line computer as a means of charging books out and in. In addition the standard equipment for a library loan desk would be included in case automation of the library system is not completed by the time the building is occupied.

Second Floor

Offices of the circulation department and the photocopying unit of the reference department (3,740 sq. ft. overall) would be located on the second floor. In addition to conventional duplicating equipment and supplies, the photocopying unit should have 2 Xerox LDX transmission machines and 1 receiver for long-distance xerography.

Group study rooms (2,160 sq. ft.).–Perhaps 10 conference rooms would be used for group study and programmed instruction, conferences, and meetings of various sorts. Each room would be equipped with an electric typewriter-type terminal on-line to the computer, a color television screen to be used as a display terminal, and a screen for slide or moving projection.

Carrels (5,720 sq. ft.) and table seats (1,680 sq. ft.).–This area would contain automated carrels for information storage and retrieval and programmed instruction. In addition, there might be separate automated carrels for audiovisual aids, nonautomated carrels, and table seating.

Third and Fourth Floors

These floors will be the same as the second and third basements, with book stacks, carrels, and table seating. For each floor the space allotment would be book stacks, 6,650 sq. ft.; carrels, 5,320 sq. ft.; and table seats, 1,330 sq. ft.

Fifth Floor

Library facilities (6,980 sq. ft.).–This area would contain a library staff and multipurpose room (1,000 sq. ft.), administrative offices (670 sq. ft.), a conference room (1,000 sq. ft.), a storage room (1,000 sq. ft.), unallocated library space which would later be finished according to need (3,310 sq. ft.), and the health sciences museum, which should be located opposite the elevators.

Conference, classroom, and multipurpose rooms (2,420 sq. ft.).–These 5 rooms would be used for research conferences, for training activities, for programmed instruction, for general meetings, and like activities. Each room should be equipped with a typewriter-type terminal.

Programmed instruction facilities (2,400 sq. ft.).–Perhaps 60 automated carrels for programmed instruction and an office for supervising and scheduling this instruction will be located on this floor.

Sixth Floor

This floor would house the various audiovisual programs: educational television and radio (3,408 sq. ft.), health sciences illustration (5,711 sq. ft.), health sciences photography (3,681 sq. ft.), and storage for the health sciences museum (1,000 sq. ft.).

Educational television and radio (3,408 sq. ft.).–This unit would include offices, studios and control rooms; workshops for maintaining equipment; storage space; and a television tape library, including an automatic tape bank or, alternately, multiple-tape players. A television tape bank should be capable of holding 1,000 or more hour-long reels of tape on racks and transferring any one of them to reading heads. Each tape would be able to be read simultaneously by up to 12 reading heads, spaced five minutes apart on the tape. With such equipment a user could request, from any carrel, a large number of lectures or other television programs and have them automatically transmitted to his carrel. If there were reading heads spaced every five minutes on the tape, the average waiting time would be less than two and one-half minutes. This would probably be a very expensive piece of equipment, but it is essential that television tapes be conveniently available on individual demand if such audiovisual aids are to be used widely enough to make significant educational impact. Alternatives would be to use several television tape players, now commercially available at moderate cost, or to have a technician continuously on call to play tapes when requested by a given carrel.

Health sciences photography (3,681 sq. ft.).–This would include staff offices and facilities for still photography, microphotography, sound moving pictures, animation, and other special projects.

Health sciences illustration (5,711 sq. ft.).–This unit would contain offices, studios, workrooms, and storage for graphic illustration, exhibit construction, silk screen, and hot-press printing. In addition to the above, 1,000 sq. ft. would be allocated to storage for the health sciences museum.

Seventh and Eighth Floors

These floors would be devoted exclusively to the applied research activities of the HSIC research unit. On the seventh floor research programs would be carried out in (*a*) library management functions (1,850 sq. ft.), (*b*) special library storage and retrieval services (2,160 sq. ft.), and (*c*) programmed instruction (9,290 sq. ft.). Offices for scientists and professional workers would be equipped with typewriter-type terminals and coaxial cable outlets. Offices for the programmed instruction section would also be equipped with terminals fitted for using the cathode-ray tube and light pencil technique. The programmed instruction section would have the following special facilities: (*a*) experimental automated instructional carrels, an instructional conference room, and an experimental classroom for perhaps 100 students; (*b*) laboratory simulation room, arranged like a physiology or biochemistry laboratory, and containing a projection booth and screen and a built-in television screen; and (*c*) 4 rooms for simulation and mock-up of various instructional sites, such as a 2-bed ward or diagnostic treatment facilities.

The following sections of the research unit would be located on the eighth floor:

Research on audiovisual programs (1,060 sq. ft.).–Offices for scientific and professional workers would be equipped with typewriter-type terminals and built-in color television tubes.

Research on automated cognitive aids (3,720 sq. ft.).–These offices would be equipped with typewriter-type terminals, and 2 offices should also have terminals with television tubes specially adapted for use with light pencils.

Research on on-line research laboratories (3,000 sq. ft.).–This section includes the computer room of HSIC, which will contain central data processing equipment, including switching equipment which may be required for operating some or all of the remote terminals. Among the types of equipment which would be needed in the HSIC building would be the main time-sharing computer, unless it were located elsewhere as in a university's central computation center, and one or more satellite computers acting as buffers between on-line remote terminals and the control time-sharing computer. These latter might be a PDP-7, a DDP-116, or an IBM-1800. Such computers would make possible microsecond and millisecond access for several simultaneous biological or behavioral experiments on a time-sharing basis. There might also be a large modular memory auxiliary to that of the main time-sharing computer. This would be necessary particularly if large amounts of text were to be read into electronic storage and stored locally rather than centrally in some national network. Large-scale storage could be added in a modular fashion as needed.

If HSIC were to participate in a national program for reading large amounts of text into electronic storage for centralized networks, or if it seems desirable to read locally produced text into storage, a photoscanner or optical character reading device might be included in the computer room.

Wet laboratories (1,230 sq. ft.).–These would be used as on-line laboratories and for work in basic general systems research. There might be several such laboratories, each with a telephone outlet and a coaxial-cable outlet for a remote computer terminal. One room should have an autoclave; 2 should be equipped for animal surgery.

In addition, there would be sections equipped with typewriter-type terminals for research on academic management functions (1,230 sq. ft.) and for research on hospital management functions (1,770 sq. ft.). An area of 1,230 sq. ft. would be kept available for any additional equipment, if needed, or for other research requirements.

Ninth Floor

This floor would contain the HSIC administrative offices (1,740 sq. ft.) and the administrative offices of the HSIC research unit (628 sq. ft.). There would also be wood, metal, glass, electronic, and photographic shops for the research unit (2,772 sq. ft.), basic research laboratories and offices (6,800 sq. ft.), and classrooms and conference rooms for training sessions and other meetings (1,260 sq. ft.).

CONCLUSIONS

The building and organization proposed above can be achieved by a process of gradual growth. Many novel technological and educational approaches are recommended. There will be numerous problems in interpreting the HSIC processes and equipment to the using community and in gaining acceptance by that community before the proposed activities can operate fully. The feasibility of such a program has been carefully analyzed, however, and it is believed that it is practicable. Furthermore, it is felt that the successful establishment of such a program can have an important impact on education, research, and service activities in the health sciences, giving personnel in these areas more rapid, efficient, and complete access to the information relevant to their activities, along with up-to-date and sophisticated techniques for manipulating that information.[12]

NOTES

[1] At the time of writing, the author was Vice President and Principal Scientist of EDUCOM, which is concerned with the use of the new information-processing technologies in higher education.

[2] Overhage, C. F. J., and Harman, R. J. (Eds.). *INTREX: Report of a Planning Conference on Information Transfer Experiments.* Cambridge, Massachusetts: M.I.T. Press, 1965.

[3] Licklider, J. C. R. *Libraries of the Future.* Cambridge, Massachusetts: M.I.T. Press, 1965.

[4] Personal communication from C. F. J. Overhage, January, 1965.

[5] Personal communication from F. H. Wagman, June, 1965.

[6] Bloomquist, H. The Status and Needs of Medical School Libraries in the United States. *J. Med. Educ.*, 38:145–163, 1963.

[7] Flood, M. M. A Stochastic Adaptive Sequential Information Dissemination System–SASIDS. In *Some Problems in Information Sciences.* Kochen, M. (Ed.). New York: Scarecrow Press, 1965, Pp. 276–288.

[8] Flood, M. M. Appendix P, Experiments on Indexing–Search and Dissemination. In *INTREX: Report of a Planning Conference on Information Transfer Experiments.* Overhage, C. F. J. and Harman, R. J. (Eds.). Cambridge, Massachusetts: M.I.T. Press, 1965, Pp. 237–241.

[9] Kochen, M., and Flood, M. M. Some Bibliographical and Sociological Devices to Improve Maintenance of Current Awareness about Literature. In *Some Problems in Information Sciences.* Kochen, M. (Ed.). New York: Scarecrow Press, 1965, Pp. 271–275.

[10] Computer Slashes Time for Lab Reports. *Med. World News*, 10:6, 40-41, 1965.

[11] Gabrieli, E. R., Vessin, V., Thorpe, J., and Palmer, R. R. C. Initial Experience with and Potential of Data Processing and Computer Techniques in a Hospital Clinical Laboratory. *Amer. J. Clinicopathol.* (in press).

[12] The author wishes to thank a number of his colleagues at the University of Michigan who took part in a series of discussions which led to the ideas presented in this paper: Alexander Barry, Wallace J. Bonk, Herbert H. Cornish, Stanford C. Ericksen, Merrill M. Flood, Robert C. Hendrix, William Higuchi, Richard Judge, Miriam L. Keller, David K. Maxfield, Kenneth Mayne, Robert H. Muller, Floyd D. Ostrander, Frederick H. Wagman, and Dean H. Wilson. He also wishes to thank Mrs. Sandra Swinehart for extensive assistance in the preparation of this manuscript.

ABOUT THE AUTHOR–Dr. James G. Miller is Vice President of the Academy for Educational Development, Inc., Washington, D.C. Previously he was Vice President for Academic Affairs of Cleveland State University. He was for many years Professor of Psychiatry and Psychology and Director of the Mental Health Research Institute at the University of Michigan. Among other academic appointments he has also been Chairman of the Department of Psychology at the University of Chicago and Chief of the Clinical Psychology Section of the Veterans Administration. It was in his capacity as Vice-President and Principal Scientist of the Inter-University Communications Council that he wrote the paper reprinted here. He holds an A.B., an A.M., an M.D. and a Ph.D. from Harvard, where he also taught.

He is a Diplomate in Clinical Psychology, a member of the American Board of Examiners in Professional Psychology and the American Board of Neurology and Psychiatry, a Fellow of the American Psychological Association and was President of that organization's Division of Clinical Psychology. He is also a member of the American Psychiatric Association, and was a charter member of the American College of Neuropsychopharmacology, the American College of Clinical Pharmacology and Chemotherapy, and the American Society for Cybernetics. He is a Co-editor of *Drugs and Behavior* (1968), and a member of the Board of Editors of *Behavioral Science*.

II.

MEDICAL LIBRARIANSHIP AS A PROFESSION

To understand a profession, one must know something about its individual practitioners and about its professional organizations. For medical librarianship, we are fortunate in having recent information on both. Miss Annan's description of thirty years of the Medical Library Association tells about its activities and its leaders, and Dr. Kronick provides characteristics and statistics on manpower in health sciences libraries.

The Medical Library Association in Retrospect, 1937–1967

by Gertrude L. Annan

A look at the records of Association meetings in 1937 and 1938 reveals that medical librarians at that time were concerned with the issues of today: training, standards, recruitment and literature control. A little later the Medical Library Association initiated formal international cooperation. How medical librarians met the "Challenge of Change" and laid the groundwork for today's accomplishment is Miss Annan's fascinating story.

The medical librarian of 1967 lives in a period of changing concepts, dramatic new methods, ever-widening scientific horizons. To meet these challenges he must welcome the future with patient flexibility and ready enthusiasm. He is aware that no generation of librarians has seen such a swift transformation of techniques and that no generation has seen such a rapid expansion of scientific knowledge. In looking toward the immediate past he may think of the medical librarian of thirty years ago as a complacent follower of accepted procedures, not as a pioneer in a brave new world. Yet the corps of trained medical librarians today and the resources of our collections and their management are dependent upon the efforts of those who were then pioneers in medical librarianship. Training, standards, recruitment, literature, control, international relations, all had continuing attention at a time when financial assistance through government funds, support by administrators, concern by scientists was almost nonexistent. Everyone using or administering medical libraries today is in their debt.

In 1937 the annual meeting was held in Richmond, Virginia, with Dr. William W. Francis of the Osler Library presiding. He was not the last on the list of physician presidents, but he served at a time when administration of the Association was becoming almost entirely in the hands of practicing librarians. Of the eighty-eight delegates representing seventy-two libraries at Richmond, only four were physicians and two dentists. Of the four physicians, one was President, one Vice President. Dr. Francis' presidential address was entitled, "At Osler's Shrine," and the formal program reflected the preoccupation with history which would continue to be evident for some years to come. The business of the Association, however, touched upon subjects and problems familiar to us today, and this small group attacked matters of significance.

As in 1967, so thirty years ago medical librarians looked to Washington, looked to an institution that had recently celebrated its centenary, the Army Medical Library. Appeals for funds were made by the Association, but these appeals were not for assisting libraries throughout the country; rather, they were for the support and maintenance of that great library itself. A depression coming in a period between two wars meant little interest in a military facility, and funds were cut drastically in 1933. Fluctuations of foreign currency further reduced the buying power to serious inadequacy. The Executive Committee of the Association reported in 1937 that, in response to action taken at a previous meeting, resolutions[1] were distributed "recommending the appropriation of adequate funds for the maintenance and growth of the Army Medical Library's Book Collection and Index Catalogue" and "requesting . . . appropriations sufficient to construct a building adequate for the purpose

SOURCE: Reprinted from Gertrude L. Annan, "The Medical Library Association in Retrospect, 1937-1967," *Bulletin of the Medical Library Association*, 55 (Oct., 1967), pp. 379-389, by permission of the publisher and the author. The first Janet Doe Lecture. Presented at the Sixty-sixth Annual Meeting of the Medical Library Association, Miami Beach, Florida, June 13, 1967.

and . . . funds for its maintenance." These were sent to the President of the United States and to the Secretary of War and brought replies which were read at the meeting. The Secretary's report adds that "The matter was also brought before our own members, with the request that each one urge his organization to adopt similar resolutions to be sent to their local congressmen, asking their support of this measure. The same action was sought from national and state medical societies, and a further appeal was made to the medical profession in general to urge congressional support. . . . Altogether over 500 individuals, organizations and publications were approached." The report points out that, "Even if we do not accomplish our immediate purpose, we have done something toward awakening a consciousness of the great worth of the Army Medical Library and its *Index-Catalogue*." It is signed by the Association's Secretary, Janet Doe.

Response to appeals for sustaining the library was generous. The following year Colonel Jones as Librarian could announce in his Annual Report for 1937/8.[2]

> The past year was noteworthy in the history of the Army Medical Library in that the Congress authorized the construction of a new Library and Museum Building, the legislation being approved by the President June 15, 1938. The whole-hearted support of the medical public and of numerous individuals, bodies, and institutions of learning . . . was a splendid tribute to the good service the Library and Museum have rendered through so many years. There were 4,104 bound volumes added . . . of which 2,292 were purchased. . . . The Library was fortunate in having the liberal appropriation of $24,500 for the purchase of books, journals, and equipment. . . . The Library receives more than 1,800 periodicals. . . . The Library loaned 14,102 items . . . more than 8 per cent over 2 years ago.

In the same report Colonel Jones told of a new service: "The Library is now prepared to assist in furnishing microfilms through the American Documentation Institute, in any quantity desired. . . . A modern camera has been installed." These were heartening words, but several years followed with little progress noted. The Report of 1941[3] announces that the site for the new building has been selected and approved by the National Parks Planning Commission. "Nothing remains but to supply some of the funds. It is a race against time."

Although the new building was still years away, 1942 may be considered as the date of the beginning of a National Library of Medicine. In that year for the first time a trained librarian was appointed to the staff. Happily, the librarian was one of force as well as capability, for Helen Norris (later Mrs. Lucké) was not one to accept conditions as they were. She writes,[4]

> I was the only library-trained person on the staff when I went there on the first of October in 1942—the first one the Library had ever had, I believe. What an appalling place it was. I asked for and received permission from Col. Jones to visit other libraries in Washington and vicinity. In New York, Dr. [Archibald] Malloch was most cordial; while I was in his office he telephoned Dr. [Alan] Gregg and announced that at last there was someone at the AML who was interested in doing something constructive. . . . On my return to Washington, I proposed to Colonel Jones that a survey of the AML be made by professional librarians, and that it be financed by the Rockefeller or Carnegie Foundation. Just the idea he had been looking for, so he said. Whereupon steps were taken to get the survey under way.

The stage was set. Colonel Jones on March 4, 1943, wrote the Executive Secretary of the American Library Association stating the approval of the War Department for a survey of the Library. Funds were made available by the Rockefeller Foundation, and a panel of distinguished librarians appointed—Keyes D. Metcalf, then Director of the Harvard University Library; L. Quincy Mumford, now Librarian of Congress; Andrew Osborn, at that time Assistant Librarian at Harvard; and three medical librarians, Janet Doe, Thomas P. Fleming, and Mary Louise Marshall. A report, but not the detailed findings, was published in 1944.[5] Those of you who know the National Library of Medicine only in its handsome building with a highly trained staff, electronic equipment, and expanding activities in scientific communication, can hardly conceive of the Army Medical Library so short a time ago. The conditions in the old building and its inadequacies have been described with appropriate humor, and need not be repeated. A few statements from the survey comparing that Library with the New York Academy of Medicine Library illuminate the situation. The Army Medical Library had twice the number of volumes, but maintained only four-fifths as many current subscriptions with a book budget 95 percent of the Academy's. There was one-tenth the number of readers, the same outside circulation, but, even then, considerably more activity in photoduplication. Of its reference services the report comments,

In the matter of answering inquiries . . . all that can be said is that the Army Medical Library's reputation, among other libraries and those individuals whose opinions were asked, has not been good in this respect. So little satisfaction has been obtained that most inquirers turned elsewhere for help. This condition is rapidly changing, however, with the advent of trained library assistants in the Army Medical Library.

An analysis of the collection itself showed that "the situation with regard to periodical holdings is all too often deplorable;" that the acquisition of monographic material was by no means comprehensive; of international congresses and government documents, incomplete and by no means outstanding; and of publications relating to allied medical sciences, particularly weak. The detailed findings and recommendations may be found in transcripts of the report. A brief summary of essential needs are cited in the letter of transmittal, as follows: The constant improvement of the quality of the staff; the establishment of an emergency shelflist; a vigorous acquisitions program; the development of a classification scheme; adoption of a standard list of subject headings; a new card catalog; a ten-year rebinding program; and modification of the building plans. Janet Doe has summarized the findings and recommendations in her article, "The Survey and After." This and Mary Louise Marshall's "Reminiscences" are in the Bulletin's special number, an anniversary issue,[6] celebrating 125 years of the Library. This, then, was the start of a new era for the old Library which soon would be transformed. Medical librarians would once more turn to Washington for assistance. In 1937, though, the idea of the Army Medical Library as a training ground for medical librarians would have been considered ludicrous; its present role in that respect was undreamed of. The training of medical librarians was such a novelty in 1937 that Isabelle T. Anderson reported on a new venture in Minnesota, commenting that

There has never been a course in Hospital Librarianship or Medical Librarianship anywhere in the world. That statement may be challenged, but we haven't heard of any. . . . This last year Mr. Walter, the Librarian of the University of Minnesota, and Miss Perrie Jones, who was formerly Institution Librarian of the Minnesota Board of Control . . . organized a course in Hospital Librarianship in connection with the University of Minnesota Library School. . . . It is mainly a lecture course, although a six weeks' internship in an approved hospital has been arranged for. The lectures include selection of books for patients, and medical reference, as well as hospital and medical library administration. . . . There have been eleven girls registered this year . . . .[7]

Miss Anderson writes[8] that Miss Jones urged Mr. Walter that a course for potential hospital librarians should be part of the library school curriculum. "As a result, a one-quarter course was offered, which included lectures on medical library practices, given by several librarians and doctors from the Twin City area. As I remember, there were lectures on medical reference books, on book selection, and ordering, on medical history, on medical periodicals. . . . Helen Norris and later Frida Pliefke participated." A young man named Thomas P. Fleming gave lectures on acquisitions and tells us, "with the exception of Norris and some of Anderson, the whole program was pointed toward the operation of a patients' library. . . . Of course, the lectures by physicians on medical terminology and history of medicine were valuable in theory . . .".[9] This pioneering venture was considered successful enough in its aim to provide graduates "doing excellent work in hospital, medical, institutional, and public libraries engaged in hospital library work".[10] Mr. Fleming, then a member of the faculty of the University of Minnesota Library School, was soon to accept the position of Medical Librarian of Columbia University, New York, where he would carry to maturity those early efforts for training medical librarians in Minnesota. He wasted little time, and an announcement appeared in the Bulletin that he would give a course on "Bibliographic and Reference Service in the Medical Sciences," in the 1939 Summer Session of the School of Library Service at Columbia. In 1948 the course was given at the same school by Estelle Brodman and was designed for the first time to cover all phases of medical library work. In 1951 a second approved course was taught by Mildred Jordan at Emory University.

These lecture courses were not supplemented by internships as were those in Minnesota. Mr. Walter had shown enthusiasm for this type of training and wrote: "One of the most practical features of the entire course is the six-weeks internship which follows the close of the classwork in June. Each student is assigned to one or more hospitals where she devotes her entire time to library work under the direction of the hospital librarian".[11] A more extensive experiment, a year long "residency in medical library work," was inaugurated in October 1940 by Mary Louise Marshall in the libraries of the Orleans Parish Medical Society and Tulane

School of Medicine. "The period of training was set at twelve months, with a two weeks' vacation, corresponding to that of a medical internship. . . . A stipend to cover board and room only has been paid. . . . The interns have worked as members of the staff under close personal direction, and have had a part in all phases of the libraries' work. Every effort has been made to explain not only methods used in our libraries, but in comparison with those used in other medical libraries."[12] In this, her presidential address in 1946, she also cited a Program of Instruction in Library Schools, 1943,[13] which advocated a year of internship after library school. She added that this would be "particularly advantageous in training for the special field of medicine in library work, since it furnishes opportunity for the student to learn the subject field, the nomenclature, the bibliography and the varying values of the different phases of medical library work. . . ."

Miss Marshall's address is a landmark in the history of medical librarianship. It was made at a time when the Association was ready and eager for action. It provoked at once animated and thoughtful discussion of varying efforts in library training and the urgent need of defining standards. William D. Postell moved that a committee be appointed to recommend the adoption of standards and a training program for medical librarianship. It was passed unanimously. There were, however, stormy years ahead. The most controversial was the program of certification. It was adopted, not without heated disagreement, at the Annual Meeting in April 1949 at Galveston, Texas. The presidential address by Janet Doe again was devoted to education. She commented, "Education for medical librarianship is at present in a healthy state of flux. A candidate taking the full library schedule of three semesters at the Columbia school, with the medical course included, will receive an M.S. degree. When there are enough applicants to justify additional facilities we hope that one or two other library schools in different sections of the country will inaugurate a medical course."[14] It is interesting to note that since that time courses have now been given throughout the country, at Catholic University, Washington, D.C., Drexel in Philadelphia, Emory at Atlanta, at the Universities of California, Illinois, Maryland, Michigan, North Carolina, Pittsburgh, Southern California, Toronto, and Western Reserve.

The story is quickly told, but in its telling there is no way of indicating the enormous contributions of many members of this Association. Each of the courses requires monitoring, and this must be repeated every fifth year to make sure the quality and content are maintained so that Association approval can be granted. Committees on Standards, Curriculum, and Certification have been actively concerned. The Booklet of Information on Certification gives a brief history of its development and cites the code in detail. Under the separate items, number five should be read with care. Here are stipulated the types of certification, Grades 1, 2, and 3. Changes have been made over the years to meet new requirements, and each change has meant as much deliberation, discussion, soul searching, and argument as the first induced.

New trends in education have been watched and evaluated. In 1958 at the meeting in Rochester, Minnesota, the President, Thomas E. Keys, instituted a day of refresher courses on practical library procedures. The twelve brief lectures[15] were each given twice, enabling those so wishing to enroll for four. A total of 290 registered. Each year since that time, except for that of the International Congress, a day of the Annual Meeting has been reserved for this program, carried out since 1963 under the auspices of the Committee on Continuing Education. Here, again, responsive to changing needs, small, informal beginnings have developed into a "curriculum planned for cyclic presentation with advanced courses building on the foundations laid by previous ones."[16] A recent offshoot of this national program has made the series of courses available regionally so that those unable to attend the Annual Meeting would have the opportunity of participation. Some have been coordinated with the national program, and all have been sponsored by regional groups of the Association.

The formation of regional groups was stimulated by the need of medical librarians to hold meetings during the war years when national meetings were omitted. In 1947 at the Annual meeting in Cleveland, a preconvention session tackled the problem of "Regional Meetings for the Medical Library Association." Mildred Jordan reported that "letters requesting a reaction to this controversial subject were sent to administrative heads of 253 member libraries."[17] Of those who replied 86 were for establishing groups, 22 against, and 49 uncommitted. Two years later Janet Doe wrote an editorial for the Bulletin, "The New Venture: Regional Meetings,"[18] telling that "the inclusion in the revised by-laws of the Medical Library Association of a section authorizing regional meetings marks the end of an old era. . . ." By that time local meetings had been held in New York, Chicago, and California. The vigorous growth of our regional groups, their effectiveness in bringing medical librarians from one locality together for educational, intellectual, and social purposes has not prevented the attendance of ever larger numbers of librarians at our annual meetings, as was feared in 1947; and some regional meetings today have a greater attendance than the 1947 meeting at which the subject was introduced.

The few librarians coming together in 1937, however, were not handicapped by the small size of the meeting, for they looked to wide horizons and were undaunted by the magnitude of problems needing solution. A Committee on Indexing Current Medical Literature, chaired by Eleanor Fair, reported on the results of a notice in the Bulletin in 1936: "Wanted: a Clinical Abstract Journal."[19] The Committee had made a study of the New York Academy of Medicine's journals to examine those carrying abstracts in English of articles appearing in foreign journals. There was not only the expected duplication in the 146 journals covered, but abstracts were so scattered that their usefulness was largely wasted. Responses to the notice varied; thirteen approvals, eight disapprovals. Questions were raised of cost and the desirability of first making sure that the duplication of abstracts would cease if a clinical abstract journal were published.

In the following year Eileen Cunningham came to the fore with a major contribution, "Problem of Abstract Publications in Medical and Allied Sciences."[20] She began, "It has been evident for some time that there has been no effort to coordinate the abstracting services in clinical medicine and the clinical specialties. . . . At present, although a tremendous amount of money and time, as well as much sincere effort, often representing personal sacrifice on the part of editors and scientists, is being expended in the publication of abstracts of medical literature, the results fall far short of the reasonable goals that should be attained as to scope, cost, economic organization, promptness of issue, and elimination of duplication." A table listed thirty-one abstract journals with their 1936 prices. "The total cost," she said, "is the very considerable sum of $1,156.00," and she pointed out that only large and well-endowed libraries could afford some of the more expensive ones, which was "especially unfortunate because the value of an abstract journal is presumably greater in a small library, where large numbers of journals containing the original material are not available." The librarian of 1967 will be glad to learn that in 1936 *Biological Abstracts* was priced at $15 and *Chemical Abstracts* at $12. Five of the German titles cost more than $100.

The chief difficulties were listed as expense, promptness, and elimination of duplication. The first recommendation was for a centralized bureau:

> A rational, business-like approach to the problem would call for the establishment of an abstracting bureau which would be national, and perhaps international, in scope. This bureau might publish two major comprehensive abstractive journals, one in the biological sciences, which would include the so-called pre-clinical sciences, and one in the clinical sciences, including all specialties. It would be desirable to issue these publications with two sets of page numbering, those for complete volume numbering, and those for sections, and that subscriptions be made available to individuals for complete volumes and for sections and combinations of sections. . . . If it were found possible to make it international in scope, a French as well as English edition could be published.

Authors' abstracts were advocated, and editors should require them routinely. Overlapping of subjects might be avoided by publication of an abstract in full in but one journal or section, with cross references wherever needed. To finance this ambitious project a committee of librarians and scientists should work out a practical plan and submit it to foundations to try to get it funded for a five-year period when, presumably, it might become self-supporting, If this were impractical, a preliminary coordinating survey of all existing abstracting services would determine the exact amount of overlapping and the needs for further coverage made apparent.

Mrs. Cunningham, in November 1937, wrote to the editors of *Biological Abstracts* expressing dismay at the proposed schedule of service charges[21] and advising that the Committee on Periodical and Serial Publications regarded it as a dangerous and unfortunate move and proposed instead a flat subscription rate of $25 to $30 for libraries. Later it was reported that beginning with vol. 13, 1939, the subscription price for the complete volume with indexes was fixed at $25.

These were the early efforts in a long struggle. They deserve a separate paper, and the reader interested in a subject still of relevance in 1967 has only to look in the cumulated index of the first forty volumes of the Bulletin. The entries indicate the story—Committee on Abstracting and Indexing; Committee on Coordinated Abstracting Service for Clinical Medicine; Joint Committee on Indexing and Abstracting Services; UNESCO Conference on Co-ordination of Medical Abstracting Services; UNESCO conferences on scientific abstracting. These and other reports give convincing evidence of long, hard work and distinguished contributions. Perhaps the climax came at the annual meeting in Philadelphia in 1948 under New Business:

> Resolved: that the Medical Library Association express to the directors of *Excerpta Medica* thanks and appreciation for their generous and genuine cooperation in endeavoring to meet the desires of medical librarians by providing a comprehensive abstract journal for medicine at reduced cost. We realize the great difficulties with which you have had to contend, and we do not mean to seem impatient. You have done remarkably well to have accomplished so much in so short a time. We look forward to the increased usefulness of *Excerpta Medica* through further lowered costs and expanded coverage as time and additional recognition and support makes these possible.[22]

A report made at the same meeting by Mrs. Cunningham summarized progress and announced that "the steps taken by *Excerpta Medica* to become a non-profit organization under Dutch law were . . . practically complete. . . . The granting of a special discount price of $250.00 from the usual list price of $342.50 to libraries in the United States subscribing to all the sections was announced. This offer is particularly generous because the full quota of 200 subscriptions originally required to obtain this discount was not reached." Expanded coverage we have today in its twenty-five sections and two more promised; but lowered costs are an idle dream. In 1967 as we meekly accept spiraling prices, often with a burdensome higher pricing for libraries, Mrs. Cunningham's persistence seems tilting at windmills. Before the war she had been active and effective in fighting the high cost of German periodicals. After the war she continued and, with Wesley Draper, prepared a study whose findings compared subscription rates of 1939 with those of 1946. She was interested in all aspects of the literature, and a brief paper of 1936 can be read today with profit, "Looking Forward: Possible Developments in the Publication of Medical Literature." Among her conclusions are that a reduction in the total number of medical journals is desirable; the elimination of serials containing reprinted material would be advisable; as well as an awareness of new developments in photographic reproduction of literature. She ended, "No one can foresee the nature of the mature development of this literature and its publication. . . . The problem is a very serious one; it challenges the best mental efforts that those concerned have to offer; its solution will require the utmost of intellectural co-operation and endeavor."[23]

At the Association's meeting in Boston in 1938 a Symposium on Medical Literature[24] was conducted by Herman H. Henkle, then Director of the School of Library Science at Simmons College. He mentioned the need for a guide to medical literature and cited Mrs. Cunningham's paper on "Reference Works in Medicine" included in the symposium. It stressed the importance of having a comprehensive outline of medical reference works and listed about 200 reference books and review journals, and was surely the forerunner of her chapter and bibliography in the first edition of the *Handbook* in 1943. In the same symposium Mr. Henkle provided a thoughtful analysis of the periodical literature of biochemistry. He wrote, "The evaluation of printed materials is a matter of primary importance to librarians. . . . This is especially true in respect to the periodical literature in the sciences. Attempts have been made with moderate success to apply objective methods of evaluation. In 1927 Gross and Gross set a pattern for the evaluation of chemical periodicals. . . ."

He concludes,

> The results of . . . such studies seem to make a definite contribution to the problem of selecting periodicals for the library; but also implicit in them is information of value in library administration. The objective data concerning the degrees of concentration and dispersion of the literature of particular subjects and the reflection in scientific literature of the interdependence of the sciences may prove especially useful in the determination of policies for the organization of subject departments and departmental libraries or for bringing together those already established.

Soon came the war years, and concern for the literature was limited chiefly to efforts to assist devastated libraries abroad and to acquire foreign publications for libraries here. With the war's end, attention once again turned to the problems of bibliographical control. In 1947 a Symposium on Medical Subject Headings was held at the Army Medical Library. Dr. Sanford Larkey said, "The bibliographical control of published materials has always been one of the major problems of librarians, and it is particularly vital and difficult in the scientific field. The difficulty was early realized by John Shaw Billings. . . . The increasing complexity of scientific literature has required elaborate and often very expensive means for dealing with it."[25] Dr. Larkey stressed the serious problems consequent to expanded war research programs and predicted that the future peacetime programs would present similar questions, with the government's increased financial support for medical research. Well worth repeating today are some of his statements of 1949 in his announcement of The Army Medical Library Research Project at the Welch Medical Library:

> This problem of bibliographical control of the results of research is as serious in medicine as it is in the other fields of science. It is becoming increasingly difficult for our indexes and abstract journals to keep up with the growing number of medical publications and with articles of medical importance in other scientific journals. These difficulties will become greater in the future as more and more money is spent on research, and particularly if there is not commensurate support for our bibliographical facilities and for our scientific libraries. It is not necessary to convince this group, the Honorary Consultants to the Army Medical Library, of the importance of medical libraries and of our bibliographical research tools. But there does not seem to be enough general recognition of the vital significance to research of libraries and bibliographical facilities. One is dismayed to see that there is little if any provision made for them in the Report of the President's Scientific Research Board or in the plans for a National Science Foundation. . . .

Dr. Larkey reported that the Army Medical Library had asked the Welch Library to consider setting up a research project under contract with the Army. Three aspects were determined upon: evaluation and study of the current indexes; a detailed study of subject headings; and a study of the possibility of using machine methods. He said, "The use of machine methods may appear somewhat Utopian, but one must look to the possibilities of the future. At present the machines are in a sense ahead of our ideas as to how they can be used and we must determine what we want them to do. Machines can probably be designed to do what we desire but it must be determined how well they do it and if it is worth doing, in terms of cost, in terms of the needs of medical research . . . ."[26]

In 1951 a terminal report of the Research Project was prepared, and a new contract announced for continuing the study. Final reports in mimeographed form were ready in 1955. Those participating under Dr. Larkey's direction were a medical research bibliographer, Dr. Williamina A. Himwich, two medical librarians, Helen G. Field and John M. Whittock, and Eugene Garfield, whose later work in the field is widely known. One of the final reports related to subject headings and subject indexing; the other to machine methods for information searching. Advocating a large-scale machine information searching system, the report concluded: "We believe that, for any of these purposes, there are very definite possibilities in the machine methods developed by the Project, and by others, particularly with the expected future improvements in these machines or by the applications of the principles of these methods to other machines. Machine methods might have other applications in the field of medicine, such as the compilation of bibliographies on special subjects, the correlation and organization of basic factual information from many sources and for analyses of various forms of medical records." In a recent letter, Dr. Garfield makes the following evaluation:

> In my opinion, the work done at the Welch Medical Library Project is the foundation for most of the important work that has been done subsequently, particularly at the National Library of Medicine, and certainly a great deal of what has been done at the Institute for Scientific Information. Additionally, it had significant effects on other institutions, including *Chemical Abstracts* and *Biological Abstracts*.
>
> The most obvious and direct relationship that I can point to is the work of the Welch Medical Library Project and the existing MEDLARS system. Not only did we do the hard work on the MESH, which is still readily visible, including the system for categorization, but we also laid the foundation for the transition to the mechanized system and, of course, as you know, I, myself, was retained as a consultant in the second stage of the mechanization of the *Index Medicus*.
>
> It was at the Welch Medical Library that I first got the idea for citation indexing and if there were time and space, I could indicate any number of other benefits that derive from this project.

Estelle Brodman has called it "the first large-scale attempt to use the methods of experimental science in bibliographic problems; as such it can obviously be incomplete and inconclusive and still be the most important modern development in medical bibliography."[27]

This project had been initiated in 1948, just ten years after Colonel Jones announced that a microfilm camera was installed in the Army Medical Library. Our use of photocopy today is so essential a part of library practice that its comparatively recent advent is hard to realize. The Bulletin in the forties reflected the interest in this new service. Mildred Walter, in "Practical Points on Microfilms," advocated its use for interlibrary loans. Thomas Keys in an editorial, January 1944, urged free microfilm copying in furtherance of research. The most prophetic words came from two librarians of the staff of Columbia University Library, Mary A. Bennett and D. H. Litchfield, who read a paper at the 1939 Annual Meeting in Newark, New Jersey, on "Problems of Microphotography."[28] In response to a student request that the Photographic Department supply microfilms of manuscripts in a Spanish library, the authors wrote, "Perhaps this is not as ludicrous as it seems at first. Who knows but what some microphotographer will evolve a method of compensating for the curve in the earth's surface, so that a librarian in Spain will hold an open book at a west window while his colleague in New York will catch its image by means of a supertelescopic lens?"

We have not yet achieved such immediate communication with our colleagues abroad, but the Association's activities in the postwar period showing increasing awareness of the needs of foreign libraries. In 1947 a Committee on International and National Cooperation was proposed, stimulated by Mrs. Cunningham. One of its suggested purposes was to "assist in helping to bring medical librarians from other countries for study and work."[29] Action was prompt. The Committee wrote to over sixty individuals connected with medical institutions abroad. "Twenty possible and eager applicants were discovered in this way. They represented ten countries: Bulgaria, Chile, China, Cuba, Hungary, India, Mexico, Sweden, Turkey, and Uruguay."[30] Funds were made available by the Rockefeller Foundation. The Committee was chaired by Janet Doe, with Scott Adams, Eileen Cunningham, Sanford Larkey, and Mary Louise Marshall as members. Their work involved sending 270 member libraries questionnaires to determine what facilities could be offered for training and advanced study. Of these, fifty-one were willing to accept interns, and eleven would take them conditionally. The first successful candidate was Lydia Pazos, Assistant to the Librarian of the Medical School at the University of Havana. Twelve other applicants were under consideration. The Committee modestly reported, "This is a time-consuming process, particularly for beginners like ourselves." In 1949 the Committee reported that two other scholarships were awarded and that the Rockefeller Foundation had renewed and increased their grant. The continuing success of this important project was due entirely to untiring efforts on the part of many librarians from coast to coast, whose functions as hosts went far beyond the training programs offered. The recent announcement of Mrs. Cunningham's generous bequest to the Association for training foreign medical librarians gives a touching reminder of her efforts in the past.

An evaluation of the first three years was included in her Committee report at the meeting in Denver, 1951.[31] A new program was also described. Funded, too, by the Rockefeller Foundation, it was a joint project with the U. S. Book Exchange for filling requests for foreign libraries. The material sent was either left over from Exchange lists or not wanted by member libraries. A total of 22,331 items were sent. The Association, with members in many countries, has ever been concerned with international activities relating to libraries and has participated in UNESCO and FID and IFLA. The high point came, of course, at the Second International Congress on Medical Librarianship in Washington in 1963, with Dr. Frank B. Rogers presiding, and with the new building he had done so much to attain available for inspection. Colonel Jones's race against time had taken twenty-one years.

These are some of the activities in which the Association has shown leadership. Some of its publications also led the way. The first edition of the *Handbook of Medical Library Practice*, with Janet Doe as editor, was surely a pioneering venture. It evolved from a primer prepared by Irene Jones from a card file compiled for her own use during her first years as a medical librarian. "Reference tools, various subject heading lists, catalogs, historical background texts, etc., in the medical and science subjects were an unknown field. Therefore, when or wherever I found something helpful in an article or book, or learned from someone, I made little file cards for future reference. . . . I decided in 1936 to put it into written form with the idea it might possibly be of some help to others."[32] This was generously turned over to a committee of the Association as a basis for a more comprehensive text that might "reflect the conclusions of many librarians instead of a single one." In 1939 the prospective *Handbook* was announced: "New libraries are constantly being organized; public librarians going into medical work wish to prepare themselves for their new field; library schools feel the want of a manual on this form of specialized library work; even seasoned medical librarians could benefit by a reliable guide in their professional problems. And yet no printed source for such information exists."[33] A special committee was appointed to serve as authors covering the subjects: the medical library and librarian; book selection and ordering; cataloging; subject headings; classification; pamphlets and miscellaneous material; reference; rare books and the history of medicine. Miss Doe wrote in the introduction to the first edition, 1943, that half of the existing medical libraries had originated since 1910.

> To staff these libraries, workers have been enticed or commandeered from general and special libraries, from library schools, from the clerical staff of hospitals . . . from doctors' offices. Seldom, indeed, has it happened that a medical library could secure a librarian with both professional library training and education or experience in the medical sciences. . . . An exceptionally definite need exists, therefore, for a means of liaison between the medical library and the sources from which it must draw its librarian. This *Handbook* attempts to fill that want.

The response was so favorable that by 1952 a fourth printing of about 1,000 copies was nearly exhausted, and plans for a revised edition were in progress, with Janet Doe and Mary Louise Marshall as editors. On its appearance in 1956, it was described in a review as "one of the most generally useful books on librarianship since the original publication of the old standby texts of Randall & Goodrich, Wilson & Tauber, Akers, Mann, and others of their kind."[34]

Another pioneering project was the inauguration of *Vital Notes on Medical Periodicals* in 1952. Mrs. Elizabeth F. Bready, then head of the Periodicals Department of the College of Physicians of Philadelphia, discussed with colleagues the time-consuming problems of establishing facts concerning the births and deaths and title changes of ever increasing numbers of journals. She suggested a continuing project and, together with Chizuru N. Boyea, of the New York Academy of Medicine Library staff, developed plans for cooperating medical librarians to pool all information of the kind. The chairman of the Association's Serials Committee, Harold Oatfield, and the President, William Postell, strongly backed the program, which was put into action by Lora Frances Davis. This important service has been well maintained by William Beatty and an alert Committee.

In 1954 a new series was inaugurated. Publication no. 1 was Estelle Brodman's contribution, *The Development of Medical Bibliography*. Slow to follow, no. 2 did not appear until Dr. Rogers' edition of the writings of John Shaw Billings in 1965.

The Bulletin itself, though of exceptionally high quality, cannot be called a pioneering feat, but it has recorded the basis of this brief account, which is surely what Dr. Brodman recently well described as "a feat of ancestor worship, a glorification of the giants of the past," but it can serve also as a background for what she calls "a study of the culture and beliefs of the society it represents at a particular period of that society's development."[35] In 1937 the Association was emerging from its first period, a period in which the bookish, scholarly physician dominated. The large libraries were chiefly collections made by practicing physicians and administered by medical societies. The contents of the Bulletin for a decade continued to reflect these interests. Articles on the history of medicine appeared regularly. In January 1945, the editors announced that ninety-seven postcards had been received in response to their request for guidance in planning future issues. Of these, thirty-seven voted to continue the present policy of alternating historical and librarianship numbers; thirty-five wished each number to contain both in equal proportions; thirteen recommended less historical material; and two, less on librarianship. A frequent feature was the listing of current sale catalogs of antiquarian book dealers. The layman's needs were considered to the extent that a Committee was appointed to consider the compilation of a list of health works recommended for lay reading. In October 1938 two were published in the Bulletin on diet and nutrition and on medical biography and history for the public. Four years later, the October issue included a bibliography of books by and about doctors, a layman's checklist for 1941. Occasionally a brief section of "Queries and Answers" brought forth questions on such varied themes as "The Handsome Men of Iowa" and "The Pearl of Allah." In contrast there were but two historical articles in 1966 and no concern for the needs of laymen. Recent emphasis is on the demands of medical research and education and on the techniques of an electronic world, unthought of in 1937.

In these years the day of the devoted amateur passed, the trained medical librarian came into being and matured, and today we look to a future of information centers and networks manned by experts with varying skills. These changing trends and developments are clearly shown in the pages of the Bulletin. Less obvious is their effect upon the Association's own role. Alfred N. Brandon's editorial in the January 1967 issue of the Bulletin provides a clue. Commenting on "Continuing (or Discontinuing) Education," he writes that "it is necessary for the MLA to subsidize" that program. "Subsidize" is the important word, for the Association, ever increasing in size, and the programs developing from small voluntary efforts into highly specialized projects, has been faced with the necessity of providing funds. The operation of the Association's business became too unwieldy to be carried on solely by the voluntary work of members, and a Central Office came into being in 1961. Although the original aims of the Association still obtain, they are increasingly difficult to carry out without financial assistance. Federal support for training programs, surveys, statistical studies, are increasingly sought to further the obvious goals of the Association. A committee to outline future programs found no crystal ball. Happily, a glance at developments in past years indicates that members of the Association have been alert to point the way, and the uncertain future will surely bring the same response.

This, the first Janet Doe Lecture, is named for one who illustrates the best in medical librarianship, serving with scholarly distinction. It is a brief survey pointing to some of the Association's significant achievements during the years of Miss Doe's greatest activity, when she and her colleagues met their "Challenge of Change" with imagination, with argument, with hard work, and with persistence. Her own words, written in 1949, give evidence of the continuing collaboration which made their progress possible: "Libraries are born of mutual needs and mutual giving, and they continue to exist and grow largely through the same process. . . . Out of this have come not alone ever growing collections: these are but the outward and visible signs of a strong inward grace. Libraries have exemplified to an outstanding degree the inestimable value of generous and continuing assistance to one another."[36]

NOTES

1 Reports. Bulletin 26: 27–30, Oct. 1937.

2 U.S. Army War Department. Surgeon General's Office. Annual Report, 1938, p. 237–240.

3 *Ibid.*, 1941, p. 246–252.

4 Personal communication.

5 American Library Association. The National Medical Library; Report of a Survey of the Army Medical Library. Chicago, 1944.

6 Bulletin 49: 251–449, July 1961.

7 *Ibid.* 26: 25, Oct. 1937.

8 Personal communication.

9 Personal communication.

10 Walter, Frank K. Training for Librarianship at the University of Minnesota. . . . Minneapolis, University of Minnesota, 1942, p. 24–25.

11 Walter, Frank K. Training for hospital librarianship. Libr. J. 63: 579–583, Aug. 1938.

12 Marshall, M. L. Training for medical librarianship. Bulletin 34: 247–252, Oct. 1946.

13 Metcalfe, K. D., and others. Program of Instruction in Library Schools. Urbana, University of Illinois Press, 1943.

14 Doe, Janet, The development of education for medical librarianship. Bulletin 37: 213–220, July 1949.

15 Abstracts of Refresher Courses to be Given May 31, 1958. *Ibid.* 46: 122–132, Jan. 1958.

16 Continuing Education: Boston, 1966. *Ibid.* 53: 659–660, Oct. 1965.

17 Jordan, Mildred. Regional meetings for the Medical Library Association. *Ibid.* 35: 309–320, Oct. 1947.

18 Doe, Janet. The new venture: regional meetings. Bulletin 38: 273–274, July 1950.

19 Wanted: A Clinical Abstract Journal. Bulletin 25: 146, Sept. 1936.

20 Cunningham, E. R. Problem of abstract publications in medical and allied sciences. Bulletin 26: 211–217, May 1938.

21 *Ibid.* 27: 63–65, Oct. 1938.

22 *Ibid.* 36: 391, Oct. 1948.

23 Cunningham, E. R. Looking forward. Bulletin 25: 100–108, Sept. 1936.

24 A Symposium on Medical Literature. Bulletin 27: 103–161, Dec. 1938.

25 Larkey, S. V. Introduction to the problems of medical subject headings. Bulletin 36: 70–81, Apr. 1948.

26 Larkey, S. V. The Army Medical Library research project at the Welch Medical Library. Bulletin 37: 121–124, Apr. 1949.

[27] Brodman, Estelle. The Development of Medical Bibliography. Baltimore, Medical Library Association, 1954, p. 174.
[28] Bennett, M. A., and Lichfield, D. H. Problems of microphotography. Bulletin 28: 105–109, 114, Dec. 1939.
[29] *Ibid.* 35: 274–275, July 1947.
[30] *Ibid.* 36: 296–298, Oct. 1948.
[31] Cunningham, E. R. Evaluation of a three-year program of international cooperation in medical librarianship. Bulletin 39: 295–305, Oct. 1951.
[32] Personal communication.
[33] Bulletin 28: 114, Dec. 1939.
[34] Libr. J. 81: 1137–1138, May 1, 1956.
[35] Brodman, Estelle. The special library, the mirror of its society. In: Marshall, J. D., ed. Approaches to Library History; Proceedings of the 2nd Library History Seminar. Tallahassee, Journal of Library History, 1966. 32 p.
[36] Doe, Janet. Growth by gift. Academy Bookman 2: 5–9, Fall 1949.

ABOUT THE AUTHOR—Gertrude L. Annan retired in 1970 from the position of Librarian of the New York Academy of Medicine which she had held since 1956. Before that she had been successively Cataloger, Head of the Rare Book Department, and Associate Librarian. She holds a B.A. in English from Brown University.

With Jacqueline Felter, she is Editor of the third edition of the *Handbook of Medical Library Practice*. She is a member of the American Library Association, the Special Libraries Association and the Bibliographical Society of America. She has held many offices in the Medical Library Association, including that of President. She also received the Association's Marcia Noyes Award, and was asked to deliver its first Janet Doe Lecture, this paper.

An Investigation of the Educational Needs of Health Sciences Library Manpower: IV. Characteristics of Manpower in Health Sciences Libraries

by Lesliebeth Rothenberg, Alan M. Rees, and David A. Kronick

What are some of the attributes of today's medical librarian? As part of a larger study of nonhospital medical librarians, the authors have found that sixty per cent of respondents are professionals. Men constitute approximately one-fifth of the respondents, and tend to enter the work force later than women. Of 728 chief librarians, fifty-seven per cent are professional librarians, possessing a graduate library degree.

Previous articles have described the objectives and design of a study of health sciences library manpower[1,2] undertaken as a joint project by the University of Texas Medical School at San Antonio and the School of Library Science at Case Western Reserve University. One part of the survey, directed to libraries, elicited data describing the total health sciences library work force in terms of size, composition, location and extent of demand for additional personnel.[3] Some 14,938 persons were identified as being involved–directly or indirectly, full- and part-time–in the provision of health sciences library services in 4,727 U.S. libraries. A 7 percent demand for professional librarians and a 3 percent demand for support personnel were found to exist reflecting budgeted, unfilled openings.

The present article reports the results of a second survey directed to individuals in the health sciences library work force. Some 3,581 health sciences library employees were requested in late 1969 to complete personal questionnaires. This population of 3,581 represented all professionals and nonprofessionals reported as employed in nonhospital, health sciences libraries and identified by name in the Survey of Health Sciences Libraries, 1969 (professional and nonprofessional being defined here in functional terms).[4] Professionals and nonprofessionals employed in health sciences libraries in hospitals were excluded since they were surveyed concurrently with this study by the American Hospital Association.

The survey instrument,[5] entitled Health Sciences Library Personnel Questionnaire, was an eight-page booklet consisting of fixed-alternative questions in four areas:

a. *Demographic Characteristics:* Age, sex.
b. *Educational Characteristics:* Academic history; current educational activity; participation in continuing education programs in library science.
c. *Employment Characteristics:* Salary, tenure and tasks performed in present position; previous library experience.
d. *Staff Characteristics:* Staff growth and skills hardest to find in prospective library employees (completed by chief librarians only.)

A response rate of approximately 70 percent was achieved. Nonrespondents included 219 chief librarians and some 900 staff librarians and support personnel, located in 446 libraries.

SOURCE: Reprinted from Lesliebeth Rothenberg, Alan M. Rees, and David A. Kronick, "An Investigation of the Educational Needs of Health Sciences Library Manpower: IV. Characteristics of Manpower in Health Sciences Libraries," *Bulletin of the Medical Library Association*, 59 (Jan. 1970), pp. 31–40, by permission of the publisher and the author. Work supported in part by Research Grant LM-00493 from the National Library of Medicine, National Institutes of Health, DHEW; David A. Kronick, Ph.D., Principal Investigator; Alan M. Rees, Co. Principal Investigator; Mrs. Leslie Rothenberg, Project Manager. The research is sponsored by the Medical Library Association. For paper V and reference to other papers in this series, see page 289 of this *Reader*.

Descriptive generalizations of professionals and nonprofessionals drawn from these data must be qualified in that the survey population of 3,581 was not chosen randomly from the total eligible population (5,666 professionals and nonprofessionals employed in nonhospital, health sciences libraries—the difference of 2,085 being accounted for by the failure of all chief librarians to identify all personnel by name). It should be noted that the analysis below reflects only the available data, and that personnel were located by sequential steps involving identification of institutions, libraries, and then names of specific individuals. Inevitably, losses resulted at each step. These limitations—loss of 1,666, and loss of 419 due to postal returns, misidentifications, changes of address, etc.—although significant, do not negate the positive value of the data.

Basic statistical data regarding the total work force in health sciences libraries are presented below in at least partial answer to the following fundamental questions:

a. What are the demographic characteristics of health sciences library employees?
b. What is the educational preparation of professionals and nonprofessionals in the work force?
c. What are the essential characteristics of the current employment of professionals and nonprofessionals?
d. What are the work histories of professionals and nonprofessionals in the work force?

DEFINITIONS

In prior survey activity, professional and nonprofessional personnel were defined in the functional terms set forth by the American Library Association in *Library Statistics: A Handbook of Concepts, Definitions and Terminology.*[4] A functional definition reflects the nature of tasks performed. This definition is now replaced by one based solely upon educational achievement, since it is important to relate professional education to manpower utilization. A *professional librarian* is defined as an individual who possesses a graduate library science degree (B.S.L.S., M.S.L.S., etc.). A *nonprofessional librarian* is defined as an individual who does not hold a graduate library science degree. A third term basic to the following discussion is that of chief librarian. A *chief librarian* is an individual in charge of a library, either as a sole individual or with responsibility for the supervision of others. A chief librarian may be either a professional or a nonprofessional. The distribution of professionals, nonprofessionals and chief librarians among respondents is shown in Fig. 1.

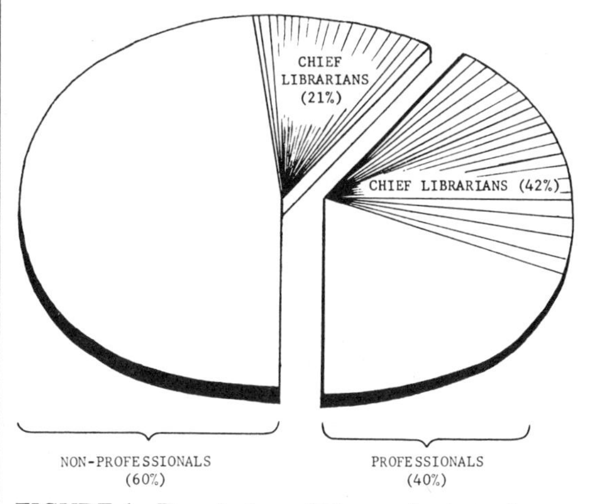

FIGURE 1 Description of Respondents to the Survey of Health Sciences Library Personnel, 1970. N = 2,461.

DEMOGRAPHIC CHARACTERISTICS

Statistics on age and sex obtained in the survey indicate that the health sciences library work force is largely female and, among professional librarians, middle-aged. Table 1 illustrates the distribution of men and women in the professional, nonprofessional and chief librarian populations, and compares these distributions to those found for the national work force and for the total library work force. Fig. 2 presents data regarding the age distributions in these three populations.

It is interesting to note that although health sciences librarianship is predominantly a female occupation, a higher percentage of men are found among health sciences librarians than in the total library work force. However, the percentage of men is lower in this population than among academic librarians (37 percent) and special librarians (26 percent).[6] Also of interest is the fact that the percentage of men in the chief librarian population is somewhat larger than would be expected considering their distribution in the professional and nonprofessional librarian populations.

TABLE 1

MALE/FEMALE RATIOS FOR PROFESSIONALS, NONPROFESSIONALS AND CHIEF LIBRARIANS IN HEALTH SCIENCES LIBRARIES, FOR THE NATIONAL WORK FORCE AND FOR THE TOTAL LIBRARY WORK FORCE

	Health Sciences Libraries				
Sex	Professional	Nonprofessional	Chief Librarians	National Work Force*	Total Library Work Force†
Male . . .	21.4%	13.2%	24.0%	63%	14.2%
Female .	78.6%	86.8%	76.0%	37%	85.7%
Ratio . .	1:3	1:5	1:3	2:1	1:5

*Bowker Annual of Library and Book Trade Information. New York: Bowker, 1969.

†U.S. Census of Population: 1960. Subject Report: Labor Reserves. Washington: Bureau of Census, 1966.

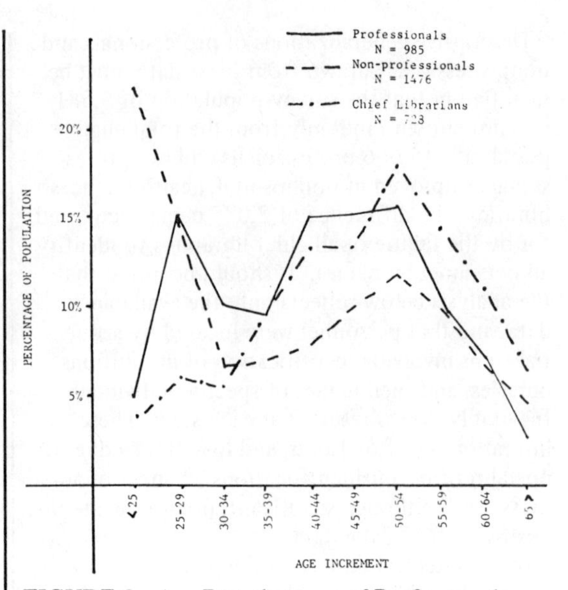

FIGURE 2 Age Distributions of Professionals, Nonprofessionals, and Chief Librarians in Responding Populations. N = 2,461.

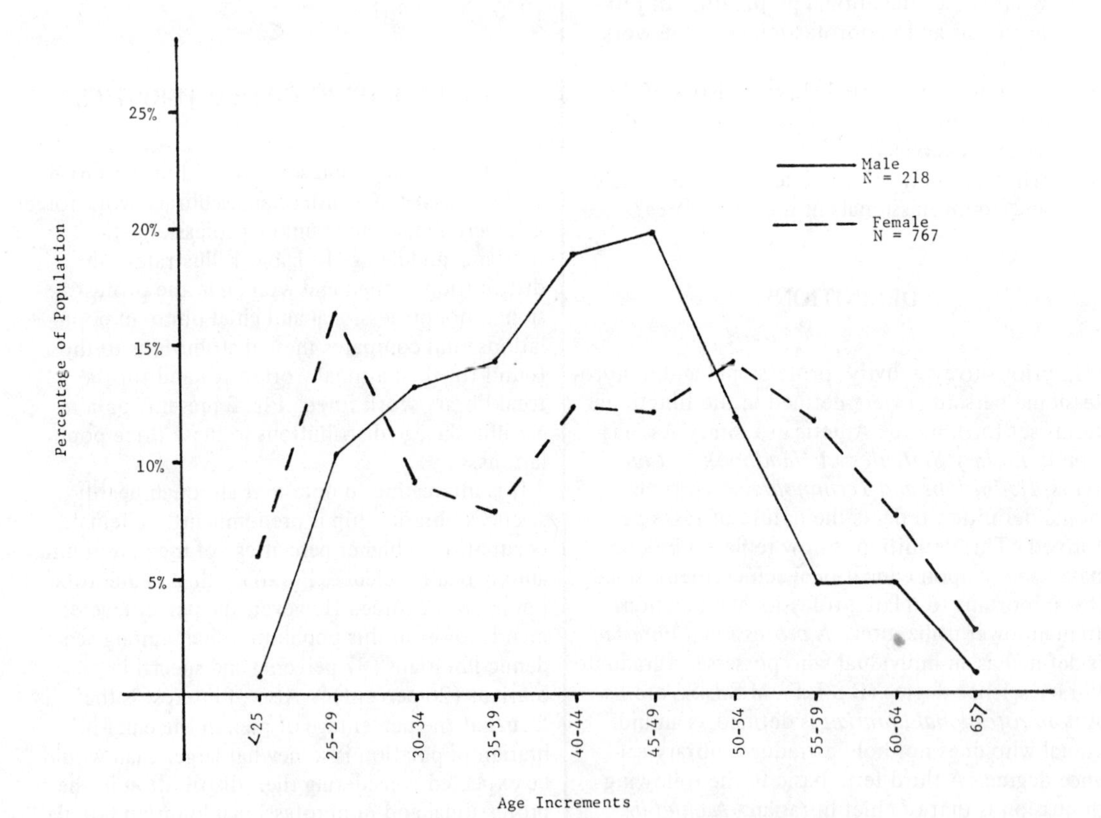

FIGURE 3 Age Distribution of Professional Librarians by Sex

Ages of professional librarians form a bimodal distribution. The two peaks occur in the age groups (25–29) and (40–54). A breakdown of this distribution by sex (Fig. 3) indicates that the first peak is due largely to a high proportion of women in the work force, while the second peak results from an increased proportion of men. This finding appears to reinforce the argument that women often tend to drop out of the work force after thirty due to family responsibilities, and that men tend to choose librarianship as a "second choice" career, entering the field at a later stage than do women. Data concerning the number of years elapsed between achievement of the bachelor degree and the M.S.L.S. for men and women appear to confirm the latter point. The time span between the bachelor degree and M.S.L.S. tends to be longer for men than for women. Ages of nonprofessionals also tend to form a bimodal distribution, although this distribution is less pronounced than in the case of the professionals. (Fig. 4)

The age distribution of chief librarians indicates that almost 60 percent of all chief librarians are between the ages of forty and fifty-nine; 17 percent are over sixty years old; and only 4 percent are less than twenty-five years old.

EDUCATIONAL ATTAINMENT

The survey data indicate that a total of 2,260 professional librarians, possessing a graduate degree in librarianship, are currently employed in health sciences libraries. Some 3 percent of this total reported Ph.D.'s in library science, with the remaining 97 percent holding the master's or bachelor's degree. The nonprofessional population, estimated at 3,400, reflects a generally high level of educational attainment. Approximately three-quarters of the group have continued their formal education beyond graduation from high school. Twenty-nine percent have completed one through three years of college; 20 percent

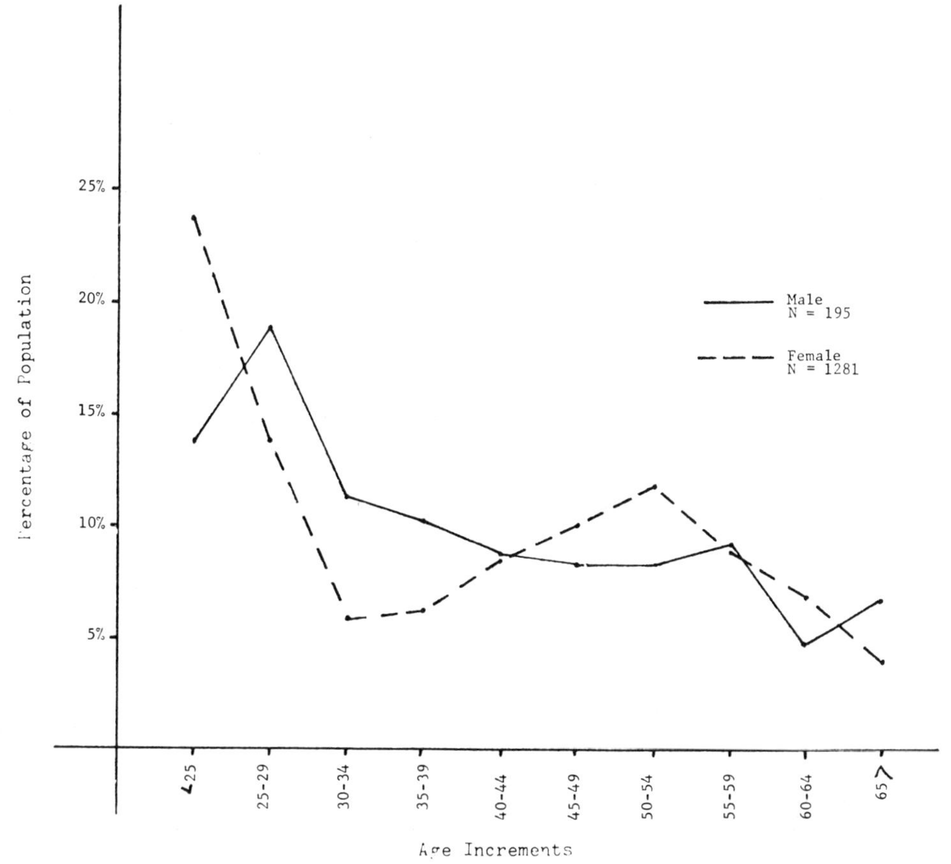

FIGURE 4 Age Distribution of Nonprofessional Library Employees by Sex

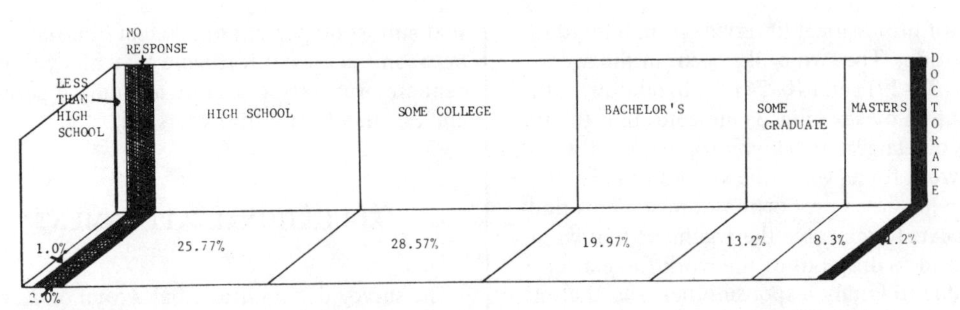

FIGURE 5 Educational Attainment of Nonprofessionals Employed in Health Science Libraries

hold bachelor's degrees; 13 percent attended graduate school; and 9.5 percent have attained graduate degrees, including a number of M.D., Ph.D., and D.D.S. degrees. The educational attainment of nonprofessionals employed in health sciences libraries is shown in Fig. 5. The data indicate that most nonprofessionals are well educated and possess the potential of performing sophisticated tasks in libraries. Their job role in relation to professionals has been investigated by means of a Job Task Index which measures the extent to which personnel, both professional and nonprofessional, perform professional tasks as defined on a graphic scale. The results of this study will be reported separately.

Professional and nonprofessional library employees reporting a college education were also asked to indicate their undergraduate majors. A large number of graduates did not have majors in either the natural or health sciences. Three-quarters of the professional librarians held bachelor's degrees in the liberal arts or social sciences, while almost the same number of the nonprofessional graduates also held degrees in the liberal arts or social sciences. Only a small percentage of each group majored in the natural or health sciences. These data have relevance to the current debate concerning the preparation of employees in health sciences libraries. In view of the fact that a majority of the present work force do not have medically-related educations, is a subject-based education in the natural or health sciences necessary for health sciences librarianship? Would the provision of subject knowledge in the health sciences and cognate areas result in an improvement in library services at least equal to the educational investment?

To provide a rough measure of the extent of formal health sciences library education, respondents were asked whether they had attended a course in medical librarianship offered by a graduate library science school. Only 36 percent of the professionals and 5 percent of the nonprofessionals responded affirmatively. It appears that most respondents in these two groups function in health sciences libraries without the benefit either of specialized health sciences library education or of educational preparation in the subject content of the health sciences. The effect of these educational limitations upon job performance remains to be explored.

NATURE OF INVOLVEMENT IN CONTINUING EDUCATION

Participation in continuing education by the survey population is of particular interest. How frequently do individuals attend continuing education programs? What factors affect their attendance at such programs? What are the expressed preferences for subject topics and how do these preferences correlate with the perceptions of chief librarians as to needed job skills?

It is apparent that frequency of attendance of continuing education programs differs significantly between professional and nonprofessional respondents. Seventy-five percent of the professionals, contrasted with 43 percent of the nonprofessionals, had attended one or more continuing education programs during the past five years. As the number of programs attended increases, the differences between the two groups remain significant. The frequency of respondents' attendance is illustrated in Fig. 6. The generally lower attendance record of nonprofessionals may be attributed to a number of factors, such as lack of professional motivation, inappropriateness of course offerings, and failure of libraries to provide release time and/or tuition waivers.

The effect of age and geographic location upon

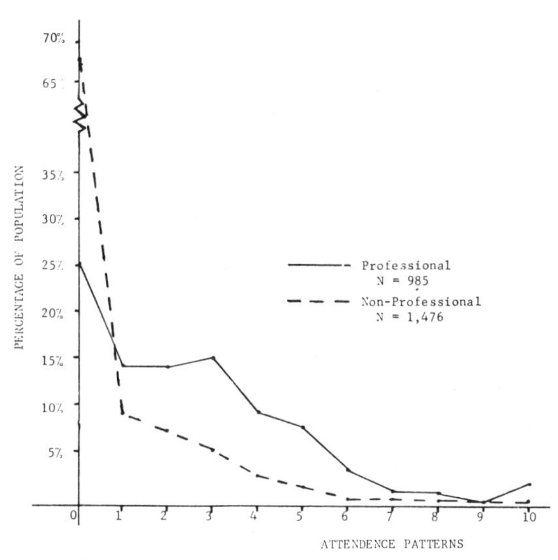

FIGURE 6 Attendance at Continuing Education Programs by Professionals and Nonprofessionals

attendance of continuing education programs was investigated. Age and attendance correlated at .133 for professional respondents and at .202 ($\alpha = .05$) for nonprofessional respondents.[7] Although age has some effect upon attendance patterns, it cannot be interpreted as a major factor. Geographic location does have a marked effect on attendance patterns for professionals, but not for nonprofessionals. Professionals in RML regions II, V, IX and XI attended continuing education courses more frequently than did professionals in other regions. It is evident that opportunities to attend continuing education programs vary from RML region to region. The effect of region is more noticeable for professionals than for nonprofessionals, perhaps because few courses are designed for the specific needs of this group.

The subject areas for continuing education programs arranged in order according to the preferences expressed by professionals and nonprofessionals are shown in Tables 2 and 3. The numbers listed for each subject topic indicate the preferential votes received. The most striking characteristic of the two lists lies in their similarity, although interesting differences in preference for continuing education subject topics appear between professionals and nonprofessionals. The ranked lists correlated at .509 ($\alpha = .05$). A major difference lies in the fact that professionals favored courses dealing with the organization of libraries, health sciences institutions and their interrelationships, while nonprofessionals preferred courses dealing with the technical procedures of library operations. Such differences were not surprising in view of the different job involvements of the two groups.

The expressed preferences for specific subject topics in continuing education courses can be presumed to reflect a self-assessment of skill deficiencies. In this connection, it is of interest to compare the self-assessment of educational needs by employees with the perceptions of employers (chief librarians). The ranks assigned to subject topics for continuing education courses by 728

TABLE 2

EXPRESSED PREFERENCE FOR CONTINUING EDUCATION PROGRAMS BY PROFESSIONAL HEALTH SCIENCE LIBRARY PERSONNEL

Preferred Education Program	Votes
1. Reference & Other Information Services	505
2. Data Processing Principles and Techniques	328
3. Systems Analysis Techniques	307
4. Material Selection and Acquisition	257
5. MEDLARS Search Procedures	243
6. Cataloging, Indexing, and Classification	231
7. Facilities & Space Planning	147
8. Use of Audiovisual Equipment	143
9. Literature of the History of Medicine	129
10. Use of Statistics in Libraries	128
11. Organization of Health Services	123
12. Scientific Terminology	110
13. Interlibrary Loan	66
14. Circulation Techniques & Procedures	59
15. Literature of Dentistry	23
16. Typing & Other Office Skills	3

TABLE 3

EXPRESSED PREFERENCE FOR CONTINUING EDUCATION PROGRAMS BY NONPROFESSIONAL HEALTH SCIENCES LIBRARY PERSONNEL

Preferred Education Program	Votes
1. Reference and Other Information Services	689
2. Cataloging, Indexing and Classification	411
3. Material Selection and Acquisition	381
4. Data Processing Principles and Techniques	319
5. Circulation Techniques and Procedures	293
6. Interlibrary Loan	242
7. MEDLARS Search Procedures	187
8. Scientific Terminology	180
9. Systems Analysis Techniques	179
10. Typing and Other Office Skills	178
11. Literature of the History of Medicine	158
12. Use of Audiovisual Equipment	153
13. Facilities and Space Planning	125
14. Organization of Health Services	103
15. Use of Statistics in Libraries	80
16. Literature of Dentistry	25

responding chief librarians are reported in Table 4. The seven subject areas receiving the highest number of votes by chief librarians were in three major areas: (a) selection, acquisition and organization of materials; (b) reference; and (c) automation. Using Spearman's coefficient of ranked correlations, it was found that the correlation between the expressed preference of professionals and the perceived needs of chief librarians was .656, while the correlation for nonprofessionals was .759. These correlations are significant at $\alpha = .01$. Thus, the expressed preferences of library personnel for areas of continuing education are closely correlated with the perceptions of chief librarians as to the skill deficiencies of their employees.

TABLE 4

CHIEF LIBRARIANS' ASSESSMENT OF LIBRARY SKILLS MOST DIFFICULT TO FIND IN PROSPECTIVE HEALTH SCIENCE LIBRARY PERSONNEL

Skill	Votes
1. Cataloging, Indexing and Classification	239
2. Reference and Other Information Services	162
3. Data Processing Principles and Techniques	130
4. Systems Analysis Techniques	129
5. Material Selection and Acquisition	120
6. Scientific Terminology	109
7. MEDLARS Search Procedures	85
8. Typing and Other Office Skills	60
9. Use of Audiovisual Equipment	55
10. Use of Statistics in Libraries	46
11. Circulation Techniques and Procedures	45
12. Interlibrary Loan	30
13. Organization of Health Services	20
14. Facilities and Space Planning	18
15. Literature of the History of Medicine	17
16. Literature of Dentistry	8

CHARACTERISTICS OF LIBRARY EMPLOYMENT

The survey findings indicate that health sciences library personnel are predominantly full-time employees, who have held their present jobs for three years. (Professionals reported a median tenure in their present jobs of 3.50 years; nonprofessionals 2.82 years. Sex does not appear to be a significant factor in job tenure.) Only one percent of the professionals and 3.5 percent of the nonprofessionals are volunteers.

Salary level and its relationship to a number of other variables characterizing library employment is a topic of obvious interest. Annual income data were therefore correlated with (a) professional/nonprofessional status, (b) sex, (c) chief librarian/staff librarian status, (d) Job Task Index scores, (e) nonprofessional educational attainment, (f) staff size and (g) geographic location.

a) Professional/nonprofessional status: Salary distribution for responding professionals and nonprofessionals is illustrated in Fig. 7. Mean income for professional librarians was $10,640 annually; for nonprofessionals, $6,510. b) Sex: Significant differences result when sex is introduced as a variable. Amongst professional librarians, men earn an average of $12,723 annually while women earn $10,044 annually ($t = 2.97$, $\alpha = .003$). Similarly, men employed as nonprofessionals receive annual salaries of $7,878 while women receive incomes averaging $6,313 ($t = 3.64$, $\alpha = .001$). It would appear that women receive less income for performing the same tasks.

c) Chief librarian/staff librarian status: Chief librarians tend to earn more than staff librarians, whether or not they possess a professional degree. A point-biserial correlation showed a .539 ($\alpha = .01$) relationship between high salary and chief librarian status. d) Job Task Index scores: Salary level and Job Task Index scores were shown to correlate at .515 for professionals and at .464 for nonprofessionals. These correlations, although statistically significant at $\alpha = .01$, do not indicate a high match between salary level and job level, i.e., tasks performed. e) Nonprofessional educational attainment: Salary level was found to correlate at .447 ($\alpha = .01$) with educational attainment for nonprofessional employees, indicating that many of these persons are probably performing jobs which could be filled by individuals having less education.

f) Staff size: Salary levels were correlated with library staff size in order to ascertain whether professionals in large libraries were paid more than those in small libraries. It was supposed that professionals in large libraries perform more specialized (i.e., more professional) tasks than professionals in small libraries and that their salaries would be consequently higher. This assumption was not confirmed in that no correlation was discovered between income and staff size for professionals.

From these correlations between salary level and other variables relating to library employment some evidence exists to indicate that the manner in which manpower is utilized in health

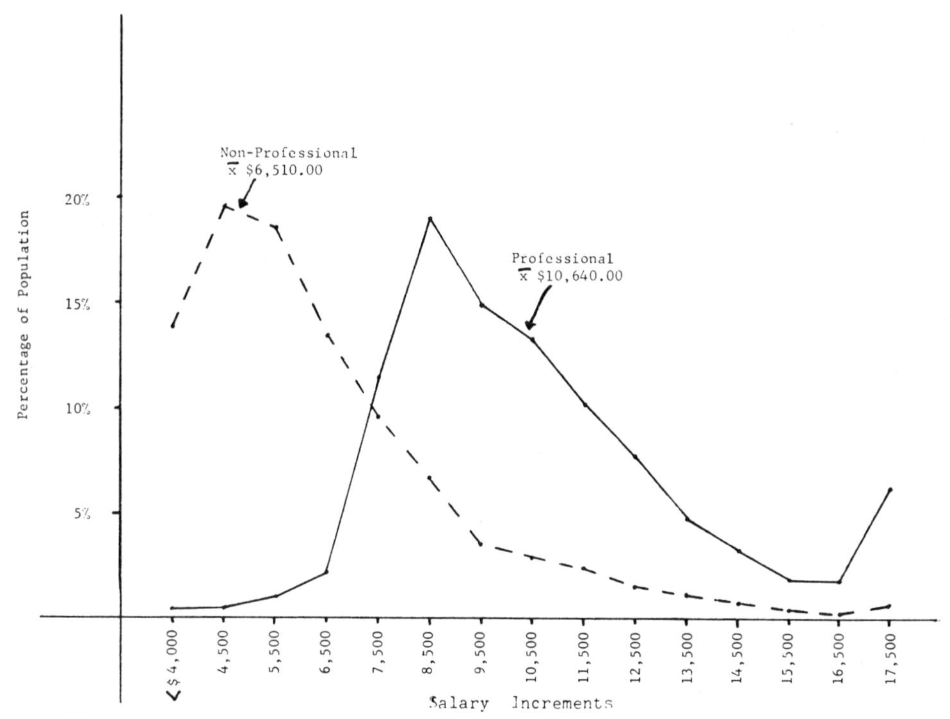

FIGURE 7 Salary Distribution for Reporting Professional and Nonprofessional Health Sciences Library Personnel

sciences libraries is far from optimal. It would appear from these correlations based upon salary and other variables that many persons are not performing jobs consistent with either their employment status as professional or nonprofessional, or with their educational attainment; that salary levels cannot be easily equated with tasks performed, and that the division of labor is no more specialized in large libraries than in small libraries. It is reasonably apparent that there is no clear distinction between the tasks performed by professionals and nonprofessionals which would indicate that employers often pay a premium for the employment of professionals at a higher rate of remuneration.

These questions warrant further study since it can be argued that many aspects of the current manpower shortage in libraries would be alleviated by more efficient utilization of available personnel.

An analysis of variance indicated that geographic location significantly affects salary level. RML regions II, IV, and VII report incomes higher than the national mean for professionals and nonprofessionals. RML region III reported an income for professionals which was higher than the national mean while incomes for nonprofessionals were lower than the national mean. Thus, variations in salary level do exist, which would allow a mobile individual to maximize his income. In order to assess the real salary gains to be obtained by moving between RML's, median salaries would have to be obtained by region controlling for work experience and cost of living variations. Mean salaries by RML regions for professionals and nonprofessionals are recorded in Table 5.

TABLE 5

SALARY BY RML REGIONS FOR PROFESSIONALS AND NONPROFESSIONALS

RML Regions	Professionals N = 975	Non-professionals N = 1416
I	$10,467	$6,287
II	10,917	6,929
III	10,819	6,006
IV	11,721	7,855
V	10,377	5,816
VI	10,109	6,003
VII	10,966	6,832
VIII	10,279	5,904
IX	10,549	6,187
X	9,279	5,979
XI	10,421	6,520
National Mean	10,638	6,509

CHARACTERISTICS OF PREVIOUS EMPLOYMENT

Sixty-one percent of the professional and 89 percent of the nonprofessional respondents reported that they had not worked in health sciences libraries prior to their present employment. Indeed, many of these individuals noted no previous work experience in any library. These data indicate that considerable on-the-job orientation is required, for both professionals and nonprofessionals, in such areas as health sciences library operations and in the literature and terminology of the health sciences.

Among the small group of professionals reporting prior work experience in health sciences libraries, about half had been employed in professional school libraries, 40 percent in hospital libraries and 12 percent in industrial settings. Only a very small number of nonprofessionals reported any work experience in health sciences libraries.

Measures of job and geographic mobility were established. Job mobility was defined as the frequency of job transfers during the last ten-year period. Geographic mobility was calculated on the basis of the number of moves during the ten-year period. The highest rate of job mobility was demonstrated by male professionals and the lowest rate by female nonprofessionals. Sixty-nine percent of the male professionals held three or more jobs during the past ten years. Half of the female professionals reported three or more jobs during that time. Mobility amongst nonprofessionals was less: 48 percent of the men and 39 percent of the women had held three or more jobs over the measured period. Geographic mobility was generally low for both populations. Half of the professionals and almost three-quarters of the nonprofessionals had not moved within the past ten years.

SUMMARY

Only basic statistical data describing select characteristics of professionals and nonprofessionals currently employed in health sciences libraries have been presented. Space limitations have precluded the presentation of the full data gathered. Detailed breakdowns of these descriptive statistics are stored on magnetic tapes and are available upon request.

A number of conclusions may be drawn from the data gathered:

1. The bimodal age distribution of the work force clearly illustrates the effects of the career patterns of women, who compose approximately four-fifths of all employees. Calculations of projected demand for manpower must account not only for expected growth in library systems and retirement at age sixty-five, but also for this "interim retirement" period at age thirty.
2. Although librarianship is a "women's career," it is evident that women are significantly underpaid when compared to men with similar educational qualifications. In addition, women are often given positions of less responsibility in libraries. These factors contribute to the softness of the professional image of librarianship.
3. Only a small proportion of the work force reported specialized education in health sciences librarianship or in the health sciences as such. If it is assumed that specialized education in these areas is required for the optimum practice of health sciences librarianship, extensive on-the-job orientation programs would be necessary for a large number of current library personnel.
4. Employee preferences for continuing education are closely matched to employer perceptions of scarce skills as identified in the survey instrument. However, based upon an analysis of the titles of courses offered during the last three MLA annual continuing education programs, it is evident that only one-half fall within the subject areas cited by employees and employers. It appears, therefore, that the focus of future MLA planning for such programs ought to take into account the preferences reported.
5. The most significant conclusion to be drawn from this study pertains to the manner in which employees are matched to library jobs. The evidence presented here, in combination with that to be presented in the discussion of the Job Task Index, points to the conclusion that many professional librarians are employed in jobs which make little, if any, use of their talents as professionals. At the same time, a significant group of nonprofessionals perform tasks normally considered to require professional training. These findings indicate that both the organi-

zation of jobs in health sciences libraries and the manner in which employees are assigned to jobs is far from optimal. These conditions may partially account for the current feeling of a "manpower crisis" in libraries, which stems more from poor utilization than scarcity.

Two areas remain to be explored. The first is related to the Job Task Index, which represents a composite score describing the job tasks performed by an individual. A subsequent article of this series will describe the Index, its statistical characteristics, and the relationship of an individual's score to his income, educational achievement, and other characteristics. The second area, yet to be reported, is concerned with the rate of growth of library staffs, losses from the work force due to retirement, job transfers, and projected demand for manpower during the seventies. Data relating to staff growth rates were obtained during the survey. However, the manner in which these data can best be interpreted, the calculation of attrition from the work force, and the identification of other factors affecting projected manpower demand have yet to be resolved.

NOTES

[1]Kronick, D. A.; Rees, A. M.; and Rothenberg, L. An investigation of the education needs of health sciences library manpower. Part I: Definition of the manpower problem and research design. Bull. Med. Libr. Ass. 58: 7–17, Jan. 1970.

[2]Rothenberg, L.; Rees, A. M.; and Kronick, D. A. An investigation of the education needs of health sciences library manpower. Part II: Health-related institutions and their library resources. Bull. Med. Libr. Ass. 58: 510–520, Oct. 1970.

[3]Rothenberg, L.; Kronick, D. A.; and Rees, A. M. An investigation of the education needs of health sciences library manpower. Part III: Manpower supply and demand in health sciences libraries. Bull. Med. Libr. Ass. 59: 21–30, Jan. 1971.

[4]American Library Association. Library Statistics: A Handbook of Concepts, Definitions and Terminology. Chicago, Illinois. 1966.

[5]The survey instrument is published in Kronick, Rees, and Rothenberg, Educational Needs of Health Sciences Library Manpower, Report No. 1. It is available on request from the authors.

[6]Schillar, A. R. Academic librarians' salaries. Coll. Res. Libr. 30: 101–111, 1969.

[7]In discussing these correlations and others described throughout the analyses, it is important to note the strength of the correlations attained. Because of the large N's in the test groups, even low correlations may attain statistical significance. The question of the meaningfulness of these "significant" correlations must then be resolved. For example, the correlation between income and age for professional librarians is .345–a correlation which is significant at $\alpha = .01$. Although the correlation attains a significant level, it does not account for a major portion of the variance. Thus, a meaningful interpretation of the correlation is complicated, and confidence in any *ex post facto* explanation set forth is correspondingly decreased.

ABOUT THE AUTHORS–Lesliebeth Rothenberg is an Instructor in the Department of Sociology, Ursuline College. She was a Research Assistant in the Case Western Reserve University School of Library Science and Instructor in its Department of Sociology. She received a B.A. from the College of William and Mary and a B.A. from Case Western Reserve University.

She is a member of the American Sociological Association and has participated with Dr. Kronick and Mr. Rees in the writing of the other articles in this series.

Alan M. Rees is Professor of Library Science and Director of the Medical Library Training Program at Case Western Reserve University. He holds a B.A. in History from the University of London, a B. Litt. in History from Oxford University and an M.S. in Library Science from Case Western Reserve University.

He has served on the Council of the American Society for Information Science and as a member of the Committee on Surveys and Statistics of the Medical Library Association. He has served as a consultant to the National Institutes of Health and the National Library of Medicine and was a lecturer for the Australian Library Association at the University of Melbourne in 1969.

Dr. David A. Kronick is Director of Medical Communications, University of Texas Medical School, San Antonio. During 1972 he studied in England under a Council on Library Resources Fellowship. He holds a B.A. in American Literature and a B.S.L.S. from Case Western Reserve University. His Ph.D. in Librarianship is from the University of Chicago. Other medical library positions he has held include:

Librarian, University of Michigan Medical School; Director, Cleveland Medical Library; and Chief, Reference Services Division, National Library of Medicine.

He has been active in the Medical Library Association, and is also a member of the American Association for the History of Medicine and the American Society for Information Science. Publications include *A History of Scientific and Technical Periodicals* (Scarecrow Press, 1962), and "Information Processing," *Encyclopaedia Britannica* (Chicago, 1968).

III.

ORGANIZATION OF A MEDICAL LIBRARY FOR SERVICE

The services of a medical library have been examined extensively by Orr and his associates. Here is presented an overview of attitudes resulting from studies of methodological tools for measuring library services and inventories of services provided. While medical schools are involved specifically, most of the opinions will be useful for other types of medical library.

The functions of a medical library which support the services described—collection, organization and retrieval of materials—are discussed in separate subsections.

User Services Offered By Medical School Libraries in 1968: Results of a National Survey Employing New Methodology

by Richard H. Orr, Harold Bloomquist, Gwendolyn S. Cruzat, and Arthur P. Schless

The most comprehensive inventory of services in medical school libraries ever attempted is summarized both quantitatively and qualitatively. On the basis of a weighting scheme established by five academic medical librarians to reflect their evaluation of different possible services, medical school library performance ranged from 38 percent to 87 percent; the median overall score was 63 percent. The summaries of individual practices and comments on them can be used as a starting point for establishing individual and general library standards of service.

INTRODUCTION

In 1968, a survey of ninety-two medical school libraries and three major nonacademic resource libraries in the continental United States was conducted by the University City Science Center employing a battery of methods developed by the Institute for Advancement of Medical Communication, which have been described earlier.[1,2] During the survey, field staff visited these libraries to carry out standardized inventory procedures, to ascertain and record service policies, and to administer standardized tests which measure capabilities for providing documents. Shortly after the survey, each library was informed of its score on these "document delivery" tests; and a report summarizing the test results and discussing their implications will be published later. The present report focuses on the survey's findings regarding service policies of medical school libraries, and more specifically on what these libraries do for individual users, as distinguished from the services they perform for other libraries.

The primary data obtained by the inventory of services to individual users provide a detailed and comprehensive picture of user services at each of the ninety-two medical school libraries. These data include: hours of "full services," as well as hours open, for each day of the week; categorized descriptions of policies on fifty-four kinds of user services; any significant variations in policies for different user groups; and certain supplementary details specifically elicited by the inventory procedure such as: exceptions to policies, charges for services, kinds of equipment employed, etc. A few preliminary findings were given at the annual meeting of the Medical Library Association in June 1968; but summarizing the large volume of survey data in a meaningful and succinct way for a publication of general interest posed several problems—in particular, how to employ categorized descriptions of service policies to arrive at an

SOURCE: Richard H. Orr, Harold Bloomquist, Gwendolyn S. Cruzat, and Arthur P. Schless, "User Services Offered by Medical School Libraries in 1968: Results of a National Survey Employing New Methodology," *Bulletin of the Medical Library Association*, 58 (Oct. 1970), pp. 455–492, by permission of the publisher and authors. The survey proper was conducted under U.S. Public Health Service Contract PH-43-68-94 from the National Library of Medicine. With the permission of the National Library of Medicine, the contractor, the University City Science Center made the survey data available to the present authors for further study and analysis. The study and secondary analyses of data reported here were supported by the U.S. Steel Foundation.

overall assessment of the breadth and depth of a library's user services. During development of the inventory procedure, a general method for converting these categorical-type data into quantitative scores had been devised;[2] but applying this method to the survey data required a suitable "weighting scheme," which did not exist as yet. We therefore decided to postpone publication until we had established such a scheme and could use it to facilitate the process of analyzing the results and summarizing the findings. Since completion of the survey proper, a small follow-on effort, which unfortunately could not be given the priority it deserved, has been devoted to establishing this weighting scheme, to "cleaning up" the primary data, to transforming these data into quantitative indices, and to carrying out secondary analyses aimed at exploring the survey's implications.

The severe practical constraints on resources available for these follow-on activities were a poor match for the challenge posed by the great wealth of data; and it soon became apparent that, should we attempt to exploit the data fully, by the time a report was ready for publication it would be of historical interest only—or, more likely, there would never be a report. This consideration forced a decision to concentrate very selectively on what we felt were the most important and useful results, even though this would mean neglecting interesting data that might be easier to digest and summarize. The decision to work toward a highly selective report was strengthened by our conviction that library surveys often fail to have much practical impact because most of the effort devoted to preparing a report is spent attempting to present as many details as possible. When this happens, the resulting report consists largely of tables showing *what* was found but offers little in the way of *so what*—that is, interpretations and conclusions, which are more likely to stimulate thought and action than is a mass of figures. On the other hand, there are reports of library surveys in which so few data are given that it is easy to dismiss the report's conclusions as unsupported opinions, unless they happen to confirm one's own beliefs. We have tried to follow a middle course in this report, which presents some of the more interesting results of the follow-on effort, discusses the implications of selected findings, and makes recommendations regarding further analyses of the present data and future surveys.[3]

METHODS

The Survey Proper

Instruments

To standardize the process of eliciting and recording service policies, the field staff followed as closely as possible the inventory procedure set forth in the Interview Guide and recorded all data on the Checklist form. These instruments, which have been described elsewhere,[2] cannot be reproduced here because of their length.[4]

Training of Field Staff

The fourteen experienced medical librarians who served as field staff met in Philadelphia on February 5-6, 1968, for a training workshop. Prior to the workshop, each was sent copies of the two instruments and asked to perform a trial run of the inventory procedure by "interviewing" himself regarding the policies of his own library. Therefore, the field staff came to the workshop already generally familiar with the instruments and primed with specific questions about any difficulties they encountered in the trial run. This preparation was important since only half a day could be devoted to this inventory procedure during the workshop, which covered the other survey procedures as well. Ideally, each member of the field staff would have been checked individually on a complete interview conducted under realistic conditions; however, this was not feasible. Rather, the group was divided into two sections, each of which collectively interviewed one of the workshop instructors, who attempted to simulate a head librarian unfamiliar with the procedure. Problems and questions that arose were then discussed with the instructor; and those common to both sections were reviewed and resolved in a final joint session.

Field Work

To minimize travel time and costs, field staff were assigned libraries in their own part of the country whenever possible; however, a field staff member's own library was always assigned to someone else. Because some members of the field staff happened to be freer to travel than others, the number of libraries assigned an individual varied from four to nine. At the time of the training workshop, a letter was sent to the head of each library to be visited; this letter described all procedures that would be carried out during the visit and requested his cooperation, including a personal interview to ascertain the service policies of his library. Individual members of the field staff then contacted their assigned libraries and scheduled their visits. Splendid cooperation by the academic medical library community expedited the field work, which was completed by early April of 1968; and in each case it was possible to interview the head, or acting head, of the library. For planning purposes, it had been estimated that interviews for the inventory of services to individual users would require about two hours, on the average. Actually, the interviews ranged in length from forty-five minutes to three hours and fifty-five minutes; but the average length was around one hour and fifty minutes, and half the interviews were completed in less than the average time.

Primary Editing and Analyses

After each visit, the field staff mailed in the completed Checklist form. The first few forms returned by an interviewer were quickly spot-checked for departures from the standardized procedure; and any significant errors of omission or commission disclosed by these spot-checks were discussed by phone. When completed Checklists for all ninety-two libraries had been returned, the process of primary, or initial, editing began. The inventory's structure permits a large number of cross-checks on the internal consistency of the recorded data. Reporting deadlines limited the amount of cross-checking that could be done at this stage; but it was possible to screen for gross inconsistencies and important omissions. Only a few such errors were detected; and these were corrected by telephone discussions with the interviewers, or in some cases with the head librarians. The primary analyses were then begun. These consisted largely of frequency and percentage tabulations of each alternative policy represented in the Checklist, compiled separately for three major user groups—faculty, medical students, and house staff. As is almost invariably the rule in surveys, some additional errors in the data were discovered in the course of these analyses; and these had to be corrected as described earlier before completion of this phase of the survey, which also included primary analyses of the even larger quantities of data collected by the other survey procedures (see "Introduction"). When the University City Science Center submitted the results of these primary analyses to the National Library of Medicine in the early part of July 1968, the survey proper was completed.

Establishing a Weighting Scheme

Selection of the Weighting Task Force

In reporting the development of a general method for establishing weighting schemes based on the differential values a criterion group assigns to alternative service policies, it had been postulated that, for establishing a definitive scheme to be used in weighting the primary data obtained in a national survey of academic medical libraries, "an appropriate criterion group would appear to be 'expert' librarians, highly respected by the medical library community and considered by their peers to be outstanding managers of academic medical libraries."[2] This report also stated, "if such a criterion group were carefully selected and large enough to be considered 'representative' of the population of such experts, but small enough to facilitate resolution of differences by discussion, it should be possible to achieve satisfactory consensus on a weighting scheme within practical constraints on time and effort." While the survey proper was underway, the problems of selecting an appropriate criterion group were discussed with Mr. Scott Adams in his capacity as President of the Medical Library Association. A limit of five members was set for the group to ensure free and informal discussion, and it was considered desirable to make this small group as heterogeneous as possible with regard to characteristics of libraries and librarians, for example, with regard to the size, geographic location, and user populations of libraries. Attempting to represent the diversity that exists within the academic biomedical library community is difficult enough when one is limited to selecting five librarians who also meet the basic qualifications, but selection problems were further complicated by the fact that funds to support the work of the group and to reimburse travel expenses were not available. The difficult task of balancing all selection considerations was undertaken with the help and advice of Mr. Adams; and the final selections were Harold Bloomquist, Alfred N. Brandon, Bernice M. Hetzner, Erich Meyerhoff, and Minnie Orfanos, each of whom accepted an invitation to serve on what will be referred to hereafter as the Weighting Task Force.

Organization of the Task Force

In June 1968, at the annual meeting of the Medical Library Association, the Weighting Task Force met very briefly to discuss how to proceed. The plans called for one of the present authors (R.O.) to arrange a suitable time and place for group sessions, to provide any materials necessary for applying the method, and to play the role of a neutral moderator-catalyst at group sessions—one who was not a member of the Task Force and whose values as a user of library services, rather than a provider, were not to be considered in achieving consensus on a weighting scheme. The economic constraints also put limits on the number and duration of group sessions; however, the members agreed that they could manage two meetings of one or two days each, and that they would work independently to prepare for the group sessions.

Initial Preparation

In preparation for the first working session, each member of the group (a) familiarized himself with what is covered in the fifty-four sections of the inventory by studying a copy of the interview Guide; (b) reviewed the general method for establishing a weighting scheme as described in a draft of the then unpublished report on the inventory[2] from which all examples of weighting schemes established in developmental trials had been deleted so as not to risk biasing the Task Force; and (c) took the first step in establishing his personal weighting scheme. The written materials for this step included a work-sheet that grouped the sections of the inventory into six broad service categories and the following instructions: "Assume you are a member of a committee charged with establishing a weighting scheme for academic biomedical libraries and allocate a quota of 1000 points among the six broad categories of service in such a way as to reflect your personal opinion on the relative 'importance' or 'value' of these service categories for an academic biomedical library in this country. In making these judgements try to ignore the relative 'cost' of providing these services and think only of the 'benefit.' " The work-sheet provided blanks for recording how many points were allotted to each service category.

First Working Session

The Task Force met for two days, July 23–24, 1968. On the first day, the group discussed problems met in preparing for the session and reviewed the results of their independent efforts. The purpose of this review was to obtain a rough idea of how much variation existed within the group so as to assess the probability of achieving consensus with the very limited number of sessions that were feasible. This review was encouraging since the differences disclosed were not disconcertingly large. The initial goal was for each member of the group to arrive at a weighting scheme reflecting his personal values; and it was emphasized that, at this stage, he should not feel any pressure to alter these values. The second step toward this goal was for each, working independently, to allot the points he had assigned to the six major service categories among the various subcategories specified on the work-sheet; and the group adjourned early on the first day to complete this independent work. On the next day, the results of this second step were compared and discussed with a view to finding out which of the differences among the emerging individual weighting schemes could be attributed to differences in interpreting the Interview Guide and the protocol for the weighting exercise, and which to real differences in personal values. Differences of the first sort were resolved by agreeing on a common interpretation. One such agreement was that, at this stage at least, only services to faculty would be considered. The rest of the second day was spent establishing a set of conventions for undertaking the third step, in which the process of allotting points to progressively finer subdivisions would continue until each of the 187 alternative policies in the inventory had been weighted and until the individual was satisfied that the resulting scheme accurately reflected his personal values.

Completion of Individual Weighting Schemes

To assure a common approach to the third step, the conventions established at the first working session were written up and distributed to the group. Each member then completed this last step independently so that his personal weighting scheme would be ready for the second working session. As described elsewhere,[2] employing hierarchical grouping to facilitate development of weighting schemes that are internally consistent is laborious in that it is often necessary to go back repeatedly and redistribute points among categories at higher levels in the hierarchy to achieve the distribution one desires at lower levels. This third step, which entailed distribution of points at the lowest or most specific level, was therefore the most time-consuming.

Second Working Session

The Task Force met again on October 25, 1968, to review the finished individual schemes and, hopefully, to achieve consensus on a single scheme acceptable to the group. Up to this time consciously exerted pressure by the group to change members' individual schemes had been minimal; nevertheless, a surprisingly rapid convergence had taken place among four of the members as the above steps were carried out and as the members repeatedly revised their schemes to satisfy themselves. At the second group session, it soon became apparent that four members of the Task Force would be able to reach agreement on a single scheme easily, without significantly compromising any of their personal values; however, the fifth member's values differed substantially from the emerging consensus. This "minority" member placed considerably more emphasis on answer services, particularly those requiring the highest levels of skills, and correspondingly less emphasis on document services, and also assigned more importance to certain personalized services currently offered by relatively few academic libraries but now becoming more feasible to perform for large numbers of users, such as systematic screening of serial literature by computer to alert individual users of items relevant to their interests. In discussing these differences, the group concluded that, although a scheme based on consensus of the majority would closely approximate the *current* values of librarians in the academic biomedical community, the minority scheme might well represent what these values will be in five or ten years, given present trends. The group had previously agreed that any weighting scheme representing an optimum, or "goal," against which the breadth and depth of a library's user services are assessed, would have to be reviewed every two or three years and revised to reflect changes in user demands and in practical feasibility—otherwise the scheme could have a stultifying influence on progress. The essential difference between the majority and minority views reduced to the question of how far ahead of the present practices of most academic biomedical libraries should the goal be set. An optimum so ambitious that very few, if any, libraries currently even approach it might be dismissed as impractically ambitious and "futuristic;" whereas, one that had already been fully attained, or surpassed, by some libraries would certainly not constitute a challenging goal for the best libraries. The minority member proposed a way, not only to resolve this dilemma, but also to arrive at a weighting scheme acceptable to the whole group without additional group sessions. Since spending time to settle all remaining differences among the majority members would be of marginal utility because these differences were already small, and since attempting to eliminate the gap between majority and minority views by discussion was likely to be unproductive, it was proposed that, for each of the 187 alternative policies represented in the inventory, the median of the five individual weighting schemes be adopted as the group value. This proposal, which the majority endorsed enthusiastically, meant that the final value for each alternative would be influenced to some degree by the minority scheme, but not so drastically as to make the result unacceptable to the majority, as might happen with an arithmetical average. Once this was settled, there was a brief discussion of how to assess service policies for medical students and other user groups when these policies differed from those for faculty. In view of the complex questions involved, and practical constraints on the Task Force, it was obvious that these questions would have to be resolved by some future group, which would have the benefit of descriptive data on differential policies from the present survey. Finally, before the group adjourned, they named one of the present authors (H.B.) as Chairman of the Weighting Task Force and authorized him to act on their behalf in making any decisions that might be required in the course of applying the final weighting scheme to score the survey data.

Final Weighting Scheme

The weighting scheme established by the Task Force is summarized later in this article (see the first two columns of Table 1); the full scheme, together with the materials used to facilitate the weighting exercise (two work-sheets and the weighting conventions adopted) are included in the Appendix.[5] In terms of effort this scheme represents the equivalent of four to five full working days on the part of each member of the group; and it is of some interest to note, in retrospect, that the weights given to the six major service categories in the final scheme differ relatively little from simple averages of the weights individual members had arrived at by the end of the first working session, when they had spent only about half this much time on the exercise. This might seem to indicate that the task could have been finished in less time than it was, and that much the same results could have been achieved, more efficiently, by accepting simple averages of their first efforts, rather than trying to explore reasons for differences by discussion. However, such a conclusion is unjustified for several reasons. First, at the midpoint of the effort, simple averages of weights for subcategories of services differed more widely from the final values; and weighting at the most specific level was still to be done. Second, simple averages of values at the midpoint of the effort obscure the sizeable differences among members that existed then, but were greatly reduced by the time the exercise ended. Last, and most important, without the process of review and discussion, the group would not have had as much confidence that the final scheme reflected their values fairly.

Secondary Editing

Before employing the weighting scheme to score the survey data, the completed Checklists were again inspected for missing data and internal consistency—this time by one of the present authors (G.C.) who, as a member of the field staff, had had extensive experience using the inventory instruments. To clarify questions about the correctness of questionable data, the libraries concerned were contacted as necessary. This round of checking and correcting data could be pursued more exhaustively than was possible during the primary editing phase. However, since there were real constraints on the time that could be devoted to this largely "volunteer" effort, secondary editing concentrated on data relating to service policies for faculty; data on policies for other user groups received little editing attention.

TABLE 1

SUMMARY OF SCORING DATA FOR 92 ACADEMIC LIBRARIES

	Weighting		% Score Relative to Optimal Library**		
	Points Alloted for Optimal Library*	% of All Points Allotted	Range	Median	Mean
Document Services (Sections 1–29)	410	43	45–89	70	69
Citation Services (Sections 30–40)	205	21	12–98	55	55
Answer Services (Sections 41–43)	150	16	13–93	80	70
Instruction and Consultation (Sections 44–47)	75	8	7–100	33	39
Facility Services (Sections 48–50)	50	5	10–100	70	69
Adjunct Services (Sections 51–54)	65	7	0–77	38	35
Overall Services (Sections 1–54)	955	100	38–87	63	61

*This column does not add to 1000 points because of the method employed for combining the weighting schemes of individual numbers of the Weighting Task Force into a group weighting scheme (see "Methods").

**[Sum of points earned on specified sections by faculty services at given library] × 100 ÷ ["Points allotted for Optimal Library" on corresponding sections]

Scoring

Scoring the inventory of a library consisted in assigning the points specified by the weighting scheme to each of the alternatives checked by the interviewer as best characterizing the library's service policy for *faculty*.[6] Although scoring could have been done strictly as a clerical procedure, it was carried out by one of the authors (H.B.) who, as a member of the Weighting Task Force, knew the intent and rationale behind the decisions on relative importance that the weighting scheme expresses. While scoring the inventories according to preestablished, explicit rules, he constantly assessed the resulting scores, to see if they made sense and were consistent with the Task Force's intent and reasoning. In this process, he found some circumstances where the original scoring rules were inadequate. These circumstances were later reviewed with another of the present authors (R.O.), and the rules were revised to accommodate these circumstances. After the scoring had been checked independently by a third individual, who applied the revised rules, a final review of the scoring led to a few further modifications of the rules. The final scoring rules, which, with one exception, are simple and explicit enough to be applied by a computer, are given in the Appendix.

Secondary Analyses

In preparation for the analyses reported here, the inventory data were keypunched selectively. For each of the ninety-two libraries surveyed, keypunched data included: interviewer's code number, length of interview, number of different user groups distinguished by the library for policy purposes, the alternative checked as characterizing policy for faculty on each of the fifty-four sections, corresponding data on policies for medical students, and the score, or points, "earned" by the given faculty policy on each section. After extensive checks for keypunching errors, a series of simple analyses, such as tabulations, and calculation of summary scores combining the points earned on sections subsumed under the six major categories of services and various subcategories, were performed and reviewed prior to carrying out more complex analyses. These analyses were all done by computer. Except for a few special programs written to provide output in a convenient form, only widely available statistical programs were utilized (e.g., Biomedical Computer Programs developed by the University of California at Los Angeles, and statistical programs written by University of Miami). Supplementary, noncoded data written in by the interviewer were selectively analyzed by hand, with emphasis on sections where it seemed likely that write-in data might be especially illuminating or interesting, and on libraries whose policies differed markedly from the norm for a given section. As was inevitable, in carrying out these manual analyses, and in reviewing the simple analytics produced by computer, some additional problems with the primary data were disclosed. Most of the problems at this stage were attributable to weaknesses in the Interview Guide rather than to interviewer errors; and those problems that might distort a library's summary scores significantly were resolved by a final editing of the primary data and by correcting all analytics produced prior to this final round of editing.

As the major results of the secondary analyses are presented and discussed, the analytic method employed will be specified unless it is obvious. In an attempt to satisfy both the readers who prefer a nontechnical exposition and those who want methodologic details, such details will be given as bracketed, highly condensed notes, couched in technical jargon for precision and conciseness, or as mathematical formulas in footnotes to tables.

SUMMARY OF SELECTED DESCRIPTIVE DATA

Plan of Presentation

As discussed earlier, the primary data obtained in the survey, which consist very largely of categorized descriptions of service policies, are difficult to summarize meaningfully, yet concisely. A simple section-by-section tabulation of the frequency with which each of the possible alternatives was checked would be relatively meaningless, or even misleading, without extensive explanation, because exactly what an alternative represents is often clear only within the context of the Interview Guide. Therefore, no attempt will be made here to summarize all the categorized descriptive data. In the Appendix, descriptive data on service policies for faculty are completely "tabulated" on a copy of the Interview Guide by noting, for each policy alternative, the number and percentage of libraries with the given policy. Here we will confine ourselves to presenting partial data from selected sections of the inventory. Choice of what to present was governed by two considerations: First, we chose findings that seemed to be of particular interest at present, or that we felt warranted comments; and second, these findings had to be a type that could be extracted from context and presented simply without distorting their meaning.

Unless specifically noted, all data and comments pertain solely to policies for faculty, which are generally at least as liberal as those for any other primary user group, and the terminology employed for service categories and specific services is that used and defined in the report of the inventory's development[2] or in the Interview Guide itself. In many cases, the primary data are grouped for presentation here, as contrasted to the detailed tabulation in the Appendix, or additional breakdowns of policy alternatives are given that are based on supplementary write-in data; therefore, even for the selected sections, this summary does not necessarily present all the data to be found in the Appendix and often incorporates data that supplement those in the Appendix. To facilitate referring from the text to the Appendix, subheadings in this part of the report show the inventory sections covered.

In presenting these miscellaneous findings, if we followed the convention of scientific writing and treated "facts" and opinions in separate parts of the paper, the reader's task of relating facts and opinions would be greatly complicated. Rather, in this part of the paper, as data are presented, we will intersperse some value judgements regarding policies that are frankly opinions; but to observe the spirit of this useful convention, we will explicitly label these opinions as "*Comments*." We feel it will be useful to comment particularly on policies that seem incompatible with modern librarianship as practiced in the academic biomedical community, even though these policies may, in some cases, have been forced on the librarian by a faculty committee, by university-wide library policies, or by the academic administration. We believe that the opinions expressed in this part of the report are generally coincident with values the Weighting Task Force embodied in the weighting scheme; however, responsibility for these opinions is ours alone.

Document Services

Availability of "In Process" Documents (Section 7)

Ten libraries indicated that they do not, as a *regular* policy, interrupt processing when a document is requested by a faculty member. Although the wording of the interview question was intended to apply only to documents being processed on the immediate premises, and therefore to processing under the library's direct control, this was apparently not completely clear since, in two of these cases, there were write-in notes explaining that processing was done elsewhere. Because of the possibility that this question was also ambiguous to others, we cannot be certain that the answers of the remaining eight libraries did not have a similar explanation; however, since the interviewers were generally conscientious about noting important qualifications to answers, it is unlikely this explanation would cover all eight. *Comments:* Unwillingness to interrupt internal processing routines to meet user needs suggests a confusion of means and ends.

Restrictions on Circulation of Serials (Section 8)

Fifteen libraries put major restrictions on circulation of serials. Grouped in order of decreasing severity of restriction: five do not circulate periodicals at all; five restrict circulation to older volumes (more than four to ten years old), at least for popular titles; and five do not circulate unbound issues. (Limiting circulation of current issues only is not considered a major restriction.) Of these fifteen libraries, four in the first group, one in the second group, and one in the third group provide free facsimile copies, at least of noncirculating materials and within quota limits; however, two libraries in the third group have no copying facilities or services. *Comments:* Drastically restricting circulation of serials markedly increases immediate, assured availability of this critical segment of the literature and also maximizes the total benefit accruing to the entire user population from a given investment in serial resources. Optimally, at least a quota of free facsimiles should be provided in lieu of circulation. Although there may be circumstances that completely rule out even limited free copying, any library that puts major restrictions on circulation of serials should have copying facilities on the premises. For the reasons discussed later, copying facilities outside the library, no matter how close by, do not eliminate the need for on-premises facilities.

Loan Periods (Sections 2, 3)

The most striking finding regarding loan periods was that fully a tenth of all the libraries permit faculty to check out nonserials for either an indefinite, or an extended period (semester or year); and almost as many have a similarly permissive policy on serial loans. Only about half of these libraries recall loans whenever documents are requested by another user. *Comments:* We believe this type of loan policy is a holdover from the past, when departments and individual researchers had no funds to develop working collections of documents they need almost continuously. Making loans recallable does not greatly reduce the loss of general utility resulting from long loan periods; and much of this loss may not be apparent to library staff. One kind of "invisible" loss is represented by users who need a document by a certain time and do not request recall because they cannot rely on recall providing it soon enough to meet the need. Although certain users may be enthusiastic about very liberal policies on loan periods, such policies do not maximize the utility of existing resources to the entire user population and cannot be defended logically unless a library, without sacrificing other services, can afford either to duplicate holdings extensively or to acquire documents useful to only a few individuals.

Routing Serials (Section 29)

Four libraries will route new issues of specific serial titles to individual faculty members; one of these libraries indicated that routing to individuals was being stopped, but routing to departments would continue. *Comments:* The above comments on long loan periods also apply to routing serials, but there seems to be even less justification for this practice, which reduces the general availability of journals at the very time when demand for them is highest. In addition, at least one of the functions previously served by routing serials —alerting individuals to articles of interest to them —can now be served by other means that do not reduce the general utility of the serial collection. (See "Citation Services" below for a description of alerting services provided by some libraries.)

Limits on Number of Documents Checked Out (Section 11)

Eight libraries limit either the number of documents a faculty member can check out at any one time, or the total number he has charged out. None of these libraries has extended or indefinite loan periods. *Comments:* Unless a library is hampered by overly long loan periods, or loan periods are not effectively enforced, there seems little justification for such limits.

Check-Out Procedures (Section 10)

Almost half of the libraries require nothing more than the faculty member's regular institutional identification and perhaps his signature; he does not need a library card, and there is no form to be filled out. The other half require a library card or completion of a check-out form; and seven libraries require both. *Comments:* We consider simple check-out procedures an important user convenience; and modern record-keeping techniques (e.g., embossed plastic identification cards) can be employed to advantage in streamlining check-out procedures while saving the time of both users and library staff.

Types of Copying Service and Charges for Staff Copying (Sections 16, 19, 21)

In about 40 percent of the libraries, faculty has the choice of using self-service copying facilities or asking library staff to make copies; whereas, roughly half provide staff service only. Of the remaining 10 percent, three libraries have only self-service facilities, and seven provide no copying services or facilities. Three of the libraries that offer staff service only have no copying facilities of their own—staff members must leave the library to copy documents. Of the eighty-two libraries that provide staff-copying service, eleven either do not charge faculty members at all for copying library-owned documents, or have policies that eliminate charges to individuals for a significant part of all such copying, e.g., quotas for free copies, not charging for the first X pages copied at any one time, etc. The cost of providing free copies is not completely absorbed by the library in all cases; one library indicated these costs are charged to the School of Medicine budget and another that the school had a special fund to cover such costs. Four of the libraries that do a considerable amount of free copying are among those that have put major restrictions on circulation of serials. Seven other libraries have policies that compensate for restrictions on circulation of serials or nonserial material in various ways—by eliminating or reducing copying charges for such material; by providing staff-copying service for noncirculating materials, but not for documents that circulate; or, in one case where the library has no copying facilities on the premises, by checking out such materials for a short time so that the user may copy them elsewhere. *Comments:* Today one can assume that any health science school has one or more copying facilities for general use, and such a facility may be relatively convenient to the library. Nevertheless, though a copying machine may be "just down the hall," there are important advantages to having copying facilities located on the library premises. Even if the library has only a self-service machine, in addition to being a real convenience to users, it can significantly reduce staff time expended on check-outs actually made only for the purpose of copying documents elsewhere; and it may reduce circulation costs more generally, since some users much prefer to carry a copy of an article away, rather than a bulky bound volume, which they have to worry about returning. At the same time, the general utility of the collection will be increased since more documents will be immediately and reliably available to users. Since a library can provide a self-service machine at no cost to itself, there must be some reason, other than budget limitations, for having no copying facilities at all within the library. For staff-service copying, in addition to most of the above advantages of on-premises facilities, there can be significant savings in labor costs if staff members are not required to carry documents to and from a machine outside the library.

Ordering Documents for Personal and Institutional Collections (Section 28)

A fifth of the libraries order at least some kinds of documents for institutional collections not under their control, and five libraries also order for personal collections of faculty members. *Comments:* Some advantages might be cited to justify ordering for institutional collections, e.g., departmental working collections. This is one way for the library to maintain up-to-date knowledge of total institutional resources and departmental needs, and it may occasionally enable the library to reduce unnecessary duplication of expensive titles by informing would-be buyers of the local availability of such titles. However, these purposes can be served in other ways; and from the user's point of view, centralized ordering has the important disadvantage of usually taking longer. Ordering original documents for personal collections would seem to require special justification where there is a good local bookstore.

I-L Borrowing and Charges (Sections 22, 25, 26, 27)

In keeping with the principle of emphasizing the function served, rather than the means of serving it, the inventory section covering policies on meeting requests for documents not in the library's collection (Section 22) did not distinguish between meeting requests by purchase or by borrowing from another library. Although a number of requests for articles from a given serial may result in a decision to subscribe to that title, and perhaps to acquire back files, the *immediate* need of the requestor is, in almost all cases, better met by interlibrary borrowing; and it seems safe to assume that the policies elicited by this section generally pertain to interlibrary borrowing, except when the document requested is a book currently in print. Therefore, with this qualification, data from this section may be interpreted as applying to I-L borrowing. Almost three-quarters of the libraries stated that they attempt to obtain any document a faculty member needs in connection with his work, regardless of the document's subject matter or its local availability. Roughly a tenth put some limitations on subject matter, and a sixth consider local accessibility; but only a few libraries put both sorts of limitation on this service. Five libraries do not allow faculty to check out original documents obtained on loan, even though the lender does not specify such a restriction. Policies on handling the costs of I-L borrowing vary widely and are complex at some libraries. Without getting mired down in details, these policies can be summarized by saying that forty-one libraries do not attempt to recover any of the "out-of-pocket" costs from the user; forty-three assess charges intended to cover, in whole or part, one or more types of costs, but not all costs. Most commonly, only the lending library's charges for copying are passed on to the user. The remaining eight libraries bill users for all costs, including postage, telephone, wire, and TWX costs. How charges are calculated also varies widely. For example, some libraries assess photocopy charges at a nominal, fixed rate per page, regardless of what the lender's copying charges happen to be; whereas, others bill users for the lender's full charges plus a flat charge for each transaction. *Comments:* This is an area in which policies are changing rapidly as the medical library community evolves toward a national system in which the conventions and values governing interlibrary borrowing differ significantly from those of the academic library community as a whole. The policies of some academic biomedical libraries seem to reflect conventions and values typical of academic libraries in general, which tend to discourage borrowing; whereas others shape their policies to the basic philosophy of regional and national biomedical library systems. Since we are committed to this philosophy, which is embodied in the Medical Library Assistance Act, we view as paradoxical and anachronistic the practice of billing a user for any of the costs of obtaining a document he needs, when his library does not happen to own it. The practice may also be questioned on a practical level. Unless charges are set at such a high level that they significantly deter interlibrary borrowing, billing individual users can cost more than the amount recovered.

Decentralization of Document Services (Sections 4, 5, 14, 15, 17, 23, 24)

Seven sections pertain, in whole or part, to accommodations by which a library can enable users to employ its document services without visiting the library or sending an agent. These accommodations include: accepting mail or phone requests for specific documents; sending these documents to the user's place of work; making renewals by mail or phone; and providing for returns by mail or library messenger, or for convenient drop-points where returns can be left. Detailed data on all seven sections will not be given here, rather we will summarize findings from three sections that seem to be most important. Only about 40 percent of the libraries accept mail and/or phone requests from faculty for specific documents in their collections; of these, two do not accept phone requests, and six require that any written requests be submitted on a library form. In contrast, 85 percent of the libraries accept mail and/or phone requests for documents that are *not* in their collection; and nearly the same proportion of all libraries with staff-copying service honor mail and/or telephone requests for facsimile copies. Explanations offered to field staff suggest that the relatively greater difficulty of packaging original documents for delivery may account, at least in part, for the less common willingness to accept requests that entail delivery of this type of material. *Comments:* At institutions where the library is not located so as to be very convenient for *all* segments of the user population, the various means for decentralizing document services are user accommodations of major importance. Today, health science institutions with widely scattered facilities are the rule rather than the exception; and a careful review of the benefit and cost of extending document services to users' work sites would undoubtedly lead to policy changes at more than a few libraries.

Citation Services

Verifying Citations When No Document Request Is Involved (Section 31)

On request, all but twenty libraries will check at least a limited number of citations for errors and completeness. Forty libraries put essentially no limits on this service; the remainder have established various limits, most of which are rather vaguely specified from the user's point of view—for example, limits defined in terms of a "reasonable" number of citations, a "reasonable" amount of time, or "as staff time permits." Only eight libraries specify relatively precise limits, such as, "a few," "not more than twenty," or "not more than one-half hour." *Comments:* This is an important service to authors, and one that has great "leverage" on the entire bibliographic system since, by improving the quality of published citations, it can reduce the future work of large numbers of users and librarians. Providing some verification service, even though it may be quite limited, is better than no service at all; but both staff and users will be happier when the limits are specified precisely. There are academic precedents for providing service above specified limits at a per citation, or hourly, rate.

Subject Searches (Section 34)

In retrospect, some weaknesses and ambiguities are apparent in the inventory section on subject searches. Interviewers' write-in notes made it possible to correct certain of these defects in editing the primary data; but some uncertainty remains about how many libraries actually do no subject searches themselves but "refer" requests to MEDLARS, and also about what referral means operationally–merely giving a MEDLARS request form to the user, offering suggestions on preparation of a search request that the user submits directly to a MEDLARS center, or taking full responsibility for mediating the request. In view of these uncertainties, the data given here will be limited to some of the findings that can be stated with considerable adsurance. At least fifteen libraries do no subject searches themselves, not even the "quick" variety; they limit faculty services in this area to "guidance," and perhaps locating existing bibliographies. At the other end of the spectrum are six libraries that not only perform exhaustive manual searches but also undertake to evaluate the relative scientific merit of items in the resulting bibliography; with one exception, such evaluation is limited to a single, relatively narrow subject field covered by a specialized information center associated with the library. From the write-in notes, it seems likely that more than two-thirds of the remaining libraries either limit manual searching entirely to quick searches, or put significant restrictions on exhaustive searches. *Comments:* There appear to be large gaps in this service area. The availability of MEDLARS service does not obviate the need for manual searches. First, the great bulk of requests can be met satisfactorily by quick searches that find a small number of pertinent citations; and MEDLARS is not designed to handle such requests. Second, when a truly exhaustive search is indicated, MEDLARS output frequently should be supplemented by manual searches of the older literature and of subject areas and types of documents not covered by MEDLARS. The earlier comments about the desirability of clearly specified limits, and about precedents for library-assessed charges for services above the limits, apply here also.

Alerting Services (Sections 38, 39)

A total of forty-four libraries offer some kind of alerting service, either designed to call attention to new documents in a relatively narrow subject area ("subject-specific"), or tailored specifically to a user's individual interests ("individual-specific"); three of these libraries do not provide individual-specific services and limit themselves to subject-specific services. The wide variety of individual-specific services is particularly interesting. Of the forty-one libraries that offer the latter type of service to faculty, around two-thirds employ manual methods solely, and about half of this group apparently limit their coverage largely to books. On request, these book-oriented services notify individual faculty members of new acquisitions, announcements of new books, or book reviews likely to be of special interest. The other half of the libraries that employ only manual methods attempt to cover journal literature as well by scanning new issues of journals or of *Index Medicus*, keeping in mind the interest profiles of individual users. Fourteen libraries rely on machine techniques almost exclusively; most of these act as the user's agent in buying and mediating one or more of the various computer-based services, such as those sold by the Institute for Scientific Information. A few libraries have acquired the magnetic tapes of one or more national services and run their own computer searches on individual users' profiles. Only four libraries seem to use both manual and machine techniques. About the only general pattern to service charges is that most of the manual services are done without charge; whereas, most, but not all, of the computer-based services entail some charges to individual users or to their departments. *Comments:* The potential demand for individualized alerting services appears to be much larger than that for one-time, retrospective, subject searches. Although it is possible to provide excellent coverage of journal literature, as well as book and technical reports, solely by manual techniques, shortage of the highly skilled manpower required and the relatively high cost per user severely restrict a library's ability to serve all potential users by manual techniques. On the other hand, for computer-based services, the cost per user tends to decrease as the number of users increases; and a given number of skilled staff can serve a much larger number of users.

Decentralization of Citation Services (Sections 32, 36)

Libraries can extend citation service to the user's work site by accepting written or telephone requests for citation verification or for subject searches. Unfortunately, the inventory instructions told interviewers to omit the section on accepting such requests for citation verification when a library indicated that it did not verify citations for faculty when they were in the library. In retrospect, we realize that, in some cases where this section was omitted, the libraries probably do verify citations when the user is not at the library, where he could presumably serve himself. Therefore, the survey findings on this user accommodation only set a lower bound on the number of libraries that accept written and/or phone requests for citation verification—at least eighty-eight libraries do so, and 80 percent of these accept both phone and written requests, though they may put more severe limits on phone requests. The section covering in absentia requests for subject searches did not have this defect; and of the sixty-nine libraries that accept such requests, five prove to be institutions that do not perform staff searches for in-person users. All but ten of these sixty-nine libraries honor both written and phone requests. *Comments:* Citation services of very frequently needed types (verification of a few citations, and quick subject searches) lend themselves particularly well to decentralization by telephone since, unlike document services, the "product" of these services can be delivered by the same medium; and often the entire transaction can be completed in less time than would be required for the user just to come to the library.

Acting as User's Agent in Tapping Other Resources (Section 40)

In addition to decentralization, libraries can extend their services, in a different sense, by acting as the user's direct agent to obtain what he needs from other resources when their own resources cannot fill the need. In acting as the user's agent, the library plays a much more active and responsible role than when it merely refers the user to another resource. As his agent, the library communicates his need and makes all necessary arrangements. Interlibrary borrowing is the prototype for this mode of extending services, which we will refer to as "coupling" with external resources. For citation services, the analog of borrowing from another library is calling on another resource to verify citations, conduct subject searches, provide alerting services, etc. Clarifying and refining a user's request for a subject search, completing a MEDLARS request form, and forwarding it to the appropriate MEDLARS center is a good example of this mode; another example is developing an appropriate interest profile for an individual and arranging with some organization for an alerting service tailored to his profile (see "Alerting Service" above). The library may or may not absorb charges for external citation services it arranges. Only a quarter of the libraries indicated that, as a regular policy, they utilize external resources (other than MEDLARS) in this manner to extend their own citation services. This low proportion is less surprising when one considers that citation verification was not explicitly covered in the wording of the inventory question, since it was assumed that almost all libraries will request help from other resources when they do not themselves own the bibliographic tools required to verify a particular citation. *Comments:* The continuing development of regional biomedical library systems, and the increasing number and variety of computer-based special services, will undoubtedly lead to rapid changes in policies regarding coupling to extend citation services; however, for the services that have a large potential demand, such as, individualized alerting services, there is a trend toward academic biomedical libraries' acquiring computer tapes prepared by others and using them as bibliographic tools different in form, but not in function, from the traditional printed tools.

Answer Services

Depth of Services (Section 41)

At least when users are at the library, over a quarter of the libraries limit their answer services for faculty to guidance or to answering only questions of "simple fact," which can be satisfied by a simple look-up in a single, standard reference tool, such as, a directory, dictionary, almanac, textbook, etc. Roughly half of all the libraries provide the next higher level of answer services and will also prepare "simple summaries" that involve the collection and synthesis of simple facts from multiple sources, e.g., a short biographical sketch based on several supplementary sources. The remaining libraries provide, in addition, a third level of service by answering questions that involve "complex facts"–where data or information from different sources are conflicting, and it is necessary to compile, compare, and contrast in preparing the answer. *Comments:* Concepts of the "health team" and the "research team" dictate that a given task be performed by whichever member of the team can do it most effectively or efficiently. As librarians come to be more commonly regarded as members of these teams, the demands for answer services at all three of the above levels will increase. That faculty members currently rely on personnel much less effective and efficient than librarians to obtain answers from the literature belies the myth that "they really want to do all their information work themselves."

Decentralization of Answer Services (Section 42)

All except four libraries allow faculty members, when they are not on the premises, to send in or phone in requests for answer services; but six of the libraries that accept such requests require that they be written. The structure of this section of the inventory does not allow one to determine with any assurance whether the level of service offered to in absentia users differs from what is provided when users are at the library and, in theory, can find their own answers. However, the write-in notes suggest that a number of libraries will do considerably more for in absentia users. *Comments:* Needs for quick answers to questions of simple fact that can be provided easily, given skilled staff and a well-chosen collection of reference tools, arise very frequently in the day-to-day work of many faculty members. To properly accommodate such needs, phone service is required. There would seem to be few other services that can earn more user appreciation at a comparable cost.

Coupling with External Resources (Section 43)

Over half the libraries indicate that they customarily act as the user's direct agent to obtain from other resources answers they can not supply. It appears that coupling for answer services may be somewhat better developed than for citation services. However, the write-in data suggest that coupling is utilized very largely for questions of simple fact, rather than for the higher levels of answer services.

Instruction and Consultation Services[7]

Instruction in Use of Information Resources (Section 44)

The instructional effort of academic medical libraries concentrates on medical students; therefore, for this section, our summary of descriptive data and comments will focus on services to medical students rather than faculty. Twenty-one libraries provide "formal" instruction (defined as required or elective courses) designed to help medical students learn to make optimal use of information media and resources; only six also offer a course for faculty members. At over half of these twenty-one libraries, the courses rely solely on passive instructional methods–lectures, assigned readings, etc.–as contrasted to methods that require the active participation of students, such as, small group seminars, practical exercises, and programmed texts. In most of the libraries that offer only "informal" instruction, aside from *ad hoc* help, such instruction consists of an orientation tour or lecture that, in about half the cases, attempts to touch upon some of "newer" types of information media and resources–such as, audiovisual materials, technical reports, citation indexes, computer-based services, and specialized information analysis centers–as well as covering the more traditional media and resources. *Comments:* Instruction is an area where there is great room for improvement. The usual orientation tour or talk accomplishes little that cannot be done better by a good written guide to the library and its services; and passive instructional modes are still as inadequate for teaching optimal use of information resources as Billings implied in 1881:

> Instruction in the history and literature of medicine forms no part of the course of medical education in

English and American schools; nor should I be disposed to recommend its introduction into the curriculum if it were to be based on French and German models [reliance on formal lectures] . . . The way to learn history and bibliography is to make them—the best work of the instructor is to show his students how to make them[8].

Help with Users' Systems (Section 46)

As a regular service, twenty-one libraries go further than merely providing *ad hoc* suggestions when a faculty member requests help in developing, organizing, or maintaining his personal library or files. Such additional help includes, at a minimum, consultation based on systematic study and analysis of his specific problems.

Facility Services[9]

Provision of Work Space for Users (Section 48)

In seven libraries, a user is expected to occupy seating space only when he is doing work that cannot be done elsewhere (e.g., work requiring use of noncirculating materials); twenty-three have less stringent limitations but expect the user to occupy seating space only when his work requires some use of library materials or staff services. The remainder, *as a matter of policy*, provides space for a variety of other kinds of activities (e.g. study and writing in general, meetings of small groups, etc.) *Comments:* If one assumes such restrictions reflect necessity, rather than philosophy regarding what library space should be used for, the fact that almost a third of all the libraries find it necessary to ration available space in this way is convincing evidence that at least this many libraries, and probably more, suffer from a truly severe shortage of user space.

Adjunct Services

Nonprint Services (Section 52)

Nearly 60 percent of the libraries handle one or more types of nonprint materials (defined to include films, photographs, audiotapes, phonograph records, models, etc., but to exclude microform copies of written materials). Of the libraries handling such material, about 80 percent loan some or all of these materials for use outside the library; and 20 percent also loan equipment for using these materials. *Comments:* Libraries have long experience in realizing maximal utility from a given investment in printed materials, and many schools have apparently found it both logical and advantageous to give the library responsibility for handling nonprint materials as well. As collections of these materials grow in size, and as their importance to the curriculum increases, the need for librarian skills in handling them will become increasingly apparent. This is a practical consideration aside from the theoretical advantages advanced by the increasingly popular "learning center" concept.

Editing Services (Section 53)

Only twenty libraries offer any editing services to faculty; and in most of these libraries, the service is limited to bibliographic "styling" (distinguished from citation verification in that it involves seeing that citations are in the particular form specified by a given journal or publisher). A few libraries also undertake simple redaction (correcting spelling, punctuation, and grammar); proofreading; editing for accuracy, brevity, and clarity; or compiling book indexes. *Comments:* Bibliographic styling demands a sensitivity to, and a trained eye for, bibliographic form that seems to be rare except in librarians and editors. When citations are being verfied for publication, and the journal or publisher to which the manuscript will be submitted is known, it requires comparatively little additional effort to style the citations appropriately; and this service is greatly appreciated by both authors and publishers.

Differential Policies for Medical Students

Although, for reasons given earlier, the effort of editing and analyzing the survey data had to be concentrated almost entirely on service policies for faculty, data on policies for medical students are accurate enough to mention certain findings that warrant comments. These findings indicate the divergence that exists on whether and how policies for medical students should differ from those for faculty and other major user groups.

Incidence of Differential Policies

The "average" library has different policies for medical students on about a tenth of the fifty-four inventory sections. However, the average obscures large differences—one library differentiates between medical students and faculty on almost half of all the sections; whereas, a quarter of the libraries have differential policies on only one section, or on none. From one section to another, the proportion of libraries with differential policies also varies widely—from half the libraries on one particular section, to none on several sections. On a total of twenty-one sections, six or more libraries provide a materially lower level of service to medical students than to faculty, and only these more common examples of differential policies will be treated here.

I-L Borrowing for Medical Students (Section 22)

Perhaps the most surprising finding is that twelve libraries apparently either will not initiate I-L requests for medical students or limit such requests so severely that they seldom, if ever, borrow for medical students. These libraries generally do not have similarly restrictive policies for graduate students in the basic sciences; and in one case, the head librarian volunteered the explanation that "medical students are not considered graduate students," but the write-in note did not indicate whether the distinction originated with the medical school library or with the university library system. Other write-ins suggest less directly that medical students are not "scholars" in the same sense that graduate students in the basic sciences are; and this distinction may well be made by other libraries that differentiate between medical and basic science students with regard to I-L borrowing. *Comments:* While it is true that, in the past, medical students at many schools may not have had much need, or time, for reading "exotic" literature, this is changing rapidly. The policy of not considering medical students eligible for interlibrary loans is not only contrary to the spirit and letter of the Medical Library Assistance Act, but it is also difficult to justify from the viewpoint of educating them to utilize library resources optimally. How can they appreciate the power and speed of today's medical library system in delivering almost any document unless they have experienced it?

Possible General Rationales for Differential Policies

For a crude analysis to explore possible general rationales, the twenty-one sections where differential policies are more common can be classified into five mutually exclusive groups: (1) those relating to decentralization of services (Sections 4, 17, 23, 24, 32, and 42); (2) those relating to coupling with other resources (Sections 22, 40, and 43); (3) sections where educational values may conceivably be involved (Sections 31, 34, 38, 39, 41, and 53); (4) sections where policies might reflect an unfavorable assessment of medical students' sense of responsibility (Sections 19 and 20); and (5) the remainder (Sections 7, 16, 46, and 50), which fit into none of the previous groups. The relatively common incidence of differential policies on sections in the first group is largely accounted for by the fact that roughly one-tenth of the libraries seem to pursue a rather consistent general policy of not decentralizing *any* type of service for medical students, as opposed to faculty. The incidence of differential policies falling in the second group cannot be accounted for similarly since there is no common core of libraries that consistently follows a general policy of not acting as medical students' agent in obtaining *any* type of service from other resources; libraries that do not borrow for medical students may very well act as their agent to obtain citation or answer services, if they do so for faculty. In the third group, where differential policies might possibly reflect a philosophy that students should learn by doing things for themselves, the proportion of libraries with such policies varies from one section to another. For example, of the libraries that do some kind of subject searches for faculty, only half also do so for medical students; but not verifying citations for students is a policy followed by approximately a quarter of the libraries that provide this service to faculty, and a similar proportion has differential policies on providing answer services. However, there is a small core of libraries that rather consistently differentiates between faculty and medical students on all sections in the third group. The two differential policies falling into the fourth group are: requiring medical students to pay cash for staff copying and for self-service copying, when faculty have the option of being billed for these same services. The final group includes such differential policies as not interrupting internal processing to meet students' document requests, and not providing staff-copying services for students; each of these policies are followed by roughly one-tenth of the libraries, but not the same tenth.

Comments on Rationales

As sending original documents to students outside the library may pose special problems at some schools, this may be a special rationale for differential policies on receiving requests from, and sending loans to, students' work sites; but a similar rationale fails to explain differential policies of not allowing students to return loans without coming to the library, not accepting in absentia requests from students for facsimile copies when staff-copying service is provided to them at the library, or not decentralizing any of the citation and answer services that are offered to students. For differential policies on any service that entails coupling with another resource, a conceivable explanation is the belief that it is somehow "improper" to call on other resources to meet medical students' needs, which appears to be the case for interlibrary borrowing at some libraries (see above); but the lack of consistency in a given library's policies on coupling tends to rule out any such general idealogical basis for differential policies on coupling. In contrast, at least some of the differential policies on citation verification, subject searching, and provision of answers are probably based on the philosophy of librarianship that emphasizes the educational value of self-service. This philosophy will not be argued here.[10,11] Another rationale is sometimes offered for differential policies on these and other services in the third group (e.g., on alerting and editing services)—namely, that a given service is not offered to students simply because they never ask for it; but this rationale is weak in several obvious respects. If the differential policies in the fourth group are based on the premise that medical students, as a group, are not fully responsible adults, these policies and any others based on this premise should be reexamined. If policies for every user group were designed primarily to prevent abuses by less responsible members of the group, services for faculty would be severely restricted. We are left with the impression that the primary aim of differential policies in general, aside from those falling in the third group and the few other exceptions noted, must be to save staff time and effort for other purposes. Various reasons have been offered for giving faculty top priority on available staff resources by restricting services to other groups, principally students; but aside from political reasons or external dictation of policy, these reasons seem to reduce to one basic argument—that services to faculty are more important in that they result in greater "benefit" to the school or society. The reasoning that medical students have more time than faculty is equivalent to saying that their time is not as valuable; and this reduces to the "greater benefit" argument. Now the "greater benefit" argument may be tenable, at least for some services and under some circumstances; but this rationale should be made explicit so it can be subjected to objective examination and careful assessment of all the values involved, and so it can stand or fall on its own merits. Later, we will present some results of exploratory analyses made in an attempt to determine whether, and how, differential policies may be associated with manpower and budget limitations.

COMPARISONS WITH DATA FROM OTHER SURVEYS

Surveys Prior to 1960

Relatively complete data are available from two systematic, objective surveys of U.S. medical school libraries that were carried out before 1960 and covered user services in some breadth and detail.[12,13] In 1952, the Medical Library Association's Committee on Criteria for Medical School Libraries sent questionnaires to libraries serving the eighty-two four-year and ten two-year medical schools operating at that time: eighty-nine questionnaires were returned. A preliminary report was published[14]; but unfortunately the final report, which contained more definitive and complete results, appeared only in mimeographed form.[15] This survey, although it focused mainly on the usual concerns of library surveys—size and qualifications of staff, size and types of user groups, and details of holdings—included a number of questions designed to obtain quantitative or descriptive data on a relatively broad spectrum of user services. These questions related to matters covered in eight of the fifty-four sections of the inventory procedure employed in the present survey. The next survey treating user services in any detail was conducted by Register in 1959,[16] who mailed a checklist type of questionnaire to eighty-two libraries serving U.S. medical schools and received sixty-seven completed questionnaires. Her checklist included some 138 "services," which were derived from an exhaustive search of the literature and were grouped into eight major categories. The approach differed from ours in that her emphasis was on what librarians do rather than on the user function served. Only about one-half of the librarian activities she listed as services are directly related to user services as we define such services,[2] and this half is redundant in our terms since several activities often serve the same basic function. Only a few of the user services she covered are not also represented explicitly in the present inventory of services: and the latter covers several types of services not represented in her checklist, e.g., loan services, paging services, and facility services.

A Recent Survey

There seems to have been only one more recent survey that included either most medical school libraries or a random sample of such libraries, covered user services in some breadth and detail, employed objective techniques, and reported data relatively completely. In April 1967, a little less than a year before the field work of the present survey, and while the instruments for that survey were being developed, Colaianni and Lewis mailed a questionnaire on "reference" services and practices to the libraries of ninety-three U.S. medical schools and received completed questionnaires from eighty-five.[17] Their questionnaire-checklist focused primarily on obtaining descriptive, and in some cases quantitative, data on the various activities the "reference" staff of an academic library may carry out, as contrasted with the totality of user services the whole library may offer. The items in their questionnaire correspond, in part, to thirteen of the nineteen inventory sections that are subsumed under citation, instruction and consultation, and adjunct services, and to three of the twenty-nine sections subsumed under document services (those relating to copying services and charges, and to routing serial titles).

Lack of Comparability Among the Surveys

Given four more-or-less overlapping surveys of the same group of libraries done at various times over a sixteen-year period, one might expect that at least some data from the different surveys would be suitable for comparisons to identify changes and trends during this period, which was a most dynamic era for medical schools and the libraries serving them. Unfortunately, it turns out that very few direct comparisons can be made with any real assurance. Some specific reasons for noncomparability were implied in describing the three other surveys. The most important general reasons are that the operational meaning of many terms employed in the previously reported surveys is not clear from the context of the questionnaires[18] and, where meaning is clear, services are often broken down differently so there is very little one-to-one correspondence of the respective data. Some of the questions used in the 1952 survey were admirably clear and precise; but, as mentioned earlier, the area of overlap with the present survey was quite limited. In scope and level of specificity, Register's survey was most similar to the present survey; however, a crucial difference makes comparisons between these two surveys of limited value. Her respondents were instructed, "If you offer a service at all, check it regardless of whether it is offered always, frequently, or only occasionally;" whereas, in the present survey, it was emphasized throughout that only the *regular* policy, applicable to all members of particular user group, was desired. Because of this difference, on many of her items that appear at all comparable with sections of the present survey, the 1959 data would be interpreted as indicating materially higher levels of service than existed in 1968 if one made the mistake of equating what a library will do occasionally, with what it will do regularly. Only relatively small changes would be expected during the short period between the 1967 survey and the present one; and, on the few points where data seem reasonably comparable, the differences are small enough to be explained by minor differences in interpretation of questions and the fact that the 1967 data include only eighty-five of the ninety-two libraries covered in the present survey.

Trends in User Services

Any attempt to "adjust" data from the different surveys to make them comparable would require many challengeable assumptions; and a formal analysis of such adjusted data for trends would be pseudo-objective at best. However, in reviewing and attempting to compare the data, certain general impressions were formed about gross changes during the period 1952 to 1968 that may be of some value.

Before offering these subjective impressions, some background information on the growth of medical school libraries and the populations they serve is appropriate. From the latest statistics on staffs and budgets that seem to be generally available, those for academic years 1962-63[19] and 1964-65,[20] and from baseline data for 1952,[15] it seems safe to postulate that from 1952 to 1968, allowing for some differences in the definitions underlying the statistics, the average size of professional staffs increased roughly two-fold, and the increase in total staff was somewhat larger. In this same period, the average library budget increased about five-fold. Simultaneously, the average number of students of all types served by these libraries increased between two and three times, while academic research manpower increased roughly four- to five-fold in terms of full-time equivalents.[21]

Now what can be said about changes in services during the period when these marked changes in academic medical libraries and their user populations were taking place, aside from what is common knowledge, e.g., that copying service and nonprint services have become more widely available, and that indexing of serial literature on receipt (which, by our definition, is not a user service in itself) has almost ceased? The general impression is one of relatively few gross changes. Other than the obvious changes already mentioned, about the only sizeable changes suggested by the data are that, since 1952, the proportion of libraries allowing use of work space for purposes not completely dependent on library materials and staff services has increased and that, since 1960 (no data are available for 1952), the proportion of libraries routing serial titles to faculty has decreased. The data available on key citation services—such as, subject searches, citation verification, and alerting services—and on instruction and consultation services, do not show large enough differences to suggest material trends either toward adding new services and user conveniences, or toward restricting services.

Because the earlier data have many gaps, major changes may have been missed in this review, and questions about the comparability of data may have led us to dismiss, as unconvincing, numerical differences that actually represent significant changes. But the hypothesis that, in general, user services have changed relatively little in terms of breadth and depth over the past two decades seems reasonable when one considers that a simple increase in volume of service proportional to the great expansion in user populations, plus inflation, would more than account for the increases in library staff and budget that have occurred. The overall picture we are left with is that increases in staff and budget have gone largely to supporting an increasing volume of service, probably at a decreasing cost per unit of service, rather than to any striking expansion of services.

SUMMARY OF QUANTITATIVE MEASURES

Scores Relative to the Optimal Library

In contrast to the difficulty of summarizing the survey's primary data, when these descriptive data are weighted and thereby transformed into numbers, the results can be expressed very concisely by converting the points "earned" by the service policies of a library into percentage scores relative to the optimal library envisioned by the Weighting Task Force, which would score 100 percent. Table 1 summarizes the national results in terms of such scores. Scores for "overall services" are set in boldface type since this measure, which we will refer to as the overall score, expresses in a single figure the breadth and depth of all services covered by the inventory. This table also summarizes scores on each of the six major categories of services, specifies the inventory sections subsumed under each category, and indicates the weight, or relative value, attached to the category. For the purpose of this report, this particular weighting scheme is a "given;" and no attempt will be made to justify it, except to state that it represents fairly the values of the Weighting Task Force on services to faculty,[22] and that its validity rests ultimately upon their qualifications as "experts."

Overall scores are distributed over a wide range and quite symmetrically on either side of the mean. [A two-tailed Kolmogorov-Smirnov test against a normal distribution with the same mean and standard deviation (10 percent) indicates the null hypothesis cannot be rejected at $P = .20$.] On all except document services, scores on specific categories of services vary even more widely than the overall scores. All this variation indicates that, among academic medical libraries, service policies are far from standardized—in fact, they are about as individualistic as men's heights.

The means for the six service categories constitute a profile of services in U.S. academic medical libraries as a whole. This national service profile shows that document, answer, and facility services are generally well developed, both relative to the optimal library and relative to other service categories; whereas, instruction and consultation, and adjunct services, are generally poorly developed.

Regional Differences

When the country is divided into eleven regions very similar to the areas of responsibility currently assigned to the Regional Medical Libraries, and the overall scores of academic medical libraries within each region are averaged, the regional means vary from 54 percent (seven points below the national mean) for the region including Illinois, Indiana, Iowa, Wisconsin, and Minnesota,[23] to 68 percent (seven points above the national mean) for the South Central Region (Arkansas, Louisiana, New Mexico, Oklahoma, and Texas). Some differences between regional means could be expected to occur strictly by chance; but it is quite unlikely that chance alone accounts for the sizeable differences between these two regional means and the national mean. [With a population mean of 61 percent and standard deviation of 10 percent, the probability that means of random samples of ten and nine libraries, respectively, will vary ±7 percent from the population mean is less than .05 when the sampling fraction is considered.] One can also conclude with reasonable confidence that at least some of the larger differences between regions on overall scores are not the result of chance alone—for example that, on the average, academic medical libraries in both the New England (Connecticut, Massachusetts, New Hampshire, Maine, Rhode Island, and Vermont) and South Central Regions have higher overall scores than those in the East Central Region (Kentucky, Michigan, and Ohio); the region including Illinois, Indiana, Iowa, Wisconsin, and Minnesota; or the region including the District of Columbia, Maryland, Virginia, and West Virginia. [Differences between the means for each of the former two regions, and the means for each of the latter three regions (six differences in all), are significant at $P = .05$ or less on two-tailed t tests using Welch's approximation for t' when Barlett's test for homogeneity of variances indicated the equality hypothesis was rejected at $P = .80$ or less. In addition, all six differences are at least 10 percent, which is the LSD at $P = .05$ for an n equal to the mean number of libraries in these five regions.] If one assumes the interviewers had no systematic bias, the conclusion that there is some association between geographical location and service policies has strong support; but then the question arises as to why such an association should exist. Later this assumption will be examined, and the results of some exploratory testing of hypotheses to explain regional differences will be discussed.

Variation in Service Profiles

Table 2 illustrates how much service profiles, as reflected by scores on the six service categories, may differ among libraries with the same overall score. These five libraries all had overall scores at the national median. As marked examples of this variation, note that Library E has well developed document services but little in the way of adjunct services, and that Library B stresses answer services but has not developed instruction and consultation services to any degree. To facilitate interpretation and comparison of service profiles on another basis, the relative position of each score within the national distribution is indicated by the italicized number, letter, or symbol in parentheses after the score. [Quartiles, rather than deciles, are shown for the service categories that subsume less than ten inventory sections since scores on these categories can take on only a limited number of different values.] On this basis, the profile for Library A can be described as above the national median on citation services and on instruction and consultation, below the median on document and answer services, and at the median on facility and adjunct services; whereas, the pattern for Library C is quite different.

Table 3 displays service profiles for six libraries that had the lowest overall scores nationally and five libraries with the highest overall scores. It can be seen that, even within these two extreme groups, service profiles can vary considerably. For example, the scores on facility services for two libraries in the high group are in the bottom quartile nationally; whereas, one library in the low group ranks in the top quartile on answer services and another is similarly outstanding on adjunct services.

Despite the variation, however, there are suggestions of certain common patterns in the profiles. Within the low group, scores on document and facility services in five of the six libraries are materially higher than overall scores; whereas, a similar or larger disproportion of scores on citation, instruction and consultation, and adjunct services are materially lower than overall scores. In the high group, common features are also present, but less obvious. In three of five cases, scores on answer services are notably higher than overall scores; whereas, most of the scores on instruction and consultation, facilities, and adjunct services are notably lower. Such intuitive impressions

TABLE 2

VARIATION IN SERVICE PROFILES AND SPECIAL INDICES AMONG FIVE LIBRARIES WITH MEDIAN OVERALL SCORES

	Library				
	A	B	C	D	E
Overall Services	63(M)	63(M)	63(M)	63(M)	63(M)
Document Services	66(7)	61(8)	68(6)	71(5)	80(2)
Citation Services	73(2)	61(4)	39(9)	76(2)	56(5)
Answer Services	37(B)	87(+)	87(+)	53(−)	60(−)
Instruction and Consultation	87(T)	7(B)	33(M)	33(M)	60(T)
Facility Services	70(M)	80(+)	80(+)	100(T)	40(B)
Adjunct Services	38(M)	77(T)	69(T)	8(B)	8(B)
Index of Service Balance					
Unweighted*	68(3)	62(M)	64(5)	49(10)	64(5)
Weighted**	76(3)	78(2)	70(5)	64(7)	61(8)
Index of Service Extension†	54(8)	62(6)	66(6)	62(6)	59(7)

Parenthetical letters and symbols indicate whether a value is equal to the national median (M), is in the top quartile (T), second quartile (+), third quartile (−), or bottom quartile (B). Parenthetical numbers show which decile the value falls in; the top tenth constitutes the first decile.

*$[300 - (D_1 + D_2 + D_3 + D_4 + D_5 + D_6)] \div 3$; where D_1 = deviation of relative score on document services from A without regard to sign, D_2 = deviation of relative score on citation services from A without regard to sign, etc.; and A = sum of relative scores on all 6 categories of services ÷ 6

**$[50 - (W_1D_1 + W_2D_2 + W_3D_3 + W_4D_4 + W_5D_5 + W_6D_6)] \div 0.5$; where D_1, D_2, etc., are same as for unweighted index and W_1, W_2, etc., are weights for the respective categories of service expressed as percentage of all points allotted.

†[Sum of points earned on Sections 4, 5, 14, 15, 17, 22, 23, 24, 32, 40, 42, 43] ÷ 290

TABLE 3

CONTRAST IN SERVICE PROFILES AND SPECIAL INDICES BETWEEN LIBRARIES WITH HIGHEST AND LOWEST OVERALL SCORES

	Library										
	Group with Lowest Overall Scores						Group with Highest Overall Scores				
	F	G	H	I	J	K	L	M	N	O	P
Overall Services	38(10)	39(10)	41(10)	42(10)	43(10)	43(10)	79(1)	79(1)	80(1)	84(1)	87(1)
Document Services	65(7)	60(8)	52(10)	45(10)	60(8)	49(10)	83(1)	83(1)	89(1)	84(1)	83(1)
Citation Services	15(10)	12(10)	34(9)	51(6)	22(10)	24(10)	88(1)	85(1)	78(2)	90(1)	98(1)
Answer Services	13(B)	47(B)	13(B)	53(−)	47(B)	93(T)	80(M)	93(T)	87(+)	93(T)	93(T)
Instruction and Consultation	7(B)	7(B)	33(M)	7(B)	20(−)	7(B)	53(+)	60(T)	60(T)	80(T)	87(T)
Facility Services	60(−)	50(−)	60(−)	60(−)	60(−)	30(B)	80(+)	40(B)	30(B)	80(+)	70(M)
Adjunct Services	15(−)	8(B)	54(T)	0(B)	8(B)	8(B)	46(+)	46(+)	69(T)	54(T)	77(T)
Index of Service Balance											
Unweighted	56(9)	57(8)	71(2)	57(6)	61(6)	52(9)	70(3)	62(M)	68(3)	82(2)	84(1)
Weighted	49(10)	53(9)	74(4)	68(M)	61(8)	56(9)	73(4)	65(7)	68(M)	85(1)	87(1)
Index of Service Extension	26(10)	31(10)	14(10)	40(10)	36(10)	57(7)	95(1)	98(1)	91(1)	95(1)	93(1)

See Table 2 for explanatory notes.

may, of course, not be confirmed by a formal analysis for patterns characteristic of the extreme groups, which has not been done in this instance; therefore, they should be considered merely as suggestive leads that it may be fruitful to explore. However, regarding general relations between category and overall scores over the entire range of the latter, more definitive statements can be made. After allowing for the fact that some service categories can be expected to be more closely related to overall scores than others because of the differential weighting built into the latter measure, it is apparent that scores on citation, answer, and adjunct services tend to be more predictive of overall scores than might be expected; whereas scores on the other categories have little or no relation to overall scores other than what is built in by differential weighting. [After observed rho's are crudely corrected by subtracting the expected correlations, residual correlations for the above variables are .30, .27, and .26, respectively, all of which are significant at P = .05 or less when n = 92.]

Index of Service Balance

By inspecting Tables 2 and 3, it can be seen that the service profiles of some libraries appear more balanced than the profiles of others in that the six service categories are more evenly developed—for example, all category scores for Libraries H and P (Table 3) are relatively uniform. Though the overall score summarizes, in a single figure, one aspect of the information conveyed by the service profile, it gives no information on this other aspect of the service profile—the degree to which the various categories of services are evenly developed. The "index of service balance," whose values are given in Tables 2 and 3, represents a crude way to summarize the latter aspect numerically. In its unweighted form, this index reflects how closely scores on different service categories agree; and its value varies from 100 percent when all six scores are identical, to 0 percent when they are maximally different. In this form, the index simply quantifies the general impression one gets by inspecting a service profile; for example, the values of the unweighted index for Libraries H and P confirm the intuitive impression of relatively even development. In its weighted form, this index does not have such a clear intuitive meaning, since deviations from even development are weighted to reflect the relative importance of each service category; but it accommodates the notion that deviations on some service categories (e.g., adjunct services) are not as important as on other categories (such as, document services).

If one postulates that an even development of services has some merit in itself and that, among libraries with the same overall score, the library with the most evenly developed services is the "best,"[24] then the index of service balance has another use, aside from merely being a convenient way to express an aspect of service profiles different from that reflected by the overall score. Theoretically, given enough manpower and money, any library could achieve a perfect overall score, that is, it could become the optimal library as far as service policies are concerned. In reality, however, these resources are always limited, and one of the central problems of library management is to develop services in such a way as to maximize the benefit that can be realized within these practical constraints. (The other central problem can be viewed as that of obtaining the support required to increase the library's contribution to the community it serves.) Assuming that the overall score is one valid, though indirect, measure of benefit, given the postulate regarding the desirability of evenness of development, the index of service balance becomes a secondary measure of benefit, which supplements the overall score. Although the manpower and money available at a given time may put an upper limit on the overall score a library can achieve, even with the best management, these practical constraints do not similarly limit the index of service balance—a library whose budget is small relative to its service load can still rank high on this index although its overall score may not be outstanding. The index of service balance (unweighted or weighted) turns out to be almost independent of the overall score. [The small correlation coefficient between overall scores and these two measures (rho = .21 for the unweighted index and .26 for the weighted index) appears to be attributable to inherent constraints on the index at the highest and lowest overall scores, since rho approaches zero over the mid-range of overall scores.] Some other properties of this index will be discussed later.

Index of Service Extension

The last index shown in Tables 2 and 3 represents an attempt to express numerically the degree to which a library extends its services by means of both decentralization and coupling. (These terms, and the concept of extension of services by these means, were introduced earlier in summarizing the descriptive data.) Originally, nine inventory sections (Sections 4, 5, 14, 15, 17, 23, 24, 32, and 42) were selected from the sections bearing directly or indirectly on decentralization, and an index of decentralization was calculated in such a way that its value would be 100 percent if a library's policies matched those of the optimal library; an index of coupling was similarly calculated based on three key sections bearing on coupling (Sections 22, 40, and 43). In exploring the relations of these two indices with category and overall scores, a few interesting findings were disclosed, for example, that the index of decentralization tends to be higher when the score on facility services is low [rho = –.24], which neatly fits with one's reasoning that libraries cramped for user work space would be more likely to decentralize their services. However, the separate indices for decentralization and coupling seemed to have no important advantages for most purposes; and they were therefore combined to form the present index of service extension.

The composite index proves to have several interesting and potentially useful properties. In scanning Table 3, one gets the impression that values for the index of service extension tend to be closely related to overall scores, and the impression is confirmed by a formal analysis. This index turns out to be a much better predictor of overall scores than would be expected solely on the basis of the weighting of the twelve sections it encompasses. If one's sole purpose were to rank libraries on a single overall measure, a greatly abbreviated version of the inventory containing only these twelve sections, rather than the fifty-four sections of the complete inventory, would give very roughly the same ranking as the regular overall score. [For this index versus overall score, rho = .83; and after a correction for expected correlation of the type described earlier, rho = .32. When the coefficient of determination is analogously corrected, the residual is .38.] Relations between this index and category scores are not particularly interesting except that there is a significant tendency for this index to be high in libraries where the adjunct services are well developed [rho = .24]. The simplest explanation of both the overall predictive power of this index and its special relation to adjunct services is that libraries tend to extend their services, and develop the adjunct services, after the highly weighted and more "basic" service categories (document, citation, and answer services) have been relatively well developed, or what is much the same—when they have sufficient resources to do all these things simultaneously. However, as will be seen later, an adequate explanation for any phenomenon encompassing a wide spectrum of services is likely to be considerably more complex than this.

EXPLORATORY ANALYSES

Complexity of Factors Influencing Service Policies

In most large libraries of any age, the collective set of written and unwritten service policies represents many separate decisions made at different times, usually by several individuals, and frequently on an *ad hoc* basis. Such collections of rules do not lend themselves handily to objective, quantitative analyses aimed at finding simple explanations for why marked differences should exist among libraries serving much the same types of users and, more specifically, why a particular library should have the service policies it does. Even if each year a complete, internally consistent set of service policies were established de novo by decisions of a single individual, who systematically assessed the relative cost-benefit of all possible alternatives with a view to maximizing the benefit that can be realized from the manpower and money available during the coming year, the resulting set of policies would defy simple explanations. Even under these ideal conditions, a host of factors will influence the decision process.

Without attempting to identify all these factors, their number and complexity can be suggested by grouping them into four broad classes according to whether they pertain to: (1) the user population (types, numbers, needs, habits, expectations, etc.); (2) the library's environment (physical accessability, characteristics of other intrainstitutional resources and of local and regional resources, relations with these resources, availability of computer facilities, etc.); (3) library characteristics (staff capabilities, physical facilities, size of collection, budget, etc.); (4) personal characteristics of the decision maker (training, experience, values, competencies, personality, etc.). For any real set of service policies, a variety of other things further increase this complexity, such as, what the library has done in the past, externally dictated policies or external constraints on the library's possible courses of action, and the fact that in most large libraries several individuals, separately or jointly, make decisions on service policies.

A final major complication adding to the difficulty of employing formal analyses to gain understanding of the "whys" is the fact that, for studying service policies, like behavioral phenomena in general, the easy and most natural mode of analysis–studying one factor at a time while ignoring all others–is seldom very illuminating and, worse, may be misleading. This mode of analysis assumes that each factor's effect is independent of the effects of other factors. Now, one can immediately think of numerous examples where this is obviously not true for library policies. For example, although an increase in the manpower and money available to a library could make possible an increase in depth and breadth of services, whether and to what extent it actually does depends on many other things, including how the size and nature of the user population may be changing, whether the librarian puts a higher value on building a collection than on expanding services, whether the library has been grossly under-funded for years and has accumulated a large housekeeping "deficit," etc. A practical consequence of the multiple influences on service policies is that more complex modes of analysis are required, and these are considerably more time-consuming and expensive, even when computers and ready-made programs for complex analyses are readily available.

Decision to Undertake Exploratory Analyses

Despite these difficulties, we decided it was important to attempt to see what might be learned about the whys before reporting the survey data. Some of the reasons for this decision are: first, the conviction expressed earlier in this article, and elsewhere,[25] that survey data *per se* have strictly limited value; second, the realization that the present survey data were uniquely well suited for such an attempt because they could be expressed in numbers reflecting the relative desirability of different policies and because they covered policies comprehensively, yet in considerable detail; and third, the fact that very few studies of library services have employed other than purely descriptive analyses, such as, simple tabulations, averages, etc. From the outset, it was apparent that the practical constraints on our effort would limit what could be done, and also that it would not be possible to collect appropriate data on each of the above four classes of factors, as would be required for any definitive study. We therefore settled for doing a strictly exploratory study, utilizing what data were readily available, in the hope that our results would suggest the promise of this approach and would stimulate definitive efforts to exploit the survey data.

One of us (R.O.) had previously worked extensively with the data on academic medical libraries published in 1966 by the Medical Library Association's Committee on Surveys and Statistics,[20] and these data had already been key-punched. These data pertain to the academic year 1964/65, three years prior to the present survey; however, they were the latest readily available data for the population of libraries included in the present survey. Of the four classes of factors that may influence policies, these statistics (which will be referred to hereafter as "MLA statistics") cover the third class fairly completely, include data on a few factors in the first class, but have very little direct or indirect bearing on factors in the second and fourth classes. Although the obsolescence of the MLA statistics, and their serious inadequacies for our purposes, considerably reduced the chance for obtaining impressive results with a limited effort, we reasoned that, if a small exploratory study employing such poorly suited data should produce any interesting results, this would be rather convincing evidence that definitive studies would have real value. On the other hand, if nothing of interest turned up rather quickly, the effort could be dropped and little would have been lost. Somewhat to our surprise, the early results were encouraging enough to warrant continuing to the limit allowed by practical constraints. Some of the results will be described.

Factors Related to Scores and Indices

The simple hypothesis, that overall scores might be related in some way to whether the school was private or state-supported, could be quickly discarded; when libraries were divided into two groups on this characteristic, the mean overall scores were almost identical. The next step was to explore how overall scores are related to a battery of characteristics, or variables, selected from the

MLA statistics. On the basis of previous experience with these statistics, the large number of variables included in this compilation were known to be highly interrelated.[25] As working with all these variables was impractical, a battery of ten was selected that seemed to cover key aspects of a library's operation and user population—total number of students in all schools served by the library, total faculty of these schools, number of professional library staff, total number of library employees, total professional salaries, head librarian's salary, total salaries and wages, total budget, total volumes, and number of serial titles currently received. The MLA statistics cover only seventy-nine of the libraries included in the present survey; and for twelve of these libraries, data on one or more of these ten variables were missing. The remaining sixty-seven libraries with complete data served as the "sample" for most of the analyses that employed the MLA statistics. This sample appears to be reasonably representative, and the overall scores of the libraries in this sample do not differ materially from those of all ninety-two libraries. [Sample mean and standard deviation are the same as for all ninety-two libraries—61 percent and 10 percent, respectively.]

The simplest mode of analysis, where only one variable at a time is considered, indicated that the only one of these variables materially related to overall scores was the total number of students; and this relation was a negative one—among the libraries with more students, there was a moderate tendency toward lower scores. Contrary to what we expected, there was apparently little or no relation between overall scores and professional staff, total employees, or budget. [Rho for total students versus overall score = −.40, significant at P = .01 when n = 67; for the other nine variables, rho did not exceed ±.15.] If taken at face value, this finding would suggest that a library's resources, including its staff and budget, have little influence on the breadth and depth of services it can offer; but this is obviously nonsense. Various ways of "unmasking" the influences of variables other than the total number of students were therefore tried. The tactic of creating new variables that represent ratios between "load" variables (total students, and students plus faculty) and resource variables (professional and total staff, budget, etc.) was not effective; none of these ratios was as strongly related to overall scores as total students alone, and the latter variable still masked any influence of resource variables.

The next step was to try looking at the other variables when the number of students was, in effect, kept constant. This technique was a little more promising, since one could see that, when this load variable was controlled, resource variables such as the number of professional staff and the budget tended to be positively related to overall scores; but these relations were not impressively strong. [Rho's for professional staff and for budget versus overall score were both +.16 when this variable was partialled out.] A "brute force" technique was then tried. With a formula that included all of these ten variables, it proved possible to "predict" a library's overall score within ±9 percent in two-thirds of the cases. [R = .52 for multiple regression on overall score with ten dependent variables, and the standard error of the estimate = 9 percent.] However, roughly two-thirds of the total predictive power of this formula was attributable to a single variable—the total number of students. [R = .44 for a multiple regression with only three variables (total students, professional staff, and serials); but rho for total students = −.44 when the other two are partialled out.]

In a further attempt to disentangle the complex interactions of these variables and the overall score, libraries were grouped according to their overall scores. Those ranking in the bottom quartile on overall score turned out to be serving, *on the average*, more than twice as many students as those ranking in the top three-quarters, but doing so with professional and total staffs of roughly the same size. When only the top quartile is considered, the relation between staff and overall score becomes strongly positive. [Rho = +.56 and +.61 for professional staff and total employees, respectively; n = 16.] But in the other quartiles, these variables are not materially related to the overall score.

From the exploratory analyses that have been described, and others of a similar kind, one can conclude that a library's overall score on services to faculty seems to be more closely associated (in a negative sense) with the number of students served, than with the number of faculty; that libraries serving one or more schools in addition to the medical school tend to be relatively understaffed and to have somewhat lower scores (these libraries average about twice as many students as those serving only a medical school); and that, although libraries with high overall scores tend to have relatively low ratios of total students to library staff, this is not sufficient by itself, since libraries ranking in the middle range had much the same student/staff ratio. It must be emphasized that all these relations are only tendencies and have frequent exceptions. A few examples should suffice to illustrate this point. Three of the nine bottom-ranking libraries serve only the medical school, and one of the five highest-ranking libraries serves several health-science schools. Among the twelve libraries with the lowest number of students per library employee, three fall in the bottom quartile on overall score; and among the nine libraries with the highest student/staff ratios, two rank in the top quartile. None of the variables in our battery of library characteristics can "explain" these exceptions. Evidently some important factors are not represented by the 10 variables employed in these explorations. Although we cannot be certain that some of the other variables included in the MLA statistics might not prove more potent than the ones employed here, we have a strong feeling that the critical missing factor, or factors, is probably not represented at all in the MLA statistics.

Others' Attempts to Relate Services to Library Characteristics

One of the very few previous studies that have attempted to find quantitative relations between library services and library characteristics is Register's study, which was referred to earlier in discussing other surveys of academic biomedical libraries.[16] In this very interesting study, as an overall index of a library's services, she used the percentage of the 138 services in her checklist that a library performed at least occasionally. She concluded that there were positive relations between this index and the size of both professional and non-professional staff and also the budget, but she emphasized the complexity and interrelatedness of factors associated with overall level of services. Our reanalysis of her data shows that, for the fourteen libraries ranking highest on her index, the means for the number of professional staff and for budget are indeed materially and significantly higher than for the whole group of libraries. However, these relations are not evident except in this top quintile. With the present survey data, similar differences cannot be demonstrated; in fact, for the top quartile on overall score, the corresponding means are somewhat lower than for the entire group. Since there were such large differences in the survey instruments and approaches (see "Earlier Surveys"), as well as in the measures employed to assess overall level of services, it is impossible to pinpoint the reasons for the difference in findings. Perhaps the fact that our library characteristic data were obsolescent accounts for the difference. However, it seems considerably more likely that differences in instruments and measures account for the different findings; she did not cover the basic document services nor facility services, and her index gave equal weight to each of the 138 services that were covered.

Reasons for Regional Differences on Overall Score

The observed regional differences in overall scores were puzzling; and in looking for patterns that might provide leads to possible explanations, a disproportionate number of libraries with relatively low scores appeared to be located in the largest metropolitan areas. To test this impression, scores for all libraries located in very large metropolitan areas with two or more medical schools were grouped: For this group, which included thirty-four libraries in the Los Angeles, San Francisco, Chicago, Detroit, New York, Philadelphia, District of Columbia-Baltimore, and Boston areas, the mean overall score is 58 percent, or 3 percent lower than the national mean; and this difference is large enough to give one some confidence it is not due to chance alone. [LSD at $P = .05$ is ± 3 percent when the sampling fraction is considered.] But this finding sheds little light on why libraries located in such areas tend to have lower scores. A variety of analyses to explore associations between regional differences and selected library characteristics (total number of students, total library employees, ratio of students to employees, and head librarian's salary) did not provide any good clues. We have pursued, in a tentative fashion, two questions that might help to focus the search for whys. First, is there something about having a number of academic medical libraries concentrated in one area that tends to reduce the probability any of them will develop overall high levels of service? Second, does the existence of large nonacademic medical libraries in some major metropolitan areas inhibit the overall development of academic libraries in some way? The present data are consistent with both of these loosely formulated hypotheses, but refinement and further testing of these hypotheses must await the collection of data on additional variables.

Rationales for Differential Policies

We were interested in seeing whether formal analyses might support our reasoning about probable rationales for differential policies on services to medical students, which was discussed earlier. For initial exploratory analyses, a crude index of "nondifferentiation" was constructed by assigning a value of one to inventory sections where there was no differentiation between faculty and medical students, and a zero value to sections where policies differed for these two user groups, and then averaging these values over all sections[26] so that the index would vary from 100 percent for a library that had no differential policies, to 0 percent when medical students were differentiated from faculty on all sections.

On first thought, it seemed that there should be a negative relation between the overall score and this index if differential policies were primarily a means to husband staff resources so that a higher level of services could be provided to faculty. But when all ninety-two libraries were included in the analysis, there proved to be no overall relation between these two measures [tau = .07]; nor was the index related to any of the ten variables in our battery of library characteristics. These findings weighed heavily against the simple hypothesis. On further thought, however, it became apparent that the hypothesis was naively simplistic in that, when services to faculty are at a low level, relatively little differentiation is possible without denying essential services to medical students; on the other hand, when the level of services to faculty is high, there are more "nonessential" services where differentiation could be practiced. Analyses provided some support for this notion; when only libaries in the top decile of overall scores are considered, there is a strong negative correlation between the two measures—in contrast to the lowest decile, where there is no material correlation. [Rho = −.69 for top ten libraries, and +.12 for the bottom ten.] However, this notion also proves too simple, because it does not explain the fact that, for libraries with overall scores between the two extreme deciles, there was a material and significant positive correlation. [Rho = .26, which is significant at P = .05 when n = 72.]

Since posing progressively more complicated hypotheses in an attempt to "explain" the relation between these two measures had reached the point of diminishing returns, another approach seemed more fruitful. The crude index of nondifferentiation was refined by postulating that the two principal rationales for differentiation of policies were the "educational value" and the "greater benefit" arguments previously discussed. A specific index was calculated to measure differentiation on those sections where the former rationale could apply (Sections 31, 34, 38, 39, 41, 42, and 43), and a similarly specific index was created for the latter rationale (based on Sections 1, 4, 6, 7, 16, 17, 22, 28, 37, 40, 43, 46, and 50). When analyzed over all libraries, both these new indices show a moderate tendency to vary together [rho = +.43]; but there are suggestions that they differ somewhat in how they relate to the overall score. Although both have a strongly negative correlation with overall scores in the top decile [rho = −.66 and −.41, respectively] and, unlike the original crude index, neither are materially related to overall scores in the mid-range, only the second index has a strong positive correlation with overall scores in the bottom decile [rho = +.05 and +.59, respectively]. However, these differences are not as clear-cut as one would like for making a definite statement.

The "brute force" approach of using our battery of ten library characteristics simultaneously in an attempt to "predict" the crude index was not as successful as it was with the overall score; a formula including all these variables had little predictive power. [R = .38.]

The main conclusion from the exploratory analyses of differential policies is that there is some objective evidence for the existence of two distinct rationales for differential policies, but that the rationales appear to be relatively independent of a library's resources and the size of its user population. These findings are not impressive *per se*; but they provide another demonstration that formal analyses with measures derived from inventory results, even with the handicaps of obsolescent and inadequate data, can be employed to gain some understanding of the very complex influences on service policies.

Libraries with No Copying Facilities

Some results of exploratory analyses to see how the 10 libraries with no copying facilities differ from other libraries will serve to illustrate a somewhat different approach to exploiting the potential of the inventory measures by objective techniques. For convenience, this group of libraries will be called Group Y and libraries with such facilities, Group X. To test the hypothesis that Group Y would have a lower overall level of services than Group X, overall scores were recalculated omitting all points earned on any of the sections relating to facsimile copying (Sections 16 through 20). Even after this adjustment, the mean overall score for Group Y was materially and significantly lower than for Group X. [Respective means were 51 and 55 percent, a difference significant at $P = .05$ on one-tailed t-test with separate estimates of variance.] On all the major service categories except document services, the means for Group Y were lower; but the differences were most clear-cut on instruction and consultation services and on adjunct services. [Means for instruction, 25 percent versus 41 percent; for adjunct services, 24 percent versus 37 percent; first difference significant at $P = .01$, and second at $P = .05$, on one-tailed t-tests with separate variance estimates.] When the two groups were compared on the battery of ten variables from the MLA statistics, clear differences were also apparent; on the average, Group Y had more students, but fewer serials, less professional staff, fewer total employees, and lower budgets than Group X. [Respective contrasts, 870 versus 618, 1.0×10^3 versus 1.5×10^3, 3.6 versus 5.1, 7.4 versus 13.1, 72.3×10^3 versus 124.0×10^3; all differences are significant at $P = .05$ or less on two-tailed tests with separate variance estimates.]

Obviously, lack of copying facilities is only part of a larger picture of a group of libraries that are generally understaffed and underbudgeted relative to their service loads. Why they are in this condition is the truly important question; but unfortunately, data on the variables that might suggest some answers are not available at present.

LIMITATIONS OF THE SURVEY DATA

Since we feel strongly that the full value of the survey data can be realized only if these data are used with full appreciation of their limitations, these limitations should be made explicit. The limitations stem from four general sources; the rationale and approach of the inventory procedure itself, the specific instruments employed to carry out the procedure, the weighting scheme and scoring measures, and the implementation of the procedure and scoring.

Inherent Limitations of the Inventory Procedure

Limitations inherent to the procedure itself have been discussed at length elsewhere;[2] here one of these limitations will be recapitulated for emphasis—that the procedure records stated policies regarding services, which do not necessarily mirror actual practices and have no necessary relation to performance in terms of either the effectiveness or the efficiency of the services provided. The inventory is not a substitute for objective, quantitative measures of performance of specific services and tests of specific capabilities, such as the Document Delivery Test,[1] nor for valid and reliable measures of utilization of specific services. Each of these three types of measures has applications for which it is uniquely well suited. The inventory's unique value is for obtaining a comprehensive picture of the breadth and depth of *all* the services a library offers to its individual users. When the day arrives that there are performance, capability, and utilization measures for each of the important services a library provides, then perhaps there will be little or no need for a procedure that elicits and records what libraries *try* to do for users, rather than what they can do *well*. This distinction is important because the gap between "try to do" and "can do well" varies from one library to another, and from one service to another within a given library. Therefore, it is essential to recognize that finding two libraries are similar with respect to their inventory data does not necessarily mean that the quality of all their services is similar. On the other hand, if they are dissimilar on the inventory, then the services they do provide are different—after all, though trying to provide a given service may not be sufficient, it is necessary.

Limitations of the Instruments

Some of the weaknesses of the instruments disclosed in the course of analyzing the survey data were implied earlier in presenting the results; and this report is not the appropriate place for a detailed treatment of these weaknesses. With few exceptions, these weaknesses did not materially affect the validity of the final data, but they added to the editing effort required and probably made the interviewer's task more difficult. In retrospect, several defects are also apparent that led to failure to capture certain useful data. For example, at the time the Interview Guide was developed, the trends toward restricting circulation of serials, and toward liberal quotas for free copying service, were not fully appreciated; and as a result, the inventory structure was not designed to handle adequately these two areas and their possible interactions. Although, given extensive editing, the accuracy of data provided by the present instrument seems adequate for most purposes; some relatively minor revisions, concentrating on sections that accounted for most interviewer errors, will probably increase accuracy and will certainly reduce the need for editing.

Limitations of Weighting Scheme and Scoring

Aside from questions that some academic medical librarians will certainly have regarding the relative values the weighting scheme reflects, the main questions about the weighting seem to be: whether the same group would decide on the same scheme if the exercise described earlier under "Methods" were repeated, or if the procedure and materials employed for the exercise were changed; whether a different group of equally qualified experts would arrive at the same scheme; and whether any scheme based on librarians' values provides an appropriate standard for assessing service policies. There is no definitive way to answer the first two questions, except by realistic trials. Until someone conducts such trials, we can only offer the opinion that weighting schemes produced under these various conditions would differ somewhat in detail, but that the relative importance attached to major categories of services and to key services would not be markedly different. This opinion is based on the experience of the Weighting Task Force in developing the scheme, and on the rather surprising degree of stability these key values showed in pilot trials with widely varying types of librarians and markedly different procedures and materials.[2] Any answer to the third type of question must be based ultimately on personal beliefs. Personally, we feel librarians' values do provide one appropriate standard, and we will argue later that internally-generated standards are the sine qua non of a true profession; but librarians' values do not constitute the only standard. Users' values, similarly mapped, can also be useful for some purposes, which will be discussed.

As to the particular scoring measures employed here to summarize survey data, facilitate comparisons, and make possible quantitative analyses, they are essentially arbitrary; and how "good" they are must be judged solely on how well they serve their purpose. A host of other measures can be devised, and undoubtedly some of them will have advantages over those employed here, at least for specific purposes.

Limitations Attributable to Implementation

Limitations of the survey results caused by imperfections in carrying out the survey, or in preparing the data and scoring, are different in that they lend themselves better to objective and precise assessment. For example, the adequacy of the training of field staff can be judged by the results of the analyses of errors reported below, which show that acceptably accurate data were obtained even though the training period was very brief. However, with longer training, the editing required would undoubtedly be reduced, and the write-in data obtained would probably be more complete.

Possibility of Systematic Errors by Interviewers

It was expected that every interviewer would make at least a few errors in recording policies; but unless an interviewer's errors are systematic in that they tend to be largely in one direction—either to raise or to lower a library's scores—these errors should largely cancel each other out when scores summarizing results on a number of sections are calculated. If an interviewer made systematic errors, and if the systematic bias thereby introduced were significant, not only would scores for the libraries he visited be biased, but regional means might also be biased since libraries were assigned to interviewers largely on a geographical basis and in some regions more than half the libraries were visited by the same interviewer. It was therefore important to try to assess the possibility of systematic errors. This would have been simple if interviewers had been assigned to libraries by some random process, because then differences between the means for the overall scores of libraries visited by each interviewer would indicate systematic biases if these differences were larger than might occur strictly by chance—should an interviewer happen to draw an atypical group of libraries. As it turned out, the means for the fourteen interviewers ranged from 55 to 72 percent, and a different approach had to be devised for assessing whether this variation simply reflected regional differences, or whether there were actually no such differences and the variation was caused by systematic biases on the part of the interviewers.

Approach to Detection of Systematic Errors

As a start, all changes in the originally recorded data made in the course of primary, secondary, and final editing were analyzed. Now, even with extensive editing by several individuals, it is likely that some errors were not detected; however, if one assumes that the undetected errors are not essentially different from those that were caught, then analyzing the latter should disclose any significant systematic biases present. The great majority of these editing changes consisted of correcting interviewer errors; but a few were recoding-type changes made in final editing to compensate for weaknesses in the inventory instrument (see "Secondary Analysis" above under "Methods"). For this analysis, all editing changes were counted as interviewer "errors" because the two types of changes could not always be clearly separated; however, since recoding changes were few in comparison to corrections of interviewer errors, and since the recoding rules were applied uniformly to all interviewers' data, confounding these two types of changes should not affect the outcome materially.

Error Analysis

There were a total of 185 nontrivial editing changes in which the alternative originally checked by the interviewer as best characterizing faculty policy was revised, an average of 2.0 changes per library. (The only trivial change was adding a "skip" mark, where this had inadvertently been omitted, so it would be clear to the keypuncher that a section of the inventory had been skipped as nonapplicable to the given library.) Only 142 of these errors would have affected scoring, since sometimes the incorrect alternative would have earned the same number of points as the correct one. For each library, a "net error" was calculated by subtracting its final overall score from what the score would have been without correcting errors; these values were then summed (taking into account whether the net errors were positive or negative) and averaged to arrive at the mean net error attributable to each interviewer.

Results

The grand mean of all interviewers' net errors was −0.2 percent, indicating that the national mean for overall scores would have been inconsequentially different if the data had not been edited. For individual interviewers, mean net errors ranged from +1.4 percent to −2.5 percent; but were less than ±1.0 percent for ten of the fourteen interviewers. If an interviewer surveyed a large number of libraries, his non-systematic, or chance, errors would cancel each other, and his mean net error would approach zero; whereas, any systematic errors would not. But each interviewer surveyed relatively few libraries; and with such a small number, it is likely that even chance errors will not cancel out completely. In the present case, one can be reasonably confident that the mean net errors of all interviewers are attributable to chance alone, and also that, if there were any systematic biases, they are negligibly small for most purposes. [Standard deviation of mean net errors from grand mean = 1.1 percent; and all interviewers means fall within the 95 percent confidence limits of +2.2 to −2.6 percent (13 d.f.).] The latter point can be illustrated if one takes the observed net errors as estimates of real, but small, systematic biases and adjusts all the regional means for these biases. The maximal adjustment would amount roughly to ±1 percent; and such small adjustments would not materially affect the previous conclusions about regional differences. As an additional check on possible interviewer bias, we analyzed the average time required by each interviewer to complete the inventory procedure, reasoning that those who typically completed interviews more rapidly might make more or different errors. It turned out there is no material relation between length of interview and overall score, number of errors, or size of errors.

Accuracy of Individual Overall Scores

Even nonsystematic errors, however, if not corrected during editing, can affect the accuracy of scores for an individual library; and, although it seems likely almost all errors that would make major differences in overall scores were corrected, we cannot rule out the possibility that the scores of at least some libraries are appreciably inaccurate because of undetected errors. To obtain a rough idea of the accuracy that can be expected, it is first necessary to estimate the probable "size" of undetected errors relative to corrected errors. There is no formal way to arrive at such an estimate, but it seems reasonably conservative to assume that, on the average, the net effect of undetected chance errors will not be more than half as large as the net effect of corrected errors would have been. Given this assumption, in ninety-five out of 100 cases, overall scores should be accurate to within roughly ±3 percent [excluding both tails of the observed symmetrical distribution of corrected net errors (mode = 0, mean = –0.2 percent), and assuming undetected net errors are half as large]. With this accuracy, it is quite unlikely that undetected errors could change a library's ranking on overall score more than one decile up or down. For scores in the top or bottom deciles, even this change is unlikely because both extreme deciles contain a relatively wide range of scores and, in addition, these ranges are separated from scores in the adjacent decile by two and three percentage points, respectively.

UTILITY OF SURVEY RESULTS

Useful applications of the inventory procedure itself have been discussed elsewhere.[2] Here we will focus on the utility of the survey results and address the questions: useful to whom, for what purposes, and when? The last question is appropriate because there are some applications that represent potentialities realizable only after certain additional work has been completed.

Present Managerial Applications

Local Management

Perhaps the most obvious application of the results is as a practical aid in the management of an academic biomedical library. By comparing the policies of his library with the national pattern on each section of the inventory, the librarian and his staff can see exactly how local services differ from national norms.[27] On sections where local policies are significantly more restrictive, an objective review of these atypical policies may indicate that a policy's original justification is no longer valid, that it is inconsistent with other policies, or that it is not in harmony with the desired service philosophy. This review will be sharpened by attempts to answer the question of what special local circumstances make the atypical policy necessary or desirable. A library saddled with undesirable policies not of its own making can use this comparison with national norms to furnish objective evidence to support arguments for changes. The library's overall score, scoring profiles, and special indices provide a basis for a similar process of comparison and policy review, but at a more general level. In addition, these quantitative measures can suggest areas where improvement and expansion of services are most needed; and they lend themselves to crude cost-benefit analyses,[2] and to setting goals for improved services in terms that are meaningful to nonlibrarian administrators. For the latter purpose, a weighting scheme established by a representative group of local faculty may be a valuable adjunct. We will venture the guess that, if the weighting exercise is conscientiously carried out,[28] such user-established schemes for weighting faculty services often will not differ greatly from the present scheme; but demonstrating this fact will greatly improve the validity of the quantitative measures in the eyes of nonlibrarians. Having a weighting scheme established by local users, particularly one that extends to the most detailed level of the inventory, also has the important advantage that it provides an excellent framework to focus discussions between users and staff aimed at identifying areas where values differ and resolving these differences by a process of mutual education.

Management at National and Regional Levels

For management of any national or regional effort to improve academic biomedical libraries—programs managed or supported by government agencies, intraprofessional efforts of the Medical Library Association, and private programs of other interested groups, such as, academic administrators—the survey results have applications closely analogous to those for local management except that attention will be centered primarily on national and regional patterns and norms, rather than the individual library. We will later offer some recommendations for specific actions to apply the results at the national level.

Research Applications

Data from the present survey offer rich opportunities for both basic research aimed at a better understanding of libraries as entities that evolve under complex and often conflicting influences, and applied research/development to improve library services. In the latter category, a host of possible projects could be suggested, varying from modest efforts that can be undertaken by individuals without special support, to ambitious programs involving a team of workers. Here we will confine ourselves to describing briefly certain efforts that are needed to extend the utility of the survey data. Perhaps the simplest effort that could make a valuable contribution is completing the process of editing and tabulating survey data that we began; much of the value of the raw data has not been extracted–for example, the large amount of write-in data, when coded and tabulated, will be a unique source of information on such matters as charges for service, instructional programs, copying equipment, internally and externally produced alerting services, library publications, etc.; and editing and tabulation will make available definitive and detailed information on policies for medical students, house staff, and the other primary user groups for which interviewers recorded data, including the general physician population in some cases. Another needed effort is the establishment of weighting schemes for services to medical students and perhaps other user groups, based on expert librarian's values; the present survey data on these user groups could then be scored and analyzed. A third type of effort required to realize the full potential of the survey data is development of materials and techniques to facilitate and simplify cost-benefit analysis employing inventory measures, which would greatly increase the practicality of this tool for management purposes. In the category of basic research, studies along the general lines we explored so tentatively would seem to have special promise. Studies designed to learn more about the various factors influencing library services, and the interactions among these factors, will be both challenging and rewarding with appropriate data on relevant characteristics of user populations, institutional environments, libraries, and librarians. A practical spin-off from such studies would be predictive formulas providing, for the first time, a sound basis for normative standards[29] on levels of support and on services that are not based on arbitrary assumptions of questionable validity, and that take into account special characteristics of local user populations and institutional environments.

Potential Applications

As we tried to imply in briefly describing some research opportunities, completion of studies and projects such as those suggested will greatly enlarge the range of applications and increase the utility of the present survey data. But full realization of the data's potential value for local and national-level management will require periodic follow-up surveys that will make it possible to assess trends and judge the effects of improvement programs with confidence, given the baseline provided by the present data.

RECOMMENDATIONS

The Case for Profession-Established and Implemented Standards

We believe that librarians' values are not only an appropriate standard for assessing library services, but also that such a profession-established standard should be the basic yardstick *if* there are effective mechanisms to ensure that three essential conditions are met. First, the basic standard must be leavened with the values of the profession's vanguard, which is not necessarily the same as its "elite." Second, the standard must be responsive to the needs and values of users and the biomedical community. Third, it must be revised and updated frequently enough to reflect both material changes in values and needs, and significant new service possibilities opened up by advances in technology and in the organization of local, regional, and national library systems. Now, associated with this belief is the conviction that a true profession can not exist unless its basic standard of performance is internally generated;[30] but it is not necessary to resort to this kind of "special pleading" to justify the belief. One can argue rather convincingly that users, on the whole, do not recognize good library services until *after* they have enjoyed such services; that their experience with library services is very limited in terms of variety and quality; and that their grasp of possible service alternatives is constrained by this narrow experience. These limitations disqualify users for the primary role in establishing yardsticks capable of accommodating the great range that currently exists in quality and breadth of services and also of expressing goals materially beyond the status quo —just as patients are not qualified for the primary role in establishing measures for assessing the quality of medical care.

The important reality, that today the standard-setting role is intimately associated with initiating change, as opposed to suffering it, is recognized in White's eloquent plea for librarians to make their values explicit so that the resulting standard can be employed to formalize decision making.

> Librarians have been unfairly condemmed as being unwilling to consider and accept change. By and large, we are innocent of this charge. What we are perhaps guiltier of is excessive introspection. We attach inherent values to our work in terms of truth, beauty and knowledge, and we usually fail to apply the more mundane and pragmatic yardsticks by which an increasingly technocratic society measures all things, including inherent values. We are offended because government programs fail to support us adequately, while these same government officials loudly proclaim that we are good and needed. We fail to understand that being good and needed is not enough. We are in desperate competition with other programs which are also good and needed.
>
> It is our failure, or rather our unwillingness to place values on what we do and how we do it, and our unwillingness to formalize the hard choices between such sometimes antagonistic factors as monetary resources, bibliographic accuracy, response time, and depth of information access, that make it difficult for us to evaluate the desirability of change. In order to make some reasonable evaluation of the validity of a proposed change, one must first have a basis for measuring and evaluating what one is presently doing.[31]

If the word "government" in this passage is modified to read "government/school," it becomes even more relevant to academic medical librarians.

Means for Establishing and Implementing Standards

Establishing a weighting scheme for the inventory represents a formalized means of making explicit the values attached to services, and conducting, analyzing, and reporting surveys based on the inventory are means for initiating and guiding changes consonant with these values. On the basis of our experience, these two means, or tools, should be in the same hands, since not only must the different activities involved be very closely coordinated, but also the knowledge and experience acquired in one activity is essential for properly carrying out the others. For example, detailed knowledge for the intent and rationale behind the weighting scheme, of how the survey instrument was designed, of how interviewers were trained, and of what problems were encountered by interviewers is important in all the processes entailed in analyzing survey data—from editing to interpretation. This background knowledge provides an appreciation of the strengths and weaknesses of data and procedures that is the best insurance against costly mistakes in performing analyses and, more importantly, against serious errors in interpretation. Likewise, the group that establishes the weighting scheme should have a good appreciation of all the other activities if the scheme, when applied, is to be faithful to their values. The necessity for close interaction among weighting, data collection, analysis, and reporting activities does not mean that the same individuals have to do everything. But there must be effective overlapping if largely different individuals are involved in these four activities.

A Program for MLA

We recommend that the Medical Library Association mount an integrated program for establishing and implementing standards on user services employing the general means described above. The Association itself should take direct responsibility for overall direction and for all key activities since many of working decisions that will be required are too important to delegate to a group not under the immediate control of the Association's elected and appointed officials. Many professional bodies, some smaller than MLA, have successfully conducted considerably more ambitious programs. This central role for the Association is feasible because all of the managerial talent and most, if not all, of the special capabilities needed can be found within the membership. It is also highly desirable, because a broad segment of the membership should be actively involved if the program is to have the widest possible support and acceptance. Although this program may start with the Medical

School Library Group, it should be rapidly extended to cover all major types of biomedical libraries.

Specific Recommendations for Program Activities

To give a more concrete idea of the kind of program envisaged, some specific recommendations for steps in such a program will be outlined without attempting to justify them in detail since the rationale in each case follows from the general line of reasoning developed earlier. Some of these steps can proceed simultaneously.

1. Establish weighting schemes based on "expert" librarians' values that are appropriate for services to medical students, house staff, other major user groups; complete the editing, coding, analysis, and reporting of the present survey data (see "Research Applications" for details). In addition to the report being a valuable contribution, this step will provide the intimate acquaintance with the instrument, raw data, and weighting exercise needed for later steps.
2. Establish user weighting schemes for services to faculty, medical students, house staff, and other major user groups, based on the values of representative national samples from these groups; analyze differences among user weighting schemes, and between these schemes and the corresponding librarian weighting schemes and report the findings. These findings will be considered by the librarian groups charged with establishing the weighting schemes employed for scoring survey data; this activity will constitute a formal mechanism to insure that the profession-established standards are responsive to user needs and values.
3. Revise the present instruments for the inventory of services to individual users to correct weaknesses and increase suitability for self-administration, keeping in mind the importance of maintaining comparability of data from one survey to the next; consider the desirability of adding sections on services to other libraries in the revised instrument; similarly revise the abbreviated form of the inventory,[2] which was designed for small libraries where service policies are relatively simple.
4. Review the crude instrument used in the present survey to collect special data on reservoir libraries[32] in conjunction with the raw data so obtained; analyze and report selected data on reservoir services; and revise that instrument to correct weaknesses and increase suitability for self-administration.
5. With the revised instruments developed in Steps 3 and 4, conduct pilot trials to ascertain the comparability of data obtained by interviewers with data obtained when the inventory is self-administered.
6. Conduct surveys of academic libraries, reservoir libraries, hospital libraries, and other major types of biomedical libraries using the appropriate revised instruments developed in Steps 3 and 4 as self-administered questionnaires; establish current librarian weighting schemes for the major user groups of each type of library; analyze and report the results of these surveys.
7. Develop plans for repeating Steps 2, 3, 4, and 6 systematically in two- or three-year cycles.[33]

NOTES

[1] Orr, Richard H.; Pings, Vern M.; Pizer, Irwin H.; Olson, Edwin E.; and Spencer, Carol C. Development of methodologic tools for planning and managing library services: II. Measuring a library's capability for providing documents. Bull. Med. Libr. Ass. 56: 241–267, July 1968.

[2] Orr, Richard H.; Pings, Vern M.; Olson, Edwin E.; and Pizer, Irwin H. Development of methodologic tools for planning and managing library services: III. Standardized inventories of library services. Bull. Med. Libr. Ass. 56: 380–403, Oct. 1968.

[3] The National Library of Medicine will release the original survey data for research and evaluation purposes, providing adequate assurance is given that the privacy of libraries surveyed will be fully protected.

[4] The 34-page Interview Guide and the 10-page Checklist employed for the inventory of services to individual users are available at cost of duplication from the Institute for Advancement of Medical Communication, 19 South 22nd Street, Philadelphia, Pennsylvania, 19103. (Request Items 7 and 8, respectively.)

[5] A copy of the Appendix (42 pages) may be obtained from the Institute for Advancement of Medical Communication, 19 South 22nd Street, Philadelphia, Pa. 19103, at cost of duplication.

[6]As explained in the Appendix, an exception to this rule was made for Sections 44 and 45, which pertain to instructional services.

[7]This category subsumes the same spectrum of services as the category called "teaching and consultation services" in the original description of the inventory.[2]

[8]Billings, John S. Our Medical Literature. International Medical Congress, 1881, Vol. 1, 54–71.

[9]This category subsumes the same spectrum of services as the category called "work-space services" in the original description of the inventory.[2]

[10]Schiller's discussion[11] can be recommended for a dispassionate examination of both sides of the question; but to our knowledge, the question as it applies specifically to medical students has not been systematically explored in print.

[11]Schiller, Anita R. Reference service: instruction or information. Libr. Q. 35: 52–60, Jan. 1965.

[12]Selected library services were covered as part of the 1952–53 Survey of Medical Education, in which all U.S. medical schools were visited; however, the published report of this survey[13] does not specify the questions asked nor give data on services, except selectively and in general terms. This study does not seem to have employed the data collected by the Committee on Criteria for Medical School Libraries at about the same time.

[13]Dietrick, John E., and Berson, Robert C. The library. In: Medical Schools in the United States at Mid-Century. New York, McGraw-Hill, 1953, p. 181–192.

[14]Medical Library Association. Committee on Criteria for Medical School Libraries. Survey of libraries in the medical schools of the U.S. and Canada. Preliminary publication of replies, June 7, 1952. Bull. Med. Libr. Ass. 41: 12–23, Jan. 1953.

[15]Medical Library Association. Committee on Criteria for Medical School Libraries. Report of the Committee on Criteria for Medical School Libraries. April 2, 1953, 7 pp., appendices and tables. (Copy supplied by Ida J. Draeger, who was chairman of committee).

[16]Register, Nancy S. Services in Medical School Libraries in the United States. Thesis, Emory University, 1960. 88 pp., appendices.

[17]Colaianni, Lois Ann, and Lewis, Robert F. Reference services in U.S. medical school libraries. Bull. Med. Libr. Ass. 57: 272–274, July 1969.

[18]Terminology problems in surveying library services are discussed elsewhere.[2]

[19]Keenan, E. L. Medical school library statistics. Bull. Med. Libr. Ass. 52: 386–409, April 1964.

[20]Medical Library Association. Committee on Surveys and Statistics. Library statistics of schools in the health sciences. Part I. Bull. Med. Libr. Ass. 54: 206–229, July 1966.

[21]U.S. Public Health Service. Biomedical Manpower for the Eighties. Resources for Medical Research, Report No. 11. Dec. 1968. 119 pp.

[22]Had the Task Force developed a weighting scheme for services to medical students, or other user groups, rather than faculty, the scheme would not necessarily be the same as the present one. For example, the value attached to facility services for students might be higher, and the value of citation services lower.

[23]The regional boundaries used for these analyses correspond to those originally employed by the National Library of Medicine for planning regionalization; in implementing the plans, boundaries for the Midwest Region were extended to include North Dakota as well as the states listed for this unnamed region. Likewise, boundaries for the Mid-Atlantic Region were extended to encompass North Carolina as well as the states listed for the other unnamed region mentioned below. The statements in this paragraph therefore do not necessarily apply to the current pattern of regionalization.

[24]The arguments in support of this proposition are complex, and presenting them here seems inappropriate. Therefore, the proposition is introduced as an unsupported postulate.

[25]Pings, V. M.; Olson, E. E.; and Orr, R. H. Summary report of a study of academic medical library statistics. Bull. Med. Libr. Ass. 57: 233–238, July 1969.

[26]A few sections were omitted in calculating this crude index because it was felt that apparent differentiation on these particular sections might be artifactual.

[27]This, and some of the other applications, require the Appendix to this report, which contains a complete tabulation of the primary data on faculty policies.

[28]An abbreviated exercise, limited to establishing weights for only the six major service categories and their main subcategories (see "First Working Session," page 459), may suffice for this particular purpose. A relatively small group of users (under 10) could carry out such an exercise in no more time than is commonly spent on many academic committee activities.

[29]To make clear which of the various senses of the term "standard(s)" is intended, we will qualify the term by adding "normative" when referring to the kind of standard that specifies "minimal," "acceptable," or "desirable" requirements. Unqualified, the term is intended to denote something used as a basis for comparison or measurement—a concept closely related to that of a "yardstick."

[30]Blau, Peter M., and Scott, W. Richard. Formal Organizations: A Comparative Approach. San Francisco, Chandler Publishing Co., 1962, p. 62–63.

[31]White, Herbert S. Professional identity: revolt of the scientists. Wilson Libr. Bull. 44: 550–554, Jan. 1970.

[32]The special instrument used for the "reservoir" inventory covers in detail all the services a library can offer to other libraries.[2] This reservoir inventory was one of the standardized procedures carried out at 15 selected libraries during the field work for the present survey (see "Introduction").

[33]The survey could not have been carried out without the help of many individuals. Specific acknowledgements are due to: first, the dedicated field staff who, in addition to one of the present authors (G.C.), included Robert W. Cryder, Head Medical Librarian, University of Iowa; Virginia H. Holtz, Associate Medical Librarian, University of Wisconsin; Lois Lehman, Head of Public Services, Hershey Medical Center Library; Francis B. O'Leary, Librarian, St. Louis Univer-

sity; Kenneth E. Moody, Librarian, Brooklyn Hospital Division of the Brooklyn-Cumberland Medical Center; Frances G. Livingston, Senior Librarian for Technical Services, University of Louisville; Eleanor E. Pasmik, Reference Librarian, New York University; Elizabeth Petgen, Librarian, Medical Library of Mecklenberg County, Charlotte, North Carolina; Mary E. Feeney, Associate Librarian, New York Academy of Medicine; Kent K. Schriefer, Assistant Director of the Libraries for Technical Processes, State University of New York at Buffalo; Lawrence E. Thomas, Assistant Librarian, University of Texas at San Antonio; Ronald M. Watterson, Head Medical Librarian, Medical College of Ohio at Toledo; and Nancy E. Whitten, Administrative Head of the Historical Section, University of California Medical Center Library, San Francisco. Second, to those who, together with three of the present authors, served as instructors in training the field staff: Edwin E. Olson, Ph.D., Senior Research Associate, Institute for Advancement of Medical Communication (now Associate Professor, School of Library and Information Services, University of Maryland); Vern M. Pings, Ph.D., Medical Librarian, Medical Library, Wayne State University; Irwin H. Pizer, Director of the Library, State University of New York, Upstate Medical Center (now Associate Director of Libraries, State University of New York at Buffalo); and Carol C. Spencer, Research Associate, Institute for Advancement of Medical Communication (now Director of Mideastern Regional Medical Library Program, College of Physicians of Philadelphia). Lastly, to Mrs. Dana Close, who was the Assistant Project Director of the survey for the University City Science Center, and who handled all arrangements with the field staff, did much of the primary editing of inventory data, carried out the primary analyses, and checked the scoring.

Miss Mary Lou Schultz wrote the special computer programs for the secondary analyses. A particular debt is owed to Mr. Scott Adams for his invaluable assistance in selecting the Weighting Task Force, and to the individual members of this group, who contributed so freely of their time and judgement. Except for their enthusiastic cooperation in making explicit the values they place on different library services, their courage in exposing these values to critical scrutiny in spirited discussions, and their willingness to reexamine and revise their positions, it would have been impossible to establish a weighting scheme acceptable to all members of the Task Force.

ABOUT THE AUTHORS—Richard H. Orr, see p. 78.

Harold Bloomquist has been Librarian of the Francis A. Countway Library of Medicine at Harvard University since 1968, following ten years of increasingly responsible positions in that library and the predecessor Harvard University Medical Library. He has an A.B. from Albion College, Michigan, and an M.S.L.S. from Columbia University. He held positions in the Columbia University Zoology-Botany and Medical Libraries before going to Harvard.

Mr. Bloomquist is presently Editor of the *Bulletin of the Medical Library Association*. His many publications include articles on writing in medicine and dentistry in addition to those more directly related to medical librarianship. With Eric Meyerhoff, he edited *Implications of Machines in Libraries: Social, Economic, and Administrative* (Chicago, Medical Library Association, 1966). One of his more important contributions was the survey which resulted in "The Status and Needs of Medical School Libraries in the United States," (*J. Med. Educ.* 38:145–163, 1963), which is discussed in Scott Adams' "Medical Libraries Are in Trouble" (page 311). He wrote the section on "Circulation; Document Reproduction" for the *Handbook of Medical Library Practice*, third edition (Chicago, Medical Library Association, 1970).

Gwendolyn S. Cruzat has recently become Assistant Professor, School of Library Science, University of Michigan. Before that, she was Research Librarian at the Wayne State University Medical Library and Assistant Librarian at the Harper Hospital in Detroit. She holds a B.A. in Mathematics from Fisk University and an M.S. in Library Service from Atlanta University and took the medical library course at Columbia University. She also served as Associate Director of the Fellowship Program in Medical Librarianship at Wayne State University and as Research Assistant for the University City Science Center and the Institute for the Advancement of Medical Communication.

Arthur P. Schless, M.D., is presently a second-year resident in the Department of Psychiatry at the University of Pennsylvania. Previous to that, he was Manager of Medical Projects at the University City Science Center, Philadelphia. His education includes a B.A. in Physics and Mathematics from the University of Pennsylvania, graduate work in those subjects at Cornell University, and an M.D. degree from the University of Pennsylvania in 1964.

His combined interest in medicine and systems analysis have led to such diverse activities as development of a regional renal dialysis program, automation of hospital clinical laboratories, work on a "*Reading Guide* and Index to the Cancer-Virology Literature" (*American Documentation* 19(2):163–167, April 1968), and his participation in the project described here.

Collection of Materials

The medical library field has many excellent bibliographic lists prepared for specific audiences, specific types and size of library and by specific methods, such as polling of librarians and/or physicians or study of requests. One of the most generally useful and used is that by Alfred N. Brandon. The introduction provides a guide to many of the other selection sources which a librarian will need.

In addition to the usual selection and acquisition problems, medical librarians are faced with the question of what to do with gifts from physicians who have built fine private libraries. Should they, through such gifts or otherwise, be building a historical collection and, if so, how can it be planned rationally?

Selected Lists of Books and Journals for the Small Medical Library

by Alfred N. Brandon

Since it is not the function of this Reader *to serve as a bibliography, the actual "Brandon list" is not included here. The introduction to this outstanding list presents its guidelines, a guide to other bibliographies and helpful hints for the novice.*

Emphasis is being placed today on the creation of "core libraries" for hospitals. With the implementation of regional medical library programs, small libraries are encouraged to purchase standard medical periodicals and books that, because of heavy usage, the regional library is unable to supply upon demand. Stearns and Ratcliff[1] have recently published their latest "core library" which may be considered the absolute minimal collection for a small hospital. Earlier published lists of recommended books and journals are now somewhat obsolete. The present "Selected List" may be considered supplemental to the condensed one compiled by Stearns and Ratcliff. It is significantly more comprehensive and will suggest additional titles for the institution which needs a more substantive collection to meet the needs and objectives of its library.

It is thought-provoking to note the increased average cost of the books and journals included in this list from its inception in 1965 to date. (See Table 1.)

TABLE 1

	1965 List	1967 List	1969 List	1971 List
Average Cost per Book	$15.00	$16.22	$17.04	$19.11
Average Cost per Journal Subscription	$13.90	$14.85	$17.61	$20.73

Based on the trend indicated in the table, hospital library budgets should allow for an approximate biennial increase of at least 10 percent for books and 15 percent for journals.

An interesting comparative analysis of various selected lists of journals for the small medical library was recently written by John A. Timour.[2] In his study, he points out that all of the starred journal titles in the 1969 edition of this list were on one or the other of the composite lists.

The three previous editions of this list have received wide acceptance and have filled a need for a selection aid for both the experienced and the untrained hospital librarian. To be a continual help, biennial revisions are a necessity. The present edition of this "Selected List of Books and Journals for the Small Medical Library" has been completely revised to reflect the suggestions made by subject specialists and medical librarians alike, and it incorporates information gleaned from additional sources.

For the very small hospital library, it will be impossible to procure all, or even a majority, of the listed books and journals. Therefore, items suggested for first purchase are noted by an asterisk.

Additional selection aids may be consulted and used in conjunction with the present list (see 3, 4, 5, 6, 7, 8, 9). An excellent *Basic List of Guides and Information Sources for Professional and Patients' Libraries in Hospitals* was published in September 1969, by the Joint Committee on Library Service in Hospitals.[10] This publication should be available for use of librarians in small medical libraries and is distributed free of charge.

Anyone wanting a more comprehensive listing of standard books and journals in the basic and

SOURCE: Reprinted from Alfred N. Brandon, "Selected List of Books and Journals for the Small Medical Library," *Bulletin of the Medical Library Association*, 59 (Apr., 1971), pp. 266–268, by permission of the publisher and the author. A fourth revised version of a paper originally published in the *Bull. Med. Libr. Ass.* 53: 329–364, July 1965; 55: 141–159, April 1967; 57: 130–150, April 1969.

medical sciences may use the syllabus prepared by Myrl Ebert for her course in Medical Librarianship given in the School of Library Science, University of North Carolina at Chapel Hill.[5]

The present list is intended as a selection aid for the small library of a hospital, society, clinic, or similar organization. It should be considered in relation to the purposes of the particular institution and the subject specialties dominant therein. Emphasis has been placed on selecting the most recent and authoritative works in the English language in each subject area. The list is by no means complete and should be supplemented by additional books and journals in the specialties of greatest interest to the clientele of the library. Very few expensive sets are noted, and inexpensive alternatives are included within the same category. No attempt has been made to list *innumerable* reference works, since the best selection of such tools is available in the "Selected Reference Aids for Small Medical Libraries" revised by Howertine Farrell Duncan, Reference Librarian, National Library of Medicine, and published in the April 1970 issue of the *Bulletin of the Medical Library Association*.[11]

The listing of books in nursing has been extensively revised with the help of Mrs. Jean Frohlich, Librarian, Sinai Hospital, Baltimore, Maryland. It may still be supplemented by three excellent lists. The "Reference Sources for Nursing," published in the April 1970 issue of *Nursing Outlook*, was initiated by the Interagency Council on Library Resources for Nursing.[12] The most complete and helpful list of materials for the nursing school library is the work compiled by Sister Mary Concordia in 1967.[13] Stearns, Ratcliff, and others published a "core nursing library" list in 1970.[14]

Although it is possible to order books directly from the publishers, it is usually more satisfactory to choose a reliable medical book dealer in one's city or region, who can obtain any of the volumes desired, and who usually offers a 10 percent discount with postage paid on books from major medical publishers in the United States. Typical of such agents are the following: Brown & Connolly, Inc., 1399 Boylston Street, Boston, Massachusetts 02115; Burns & MacEachern Limited, 62 Railside Road, Don Mills, Ontario, Canada; Login Bros. Book Company, Inc., 1445 West Jackson Boulevard, Chicago, Illinois 60607; Eliot Books, Inc., 35-53 24th Street, Long Island City, New York 11106; Majors Scientific Books, Inc., 139 Forrest Avenue, N.E., Atlanta, Georgia 30303; Majors Scientific Books, Inc., 147 South Liberty Street, New Orleans, Louisiana 70112; Majors Scientific Books, Inc., 8911 Directors Row, Dallas, Texas 75247; Majors Scientific Books, Inc., 6632 South Main Street, Houston, Texas 77025; Mathews Medical Books, 3140 Park Avenue, St. Louis, Missouri 63104; Rittenhouse Book Store, 1706 Rittenhouse Square, Philadelphia, Pennsylvania 19103; and J. W. Stacey, Inc., 5255 East Don Julian Road, City of Industry, California 91747.

Similarly, journals can be ordered through an agent, thus saving time in correspondence, purchase orders, and processing multiple invoices. Today, most journal agents are charging a service fee ranging from 3 to 10 percent. Before placing subscriptions with any agent, the librarian should ascertain the amount of such service charges. It is advisable to consult with other medical or university librarians in one's area prior to choosing a subscription agent. Typical of these agents are the following: F. W. Faxon Company, Inc., 515-525 Hyde Park Avenue, Boston, Massachusetts 02131; Hanson-Bennett Magazine Agency, 180 North Wabash Avenue, Chicago, Illinois 60601; Majors Scientific Books, Inc., 8911 Directors Row, Dallas, Texas 75247; Moore-Cottrell Subscription Agencies, Inc., North Cohocton, New York 14868; and Read-More Publications, Inc., 140 Cedar Street, New York, New York 10006.

A great many changes have occurred since this list was originally published. Many new editions of standard works have appeared. In instances where more recent books have been published, they have supplanted out-of-print or older works in the same field if they are just as authoritative. In citing the books, the entry used by the Library of Congress is generally followed. If a work has more than two authors or editors, the phrase "[and others]" is used after the name of the senior author or editor.

NOTES

[1] Stearns, Norman S., and Ratcliff, Wendy W. An integrated health-science core library for physicians, nurses and allied health practitioners in community hospitals. New Eng. J. Med. 283: 1489-1498, Dec. 31, 1970.

[2]Timour, John A. Selected lists of journals for the small medical library: a comparative analysis. Bull. Med. Libr. Ass. 59: 87–93, Jan. 1971.

[3]American Hospital Association. Health Services Administration: Suggested References. Chicago, The Association, 1968. 24 p. Free.

[4]C D reference list of current medical books: fourth annual edition. Canad. Doctor 35:39 +, Jan. 1969. (Single copy free from publisher.)

[5]Ebert, Myrl. Introduction to the Literature of the Medical Sciences. 3d ed. Chapel Hill, The Student Stores of the University of North Carolina, 1970. 125 p. $3.00.

[6]Library Association. Books and Periodicals for Medical Libraries in Hospitals. 3d ed. London, The Association, 1966. 31 p.

[7]Roy, Donald E., and Morgan, Virginia W. Books for the hospital emergency service. Bull. Med. Libr. Ass. 54: 243–250, July 1966.

[8]U.S. Veterans Administration. Medical and General Reference Library. Basic List of Books and Journals for Veterans Administration Medical Libraries. 1967 Revision. 31 p. (G-14, M-2, Part XIII, August 15, 1967). (Available upon request from U.S. Veterans Administration, H Street and Vermont Avenue, N.W., Washington, D.C. 20420.)

[9]*Id.* Medical Specialty Checklist for Veterans Administration Medical Libraries. (G-15, M-2, Part XIII). (Ten parts were published from September 1968 through July 1970: Urology, Pathology, Surgery, Radiology, Psychiatry, Internal Medicine, Neurology and Neurosurgery, Dermatology, Gastroenterology, and Anesthesiology. Other parts are in progress. These are available upon request from the U.S. Veterans Administration.)

[10]Council of National Library Associations. Joint Committee on Library Service in Hospitals. Basic List of Guides and Information Sources for Professional and Patients' Libraries in Hospitals. Chicago, 1969. 15 p. (Single copy free from the Medical Library Association.)

[11]Duncan, Howertine Farrell. Selected reference aids for small medical libraries. Bull. Med. Libr. Ass. 58: 134–158, April 1970. (Single reprint free from the National Library of Medicine.)

[12]Interagency Council on Library Resources for Nursing. Reference sources for nursing. Nurs. Outlook 18: 47–52, April 1970. (Single reprint free from the Library, American Journal of Nursing Company.)

[13]Mary Concordia, *Sister*. Basic Book and Periodical List: Nursing School and Small Medical Library. 4th ed. Peru, Illinois, St. Bede Abbey Press, 1967. 144 p. (Available from the author at St. Mary's Hospital, La Salle, Illinois. $5.00).

[14]Stearns, Norman S., Ratcliff, Wendy W., Getchell, Marjorie E., and Zeller, Karen. A core nursing library for practitioners. Amer. J. Nurs. 70: 818–823, April 1970.

ABOUT THE AUTHOR–Alfred N. Brandon is Chairman, Department of Library Science, at the Mount Sinai School of Medicine of The City University of New York. Prior to accepting this position, he was Director of the Welch Medical Library, Johns Hopkins University School of Medicine, and Head Librarian of the University of Kentucky Medical Center and of Loma Linda University. His degrees include a Th.B. from Atlantic Union College, South Lancaster, Massachusetts, a B.S.L.S. from Syracuse University, an M.S.L.S. from the University of Illinois, and an M.A. in History from the University of Michigan.

He has been a consultant on library building plans for a number of medical schools and has held lectureships at Syracuse University and the University of Maryland library schools. The list to which this paper is an introduction was first published in 1965 and it has subsequently gained wide recognition as simply "the Brandon list." He has been President of the Medical Library Association and was chosen as its Janet Doe Lecturer in 1969. He wrote the first chapter, "The Emergence of the Modern Medical Library," for the *Handbook of Medical Library Practice*, third edition (Chicago, Medical Library Association, 1970).

Treasure or White Elephant?

by Helen Crawford

An integral part of collecting is determining what should be discarded and when. In the case of gifts, one must decide whether they should be added to the small library. Miss Crawford's experience of years is condensed into her terse advice.

This whole thing started with a question which someone raised last year: "I had a lot of books given to me and a librarian who saw them said, 'These are treasures and should be kept.'" The question is, what is a treasure and *should* you keep it? It seems anomalous, but the smaller the library, the more selective it has to be. A large library with a large responsibility can afford to keep more marginal items than a small library with a sharply defined responsibility and much less space.

Anyone can recognize that an American book published before the Civil War should be investigated and, perhaps, an outside opinion solicited. What we need are some general principles for disposal of the run-of-the-mill volumes, the 1910 textbook, the systems of medicine and surgery, the well-bound, highly illustrated and expensive edition-before-the-last of a standard text. Medical people are generous and this is a recurring problem everywhere.

Let one start with the donor, usually a physician or his widow. He bought the books as part of his professional equipment. He used them through the years of his practice, and presumably got full value from the investment. No matter what the initial cost and the present condition of the books, the depreciation rate is high because the rate of obsolescence is high. If the library offered to you, as is usually the case, consists of the doctor's medical school textbooks with a scattering of more recent publications, it has already outlived its practical value.

On the other hand, if it is a collection of real rarities, it may not belong in a small library at all. A shelf of seventeenth century books may have value but no practical usefulness in a hospital setting, whatever the wishes of the donor. I have on more than one occasion seen such volumes locked up in a special case in a hospital library, pointed to with pride, but I have rarely been permitted to examine them; sometimes the librarian cannot even tell me the titles, although she assures me they are treasures. It is wasteful to have the source materials of science dispersed in this way, unrecorded, unknown (except in a very narrow circle), and unused.

But here you are, on the spot. Say the widow of a much-loved doctor on your staff offers you his library, what do you do? The books are sacred to her because she knows how much her husband valued them and was probably conscious of the amount of money spent on them over the years. She may have given his associates their pick of some of the most recent books, and what you have is several dozen or several hundred volumes—an old Cecil, an Eastman, a Todd and Stanford, an anatomy, perhaps a set of Tice or Lewis or the *Oxford Medicine*, in mint condition with the revision pages present in their original wrappers. There is likely to be an old *PDR*, a few books from pharmaceutical houses, a shabby dictionary. If the collection has been accumulating for a longer time, there might be a nondescript edition of Osler, a Howell's *Physiology*, a *Reference Handbook* or some old books on therapeutics (than which nothing is deader). They are not new enough to be reliable and not old enough to be quaint.

The question of value is at the basis of any decision on gift books, and whenever we talk about value we get involved in semantics: value to whom and value for what? We may think of the value of

SOURCE: Reprinted from Helen Crawford, "Treasure or White Elephant?" *Bulletin of the Medical Library Association*, 58 (July, 1970), pp. 336–340, by permission of the publisher and the author. Copyright © 1970 by the Medical Library association. Presented on the Medical Library Seminar series of the Television/Radio Conferences sponsored by the University of Wisconsin Division of Postgraduate Education.

the gift to the donor, as I have indicated—and not only emotional but monetary value; value to our clientele; and value to us, in the work we do for our clientele. The commercial value is another matter entirely, which I will discuss later on. What I am concerned with here is the usefulness of the book to your operation.

Value is a factor of age, of subject matter, of type of publication, of condition, and of local significance. One should not attempt to serve 1969 physicians with 1910 books any more than a physician would retain a piece of 1910 X-ray equipment. The trouble is that books don't age at the same rate; whereas a 1940 book on therapy would be ludicrous, a 1920 anatomy might be perfectly usable. From a historical point of view, an 1870 surgery should probably be discarded whereas an 1870 bacteriology text would have appeared in the infancy of a science and could be getting scarce.

First, there is the question of the aging textbook. It was probably issued in a large edition and has, perhaps, been superseded by a later edition. Would you like your physician to treat your infection from a pre-antibiotic Cecil? If not, discard it. On the other hand, what if it is a first edition of, say, Holt's *Diseases of Infancy and Childhood* or the Osler textbook? Again, even though it may not belong in your library, it should perhaps be preserved.

Secondly, there is the ageless monograph, that is, a thorough presentation on a narrow subject (such as the kidney) as compared with a textbook which is more general and more frequently revised. If so, it has a longer life and even, perhaps, permanent usefulness in the library because later authors may not repeat the painstaking historical review. Cushing's *Pituitary Gland* is an example of an important monograph, or Ewing's *Neoplastic Diseases*, which gave everything known about the subject at the time and serves as the take-off point for every succeeding writer. In general, the more specific and more special the subject, the more valuable the book is likely to be. This is not to say that you should retain it in your library but you should at least consider whether it should be offered to another library or, possibly, sold.

Books in the specialties are likely to have a longer life than general titles issued in very large editions. Books in orthopedics or plastic surgery or ophthalmology or anesthesia are in this category. There are always takers for Albee's *Bone-graft Surgery*, or Codman's *The Shoulder;* for Gillies' *Plastic Surgery of the Face,* for Labat's *Regional Anesthesia* and Fuchs' *Diseases of the Eye*. Bunnell's *Surgery of the Hand* has become a modern classic, and many young ophthalmologists are on the lookout for the *Strabismus Symposium* of 1962. I asked a young pathologist on our staff what older volumes he yearned for; he mentioned particularly Wells' *Chemical Pathology* and Wilson's *The Cell.*

Psychology and neurology are in a class by themselves because they are less dated by the passage of years and are, in fact, more likely to grow in value as they become scarce. Many of the Gowers books of the 1880's and 1890's, for instance, are selling in three figures, and the prices for publications of leaders in the psychoanalytic movement reflect the widening demand.

Thirdly, there is one category of books that will always be found useful to someone: medical history and biography. Unfortunately, they don't often turn up in the collections offered to us. A Garrison or some other good history of medicine, a history of nursing, a biography of Osler or Welch or Cushing should be kept for reference or offered to another library. Books such as Cannon's *Way of an Investigator* will never grow old.

Just a word of warning: dealers are not interested in shabby cast-offs. Libraries are concerned with content and do not mind library discards, even rebinds, if the general condition is good. The typical collector, however, is looking for a copy of Osler, first edition, first issue, in mint condition, uncut and unopened, with paper wrapper intact, if it ever had one, and preferably with an inscription from the author to a prominent contemporary. Of course the older the imprint the less likely it is to have all these desirable qualities.

It is axiomatic in the book trade that unsophisticated people inheriting a collection of books keep the plush-covered portfolio on Picturesque Venice and throw away the periodicals and pamphlets. I will not discuss the subject of medical journals because everyone knows their value and has a cooperative method of exchanging them. Pamphlets, on the other hand, are ephemeral. Because most copies are thrown away, the few that remain have the value of scarcity. Whether they have any intrinsic worth depends on their age, their subject matter, their local pertinence. Some of the history of the public health campaigns of the past 100 years will be culled from the "swat the fly" "clean milk" and TB publicity material of the early years of this century. The antivivisection pamphlet, the promotions for bitter snake root, and other off-beat subjects, especially if they date from the nineteenth century, should be passed on to a historical collection. Perhaps a local historical society might have an interest in some of them particularly if they have local pertinence. I have been amazed in my recent attendance at book auctions at the prices fetched by eighteenth and nineteenth century pamphlets on cholera, insanity, gout, tetanus, fever; elegies of doctors, controversies, lectures on medical education, reports on the health resorts and cures. This type of pamphlet has now been superseded by the journal article. The price reflects their scarcity and, sometimes, the efforts of collectors to assemble every scrap published by some writer important to them.

The highly illustrated book, especially in a field that does not change readily, always finds takers at our giveaways. I find that students pick up orthopedic books because the skeleton does not change through the years, although the surgical approach to it may be modified. Such an old standby as the *Ciba Collection of Medical Illustrations* by the artist Netter is out of print and should be retained.

In a long experience with gift collections, I have observed that, if there is one interesting book in a gift lot, there will be others, unless, of course, the interesting book was given to the donor and does not represent his own book-buying habits. I am also very suspicious of the book in mint condition that gives no sign of having been opened. The really useful book, like the copies of Gray's *Anatomy* that come our way, are likely to be shabby and shaken.

The condition of a volume has a great deal to do with its value. Using a book with a broken back and pages falling out is irksome and a collection of such castoffs makes a sad-looking library. By all means, if a good copy comes in, use it as a replacement and throw away the old one. Other broken-backed war horses may not be worth the effort of processing.

It is no coincidence that British libraries such as the British Museum have a traditional title of "keeper of printed books." Librarians are by nature or by nurture "keepers" and they are expected to be able to produce on demand the publications that everyone else consigned to the wastebasket on receipt. The tendency, therefore, is to keep everything that comes to hand that may be remotely useful, without stopping to think that we might trust a larger library to hang on to fringe publications for us. The whole emphasis in the library network concept is on adjusting the depth of coverage to the size of the service unit. We can all point to the occasion when we "just happened to keep" something that was asked for later; sometimes this represents real prescience, more often overcautiousness. We forget the scarce shelf space the publication may have occupied for far too many months before use.

However, there is one type of material that falls squarely in our lap: publications about our own institutions and personnel. No other library can possibly have much interest in collecting this local material. It may be that no one else in one's institution has a sense of historical continuity. Office files are cleared out periodically and all the "junk" discarded. However, when the time comes to celebrate the fiftieth anniversary, where does everyone turn for records of the twenty-fifth celebration? You know where. What is loosely called "archives" should be the definite responsibility of someone in your institution if the library is not nominated for his honor.

There are several other outlets for material with local interest or of concern to other professional organizations. I mentioned pamphlet material earlier. There is also the category of old statistical and other reports; these can be very difficult to complete and it is a good idea to offer them to a larger library that might be collecting. The voluntary organizations—the TB Association, particularly—are often trying to reassemble their own publications of the earlier years when filing was more haphazard.

Some groups, such as the Wisconsin Nurses Association, have a history committee which solicits gifts to be offered to the Marquette Nursing Library or the Middleton Library. Mrs. Signe Cooper, the present chairman, has found from her own work in history how incomplete the published record is, especially for local history. Because nursing is a relatively young profession, it may not be recognized that part of the history lies in the old nursing text that you might discard without hesitation. National nursing associations are encouraging their constituent associations to be concerned for the preservation of these materials.

Sometimes there is nothing so expensive as a gift. Shelves well filled, even with outdated books, can encourage your administrators to assume they have a useful library. An associate of mine recently went through one of these collections and found only one volume out of five that was worth saving.

There is also another economic principle involved. Space in hospitals and medical centers is high-cost and always in short supply. The library has to compete for its little area with other needs given a high priority because they concern direct patient care. If your business manager ever calculated the annual cost of keeping a book on the shelf in your library, you might find yourself called on to justify every inch with use figures.

What is to be done with the books you don't want? Once they are added to the library there may be regulations and formal procedures before they can be thrown out. I read of one college librarian whose faculty raised such a storm when he openly threw *books* in the trash that he was driven to sneaking them out to the dump at night.

However, gift books are usually considered expendable. You can give them away or sell them and the one may be almost as difficult as the other. Some of the larger libraries in the state belong to the Medical Library Association and have access to its exchange. The $50 a year fee seems expensive, but every member library can share in the hundreds of thousands of items that the hundreds of institutional members throughout the world offer to each other. The only requirement is that the member offer a list of its own duplicates at least once in two years. Smaller libraries profit particularly from the exchange because they need chiefly the more common journals and they receive more than they give. Don't offer on your own lists outdated texts, the same titles other libraries will be offering on theirs; and don't be tempted to request books and journal titles that are not really essential. I commented to a very experienced medical librarian one time, "I wonder why some libraries ask for the publications they do from exchange lists." He responded, rather cynically, "They check them because they are offered." Completing runs of journals entirely by exchange can be a time-consuming business, and one should consider whether buying essential titles might be cheaper.

If there is a residue of books not suitable or not wanted on exchange, have a giveaway before throwing them in the trash. Medical students and younger physicians are often grateful for an edition of Cecil that has a chapter omitted from later editions, or sound books in the specialties. Anatomies are always in demand.

Markets for secondhand medical books are not available in some parts of the country and selling them means essentially selling by mail. Compiling your list, with notes of condition, and offering it to dealers takes time, and costs money. (A recent estimate said that a dictated letter costs about $2.50.) Answers may not be prompt and when they do come you may have forgotten just what you did with the books and, besides, are too busy to complete the transaction immediately. The amount offered may also seem inadequate for the work involved in packing and shipping, and you may be sorry you started the whole thing.

How do you decide what a book is worth? In the simplest sense, it is worth what someone will give you for it. Suppose you bought a brand-new $20 medical book yesterday, stamped it and then decided to sell it. The minute it leaves the bookshop shelves and is marked in any way it becomes a secondhand book. I believe that students consider themselves fortunate to get half the purchase price for recent textbooks in good condition. Dealers in general cannot afford to give more than a third of the final sale price of a book if they are to provide shelf space and catalog or promotion costs until it is sold. (One collector I know said that he automatically doubled the purchase price of a book in his mind when he bought it, to allow for the shelving cost at New York rental rates).

This is not to say that selling gift books cannot be feasible and profitable at times. The books would have to be in one of the more unusual categories I mentioned–histories, monographs, first editions–but a long run of a standard journal might bring in some funds for additional subscriptions. Again, you may receive no offers for the common journals, but something like *Anesthesiology* or *Blood* or the *Journal of Bone and Joint Surgery* or *Journal of Clinical Investigation* would have resale value. Broken runs fetch a rather low per-issue price.

Gifts with strings attached can strangle a library. Most libraries have learned that a collection offered on condition that it be kept intact is nothing but an incubus. A collection isolated from the rest of the library and not refreshed by addition of new material is like a stagnant lake, outside the live and growing activities of the library. It must be protected by special rules, and access is made more difficult by special permits or keys. Disposing of the collection when it no longer meets a need may also be impossible because of legal restrictions.

The donor who gives books to the library but maintains his emotional ownership of them can be prickly about the use or safekeeping of "his" books, but more often he has an ongoing interest in the library and continues to be a benefactor. A colleague in another institution has a lovely and varied browsing collection, entirely the gift of a widely read and generous faculty member.

Gifts of journals can be very helpful to a library,

especially if the donor can be persuaded to contribute them as they come out without waiting for his wife or his secretary to dig in her heels at housecleaning time. However, subscriptions should be entered for the really necessary journals because of the frustration and expense of late receipt and broken runs.

At some point in her experience, every librarian has to establish a policy concerning nonbook materials: portraits, instruments, statuary, even the desk or chair used by a founder. The library committee and the administration should decide whether they want a library or a library-museum; if the latter, adequate space should be provided for proper display or storage of these too-solid items. I worked in one university library where the problem was solved by placing a series of busts on the cornice behind the reference desk. They chinned themselves benignly there, serving no artistic or functional purpose but not getting in the way. We are delighted to have an oil portrait of Dr. Middleton prominently mounted in our library, and portraits and memorabilia of faculty members are welcome additions to our local history resources. However, I do not know what we should do with a framed engraving of Harvey demonstrating to Charles I; it is highly pertinent, but nearly four feet square.

An attractive exhibit case can be an asset to a library, but the care and feeding of exhibits is very expensive in time and the librarian may wish to limit the extent of the exhibit area.

You are fortunate if some of your physicians and house staff are collectors, even in a small way. They can tell you the contemporary books that are valued in their specialties and hard to find. Reading medical biography alerts one to the significant names in 19th century American medicine—the early Philadelphia physicians, the Johns Hopkins founders, the Ohio River school, the Chicago group.

The only way to learn what is important is by experience. You will make mistakes. A resident will be appalled to hear that you threw away a volume five years ago that he would give his eyeteeth for. (There are fads in book collecting and certain titles become prestige items when they go out of print.) But meanwhile you have been using the space it occupied for a livelier title and your energies have not been dissipated by hanging on to a lot of useless material for fear of making a mistake. Perhaps setting aside a few borderline volumes for a second inspection will be enough to solidify the decision.

Being a keeper myself, I find that I have to be either rested or desperate before I can throw anything away. I can recall just the state of desperation I had reached before I recommended discarding some file cases of reprints twenty years ago when reprints were less valued than today and the space was acutely needed. A faculty member always needles me about the decision. I am sure he is right about the current commercial value of some of the reprints, but the space was indispensable to us for many years, and so far as service is concerned, they have never once been missed. There can be quite a canyon between value and usefulness.

ABOUT THE AUTHOR—Since retirement in 1971 from the position of Librarian and Associate Professor of Medical Librarianship at the University of Wisconsin (Madison), Helen Crawford is Resident Consultant at the Texas Tech University School of Medicine in Lubbock to help get a new medical library started. She has a B.A. in German from the University of North Dakota and a B.S.L.S. from Simmons. She also attended the University of Chicago in 1944-1945.

Miss Crawford has been active in the Medical Library Association for many years and will serve as its President in 1972/1973. She served on the Joint Committee on Health Science Library Standards in 1969, is a past Chairman of the Exchange Committee of the MLA and also of its Midwest Regional Group, and has been a member of the Executive Board previously. In addition to book selection and the history of medicine, Miss Crawford's varied interests include administration, reference, and building planning, and that which led to her writing the section on "Preservation of Library Materials" in the *Handbook of Medical Library Practice*, third edition (Chicago, Medical Library Association, 1970).

Collecting for the History of Medicine

by Gertrude L. Annan

The historical collection at the New York Academy of Medicine and experience in acquiring it form the backdrop for a realistic discussion of how to collect and how not to. Examples of mistakes that should be avoided will prove particularly useful.

Few medical libraries planning a historical collection begin without some resources. There are usually at least a few volumes or small groups of material which point in specific directions to guide the librarian in adding to or in weeding from the shelves. Weeding and building the collection must of course be based on the same principles.

A major point to remember is that the value of any item in any collection does not depend upon its market value. It is the value of the particular text within the particular collection. Nothing should be added to or discarded from a collection because it is expensive or not expensive. The item itself, the text in the collection, is the only concern in passing judgment. A knowledge of prices and values is useful for a librarian to have, particularly when buying early materials or collectors' items of later periods, and in judging the disposal of duplicates. Unfortunately, there is no easy way to learn the values of these historical materials. It is a life's work, and takes many years of reading sale catalogs, following book auction prices, and realizing the fluctuations in the antiquarian book market, because this, as in all commodities, follows supply and demand.

The librarian, however, can be comforted by the fact that he is not expected to be an expert in the prices of rare books. He is not a dealer nor should he assume that prerogative. The Antiquarian Booksellers Association of America issues a directory of members which includes also brief general information about books and values. This emphasizes that dealers are appraisers, that it is their business to be concerned with the ever changing picture of prices in the rare book market. This was rightly stressed at a meeting of ALA's Rare Book Section in 1967. Here the librarian was advised that he should not appraise except in certain cases, for example, when there is a donor who gives a few items and wishes evaluation for income tax purposes. If they are not very valuable and the librarian feels capable of appraising them, this may be done. If the gift is an expensive book, or a collection, then the librarian should feel free to tell the donor that he should have a professional appraisal. Some donors will offer to pay for this; others expect the library to cover the expense, often 10 percent of the value. As the Internal Revenue Service is much more strict than formerly, a professional appraisal is a protection for both donor and library. This same advice serves to help the librarian receiving demands for appraisals from those unfamiliar with the many problems appraising may cause. A firm rule, gently stated, should meet with understanding. Such a rule should cover all requests, including those frequent demands for assigning the costs of secondhand books without any examination of copies. Librarians can say with authority that they are not dealers, no matter how many years they have spent in historical collections. Librarians with such expertise are the most adamant in refusing.

The same general attitude may be assumed toward disposal of duplicates or other unwanted volumes. Practical advice given at ALA's meeting of the Rare Book Section was quoted in *Antiquarian Bookman:*

> The usual method for the disposition of special collections is the tried and true one of establishing a relationship with a number of booksellers who know the collections in the library; are likely to want the type of

SOURCE: Reprinted from Gertrude L. Annan, "Collecting for the History of Medicine," *Bulletin of the Medical Library Association*, 58 (July, 1970), pp. 330-335, by permission of the publisher and the author. Based on a lecture given at the Institute sponsored by the Committee on Continuing Education, Medical Library Association, in Denver, Colorado, on June 5, 1968.

duplicates which may show up in it and in turn likely to be able to offer, at the time or later, something wanted or needed by the library. Except for the simple and obvious requirements of notations or receipt and credit memoranda, the arrangement seems always to be an informal, if not unofficial one based on the indispensable factor of mutual trust between librarian and bookseller. And it seems to work with all parties benefiting.

I cannot emphasize too strongly this point of view. Some medical libraries send priced lists of duplicates to libraries and patrons. Financially, this is impractical. The staff must spend in staff time an equivalent of whatever profits accrue. Perhaps more important, however, is the danger of upsetting library-dealer relationships. Every librarian with a historical collection knows the dependence upon a friendly dealer in building a collection. When librarians appraise duplicates, price them low for the benefit of their own clientele and their colleagues in other libraries, they are appreciated by those who benefit. It can hardly fail, though, to make difficulties for dealers. More than once items worth about $75 have been listed at the very low price of $5. The physician who orders one of these after it has been sold may try to get another copy from a dealer who expects to get the market value. The prospective buyer will probably not consider that the price of the duplicate was particularly small, but rather claim the dealer is a pirate. Examples of this are many. One man, outraged because a dealer priced an important contribution at the then market price of $250, has never been convinced that the library's $40 was in error, rather than the dealer's. Confidence in a dealer's integrity may be unwittingly destroyed. Furthermore, a dealer should not be asked to offer special prices or reductions to those who are not regular customers. A client of long standing may hope for special privileges and consideration, not a stranger. It is unrealistic to demand from a book dealer what one would not expect other business men, such as antique dealers, to offer. Librarians, then, wishing to please their clientele with underpriced material should state very explicitly at the top of the list of duplicates that these prices do not reflect the market value but are priced below it for the benefit of friends and colleagues. Otherwise, the librarian would do well to have a professional appraiser engaged. This would protect dealers and prevent knowledgeable collectors from snapping up bargains with the intention of selling them at a profit.

Although the librarian cannot suddenly overnight become an expert in book values, he can learn about the different types of material and what makes them rare. It is seldom that there is only one factor. Today a book is not as a rule valuable for age alone, scarcity alone, size alone, beauty or typography alone, provenance alone, or type of publication alone. The one single factor of great importance is that of contribution to knowledge. This should be emphasized, because twenty years ago the most important factor was age, and librarians collected chiefly the classics of medicine, early editions, manuscripts, sixteenth century publications, and early Americana.

At the New York Academy of Medicine Library in the thirties and forties the money available for the purchase of rare books was so very little that it was impossible to add to our incunabula, medieval manuscripts, or the most costly of the sixteenth century items. The few hundred dollars regularly available were spent with care, consideration, and no little anxiety, on important texts of the seventeenth to nineteenth centuries, the very material which has since then risen so spectacularly in price. There was no prevision that this would be so. Poverty of funds dictated that the early classics other libraries were adding were far too costly. There are many examples of low-cost purchases. An eighteenth century Italian book concerning a hospital which treated patients with mental illnesses, acquired for $8.00, was offered not long ago for $275. The value of Carpue's small piece on plastic surgery of 1816 has soared unbelievably since 1929 when the Academy's copy, described even then as scarce, was bought for ten shillings. Editions of Hippocrates and Galen, or fifteenth and sixteenth century texts, have not risen in value as astronomically. Some are very little higher, a few even lower. Important contributions, however, have steadily increased. Even the *Wall Street Journal* published an article on the subject. Libraries do not buy for investment, but there is satisfaction in knowing that scientific texts have gone up in value as some literary and ecclesiastical volumes declined. A collection of 112 editions of the *Vicar of Wakefield* was presented to the Academy, because Goldsmith studied medicine. The donor was proud of the first edition obtained for $4,000. Kept in the vault for some years, it was finally removed when it was apparent that tastes had changed so much that its price had sunk to $400.

Although the librarian need not try to become an expert in market prices, he should turn his attention to a consideration of the types of publication which may have value in a historical collection. The first and most needed lesson is to learn that the large handsome volume may well be of much less value, intrinsically and financially, than a small unattractive piece. The first edition of Harvey, beyond question the most costly of all printed medical books, is in reality a poorly printed pamphlet on poor quality paper. Many years spent in working with early material have taught that the librarian should and must learn that above all the small fragile piece must be of concern. The New York Academy of Medicine Library was extraordinarily fortunate in having a man of remarkable foresight in the nineteenth century who saved thousands of pamphlets, chiefly in bound volumes, that his contemporaries were discarding as worthless. He knew instinctively what the historian of the future would want saved for his needs. One of our most valuable Americana, Samuel Bard's thirty-three-page tract on diphtheria, 1771, Dr. Samuel Purple literally retrieved from an ashcan. Early nineteenth century murder trials containing medical testimony by leading physicians of the day are in some cases unique survivors. One of our most knowledgeable medical bookmen, seeing the many bound volumes containing these pamphlets, estimated that if put up for sale they would bring at least six million dollars. Often today, when pamphlets are offered at very high prices in sales catalogs, the staff checks to see if our copies are safely in the locked precincts of the Rare Book Department. Last year Ashbel Smith's early Texas medical imprint, *An Account of the Yellow Fever*, Galveston, 1839, was offered for $1,500. Our copy was immediately rescued from the pamphlet file in the main collection, where an unscrupulous reader might be tempted to take it away in a convenient pocket. The very next day after that incident, Goodspeed's *The Month* described an early eighteenth century Boston pamphlet on inoculation for sale at $1,600. Our holdings of those early smallpox pieces are most distinguished, and as this particular one was not present, an immediate telephone call ordered it. Unfortunately it was sold. At the time there were no funds for such a purchase, but its importance to our already fine holdings would surely be of sufficient persuasion to attract funds from some of our Friends. These two incidents are cited to emphasize how valuable pamphlet material may be and how little today age is a factor. Twenty years ago the inoculation pamphlet would have been very costly, the Smith, not at all.

Other material often slighted by librarians are annual reports and annual school catalogs. Those who have little historical insight often discard potential treasures. A member of the Library Committee of the Academy advised that instead of careful weeding of hospital reports we should discard them all. The previous day another Committee member, an astute bookman, telephoned to say that he had been going through similar material at a local dealer's, found some interesting reports he was sending to us, and he would buy for his own library any we did not need. There were many early reports of the Institute of Living in Hartford, Connecticut, only one of which we lacked. The Menninger Foundation, *Short Title Catalogue of the Rare & Historical Collection*, Topeka, 1967, has a splendid listing of hospital reports, pp. 48-63, which should assist any librarian in demonstrating the value of retaining them. With these as with other desiderata, judgment must be determined on the importance of the material to the library and its users. A report that lists donors to an unfamiliar small hospital may be discarded without concern, but reports containing information which will be of obvious use to the historian should receive careful consideration.

Nor should the lowly reprint be scorned, even if the original journal article is in the collection. Reprints of outstanding contributions to science, especially those signed by the authors, are collectors' items of great cost. Librarians must look at reprints, not as trash to be thrown out without question, but rather as potential rarities. The staff of the Academy library are well aware that out-of-date, unwanted textbooks, particularly duplicates, may be discarded without further questioning, but pamphlet material, small pieces, must have authoritative judgement passed upon them. A duplicate pamphlet, Philadelphia, 1837, Jean Baptiste Bouillaud, *New Researches on Acute Articular Rheumatism*, was sent for decision. Fortuitously, the previous day it had been noticed for sale in a catalog at $75, so that, obviously, its fate was not wastbasket. Librarians cannot be expected to be knowledgable about such items, but must be aware of general principles, and must at least question the importance of a text. The reprint of Oliver Wendell Holmes' paper on puerperal fever is hardly a handsome publication, but is many times more valuable than a copy of the journal from which it was reprinted. Claude Bernard, Lister, Roentgen, all the giants of medicine are collected in reprint form. Twentieth century giants are no less important. A library exhibit, "Yesterday's Throwaways, Today's Treasures," brought together astonishingly valuable pieces, surprising to librarians and collectors alike.

Alert to these considerations, the librarian faced with building a collection must begin by having a written plan, the product of consultation with bookmen, collectors, dealers, even more than with historians, unless the latter are bookmen as well as historians. The historians are enormously helpful in determining policies, but their own specialized interests may on occasion prevent objective planning. The collection must be planned for the future as well as the present, and one must consider the holdings already available, and the possibility of adding collections being built by those close to the library, but since it is obvious that too broad an acquisitions policy prevents rather than stimulates wise collecting, the librarian cannot please every historian by collecting in his field. The physician who is shocked to find the library does not have anything about the materia medica of Madagascar may insist that such a collection be inaugurated. Such a collection might be most appropriate, but decision should be reached only after extensive efforts to determine how it fits into the present collection, where other collections are, who are experts in the field to advise, what dealers can help. In some fields expertise is far more important than available funds. Money is necessary for most collecting, but time and expertise are far more necessary. Here the dealer can be expert consultant, a friend in need as well as a bookseller. Librarians without contacts with dealers should acquire a directory of the members of the Antiquarian Booksellers Association of America from their Center at 630 Fifth Avenue, New York, and make an effort to meet and know any geographically convenient one who may cover medicine and science. The librarian, the bookman, the historian, the dealer all have vital roles to play.

Changes in the study of the history of medicine in these twenty years have been as great as those in collecting. When Dr. Richard Shryock was Director of the Institute of the History of Medicine at Johns Hopkins University, he reported that those applying to study there were from other disciplines rather than medicine. A major reason was that at the time there were few opportunities for full-time historians of medicine. Today the situation is in reverse, with chairs not filled because there are not enough trained applicants. On the other hand, in the training of rare book librarians, for the first time there are opportunities to learn that expertise outside in-service learning. The establishment of a Rare Book Section of the Association of College and Research Libraries, and the pioneering at the Lilly Library in training rare book librarians are major and exciting and badly needed steps toward supporting and providing the expertise so necessary. The same may be said of advancement in the care and processing of archives. When the Academy started its archival program, there were no guidelines or sources of information and advice. Today the Society of American Archivists has annual meetings of great practical value and publishes an important journal. This supplements Theodore R. Schellenberg's *The Management of Archives*, New York, 1965. Oral history, too, has grown up in this same period. Librarians must concern themselves with the records of their own institutions, and encourage administration to insist upon saving and preserving them. Gilbert Clausman, Librarian of the New York University Medical Center established a model program, and others in the New York metropolitan area have been alerted to the importance of establishing and maintaining these services in accordance with the size and age of the facility. Some hospitals have lost all records of their distinguished history. Others are more fortunate in early administrators who realized the value to the institution for information and in public relations as well as the history of medicine.

Establishing the institution's own records is surely the first step in building a historical collection. Then decisions must be made regarding the scope of the collection. This depends upon the goals, upon the teaching needs, upon the special interests of the institution. The greatest danger is to be too ambitious in scope. Lee Ash has said in a survey he made of a library in Canada (quoted on the cover of an issue of the *Antiquarian Bookman*): "A good collection is expensive: a poor collection is extravagant and wasteful." An examination of several collections may show this, so we may first look at some of the collections given over the years to the New York Academy of Medicine. The Streeter Collection, purchased by a group of Fellows of the Academy in 1928, is a particularly good example. It was brought together by a physician who bought whatever appealed to him without any special plan or design, and without any expertise, without knowledge of condition of copies, of editions, of importance of texts.

Some of these volumes are highlights of the library today, such as the superlative illuminated English manuscript of Guy de Chauliac. But as a collection it can only be called extravagant and wasteful, or more properly it may be said that it was not a collection, but a group of books which have been scattered through the Academy's library. A few years later, Dr. Margaret Barclay Wilson presented her collection on foods and cookery, some 4,000 items relating to the subject. This is not as extravagant and wasteful, for it has a basic idea and brings together volumes and information belonging together. Unfortunately, she, too, was not advised about condition of copies, or selection of editions or texts, but added whatever came her way, so that there is great unevenness, with excellent holdings by one author, but no important edition by such a figure as Brillat-Savarin. On the other hand, it was wasteful to have this collection given to a medical library where it is seldom that readers wish to know what an Italian kitchen of the sixteenth century looked like, how poultry was carved in the seventeenth century, or how elegantly an eighteenth century table could be decorated. This is surely out of scope in a medical library, except for texts on nutrition and diet. It is especially sad to see a collection brought together with such love and interest little used and not being added to as such a collection might be in a more appropriate home.

Several collections received in the last decade are worthy of examination as models to follow. Rufus Cole, Director of the Hospital of Rockefeller Institute, interested in the development of scientific research, collected the writings of Francesco Redi, an eminent Italian experimental physiologist of the seventeenth century. From this one author his efforts were extended to assembling the writings of Redi's colleagues. Redi was a member of the Accademia del Cimento, that first great scientific society whose writings reflected the ferment, the exciting and varied experiments of the scientists of the period. Here are the works of Bellini, Borelli, Steno, Kircher, Malpighi, Magalotti, and others, all in one place for the historian of experimental science in that century, a superb concept for a collection. Fenwick Beekman's John Hunter collection is of equal importance, uniting not only the many contributions of that great surgeon, but also the work of his contemporaries. Another small group of material Dr. Beekman collected may be called unique, and is surely fascinating, if not a little macabre. It relates to the resurrectionists, that notorious pair, Burke and Hare, who robbed graveyards for the benefit of surgeons wishing bodies for dissection. One volume contains pictures in color of "Daft Jamie" and other victims, many balads, a woodcut of the scene of the execution, and a letter written by William Burke, addressed to the keeper of the "Lock up House," on the night before the hanging. Again, the historian has in one place a treasure of information.

A totally different kind of collection came to the Academy, one that required little in money, but much in thought, perseverance, enthusiasm, even dedication. Michael Davis for over fifty years was intimately involved with medico-socio-economic movements of the period which led to Medicare. He saved correspondence, published and unpublished reports, legislation, pamphlets, books, a mine of pertinent information that anyone wishing to report on these events in the history of health care and economics must consult. This collection can serve as a classic example of what may be accomplished by one man deeply concerned in his work.

Most large collections are the result of amalgamation of a number of these personal collections, and the librarian must work toward coordinating them, supplementing, not allowing them to stagnate. A dynamic program should be encouraged, and the various collections placed within a general scheme so that progress may be made in developing the collection as a whole, rather than separate goals pointing in many directions. With large collections this is difficult, but planning should be started early. Sir William Osler's collection, remarkably varied in scope, was carefully structured. This was possible only because of his varied interests and wide reading in the history of medicine. Also, he had the good fortune of pioneering at a time when it was possible to haunt bookstores for great bargains. His careful planning, however, is still pertinent to the librarian.

Acquiring material is only the first step for the librarian; it must be cataloged, it must be cared for. Too many libraries, overburdened with many activities, have put aside for the future the care and cataloging of their gifts and purchases. This discourages donors who prefer to give to institutions which obviously cherish their gifts and make them available. Often it has been difficult to persuade donors to send manuscripts and other archival material to the appropriate library because previous gifts have not been unpacked and cataloged. Since the Academy library has always made every effort to process such material it has been the reluctant recipient of many items more properly offered elsewhere. Librarians wishing to encourage donations should emphasize their willingness to care for them.

Preservation is a most important problem today. Fortunately, there is now information available, although it is not always a simple matter to find an expert. Yet expertise in this field is all important. Much damage has been done by amateur mending, by accepting a salesman's words about laminators or supplies, by lack of interest, by assuming every large library must know what procedures should be correct. Librarians should at least learn what not to do, should feel a grave responsibility to keep up with the literature on the subject, should not order supplies and equipment without consulting the enormously useful publication of Talas, Division of Technical Library Service, *Tools & Supplies for Bookbinding; Book Repair; Book Conservation*, New York, 1967 and Supplement, 1968. The series of pamphlets issued by the Barrow Laboratory: Permanent Durable Book Paper, The Virginia State Library, Richmond, should be at hand. Articles by Frazer Poole, Preservation Officer, Library of Congress, Paul Banks, Conservator of the Newberry Library, and Hannah B. Friedman, Collections Preservation Coordinator at the New York Public Library, appear in the literature. Workshops by such an expert as Carolyn Horton are of great importance for all staff members.

There are of course differing opinions and methods, and each librarian must use judgment. A rare book librarian who recommended that materials in a library should be divided for preservation procedures, the sheep from the goats, should surely pause at the awesome responsibility of these decisions. They should not be left to the whim of a staff member. Experience has taught that unless one knows that a Roentgen reprint is of great value it is apt to be treated as any other reprint, and tragic errors have been made by unknowledgeable treatment, with stiff hinges cutting through fragile title-pages. The advice—at least do no harm—should be a command for all types of material, old, new, fragile, ugly, and handsome.

Any collection is brought together for the future as well as the present. It is a heritage from one generation to another, or from many centuries to another. It may be of staggering financial worth or it may in its initial stages be modestly collected as those of Samuel Smith Purple and Michael Davis. Time, interest, knowledge of a subject, enthusiasm, and determination bring rich rewards to library and librarian.

ABOUT THE AUTHOR—See page 135.

Organization of Materials

Classification and cataloging in a medical library differ in subject from that in other libraries, but vary little in basic operation. More and more, with the inception of the National Library of Medicine's *Current Catalog*, libraries are using the *National Library of Medicine Classification* and its *Medical Subject Headings* (MeSH).

One user's experience with revising his catalog when *MeSH* is updated will serve to illustrate attributes of that standardized vocabulary and of the procedures involved with keeping the card catalog up to date.

Many medical libraries have automated various cataloging routines. From among all the experiences with mechanized catalogs, we have chosen the story of a failure with the idea that more can be learned from one honest mistake than from many partial successes.

Problems of Medical Subject Cataloging

by Frank B. Rogers

A description of the nature and extent of the work required to update a library subject catalog for books provides a basis for a discussion of the effects of subheadings on book cataloging and periodical indexing, general comparisons of a book catalog and a periodical index, and a philosophical look at the MeSH system.

It is an honor to be asked to present the second annual Janet Doe Lecture. Janet Doe is a great figure in medical librarianship, a great contributor to the development of this field. I have had occasion in the past to seek her advice and help many times, and it was always given generously and wisely; there are many in this Association who would join me in that avowal.

Of Miss Doe's many interests, a special one is cataloging, and particularly subject cataloging. Our Association has not shown much interest in this area in late years, as if these problems were such that they could be left to others to solve for us. It is my hope that the emphasis on this subject in the program of the 1968 Annual Meeting of the Medical Library Association will serve to provoke a renewed interest in and attention to that technical area which, in my mind, more than any other tends to define and illuminate the special job and the special glory of the special librarian.

The charge given to the Janet Doe lecturer is that he speak on some historical or philosophical aspect of medical librarianship. My remarks may seem to fall short on this score, for what I have to say deals largely with description, in considerable detail, of an attack on an operational problem in a single library. I justify this by my feeling that the University of Colorado Medical Center Library is fairly typical, in most ways, of that group made up of about one hundred of the larger medical libraries of the United States. And I justify it, in a larger sense, by quoting the remark of Alvan Feinstein, who said that he doubted that it was the case that Isaac Newton sat down one fine evening and decided that he would posit the notion of gravity, and that he would then go outdoors the next day to see if any apples were falling.[1] What I want to do first is to count some apples and see where they are falling. After this, it is unfortunately unlikely that I shall come up with any such elegant notion as a bibliothecal theory of gravitation. It is a regrettable but almost inevitable fact that, in this era of burgeoning social complexity, more and more the theoretician and the practitioner are no longer combined in a single person, but are different persons pursuing their disparate but equally important tasks. I take it that it is the duty of the practitioner to point out to the theoretician *where he should look*. Again, in the phrase of Dr. Feinstein, it is not the case that one fine day Linus Pauling decided to do some hemoglobin electrophoresis on the notion that it might have something to do with blood dyscrasias. Practitioners had told him where to look. They had identified the sickling trait, and Pauling's elegant work provided explanations which advance both theory and practice thereafter.[1] The best I can hope to do here is to identify some of the sickling traits of subject cataloging.

The University of Colorado Medical Center Library holds upwards of 85,000 volumes, the greater portion of which are imprints of the last two decades. It has a divided catalog, for which I have my predecessor to thank, and I offer these thanks fervently. There is no doubt in my mind but that the separate subject catalog is preferable from the library patron's point of view, and highly preferable from the librarian-practitioner's point of

SOURCE: Reprinted from Frank B. Rogers, "Problems of Medical Subject Cataloging," *Bulletin of the Medical Library Association*, 56 (Oct., 1968), pp. 355–364, by permission of the publisher and the author. The second Janet Doe Lecture. Presented at the Sixty-seventh Annual Meeting of the Medical Library Association, Denver, Colorado, June 11, 1968.

view, in that catalog maintenance is greatly facilitated. In this subject catalog are represented imprints of 1946 or later date; we place our reliance on printed bibliographies, such as the *Index-Catalogue*, for imprints of an earlier date. And since studies have shown us that only 15 percent of the action in our Library concerns earlier materials, and that most of this concerns serials rather than monographs, we are content with this arrangement.

The separate subject catalog provides the opportunity to file subject cards behind guide cards which bear the subject headings. It is our practice to file subject cards in reverse chronological order, so that the latest work always first engages the attention. Only current editions are represented in our subject catalog; earlier editions are to be found in the separate author catalog.

In 1965, our subject catalog was thoroughly revised to accept the National Library of Medicine's *Medical Subject Headings (MeSH)* as the subject heading authority. In 1966, the subject catalog was again revised to reflect the introduction of standard subheadings into the system. We procured a set of these standard subheadings on preprinted center-cut guide cards to go with our left-cut guide cards bearing main headings. We adopted the forty-two topical subheadings then in the *MeSH* system and the four additional topical subheadings (e.g., *in infancy & childhood*) authorized by *MeSH* for book cataloging. We also adopted twenty-one of the form subheadings authorized, rejecting only a few, such as *juvenile literature*, as being unsuitable for the scope of our collection. At the same time, on a purely intuitive basis, we made the decision that we would divide main headings by either topical or form subheadings, placing them within a single alphabet arrangement, but that we would not subdivide a topical subheading by a form subheading, or vice versa.

There are two main reasons for adopting the *MeSH* system. First, maintaining a subject heading authority list is a task of a high order, requiring much skill and many man-hours of effort; we wished to take advantage of the effort already performed at the National Library of Medicine, which we could not afford to duplicate even if we could muster the skill and resources. Second, we wished to take the greatest possible advantage of the centralized cataloging product of NLM, being made available in the *NLM Current Catalog*, for the same reasons.

Then in 1967, *MeSH* introduced 200 new main headings, and made slight changes of form in an additional fifty main headings, for a total new authority list of about 6,600 main headings. It also introduced eleven new subheadings to the apparatus. This called for another revision of our subject catalog, the third in what is now clearly an annual series. What I want to document for you is what happened in this third revision and what some of the implications are of the difficulties encountered.

I performed the revision of the subject catalog myself, and it required 240 man-hours, or six man-weeks. While I happen to find this kind of task congenial, I do begrudge the long hours involved. Because of the fact that this was a third revision, and because of certain peculiarities of our catalog, such as that the earlier subject cards do not bear subject tracings, something more than merely taking care of the new changes was involved, but I am unable to say just how much time these extraneous factors amounted to.

There is another possible circumstance which must be alluded to. In revising a subject catalog, one is dealing with a corpus that is fixed in size at that moment in time, and there is a danger that one will yield to the temptation of revising it as a fixed item, as one would index an individual book or arrange a one-time bibliography, rather than revising it prospectively with an eye to the next decade's library patrons. I strove to avoid this hazard, and some evidence that I may have succeeded in large measure is the fact that at the end of the revision there were 882 main headings which held but a single entry behind them.

My method of work was crude because of the time limitations involved. My sources of information were limited to the title of the book, the tracings on the card, and the guide card heading under which it was filed. Seldom did I succumb to the longing to reexamine the book itself, which of course would have been desirable ideally.

I moved cards around at will, placing them under new headings and new subheadings. At the conclusion of the exercise, the entire subject catalog was filmed and reproduced on paper slips. A library assistant then spent seventeen weeks, first making the tracings on the slips agree with the actual point of filing, then rearranging the slips in call number order, and then transferring the new valid information to the shelflist. It was in the course of this exercise that the data to be exhibited were collected.

We found that the number of cards representing books was 21,600, pertaining to 16,000 volumes, but only 13,000 titles. (Cards under the subheadings *abstracts, indexes,* and *periodicals* are not considered in this study.) Considering the rate of processing, it is difficult to see how the job could have been done in a shorter period of time.

TABLE 1

UNIVERSITY OF COLORADO MEDICAL CENTER SUBJECT CATALOG 1946-1967

Total cards representing books	21,604
Total volumes represented	16,028
less multivolume works, duplicates, superseded editions	3,050
Total book titles represented	12,978
Librarian man/hours to edit (average 40 seconds per card)	240
Library assistant man/hours to post (average 3 minutes per title)	680

The average number of subject cards per title was 1.66. When single card titles are eliminated, the remaining titles show a representation by an average 2.55 cards, which happens to be identical to the ratio of the *Cumulated Index Medicus* of 1966.

TABLE 2

SUBJECT CARDS PER TITLE

Average subject cards per title	1.66
Titles represented by single card only	7,411
Titles represented by multiple subject cards	5,567
Cards representing multiple-card books	14,193
Average subject cards per multiple-card book	2.55

Of the 21,600 cards, 17,600 were under undivided headings or "up front," and 4,000 cards were under subheadings. Of the 6,600 main headings available in the system, only 42 percent had been utilized, and of these, only one-quarter had been divided by subheadings.

The number of main headings used is neither surprising nor disturbing; the Colorado set is simply a subset of *MeSH*, a subset which may be enlarged as the need becomes manifest. The low proportion of use of subheadings is somewhat startling, but it must be remembered that to a certain extent this is an artificial situation, i.e., in editing the older material there may not be enough information available in title and tracings, unequivocally, to warrant assignment of subheadings.

TABLE 3

HEADINGS USED

Cards representing books	21,604
Cards–undivided headings or "up front"	17,637
Cards under subheadings	3,967
under FORM subheadings	1,318
under TOPICAL subheadings	2,649
Number of main headings used	2,772
Number of undivided main headings	2,058
Average card density per undivided heading (or "up front")	8.6

TABLE 4

SUBHEADING DENSITIES

Number of divided main headings	714
divided by FORM subheading only	234
divided by TOPICAL, or TOPICAL and FORM	480
Number of cards under FORM subheadings (18)	1,318
Number of MH/SH (FORM) combinations	629
Average card density per MH/SH (FORM) combination	2.1
Number of cards under TOPICAL subheadings (57)	2,649
Number of MH/SH (TOPICAL) combinations	831
Average card density per MH/SH (TOPICAL) combination	3.2

Table 4 displays subheading usage. It shows that the number of new "access points" created in the subject catalog was 629 with the use of eighteen form subheadings, and 831 with the use of fifty-seven topical subheadings. This tends to confirm what we might have expected in terms of proportional use. We may note that the inclusion of *history* under topical subheadings, rather than under form subheadings where it would have been just as appropriate, tends to distort the picture.

TABLE 5

ACCESS POINT DENSITY

Main headings available	6,600
Main headings used	2,772
"Access Points" used	4,232
Main headings	2,772
MH/SH combinations (FORM)	629
MH/SH combinations (TOPICAL)	831
Total MH/SH combinations	1,460
Average card density per "access point"	5.1

Table 5 summarizes the usage in the Colorado catalog. It shows that the use of subheadings has increased the number of access points by 50 percent, and has reduced the average density of posting under each access point from 7.8 to 5.1, a decrease of 35 percent.

Now let us recall that *MeSH* was created as a common subject heading authority list for indexing journal articles as well as for cataloging books. The rationale for this position is that it is too costly to maintain two separate authority lists, even if there were otherwise some positive reason for doing so, and that a single list facilitates the library patron's use of what is inherently a complicated apparatus. This position seems sound.

With this in mind, it may prove interesting to compare practice in the Colorado catalog with *Index Medicus* practice, using 1966 as an example. Table 6 gives the basic facts for the *Cumulated Index Medicus*, 1966.

TABLE 6

CUMULATED INDEX MEDICUS 1966

Total articles indexed	157,798
Total citations printed	402,908
Average citations per article	2.55
Number undivided or "up front"	186,139
Number subheaded	216,769
Total "access points" used	36,154
Average citations per "access point"	11.1

These figures pertain only to the printed subject section for the year stated. The term "access point" is defined in the same manner as for the Colorado catalog earlier.

Table 7 juxtaposes the two sets of figures. First, one must adjust to the fact that the *Index Medicus* corpus is more than twelve times the size of the Colorado catalog, despite the discrepancy in number of years covered. One sees that the greatest disproportion occurs in the frequency of use of subheadings. One also sees that this indeed must occur, as the number of access points in the *IM* case exceeds the total number of cards in the Colorado catalog.

TABLE 7

INDEX USE AND CATALOG USE

	Index Medicus	U. Colorado
Articles indexed/Titles in catalog	157,798	12,798
Citations printed/Cards in catalog	402,908	21,604
Average citations/cards per article/title	2.55	1.66
Number undivided	186,139	17,637
Number subheaded	216,769	3,967
Total "access points" used	36,154	4,232
Average density per "access point"	11.1	5.1

Table 8 compares catalog and index use of the body of forty-two topical subheadings available in 1966. Subheadings printed in capitals are those which fall in other percentiles in the opposite list. The two central columns indicate the number of times each subheading was used, with the figure for *IM* being derived by dividing the actual figure by a factor of a little more than twelve–in other words, the *IM* number is the number of times the subheading would have been used in indexing the same number of items represented in the Colorado catalog.

TABLE 8

HEAVY-USE SUBHEADINGS

Rank	U. Colorado	Times Used	Times Used	*Index Medicus*	Rank
1	HISTORY	549	1880	metabolism	1
2	surgery	274	1524	PHARMACODYNAMICS	2
3	therapy	165	1287	etiology	3
4	physiology	144	1257	diagnosis	4
5	diagnosis	110	1081	therapeutic use	5
6	metabolism	106	1066	surgery	6
7	therapeutic use	96	1030	COMPLICATIONS	7
8	ANATOMY & HISTOLOGY	95	861	drug therapy	8
9	NURSING	58	770	physiology	9
10	etiology	57	737	pathology	10
11	drug therapy	48	643	DRUG EFFECTS	11
12	pathology	46	523	therapy	12

12 subheadings–66 percent of all topical use

12 subheadings–71 percent of all use

TABLE 9

LEAST-USE SUBHEADINGS

Rank	U. Colorado	Times Used	Times Used	*Index Medicus*	Rank
31	classification	7	103	RADIATION EFFECTS	31
32	ADVERSE EFFECTS	6	89	administration & dosage	32
33	VETERINARY	6	85	BLOOD SUPPLY	33
34	CYTOLOGY	5	83	isolation & purification	34
35	administration & dosage	4	71	poisoning	35
36	ENZYMOLOGY	3	70	congenital	36
37	injuries	3	58	pathogenicity	37
38	poisoning	3	47	injuries	38
39	COMPLICATIONS	2	41	INNERVATION	39
40	congenital	1	40	EMBRYOLOGY	40
41	isolation & purification	0	37	classification	41
42	pathogenicity	0	12	NURSING	42

TABLE 10

WIDE RANK VARIATIONS

Rank	U. Colorado	Times Used	Times Used	*Index Medicus*	Rank
1	HISTORY	549	1524	PHARMACODYNAMICS	2
8	NURSING	58	1030	COMPLICATIONS	7
22	PHARMACODYNAMICS	12	142	HISTORY	25
39	COMPLICATIONS	2	12	NURSING	42

Table 9 shows the other end of the line. Again, the subheadings printed in caps are those which do not match this percentile in the opposite list.

Table 10 shows where the widest discrepancies lie. It is easy to see why this should be so, considering the differences that naturally exist as between the two bodies of material.

It will be remembered that eleven new subheadings were introduced in 1967. Table 11 shows their use in the University of Colorado catalog.

TABLE 11

SUBHEADINGS INTRODUCED 1967

	Times Used at U. Colorado
analysis	12
blood	9
cerebrospinal fluid	0
chemically induced	1
diagnostic use	0
education	43
microbiology	0
mortality	0
radiography	120
rehabilitation	39
urine	3

The three new subheadings, *radiography, rehabilitation*, and *education*, are fairly useful. The remainder are of little help.

After the 1967 subheadings have been incorporated, and considering the use of form subheadings as well, the highest use and lowest use groups in the Colorado catalog appear as in Table 12. In the highest use group in the left hand column, note that the new appearances, signaled by capitalization, include six subheadings, one of which is a 1967 topical addition, *radiology*. In the lowest use group in the right column, note that there are six new members, all of which are 1967 additions.

Table 13 is a list of the twenty main headings with the highest posting densities in the Colorado catalog. The list holds no surprises, except perhaps for the inclusion of PERSONALITY. Note that many of these heavy-use main headings are themselves, in another incarnation, identical with subheading concepts. Recall that these twenty headings, and their 131 subheading combinations, represent only 3 percent of the total access points used but accommodate over 11 percent of the total catalog entries.

With this as background, I offer the following observations:

TABLE 12

HIGHEST AND LOWEST USE–U. COLORADO

Highest		Lowest	
history	549	enzymology	3
surgery	274	injuries	3
IN INFANCY & CHILDHOOD	258	poisoning	3
ATLASES	234	URINE	3
NURSING TEXTS	217	complications	2
BIBLIOGRAPHY .'	193	CHEMICALLY INDUCED	1
therapy	165	congenital	1
physiology	144	CEREBROSPINAL FLUID	0
RADIOGRAPHY	120	DIAGNOSTIC USE	0
DIRECTORIES	115	isolation & purification	0
diagnosis	110	MICROBIOLOGY	0
metabolism	106	MORTALITY	0
therapeutic use	96	pathogenicity	0

TABLE 13

MAIN HEADINGS WITH HIGHEST POSTING DENSITIES–U. COLORADO

	Total Cards	Up Front	Number Subheadings	Density Per Subheading	Form Subheadings	Density Per Form SH	Topical SH	Density Per Topical SH
Biochemistry	169	158	5	2.2	4	2.2	1	1.0
Biology	86	58	9	3.1	7	2.3	2	6.0
Brain	108	28	8	10.0	1	19.0	7	9.0
Child Psychology	95	95						
Education	119	110	4	2.2	3	2.7	1	1.0
Education, Nursing	150	148	1	2.0	1	2.0		
History of Medicine	94	82	3	4.0	3	4.0		
Medicine	106	46	6	10.0	6	10.0		
Neoplasms	150	35	22	5.3	6	3.0	16	6.3
Nursing	126	103	7	3.3	7	3.3		
Personality	101	92	1	9.0			1	9.0
Pharmacology	92	69	5	4.6	4	4.5	1	5.0
Physiology	97	65	8	4.0	7	4.6	1	1.0
Psychiatry	195	156	11	3.5	8	2.1	3	7.3
Psychoanalysis	163	142	7	3.0	4	1.5	3	5.0
Psychology	91	64	5	5.4	4	5.5	1	5.0
Psychotherapy	141	139	2	1.0	1	1.0	1	1.0
Public Health	98	59	10	3.9	8	2.4	2	10.0
Science	111	27	8	10.5	7	4.0	1*	57.0
Surgery	144	75	9	7.7	6	3.7	3	16.0
Composite	122	88	6.6	5.1	4.4	4.0	2.2	7.0

*History.

(1) The number of items cataloged for the *Index Medicus* being far larger than the number of items in the average library subject catalog, it is reasonable to expect that the library catalog may require a lesser number of access points than does the *Index* and that this smaller set may be a subset of the larger.

(2) When additions and changes are made to subject heading authority lists, as is inevitable, demands on the time of librarians, necessitated for revision of subject catalogs, is far from being negligible.

On this second point, there emerges another notion of great importance—the use of machine or computer systems has little or no bearing on the amount of librarian man-hours required for subject catalog revision. Consider the following instances:

(a) In the case of a new term, such as PARKINSONISM, being substituted in a one-for-one exchange for an old term, such as PARALYSIS AGITANS, there is no problem in either a machine or a manual system. In the machine, we simply substitute one code for another; in the subject portion of a divided catalog, we simply remove a block of cards from behind one guide card and place them behind a new guide card; and to me, there does not seem to be a requirement for modifying the shelflist records in such instances.

(b) But in the case of new main headings which do not have this one-for-one equivalency with the old, as for example, the new KIDNEY CORTEX NECROSIS and KIDNEY FAILURE, CHRONIC, which were formerly not differentiated from the broader term KIDNEY DISEASES, there is no solution possible except a reexamination of all of the material under the older term. In these cases, there is at least some comfort in the thought that only particular areas of the subject catalog, e.g., KIDNEY DISEASES, need be examined to establish which items are now to be cataloged under newly established headings, e.g., KIDNEY CORTEX NECROSIS.

(c) In the case of the introduction of additional new subheadings, however, in the majority of instances no such limitation of effort is possible. Often the entire file must be reexamined. All candidates for inclusion under the subheading *blood* are certainly not going to be found under the main heading BLOOD. And where, for another example, would one be expected to look for material now eligible for inclusion under the new subheading *diagnostic use*? The problem of dealing with new additions to a subheading list is far more severe than dealing with the problem of new main headings.

There is no question but that, to remain viable and useful, subject heading authority lists must undergo changes and must receive new additions from time to time. What I want to warn against is the easy and fatal assumption that massive proliferation of terms brings with it no penalties. It is understandable that the tired indexer or the tired subject cataloger or the tired reference librarian may at some particular moment long for the inclusion of a new and very specific term in the system because its presence would dispel the particular concern of the moment. Any coordinate indexing system, as Calvin Mooers pointed out long ago, must favor the descriptor end of the subject heading-descriptor continuum. The more minutely precise and limited and precoordinated are our terms, the further are we drifting from the principle of coordinate indexing and the less useful that mechanism becomes. As an example, I exhibit a partial list of some main subject headings suggested for addition to the *MeSH* list. These are in the field of alcohol studies. (Table 14).

TABLE 14

SUGGESTED MAIN HEADINGS

Adaptation to alcohol
Alcoholic brain disease
Alcoholic hallucinosis
Alcoholic intoxication
Alcoholic paranoid states
Alcoholic psychoses
Alcoholism
Aversion therapy of alcoholism
Chronic alcoholic psychosis
Dependence on alcohol
Deviant drinking
Drinking behavior
Drinking pattern
Early skid career pattern
Endogenous alcoholic
Exogenous alcoholic
Hidden alcoholic
Lay therapy
Nonaddictive pathological alcoholic
Nonbeverage alcohol drinking
Pathological intoxication
Physiologic dependence on alcohol
Plateau drinker
Prealcoholic personality
Psychological adaptation to alcohol
Psychological dependence on alcohol
Remission of alcoholism
Research on alcoholism
Ritual drinker
Schizophrenic drinker
Situational drinker
Social drinker
Solitary drinker
Successfully arrested alcoholic
Symptomatic drinking
Teetotalism
Withdrawal syndrome (alcohol)

Actually, these suggested alcohol headings constituted 10 percent of the entire list of headings suggested by a group of behavioral scientists. The field of work of the most active member of this group is evident. He is thinking of a list of headings suitable for his private files of material, which contain nothing but alcohol studies. It would be fatal to adopt such a list as part of a general scheme. In contrast, I exhibit in Table 15 a list of the more descriptor-like subject headings now available in *MeSH*.

TABLE 15

NLM *MeSH* HEADINGS

Alcohol deterrents
Alcoholic beverages
Alcoholic intoxication
Alcoholism
Korsakoff's syndrome
Psychoses, alcoholic
Temperance

This is as it should be. While we are on the topic, I should like to allude to the problem of subject heading equivalency, the reduction of separate authority lists to an overall authority list. All studies in this area which I have seen are vastly oversimplified and contain many illusions when they imply that all that is needed for consolidation of lists is an act of will. Table 16 shows the list of current Library of Congress headings on this topic.

TABLE 16

LC SUBJECT HEADINGS, SEVENTH EDITION 1966

Alcohol in the body
Alcoholics
Alcoholism
Alcoholism and crime
Alcoholism and employment
Alcoholism and religion
Cocktails
Drinking and traffic accidents
Drinking in literature
Drinking on aircraft
Drunkenness (Criminal law)
Liquor laws
Liquor problem
Liquor traffic
Liquors
Prohibition
Punched card systems–alcohol
Temperance
Temperance and religion
Wine in literature

Surely these show that the Library of Congress and the National Library of Medicine have different fields of interest and that the search for subject heading standardization is going to be one of the most resistant areas to effective compromise in the entirely laudable efforts that are now underway to achieve greater cataloging standardization among the several national library systems.

I have described the efforts required to conform to the 1967 changes in *MeSH*. Soon I shall have to tackle the problems, till now postponed, of 1968 *MeSH* changes. These changes are enormous, including main heading additions totaling more than 10 percent of the entire list, and including additional subheadings. The subheading changes are more numerous than the mere number of subheadings added; they embrace the extension of existing subheadings to additional categories. While the number of subheadings has increased by 46 percent in a period of two years, the available subheading-category combinations have increased by 76 percent. And when the 1968 revisions are completed, the 1969 changes will be at hand.

To my colleagues at the National Library of Medicine who are in charge of the *MeSH* operation, I would wish to say the following. I applaud the generally fine work which you have performed in keeping the *MeSH* list viable. I ask you never to forget that in adding new main headings to the list, one of the most important points is to establish the relationship of the new heading to the headings in the existing corpus. This implies especial care in establishing the cross-reference structure, which has negative as well as positive aspects.

Cross-referencing is inherently complicated enough without complicating it further with the addition of what I would call "gratuitous" cross-references. The first two examples in Table 17 are of this type. If this type of cross-reference is included–the gratuitous cross-reference of the type "Leukemia *see also* Anemia"–there is no limit whatsoever which can be imposed on the extent of the cross-reference system.

TABLE 17

CROSS-REFERENCE PROBLEMS

Thermography
  XR Autonomic dysfunction
  XR Body temperature
  XR Paraplegia
Cystic fibrosis
  See also related Sweating
Anoxia (C17)
Cerebral anoxia (C8, C10)

The third pair in Table 17 is an example on the other side. Great care must be exercised to provide crosses between closely related headings of this kind.

But the main thing I want to say to my *MeSH* colleagues is this–I plead for an early stabilization of topical subheadings. There is some evidence to suggest that the subheadings of maximal usefulness have already been discovered and adopted and that extensive further elaboration of the list is not warranted.

To my colleagues in the subject cataloging departments of the many medical libraries across the country and to my colleagues in reference services, I would like to say the following. Let us not lightly recommend changes in what is really a very delicate structure without realizing all the different aspects which are at stake. There is, for example, the problem of achieving indexer and system consistency, as well as the problem of trying to achieve instant user satisfaction in 100 percent of cases. Let us not naively imagine that parts of the system can be tampered with without causing reverberations throughout the system. Let us recognize and support the *MeSH* system for what it is, a legitimate compromise between the descriptor-oriented terms of a computer coordinate-indexing system, and the subject-heading-oriented terms of the conventional card catalog.

Finally, let us realize that we are up against some tough professional problems in the field of subject cataloging and that these problems are crucial to the nature and adequacy of the services which we can provide. Neither Billings nor Cutter found permanent solutions to these problems, nor do today's computer systems figure in any central way in their solution. We need new ideas, large and small and medium-sized. Perhaps, for example, we should probe further into the notion of time-segmentation of subject catalogs, it being evident that this is the factor which "solves" the situation for the *Index Medicus*, and is absent in large part from our library catalogs. But "time-segmentation" is just a phrase. What we need is to explore some possible operational systems, weighing what we must yield for what it is possible to achieve, and never being seduced into the notion that we can get something for nothing.

NOTE

[1]The statements of Dr. Feinstein are those made by him in the course of a lecture at the University of Colorado in the Spring of 1968. Cf. his *Clinical Judgment* (Baltimore, Williams & Wilkins, 1967).

ABOUT THE AUTHOR–Dr. Frank Bradway Rogers is Librarian and Professor of Medical Bibliography, University of Colorado. He went to that position after serving for fourteen years as Director of the National Library of Medicine and its predecessors, the Armed Forces Medical Library and the Army Medical Library. His undergraduate education was obtained at Yale, and he received his M.D. from Ohio State University. He has an M.S.L.S. from Columbia University.

Dr. Rogers left a career in surgery in the U.S. Army Medical Corps when he was appointed Director of the Army Medical Library. During his administration of the Library, it gained a Congressional charter for the national function it was already accepting, with consequent name change, the dream of a new building was brought to fruition, and MEDLARS (Medical Literature Analysis and Retrieval System) was initiated. He has been recognized for these achievements and his scholarship by such awards as the Public Health Service's Distinguished Service Medal, the American Library Association's Melvil Dewey Medal, and the Medical Library Association's Marcia C. Noyes Award, Barnard Memorial Prize, and the Janet Doe lectureship, for which this paper was written.

He is a Past President of the Medical Library Association and of the American Association for the History of Medicine.

Mechanization of Library Procedures in the Medium-sized Medical Library: VIII. Suspension of Computer Catalog

by Doris Bolef, Lynda Van Wagoner, and Estelle Brodman

The following paper is unusual in its reporting of the discontinuation rather than the introduction of a computer system. Reasons for discontinuation center around problems in cumulating the book catalog, difficulties in correcting and updating it, and program problems. The faults are being examined carefully for their use in planning a new system.

INTRODUCTION

The literature of librarianship is replete with articles about newly installed computer systems which are hailed by their makers as the answer to all the problems the flesh of librarianship is heir to. Not so often is the demise of the vaunted system described in the literature, complete with the reasons why it failed. This is to be expected. After all, how many times does one read an article titled, "How I Treated Forty Consecutive Cases of Appendicitis Incorrectly"? Nevertheless, it is incumbent upon those who report purported new advances also to report when the new advance turns out to be neither new nor an advance. The Washington University School of Medicine Library has just put the computer-based acquisitions/cataloging system it reported as in operation in 1963[1] to a new and more severe test than it had ever had before, and under these conditions of strain, the system broke down. Together with serious doubts about the desirability of the results obtained,[2] this breakdown has caused the Library to decide to abandon the present system entirely and to design an entirely new one. The reasons for the breakdown are explained in this article, and the plans for the future now being considered are described, in the hope that such a description will be as helpful to those working in the field as was the original discussion.

EXPERIENCE

The original acquisitions/cataloging system at the Washington University School of Medicine Library was designed for the following purposes:[1,3]

1. To produce, from a single keyboarded card source, multiple printouts: of both acquisitions and fiscal records and author, title, and subject catalogs.
2. To provide Washington University Medical Center personnel and interested persons from other institutions with copies of a printed *Catalog of Books*.

Until recently the *Catalog of Books* has been used merely as a supplement to the traditional card catalog, but it is obviously useless to have a computer catalog and a manual catalog side by side. In September 1968, therefore, a four-month experiment was begun[2] to determine what would happen if that portion of the card catalog whose contents were also in the computer store and computer-produced catalogs (i.e., items acquired since

SOURCE: Reprinted from Doris Bolef, Lynda Van Wagoner, and Estelle Brodman, "Mechanization of Library Procedures in the Medium-Sized Medical Library: VIII. Suspension of Computer Catalog," *Bulletin of the Medical Library Association,* 57 (July, 1969), pp. 264-266, by permission of the publisher and the authors. Earlier articles in this series appear in the *Bulletin* 51: 313-338, July 1963; *Ibid.*, 52: 370-385, Apr. 1964; *Ibid.*, 53: 99-101, 305-328, July 1965; *Ibid.*, 54: 259-260, July 1966; *Ibid.*, 56: 59-70, 71-79, Jan. 1968; *Ibid.*, 56: 123-131, Apr. 1968; *Ibid.*, 57: 260-263, July 1969. Article XII appears on page 254 of this *Reader*.

January 1, 1965) were made inaccessible and readers had to rely on the printouts alone.

One printed catalog covered the years 1965-67, and another 1967. An additional printout covered the period January-June, 1968, and thereafter cumulated monthly printouts were produced. There were in all cases main entry and subject lists, and since 1967, title lists as well. In addition to the computer printouts, because of the time lag between the cataloging of a book and its appearance in the monthly printout, a card catalog of these items was also maintained, and weeded each month as the new printout was received.

DISCUSSION

For the most part, readers accepted the new system with resignation, except for a few who objected to the necessity for searching multiple alphabets when the dates for an item were not known. One reader remarked that it made no difference to him how the cataloging information was presented, so long as it was all there. The staff, on the other hand, found the five alphabets a serious difficulty.

The acquisitions/cataloging system was originally designed around a single-input multiple-output concept, as noted above. A record could be initiated by the Acquisitions Section and added to or changed by the Cataloging Section. In actual practice, however, there were many differences between these records. For example, the Acquisitions Section might order a series under a series title, leaving to the Cataloging Section the expansion of the single record into the necessary number of individual ones. On the other hand, the Acquisitions Section might separate records for volumes normally considered by the Cataloging Section to be part of a set—say a twenty-four volume encyclopedia which appeared over a period of years, for which twenty-four separate entries would be made by the Acquisitions Section as each volume was received and payment for it approved. It was thought that provision had been made for this in the original systems design, but this proved not to be so.

Another serious difficulty was in the inflexibility of any printed record—once a record is printed, it is there to stay. Thus deletions can not be made retrospectively. For example, the Nursing School Library was being disbanded, but the records for it in the printed *Catalog of Books* could not be expunged, and it became necessary to paste a general statement on the cover of each copy in the Library. Copies already distributed could not even have that updating.

It was soon obvious, also, that serious limitations were present on the number of records which could be handled at any one time. For example, the Dental Library holdings were to be added to the computer store, and 600 records were made ready at one fell swoop. Grave difficulties were encountered; the computer refused over and over again to accept them. Finally the input was broken down into smaller chunks and added gradually. The explanation here was that the internal storage capacity of the IBM 1401 was limited. In the particular design and with the particular programming language used (SPS), a considerable fraction of the 8,000 byte storage capacity had to be taken up with instructions to the computer. To make the most efficient use of the core storage remaining for manipulation, there was considerable moving about internally of the data fed into the machine. Unfortunately, it appears that data do not move about and out of specific addresses quickly, but keep building up so that the computer becomes overloaded beyond its storage capacity. It was felt that a larger computer might have obviated this problem. This is a problem also encountered at the SUNY Bio-medical Communication Network.[4]

The poor quality of the program arose in part because of the high systems analyst and programmer turnover, which brought a series of persons, each with a different background, to work on it. Not one of them was able to see it through to conclusion, or (in spite of reams of manual sheets) to provide sufficient documentation so that the person following could understand fully what had gone before. Even debugging had been sketchy. The result was a patchwork so difficult to understand that necessary changes, not anticipated when the program was first put into operation, could not now be made.

The system worked comparatively well for some time: after all, several annual volumes of the *Catalog of Books* were produced. However, using the printed catalog as a supplement to the card catalog requires one level of accuracy and speed; using the printed catalog to replace the card catalog requires a higher level of accuracy and speed. The system provided the first but not the second level of accuracy.

In retrospect, given the requirements originally set forth—single acquisitions/cataloging input and multiple outputs—and the constraints of the capabilities of the IBM 1401 8K computer available when the program was being written, it is not surprising that serious flaws became apparent.

If anything has been learned from this experience it is the old cliché that much more serious thought and preparation must go into the design of a system and its documentation than is generally realized. It cannot be stressed too often that what are problems for the computer are not at all problems for the human, and vice versa.

It is also obvious that designing a cataloging computer system requires catalogers to reverse their normal patterns of thought. Accustomed as they are to the application of a generalized rule to a specific item to be cataloged, the catalogers designing the system must instead generalize from each specific case to the longest, largest, most numerous, most complex situation possible. Provision must be made for all the rules that do not follow logical patterns. All the possible variations to which publishers are prone must thus be considered in advance.

PRESENT SITUATION

Despite the inconveniences and problems encountered during the four-month test, it has been concluded that a good computer-produced catalog is desirable. The Library is therefore now engaged in rethinking the entire acquisitions/cataloging system, expecting to base it on the IBM 360/50 now available. Other changes include breaking the record into an acquisitions record and a cataloging one. The possibility of optical scanning, rather than keypunching, is being investigated. It is hoped to produce catalog cards as well as a printed record, both by way of the computer. Finally, it is expected that in the new system the printouts will be cumulated each month, to do away with the multiple alphabets, and that the printouts will be produced in only a small number of copies for internal use in the Library, with printed cumulated catalogs at rarer intervals. The reason for the latter is given in another article.[2]

Surprisingly enough, in spite of this bruising first experience, the plans for the second attempt to provide a viable computerized acquisitions/cataloging system are being undertaken in a spirit of renewed hope. The Library will, of course, report its results promptly.

NOTES

[1] Moore, Evelyn A.; Brodman, Estelle; and Cohen, Geraldine S. Mechanization of library procedures in the medium-sized medical library: III. Acquisitions and cataloging. Bull. Med. Libr. Ass. 53: 305-328, July 1965.

[2] Brodman, Estelle, and Bolef, Doris. Printed catalogs: retrospect and prospect. Spec. Libr. 68: 783-788, Dec. 1968.

[3] Brodman, Estelle, and Cohen, Geraldine S. Changes in acquisitions-cataloging methods at Washington University School of Medicine Library. Bull. Med. Libr. Ass. 54: 259-260, July 1966.

[4] Library Bulletin, SUNY Upstate Medical Center Library 8: 130-131, Dec. 1968.

ABOUT THE AUTHORS—Mrs. Doris Bolef is Deputy Librarian of the Washington University School of Medicine. She has a B.S. in Education from Temple University, a B.S.L.S. from Drexel University, and an M.S.L.S. from Columbia University. She has served as librarian consultant for a number of nursing school libraries, including the Bellevue Schools of Nursing in New York City. Besides holding positions in other kinds of special library, she was Cataloger at the Falk Library of the Health Professions at the University of Pittsburgh before going to Washington University School of Medicine, first as Cataloger and then as Assistant Librarian for Technical Services before receiving her present assignment.

She has held offices in the Special Libraries Association and the Medical Library Association. Her extracurricular interests include membership on the National Board of the Women's International League for Peace and Freedom.

Lynda Van Wagoner was Cataloger and then Head of Technical Services at Washington University School of Medicine. She holds a B.A. in Nursing from Brigham Young University and an M.S.L.S. from the University of Washington. She had previously worked at the Malcolm Bliss Mental Health Center in St. Louis and at the St. Louis University School of Medicine Library. She is now in Salt Lake City, and combines raising a family with part-time work as a medical abstractor and special research assistant in the Medical Records Department at Cottonwood Hospital, Murray, Utah.

Dr. Estelle Brodman is Librarian and Professor of Medical History at the Washington University

School of Medicine. Her previous library positions were at the National Library of Medicine, Columbia University Medical Library and Cornell University Nursing School. Her Ph.D. in the History of Medicine from Columbia University followed a B.A. in Histology and Embryology from Cornell University and a B.S. and M.S.L.S. from Columbia University.

She wrote *Development of Medical Bibliography* (Medical Library Association, 1964). Other interests include the philosophical and social bases of the education of information specialists, and the impact of new technologies on science and librarianship and on their interrelationships. She is author of "Automation in Medical Libraries" in *Handbook of Medical Library Practice*, third edition (Chicago, Medical Library Association, 1970). She has received such honors as the Marcia C. Noyes Award and the Janet Doe lectureship (both of the Medical Library Association) and the Presidency of the Medical Library Association. She was a Member of the President's National Advisory Commission on Libraries and was Visiting Professor (under a Rockefeller Foundation Fellowship) at Keio University, Tokyo, in 1962. She has been a consultant for documentation to the World Health Organization Regional Office for South East Asia and to the Central Family Planning Council in New Delhi. She was recognized as Woman of the Year by the St. Louis Chapter of the American Association of University Women.

Retrieval of Materials

While the library user will be guided to books and other general sources by the card catalog, he must rely on abstracting and indexing services to find specific information in journal articles. To provide the best service from these abstracting and indexing publications, the medical librarian must understand their history, function and data bases from the point of view of the publisher, the librarian and the scientist user. He must study formal evaluations for what he can learn of their value and of their characteristics. And he must be conscious of every way in which he can make easier the interaction between the scientist and the service.

The first three papers cover the history, function and data bases of abstracting and indexing services from the various points of view. The next two describe evaluations. The Beatty paper is an excellent introduction of these important sources to the scientist, and the last two suggest how the library can assist the user in his own file maintenance and how new techniques of access to abstracting and indexing services are likely to assist him.

Bibliographic Organization in the Biomedical Sciences

by Scott Adams

Specific bibliographic tools are discussed in the framework of the developments in the political and scientific communities which have made them possible.

Bibliography in the sciences is functional in the sense used by the late Mortimer Taube.[1] It exists to serve the particular purposes of segments of the scientific community. In its totality (and totality means here the spectrum of secondary publication: indexes, abstracts, bibliographies, review papers, handbooks, compendia) it constitutes the scientific record, which is as much an institution of science as the scientific society.

It follows that a study of the shapes and forms taken by this record, its morphology, transcends a critical analysis of the published products. A comprehensive sociological study of the relationships of the scientific community to this institution has yet to be accomplished.[2] This essay on developments in the organization of biomedical bibliography, however, is more concerned with the roles played by various groups, both governmental and private, in relation to the planning, organization, and development of the scientific record, than it is with enumerating and classifying bibliographical products.

Quis custodiet ipsos custodes? or, in a more modern paraphrase, "Who takes care of the caretaker's daughter?" Given a complex scientific society, fragmented into many communities, who becomes responsible for overseeing the planning and organizing of scientific bibliography? This question underlies the classic problems of overlap, duplication, and omission discussed by Henkle in 1951.[3] Efforts to answer it epitomize the history of scientific bibliography ever since World War II.

Attention in turn has been focused on roles and responsibilities proper to individual scientists (as in the Weinberg Report), to scientific societies (such as the American Psychological Association), to umbrella scientific organizations and international scientific unions (as evidenced by the Biological Sciences Communication Project of the American Institute of Biological Sciences, or the Abstracting Board of the International Council of Scientific Unions), to government agencies (National Research Council, National Science Foundation, Public Health Service, and Office of Science and Technology), and to international organizations and supranational bodies (International Federation for Documentation, the International Council of Scientific Unions, UNESCO, and the World Health Organization).

All these agencies, groups, and institutions (and more besides) have been involved in one way or another in bibliographic organization and planning for the biomedical sciences over the past 15 years. Out of these manifold, and at times conflicting efforts, three major trends have emerged: 1. the impact of the scientific revolution in the biomedical sciences; 2. the increasing support and planning role of agencies and government; and 3. the impact of computer technology.

Underlying the support and planning role of government agencies and their drive to develop mechanized information processing systems is the generalized discomforture of the scientific community as it adapts to the requirements of the scientific revolution. All scientific institutions, including the scientific record, have been subjected to stress by the needs of society to mold science to its purposes and simultaneously to foster its development. The rise of interdisciplinary science for the accomplishment of categorical or mission-

SOURCE: Reprinted from Scott Adams, "Bibliographic Organization in the Biomedical Sciences," *Wilson Library Bulletin,* 40 (Apr., 1966), pp. 714–718, by permission of the publisher and the author.

oriented research, with its new organizational forms and requirements, is one of the outstanding features of this revolution.

This trend was established earlier and proceeded faster in the biomedical sciences than in any other areas of science. The founding of the National Cancer Institute in 1935 established a prototype for large-scale federal funding of disease-oriented research. The many mission-oriented research programs, promoted by recent institutes in heart disease, mental health, neurological diseases, and blindness, have accelerated the trend of assembling scientists from various disciplines to work on health problems on the frontiers of knowledge. As a result of this interdisciplinary trend, the older forms of bibliographic organization by discipline have grown progressively less useful, while at the same time there have been multiple efforts to reconstitute bibliographic organization into new forms.

Generally speaking, the information requirements of interdisciplinary groups as they affect bibliographic organization are threefold:

1. A number of such groups express a need for a basic bibliography to assemble previous contributions of all disciplines bearing on the problem area. Examples are the *Bibliography of the Research in Tissue Culture* (1953), and the *Bibliography of World Literature on Mental Retardation* (1964). In rapidly developing interdisciplinary fields, their chief role appears to be that of assisting the scientists engaged in defining the field and in providing them with a common record of its antecedents.
2. Far more prevalent is the need for a specially packaged current-awareness service to keep up with the rapid development of the field. Such services may take many forms, ranging from the *Current Contents* series produced by the Institute for Scientific Information, to the recurring bibliographies developed under the MEDLARS program. When the most comprehensive English-language abstracting service in the medical sciences, the *Excerpta Medica*, was established in 1947, it initially had 15 sections organized by classic disciplinary and professional fields: anatomy, physiology, surgery, pediatrics, etc. *Excerpta Medica* now produces 33 abstract series, including such disease-oriented titles as: *Cancer in Children*, *Diabetes Research*, *Glaucoma Review*, *Multiple Sclerosis Abstracts*, and *Muscular Dystrophy Abstracts*. From a systems-planning point of view, the proliferation of multiple, uncoordinated efforts in establishing current-awareness services has created a new set of problems.
3. Of equal importance for rapidly developing interdisciplinary fields is the need to evaluate, consolidate, and synthesize the new information being generated. The critical review functions to synthesize ongoing work, and to give the field a sense of direction. Generally speaking, there are two types of reviews: those which attempt to record all contributions to a field without significant evaluation or synthesis, and those which are highly selective and problem-oriented. The classic models are the *Jahresbericht* and the *Fortschritte*. The popularity of the *Advances* series of Academic Press testifies to a contemporary need for the latter type. To provide control for this highly popular form of bibliography, the National Library of Medicine established its *Bibliography of Medical Reviews* as a by-product of its indexing in 1956.

Agencies of government, and not only in the United States, have been simultaneously the instruments of public policy responsible for the acceleration of the scientific revolution, and the patrons of the scientific communities primarily affected by the resultant stresses. It is understandable, therefore, that as the defense, health, prosperity, and welfare of the country require acceleration of the scientific effort in the public interest, the scientific information problem, to which bibliographic organization is central, has achieved significant political proportions.

The date Sputnik I was launched, October 4, 1957, is generally believed to have initiated political interest in scientific and technical information. While Sputnik I accelerated this political interest in both the Congress and the Executive Branch, and added thereby another dimension to this complex problem, governmental agencies had been concerned with the organizational problem long before.

In addition to proposing MEMEX in a now-historical paper,[4] Vannevar Bush committed the government to two other actions. First, he organized the Office of the Publication Board to provide for the release of large numbers of classified reports, generated by the Office of Scientific Research and Development and other wartime agencies, to the scientific and technical communities; second, in *Science, The Endless Frontier*,[5] he devoted considerable attention to the government's new responsibilities for encouraging the publication and dissemination of scientific knowledge. The first suggestion led to new federal agency systems for the bibliographic organization of the report literature produced by the defense agencies, Atomic Energy Commission, and National Aeronautics and Space Agency; the second led to the provision for an Office of Scientific Information (OSI) in the National Science Foundation upon its establishment in 1950.

Meanwhile, other executive agencies had been responding to observed needs to provide organization for the scientific literature of their fields. When the Atomic Energy Commission was launched in 1946, it had a statutory mandate to provide for the dissemination of scientific and technical information in the nuclear sciences, and developed sophisticated systems to this end. In 1948, the Army Medical Library contracted with the Welch Medical Library of Johns Hopkins Hospital to study problems related to medical indexing and its organization.

While efforts to establish responsible roles for government agencies preceded Sputnik I, they were greatly expanded as a result of political reaction to this event. The Office of Scientific Information became the Office of Science Information Service, National Science Foundation, with new authorities under the National Defense Education Act of 1958 to "provide, or arrange for the provision of, indexing, abstracting, translating and other services leading to a more effective dissemination of scientific information." The Senate Committee on Government Organization began its series of inquiries and studies into agency programs for the organization and dissemination of scientific information, and the Baker Committee made its report.

The 1958 report of the Panel on Scientific Information of the President's Science Advisory Committee (with W. O. Baker as chairman) is still a cornerstone of federal policy relating to bibliographic organization.[6] Rejecting the concept of a monolithic federal information agency comparable to the Soviet VINITI (which had been established in 1952) as inappropriate to a democratic society, the report called for the strengthening of services created by the scientific community, and their improved coordination.

While the Crawford Report of 1962[7] emphasized federal agency responsibilities for scientific and technical information of their own generation (STINFO) and the Weinberg Report of 1963[8] stressed the responsibility of individual scientists, the federal posture has consistently been one of cooperation with the scientific community. The federal role has been one of stimulating, supporting, and studying, rather than of planning and operating, other than for the mission-oriented needs of individual agencies.

As yet, little evidence has accumulated to suggest that agencies of government have been more or less successful than other groups in rationalizing the organization of bibliography in the sciences. The most imaginative effort to date has been the report of Robert Heller Associates, conducted on behalf of the National Federation of Science Abstracting and Indexing Services, with funds from NSF. This report posited an "Organization X" to serve as a clearinghouse, receiving abstracts from the classic, discipline-oriented services (*Biological Abstracts, Chemical Abstracts*, etc.) and repackaging them for multiple, mission-oriented purposes. Many reviewers, however, agreed on its impracticability.

Presently, the government agencies with membership on COSATI are exploring the ramifications of the "delegated agency" concept, through which each of the agencies would accept responsibility for the support and strengthening of information services in those fields of science most nearly related to its mission. Under this concept the Department of Health, Education, and Welfare has a governmental responsibility for organizing biomedical bibliography.

At the root of functional bibliographic organization lies the problem of breaking up the published literature into discrete units, and then reassembling the units, be they citations or abstracts, into desirable and logical arrangements for access to information. The high costs of bibliographic work are associated with the reiterative manual review of multiple sources (incidental to the identification of units in either the original published literature or existing bibliographic sources) to locate and transcribe the materials. How much better to have a computer, which can process and store unit bibliographical records, perform this search, manipulation, and organization in accordance with instructions. How much better yet, in these days of interdisciplinary science, to have standardized unit bibliographic records among large computer systems, so that records created for one large system can be made available for the use of another.

These are the motivations which have led to the development of computer-based systems for bibliographic purposes, and which underlie efforts to standardize them.

Biological Abstracts, with funds from NSF, initiated BASIC (Biological Abstracts Subjects in Context), a computer-prepared permuted title index, in October 1961. Under continuing development since then, the Biological Abstracts system is producing an additional publication, *Bio-Research Titles*, a monthly index service. Biological Abstracts is also developing an experimental abstract search service, BIOCOM.

The NLM has been operating MEDLARS (Medical Literature Analysis and Retrieval System) successfully since January 1964 as both a publication system and a search system.[9] It is as a publication system that MEDLARS has great significance for bibliographic organization. Using a new photocomposing device, which produces typographically acceptable computer print-out at the speed of a page of three-column text per minute, MEDLARS prepares the monthly *Index Medicus* and its 6,000-page annual cumulation. Starting in January 1966, it will also produce a biweekly *Current Catalog*, which will cumulate quarterly and annually to form the Library's book catalog.

More significant is the use to which the system is being put to produce specialized indexes, or recurring bibliographies of prearranged periodicity. By agreement with the American Dental Association, it is producing a bimonthly *Index to Dental Literature*; with the American Rheumatism Association, it is producing an *Index to Rheumatology*. A list of such bibliographic services published, or ready for publication includes: *Cerebrovascular Bibliography; Index to Rheumatology; Index to Dental Literature; Fibrinolysis, Thrombolysis, and Blood Clotting Bibliography of Medical Education*; and *International Nursing Index*. Fifteen more are at various stages of planning or development.

The underlying concept is that a large data base, or pool of machine-readable bibliographic unit records, can be drawn upon to provide multiple bibliographic current-awareness services of the type required by modern science. The capital investment in indexing is made once; at small incremental costs multiple uses can be made economically.

The introduction of computer technology to repackage the bibliographic record of the biomedical sciences creates an enormous potential for meeting the needs of contemporary science. It does not necessarily contribute to the type of systematic planning implied in the phrase "bibliographic organization," other than to suggest that a systems pattern of centralized analysis and multiple decentralized syntheses is emerging. The *Index Medicus* and multiple derivative bibliographic products of indefinite duration may coexist successfully. Similarly, *Biological Abstracts* and derivative specialized services will develop.

Two questions remain. Can the large, centralized processing systems develop both technical compatibility and a community of interest so they may either interchange bibliographic units, or provide a supply of standardized units for melding to a mission-oriented service? And at what point in time will it become no longer feasible or desirable to produce a comprehensive *printed* record, such as the *Index Medicus*, but depend on copies of a tape store for retrospective search, and on multiple *ad hoc* products for current awareness?

NOTES

[1] Mortimer Taube. "Functional Approach to Bibliographic Organization: A Critique and a Proposal." J. H. Shera and M. E. Egan, eds. *Bibliographic Organization*. Chicago, 1951. pp. 57–81.

[2] But see *Reports of the American Psychological Association's Project on Scientific Information Exchange in Psychology*. Washington, D.C., American Psychological Association, 1963, vol. 1.

[3] Herman H. Henkle. "The Natural Sciences. . . ." Shera and Egan, eds., *op. cit.*, pp. 140-60.

[4] Vannevar Bush. "As We Think," *Atlantic Monthly*, vol. 176, pp. 101–08, 1945.

[5] ———. *Science, The Endless Frontier*. Washington, D.C., GPO, 1945.

[6] President's Science Advisory Committee. *Science, Government, and Information*. Washington, D.C., GPO, 1963, p. 8.

[7] *Ibid.*, pp. 44–51.

[8] *Ibid.*

[9] L. Karel, C. S. Austin, and M. M. Cummings. "Computerized Bibliographic Services for Biomedicine," *Science*, vol. 148, pp. 766–72, 1965.

ABOUT THE AUTHOR–Most recently, Scott Adams has been deeply involved with UNISIST, writing the synoptic version of the feasibility study on a World Science Information System, and working with all participating countries in the successful completion of the Intergovernmental Conference for the Establishment of a World Science Information System (UNISIST), held in Paris, October 4-8, 1971. Prior to that he was Deputy Director of the National Library of Medicine, Program Director for Science Information at the National Science Foundation, and Librarian at the National Institutes of Health. He has an A.B. in English from Yale and a B.S.L.S. from Columbia.

He has long been interested in international communication of information. He has served on such international advisory committees as that of UNESCO for Documentation, Libraries and Archives, that for UNISIST, and the Biomedical Information Policy Group of OECD. He was Honorary President of the Third International Congress for Medical Librarianship. He is a Past President of the Medical Library Association and of the American Documentation Institute. He has received the Special Service Award of the Public Health Service and the Medical Library Association's Ida & George Eliot Award for his paper on "Medical Library Resources and Their Development," which appears in this *Reader* under the title "Medical Libraries Are in Trouble" (page 311). He wrote the chapter on "The National Library of Medicine" for the *Handbook of Medical Library Practice*, third edition (Chicago, Medical Library Association, 1970).

Plus ça change...

by A. W. Green

The history of Excerpta Medica and its current computerization activities are described and compared with those of Index Medicus. In the framework of problems in the total biomedical communications system, suggestions for coordinated exploitation of biomedical bibliographic control are made.

THE EXCERPTA MEDICA FOUNDATION

The twenty-first anniversary of the Excerpta Medica Foundation in January of this year was marked in a highly appropriate manner by the publication of the first abstracts to be stored in the EMF data bank.

The Excerpta Medica Foundation, conceived in 1946 and active by 1948, was established with the objective of advancing the progress of the biomedical sciences and their application through publication of a co-ordinated series of abstracting journals in English. Each abstracting journal is devoted to a more or less specific aspect of the biomedical sciences, such as Physiology or Biochemistry. In 1947, 15 such journals were projected. At present there are 34 and it has been announced that this number will increase to 55 during 1969.

The original concept was visionary, especially when the contemporary situation of post-war bibliographical chaos is taken into consideration. There is no other comprehensive abstracting service providing coverage of the biomedical sciences. The expansion and increasing sophistication of the total system of literature control achieved by EMF indicate administrative qualities of the highest order and an official history of the Foundation would make interesting reading. From humble, makeshift beginnings of the sort which seem to characterize all great ventures in bibliography and lexicography,[1] the EMF has developed into a vast enterprise with international ramifications. There are offices in Amsterdam, Buenos Aires, London, Milan, New York, Paris and Tokyo. The number of permanent staff exceeds 500, together with some 4,000 persons serving on a voluntary basis, giving rise to a complex structured network of chief and executive editors, abstractors, translators, style experts and finally the category of experts which has made modern bibliographical control possible—the computer men. In common with *Chemical abstracts*, *Science citation index*, *Biological abstracts* and *Index medicus*, *Excerpta medica* has resorted to the computer.

THE COMPUTER AND BIBLIOGRAPHICAL CONTROL

The computer is ideally suited to the production of bibliographies and indexes. Once the item, consisting of the standard identifying characteristics of the journal articles together with descriptors, has been entered into the system, the data can be manipulated to produce any required output in printed form. There is no doubt that computer-produced bibliographies and indexes are more economic. When the objectives of the NLM, MEDLARS (National Library of Medicine, Medical Literature Analysis and Retrieval System), were formulated,[2] economic production of the printed *Index Medicus* was the primary consideration because the traditional method was proving totally inadequate to cope with the volume of literature. The vast store of data on magnetic tape which accumulates as a result of the primary objective represents a tantalizing solution to all future problems

---

SOURCE: Reprinted from A. W. Green, "Plus ça change . . . ," *Library Association Record*, 71 (June, 1969), pp. 180–181, by permission of the publisher and the author.

of bibliographical control. Remote interrogation of a central store or decentralization of the central store by duplication of the magnetic tapes are not futuristic solutions to a perennial problem.

ROYAL SOCIETY EMPIRE SCIENTIFIC CONFERENCE

It is interesting to recall the Royal Society Empire Scientific Conference which, by coincidence, was held in 1948. At this conference, Professor Bernal suggested a formula for more efficient communication and dissemination of scientific research based on central organizations referred to as National Distributing Authorities. Basically the idea was that all original manuscripts could be submitted to a central national editorial board. Abstracts would be published rapidly and a copy of the original made available to anyone who requested it.[3,4]

COPYRIGHT

EMF now possesses, albeit in embryonic form, the machinery to put such a scheme into operation. The question of centralized publication has been the subject of recurring debate. The arguments can be tabulated by any first-year student librarian. There is the fundamental conflict between the profit motive underlying commercial publication which has to be reconciled with conscientious publishing and efficient, i.e. economic communication and dissemination. The anomalies of the existing system proliferate:

© 1967. *McGraw-Hill Publishing Company Limited. All rights reserved. No part of this publication may be reproduced, stored in a retrieval system, or transmitted in any form or by any means, electronic, mechanical, photocopying, recording or otherwise, without the prior permission of McGraw-Hill Publishing Company Limited.*

© 1969. *Excerpta Medica Foundation. The copyright of the abstracts, titles and indexes included in this issue is the property of the Excerpta Medica Foundation. No part of this publication may be reproduced in any form by print, photoprint, microfilm or by any other means without written permission from the publisher.*

The EMF System, the full name of which is Excerpta Medica Automated Storage and Retrieval Program of Biomedical Information, is, unlike the NLM MEDLARS, based on a micro-filmed store of all the articles abstracted since 1960. This store of microfilmed journals may already constitute an infringement of copyright. Further exploitation of the store must inevitably involve further infringement, unless a complex system is devised to compensate publishers for loss of income.

THE STATE AND THE SYSTEM

There are numerous arguments for retaining the existing system based on traditional commercial publishing, but the overwhelming argument in favour of centralized publication is that most research is financed directly or indirectly by the State. It seems unreasonable that the State should subsequently incur permanent financial responsibility for the acquisition and indefinite storage of multiple copies of any given document in libraries of universities and research institutions. Against this it is argued that State involvement in research already bears a dangerous resemblance to a monopoly. This, however, brings into question the entire philosophy of State-sponsored research.

The number of research workers is steadily increasing; if the existing formula of success prevails (that is, "publish or perish") for the next generation, the retrieval problem will assume even greater proportions.[5]

MERITS AND DEMERITS

Thus the EMF system presents some interesting possibilities for the rationalization of the entire system of scientific communication.

The success and potential of *EM* draw attention to several points worthy of examination in the light of possible future developments. Firstly, are abstracts necessary in a mechanized retrieval system? If they could be made available with the same rapidity as *Current contents*, they would indeed provide an invaluable service, but the delay is likely to be four to five months.

There is little question that both *EM* and the *Index medicus* in their printed forms serve a valuable function because of their different presentation and will continue to do so. Against this must be set the difference in price: the projected 55 sections will cost approximately $2,500 per annum based on present rates. Admittedly, few libraries will subscribe to all sections but the *Cumulated index medicus* for one year costs less than $100.

Both *IM* and *EM* cover approximately 3,000 journals. The *EM* journals are selected according to scientific merit and on the principle of geographic representation. Thus although there is a wide variation in cost, coverage would appear similar, although examination of the NFSAIS[6] guide reveals that *EM* covers only 19 of the sub-divisions whereas *IM* covers 31.

MEDLARS has been operational since 1964 and the MEDLARS staff at the National Library of Medicine has accumulated considerable experience. There is no complacency. "In order to survive, a system must monitor itself, evaluate its performance and upgrade it wherever possible." *EM* would appear to have neglected this accumulation of experience. If the two retrieval systems were based on diametrically opposed principles there would be no reason for criticism but, apart from the fact that abstracts will be stored as well as the document description and descriptors, there is little difference. *EM* does claim a thesaurus (EMCLASS) of 40,000 terms correlated with 500,000 synonyms, whereas MeSH (Medical Subject Headings) consists of a mere 7,000 terms, but until *EM* has been operational and its performance evaluated, such figures are meaningless.[7,8]

An evaluation of the MEDLARS demand search service revealed that the average recall and precision is 58 per cent and 50 per cent respectively. Amongst the recommendations made with the intention of improving system performance, it was suggested that the updating methods for MEDLARS thesaurus, MeSH, should be thoroughly reappraised and that more emphasis should be placed on sought terms, i.e. *as reflected in the demands placed upon the system.*[9]

CO-ORDINATION

Co-operation was the subject of a considerable amount of attention in 1949;[10,11] it seems unfortunate that the EMF and the NLM have not seen fit to collaborate closely, concentrating on the perfection of a single computerized retrieval system.

Although co-ordination at source of the various systems is now impossible, it would appear that there is a definite case to be made for the establishment of a centralized service to exploit all the services now available. The Office for Scientific and Technical Information exists to co-ordinate information services in the United Kingdom. OSTI has financed a project for co-ordinated exploitation of the various information services available in the chemical field. This project, based on the faculties of Physical and Biological Sciences at Oxford, could well be imitated in the biomedical sciences.

NOTES

1 Brodman, Estelle. *The development of medical bibliography*. Chicago, Medical Library Association, 1954.

2 National Library of Medicine. *The MEDLARS story.* US Dept. Health, Education, and Welfare. Public Health Service, 1963.

3 *Royal Society Empire Scientific Conference, 21 June–2 July 1948. Report and papers submitted*. London, The Royal Society, 1948. 253–258.

4 Publication and classification of scientific knowledge. *Nature*, **160** (4071) November 1947, 649–650.

5 Price, Derek J. de Solla. *Little science, big science*. New York, Columbia University Press, 1963.

6 National Federation of Science Abstracting and Indexing Services. *A guide to the world's abstracting and indexing services in science and technology*. Washington, D.C., NFSIS, 1963.

7 Excerpta Medica Foundation. *A brief outline of the Excerpta Medica Foundation program for the automated storage and retrieval of medical information*. Amsterdam, EMF, 1968.

8 Excerpta Medica Foundation Catalogue, 1963.

9 Lancaster, F. W. *Evaluation of the MEDLARS demand search service*. US Dept. Health, Education, and Welfare. Public Health Service, 1968.

10 Cunningham, Eileen R. Medical and science abstracting; conclusions and recommendations from two international conferences. *Bull. Med. Lib. Assn.,* **38** (2) April 1950, 125–134.

11 Cunningham, Eileen R. Report of the committee on a co-ordinated abstracting service for clinical medicine. *Bull. Med. Lib. Assn.,* **37** (4) October 1949, 344–347.

ABOUT THE AUTHOR—Arthur W. Green is Librarian of the Commonwealth Institute of Entomology, London. Previously he served as Deputy Librarian, National Coal Board, London and Assistant Librarian, National Institute for Medical Research, London. After five years teaching, studying and bookselling in France, Germany, and Switzerland respectively, and two years' study at the School of Librarianship, Polytechnic of North London, he qualified as a chartered librarian (A.L.A.).

As evidenced in this paper, he is interested in first principles required in an effective information system.

Keys to the Medical Literature

by William K. Beatty

This paper provides a model user's guide to secondary sources of biomedical information. At the same time, it gives the librarian a concise summary of the key sources in the field.

The old invitation to "Come you now and sit with me, Underneath the medlar tree" has taken on a less romantic tinge in the 1960's. The quiet country landscape has been stripped of its trees to provide paper for the burgeoning medical literature, and the medlars themselves have turned into a whirring blinking computer system. The *Med*ical *L*iterature *A*nalysis and *R*etrieval *S*ystem at the National Library of Medicine lies at the core of much of the practice and most of the theory of modern bibliographic control of the medical literature. The reader's problem is no longer that of finding material, but rather of winnowing pertinent articles, books, and reports out of the vast mass that is piling up both in this country and abroad. There are several "keys," physical and mental, that will help to accomplish this. The physical "keys" include an up-to-date medical library, and the mental "keys" include a logical mind, a good imagination, and an awareness of the basic methods for searching the literature.

Before you start your search you should sit down and think. Do you have a clear picture of just what is involved in the subject? Are you interested in etiology, medical or surgical treatment, complications, or some other particular aspect of the subject? Are you going to be dealing with humans, animals, or both? Do you want only English language articles, or can you use one or more foreign languages? Will you cover only the current literature, or will you go back five or more years? The answers to these questions will help to define your problem and make your search more effective. You will want to take advantage of both the mental and physical keys, so keep in mind the help that your reference librarians can give you. Dragons are almost as extinct on library staffs as they are in the outside world, and you may be pleasantly surprised by the interest and usefulness of your librarian.

If you want two or three good, recent articles on a subject, for basic information or for preparing a report, you would probably not be overjoyed to have the current issue of each of the 19,000 medical and related journals that are now pouring out of almost a hundred different countries dumped in your lap. What you want are references to two or three articles in English, in journals that are in the library of your school or hospital. The best guide for this is the "new" *Index Medicus.*

Index Medicus is your first "key" to current medical articles, and you will find it a great timesaver. This monthly index to 2,300 journals is one of the products of Medlars. Each issue is divided into five parts. The first, the introduction, is short, clear, and informative. The second and third parts contain the subject and name sections of the *Bibliography of Medical Reviews*. The fourth and fifth parts contain the subject and name sections for the body of the *Index Medicus* itself, and it is in the fourth part that you will look for your two or three articles.

If your subject is retinal detachment the pertinent page in a recent (October, 1967) issue of *Index Medicus* would look like this (Fig. 1). Depending on your requirements you can select your articles from the general heading or one of the subheadings. English articles appear at the head of each subject or subheading. These are followed by the foreign-language articles which have not only the square bracket preceding them but an abbreviation for the language given at the end of each citation. If you are looking for recent articles on therapy of retinal detachment you will find one by Cox under the subheading "therapy" (Fig. 1). If you want more references on this subject you

SOURCE: Reprinted from William K. Beatty, "Keys to the Medical Literature," *The New Physician*, 18 (Aug., 1969), pp. 634–641, by permission of the publisher and the author.

INDEX MEDICUS

studied with linearly ...
Boll Soc Ital Biol Sper 42:1420-2, 31 Oct 66 (It)
[Fractional sleep in the monomodal canal of the information transmission system and the role of the feed-back in the control of afferent pulses of the input system] Ataev MM
Izv Akad Nauk SSSR [Biol] 2:230-43, Mar-Apr 66 (Rus)
[Macular representation in the visual cortex. Electrophysiological analysis in man] Aranda L, et al.
Neurocirugia 23:41-3, Jan-Dec 65 (Sp)

PHYSIOPATHOLOGY

Studies of dark adaptation of discrete paracentral retinal areas in glaucomatous subjects. Zuege P, et al.
Amer J Ophthal 64:56-63, Jul 67

RADIATION EFFECTS

Retinal lesions produced by Q-switced lasers. Bergqvist T, et al. Acta Ophthal (Kobenhavn) 44:853-63, 1966
Alterations in the fine structure of the mature retina of dogs irradiated as neonates. Shively JN, et al. Exp Eye Res 6:278-82, Jul 67
Provitamin A2: electroretinographic measurements of its effect on photopic sensitivity in chicks. Auerbach E, et al. Nature (London) 211:77-8, 2 Jul 66
Molecular and thermal origins of fast photoelectric effects in the squid retina. Hagins WA, et al. Science 157:813-6, 18 Aug 67

X RETINAL DETACHMENT (C11)

[Postoperative detachment of the retina. Mechanism and prospects of prevention] Bessière E.
Annee Ther Clin Ophtal 17:209-18, 1966 (Fr)

COMPLICATIONS

Homocystinuria and ocular defects. Presley GD, et al.
Amer J Ophthal 63:1723-7, Jun 67
Vitreoretinal traction in serous and hemorrhagic macular retinopathy. A biomicroscopic study Tolentino FI, et al.
Arch Ophthal (Chicago) 78:23-30, Jul 67
[Malignant melanic tumor of the choroid revealed by a spinal metastasis] Auvert B, et al.
Ann Oculist (Paris) 199:1079-87, Nov 66 (Fr)

Annee Ther ...

THERAPY

X The manifestations and current therapy of the retinal detachment disease. Cox MS Jr.
Amer J Med Sci 254:236-42, Aug 67
[Current status of photocoagulation in the therapy of diseases of the fundus oculi] Meyer-Schwickerath G.
Annee Ther Clin Ophtal 13:55-67, 1962 (Fr)

RETINAL HEMORRHAGE (C8, C11)

[Hyperuricemia and gout in retinal vascular accidents. New etiological and therapeutic data] Bourde C.
Annee Ther Clin Ophtal 14:91-113, 1963 (Fr)

ETIOLOGY

Hyperviscosity syndrome in multiple myeloma. Kopp WL, et al. Amer J Med 43:141-6, Jul 67
Hemorrhage in hyaline bodies (drusen) of the optic disc during an attack of migraine. Gaynes PM, et al.
Amer J Ophthal 63:1693-6, Jun 67
Dermal vasculitis with retinal involvement. McCarthy JT, et al. Arch Derm (Chicago) 96:109-10, Jul 67
[Anomalies of platelet aggregation during Waldenström's disease. (Apropos of 3 cases)] Doumenc J, et al.
Nouv Rev Franc Hemat 6:734-8, Sep-Oct 66 (Fr)

RETINAL PIGMENTS (D10)

Rhodopsin kinetics and rod adaptation in Oguchi's disease. Carr RE, et al. Invest Ophthal 6:426-36, Aug 67
A thermal component of excitation in the lateral eye of Limulus. Srebro R.
J Physiol (London) 187:417-25, Nov 66
[Life and death of the pigmented epithelium of the retina] Hervouet F.
Annee Ther Clin Ophtal 14:115-22, 1963 (Fr)

ANALYSIS

Pigmented iris and retrocorneal membrane simulating an iris melanoma. Haver RP.
Arch Ophthal (Chicago) 78:55-7, Jul 67

Laser photocoagula... al.
Trans Amer Acad Op... Nov-Dec 66

RETINITIS PIGMENTOSA (C11)

COMPLICATIONS

[Neuromuscular syndromes in so-called atypical retinitis pigmentosa as a hint to a fat metabolism disorder] Dieckmann H, et al.
Verh Deutsch Ges Inn Med 71:634-7, 1965 (Ger)

DIAGNOSIS

Pigmentary degeneration of the retina: early diagnosis and natural history. Sunga RN, et al.
Invest Ophthal 6:309-25, Jun 67

URINE

[Studies on a melanocyte-stimulating hormone-like substance in the urine, with reference to retinitis pigmentosa] Aonuma S, et al.
Folia Endocr Jap 42:512-20, 20 Aug 66 (Jap)

RETINOBLASTOMA (C2, C11)

COMPLICATIONS

Invasion of choroid and sclera by retinoblastoma following photocoagulation. Howard GM.
Trans Amer Acad Ophthal Otolaryng 70:984-9, Nov-Dec 66

RADIOTHERAPY

Retinoblastoma, megavoltage, therapy and unilateral disease. Bagshaw MA, et al.
Trans Amer Acad Ophthal Otolaryng 70:944-50, Nov-Dec 66

SURGERY

Invasion of choroid and sclera by retinoblastoma following photocoagulation. Howard GM.

Part 2 of the January issue contains a categorized list of subject headings, including cross references. Their location in the categorized list is indicated by the letter-number designations (A1, B1, etc.), following each subject heading. 677

Fig. 1 Page from Subject Section, Oct. 1967, issue of Index Medicus, showing section on "Retinal Detachment," and reference to article by Cox under subheading "Therapy."

would go back to the September, August, etc, issues.

If you had heard, on the ward or in the lecture room, that Cox had recently written a good article on retinal detachment, you would go directly to the Name section and find the citation (Fig. 2) under the author. The attending physician or the lecturer might have remembered the name of the second or third author rather than of the first, and then you would have found a cross reference (in the Name Section) that would have referred you to the senior author and the citation.

The term "Name Section" is used here, rather than "Author Section," because this section includes more than authors. If you are seeking an obituary or biographical article on a particular person you would locate it in the "Name" section.

If you have to do some further searching, and have exhausted the monthly issues of the current year, you would turn to the *Cumulated Index Medicus*. This cumulates the 12 monthly issues for each year into one annual arrangement for subjects and another annual arrangement for names. Here (Fig. 3) you will find a much larger number of articles, and two additional elements of the arrangement will become evident. Under the subheading "Etiology" you will see that the English language articles, at the top of the subsection, are arranged alphabetically by journal title. The foreign language articles are arranged alphabetically by language, and, within each language, alphabetically by journal title. This format can be helpful if you want to limit your searching to one or two specific journals, or if you read a foreign language and want to coordinate your subject search with some practice in that language.

With the aid of the current issues of *Index Medicus* and a year or two of the *Cumulated Index Medicus* you will probably be able to dig out as many references as you need. You could then jot these citations down on the backs of old grocery lists or whatever scraps of paper you may have in your pocket, or you might try a reference slip (Fig. 4). Such a slip will remind you to copy down all the data you need in order to locate the article. A group of such slips forms a handily managed packet that will fit easily into a pocket, whereas grocery lists, etc, are usually of different sizes and are quite likely to be thrown away if you

INDEX MEDICUS

Cortese I, Macri G, Rubino M: Influenza dell'enteramina sulla stimolazione della sete nell'uomo, nella cavia, nel topo e nella rana. Arch Ital Sci Farmacol 15:177-82, Jul-Oct 65 (It)
Cortese I see Zamboni P
Cortesi S, Fontanin O, Xodo P, et al: Influenza della circolazione extracorporea sulle resistenze osmotiche e termiche eritrocitarie. Minerva Med 58:2153-5, 9 Jun 67 (It)
Cortesi S, Vettore L, Ancona G, et al: Comportamento della colinesterasi plasmatica in corso di emodialisi. Minerva Med 58:2103-5, 6 Jun 67 (It)
Cortesini R: Problemi organizzativi di un reparto dialisi e trapianti renali. Minerva Med 58:2066-71, 6 Jun 67 (It)
Cortiñas JJ see Murphy G
Corwin JH, Ferguson EF Jr, Moseley T, et al: Carcinoma of the male breast. Southern Med J 60:777-80, Jul 67
Cory RP, Wold F: Isolation and characterization of enolase from rainbow trout (Salmo gairdnerii gairdnerii). Biochemistry (Wash) 5:3131-7, Oct 66
Cosar C see Bénazet F
Coscas G, Kalimi G: La correction optique des aphaques. Arch Ophtal (Paris) 26:599-608, Sep 66 (Fr)
Coscas G see Bouniq C
Coscia L, Causa P, De Natale G: A new synthetic analgesic drug, p-phenetidine-alpha-N-n-propylpropionamide (FC 379). Arch Int Pharmacodyn 164:331-9, Dec 66
Coscia L, De Natale G, Causa P: General pharmacological properties of p-phenetidine-alpha-N-n-propylpropionamide (FC 379). Arch Int Pharmacodyn 164:340-4, Dec 66
Coscia L see Causa P
Cosemans J see Gyselen A
Cosgrove JB see Murphy BE
Coskey R, Haldin R, Pinkus H: Lupus vulgaris. Arch Derm (Chicago) 96:107-8, Jul 67
Coskey RJ, Mehregan AH: Granuloma pyogenicum with multiple satellite recurrences. Arch Derm (Chicago) 96:71-3, Jul 67
Coskey RL, Magidson O: Electrocardiographic response to selective coronary arteriography. Brit Heart J 29:512-9, Jul 67
Cossa GA see De Marchi F
Cossart YE: Marker studies of poliovirus. Nature (London) 211:1432, 24 Sep 66
Cossins EA see Wong KF
Cosson G see Leclerc M
Costa A, Cottino F: An epidemic of acute nodular goitre. Lancet 2:50, 1 Jul 67
Costa AL, Spadaro M, Mundo A: Sui rapporti tra lisozima e tasso di colesterolo surrenale nei ratti pan-irradiati. Boll Soc Ital Biol Sper 42:1280-3, 15 Oct 66 (It)
Costa AL see Spadaro M
Costa C see Zappia V
Costa E see Boullin DJ
Costa LD, Horwitz M, Vaughan HG Jr: Effects of stimulus uncertainty ... [torn]

Cottier H see Wagner HP
Cottino F see Costa A
Cottino F see Magro G
Cottle MK, Mitchell R: Degeneration time for optimal staining by Nauta technique. A study on transected vagal fibers of the cat. J Comp Neurol 128:209-22, Oct 66
Cotton DW see Mier PD
Cotton WR: Pulp response to an airstream directed into human cavity preparations. Oral Surg 24:78-88, Jul 67
Cotton WR see Russell JR
Cottrell GA: Occurrence of dopamine and noradrenaline in the nervous tissue of some invertebrate species. Brit J Pharmacol 29:63-9, Jan 67
Couch NP: Supply and demand in kidney and liver transplantation: a statistical survey. Transplantation 4:587-95, Sep 66
Couch NP, Wheeler HB, Hyatt DF, et al: Factors influencing limb survival after femoropopliteal reconstruction. Arch Surg (Chicago) 95:163-9, Aug 67
Coughlan MP see Winder FG
Coughlin CA: Spheroplast production in thymine starvation. Nature (London) 212:633-5, 5 Nov 66
Coul AA op de: The effect of ACTH and corticosteroids on the brain. Psychiat Neurol Neurochir 69:385-98, Nov Dec 66 (66 ref)
Coules J, Avery DL: Human performance and basal skin conductance in a vigilance-type task with and without knowledge of results. Percept Motor Skills 23:1295-302, Dec 66
Coullaud D, Lévêque J: Action du métoclopramide sur différentes portions de l'intestin isolé de lapin, et sur l'intestin "in situ". Path Biol (Paris) 14:963-5, Oct 66 (Fr)
Coulombe MJ see Spencer RP
Coulshed N see Epstein EJ
Coulson RA, Hernandez T: Changes in free amino acids of caymans after feeding. Amer J Physiol 212:1308-12, Jun 67
Coulson RA see Hernandez T
Coultate TP see Dennis DT
Coulter NA Jr see Kunz AL
Coulter SK see Hingtgen JN
Counsell LA: Inverted premolar. Oral Surg 24:210, Aug 67
Counsell RE, Adelstein GW: Anabolic agents. 19-Nor- and 19-substituted 5alpha-androst-2-ene derivatives. J Med Chem 9:685-9, Sep 66
Counsell RE, Klimstra PD, Elton RL, et al: Chemical and biological properties of some 17-substituted estradiol derivatives. J Med Chem 9:689-92, Sep 66
Counsell RE, Willette RE: Synthesis of 14-C-labeled isomers of dichlorodiphenyldichloroethanes (DDD). J Pharm Sci 55:1012-5, Oct 66
Counsell RE see Klimstra PD
Counts RM: Family crises and the impulsive adolescent. Arch Gen Psychiat (Chicago) 17:64-71 ...
Courbier R see Gérard R
Coursin DB see Lowe ... [torn]

Cowden JE: Institutional and post-release adjustment of neurotic and social delinquents. J Clin Psychol 22:477, Oct 66
Cowden RR see Alvarez MR
Cowden RR see Levi JU
Cowden RR see Malone WF
Cowell TK, Marsden CD, Owen DA: Objective measurement of parkinsonian tremor. Lancet 2:1278-9, 18 Dec 65
Cowen DL, Burtis B, Youmans J: Prolonged coma after acetohexamide ingestion. JAMA 201:155-6, 10 Jul 67
Cowie AT see Watson SC
Cowie V, Gammack DB: Serum proteins in Huntington's chorea. Brit J Psychiat 112:723-6, Jul 66
Cowley JJ, Griesel RD: The effect on growth and behaviour of rehabilitating first and second generation low protein rats. Anim Behav 14:506-17, Oct 66
Cowsert MK Jr, Carrier O Jr, Crowell JW: The effect of hemorrhagic shock on blood uric acid level. Canad J Physiol Pharmacol 44:861-4, Sep 66
Cox AG see Abernethy RJ
Cox AJ, Reaven EP: Histidine and keratohyalin granules. J Invest Derm 49:31-4, Jul 67
Cox CP, Leaverton PE: Statistical procedures for bioassays when the condition of similarity does not obtain. J Pharm Sci 55:716-23, Jul 66
Cox CS: Bacterial survival in suspension in polyethylene glycol solutions. J Gen Microbiol 45:275-81, Nov 66
Cox CS: The survival of Escherichia coli in nitrogen atmospheres under changing conditions of relative humidity. J Gen Microbiol 45:283-8, Nov 66
Cox DR: The null distribution of the first serial correlation coefficient. Biometrika 53:623-6, Dec 66
Cox EF: Hemobilia following percutaneous needle biopsy of the liver. Arch Surg (Chicago) 95:198-201, Aug 67
Cox FE: Acquired immunity to Plasmodium vinckei in mice. Parasitology 56:719-32, Nov 66
Cox FE, Vickerman K: Pinocytosis in Plasmodium vinckei. Ann Trop Med Parasit 60:293-6, Sep 66
Cox FE, Voller A: Cross-immunity between the malaria parasites of rodents. Ann Trop Med Parasit 60:297-303, Sep 66
Cox FE see Vickerman K
X Cox MS Jr: The manifestations and current therapy of the retinal detachment disease. Amer J Med Sci 254:236-42, Aug 67
Cox PA, Keshishian JM, Blades BB: Traumatic arteriovenous fistula of the chest wall and lung. Secondary to insertion of an intercostal catheter. J Thorac Cardiov Surg 54:109-12, Jul 67
Cox PJ see Adels BR
Cox R see Demott BJ
Cox RM see Fay P
Cox RP see Griffin MJ
Cox RW, Grant RA, Horne RW: The assembly of ... to form native ... [torn]

Fig. 2 Page from Name Section, Oct. 1967, issue of Index Medicus, showing reference to article by Cox.

happen to look at the wrong side first when you take one out of your pocket.

Review articles are among the most important and useful in the literature. If you want a picture of the current state of a particular subject, or if you want to find out how a certain therapy or operative procedure has developed, you will stand a good chance of finding the information you want in a review article. The only problem, then, is to find that review article.

"BMR" are easy initials to remember. Bibliographically speaking, they stand for another "key," the *Bibliography of Medical Reviews*, which makes up the second and third parts of the monthly issues of *Index Medicus*. These pages are also published as a separate monthly journal, and are cumulated into an annual arrangement with the same title.

The BMR has the same basic arrangement as the *Index Medicus*. For example, if you look under "Retina" in the October, 1967, BMR subject section of *Index Medicus* you will find a reference to an article by Campbell. To give you an idea of the depth of the review the index entry gives the number of references cited by the author; in this case, 206. This bit of information not only gives you a clue as to the coverage of the article but also, where several reviews are listed on the same subject, permits you to choose a review by size. If you have an author of a specific review article, you would go first to the Name rather than the Subject Section.

Review articles generally require some time for digestion. If your library has a photocopier you might consider having a copy made of the review you have found. You will then take only those pages from the journal that you need, read them at your leisure, and, possibly, check off appropriate references in the article's bibliography as you follow up on them later.

The symbols following the subject headings in *Index Medicus* and its annual cumulation are guides to the Medlars list of subject headings. This list, called *Me*dical *S*ubject *H*eadings (MeSH), will be useful in helping you to understand the production and arrangement of *Index Medicus*. MeSH is published each year as part 2 of the January issue of *Index Medicus*. It consists of three parts: an introduction, an alphabetical list and categorized lists. This introduction is worth a few minutes of your time since it explains the purpose, cross references, subheadings, and other elements of the list. The final section of the introduction draws attention to headings that have been added or deleted during the past year. Medical terminology is always growing and changing, and the subject headings appropriate for today may very well not have been the ones used for that subject 10 or 20 years ago. Whenever you make a subject search for articles or books you will want to be sure that you are searching under the terms in use at that time. Textbooks and dictionaries, contemporaneous with the period of your search, can be helpful in providing subject headings under which material was indexed.

The alphabetical list of subject headings shows

RETINAL DETACHMENT **CUMULATED INDEX MEDICUS**

deficiency] Yano T
Acta Soc Ophthal Jap 68:1808-20, Oct 64 (Jap)

RADIATION EFFECTS

Observations on early pathologic effects of photic injury to the rabbit retina. Fine BS, et al. Acta Ophthal (Kobenhavn) 43:684-91, 1965
Chorioretinal lesions produced by laser on monkeys and rabbits. Santos R, et al. Amer J Ophthal 61:230-40, Feb 66
The threshold of the retina to damage by laser energy. Campbell CJ, et al. Arch Ophthal (Chicago) 76:437-42, Sep 66
Is there a hazard in laser photocoagulation? Mellerio J. Brit Med J 5489:719, 19 Mar 66
Quantum energy specificity of simple photoreceptor units. Dawson WW. Nature (London) 208:589-90, 6 Nov 65
Effects of laser radiation on the mammalian eye. Ham WT Jr, et al. Trans NY Acad Sci 28:517-26, Feb 66 (32 ref.)
Eclipse burns in humans and laboratory threshold measurements in rabbits. SAM-TR-66-45. Allen RG Jr, et al. US Air Force Sch Aerospace Med 1-5, May 66
[Radiation injury of the retina induced by roentgen rays in newborn mice] Fischer H. Radiobiol Radiother (Berlin) 6:439-45, 1965 (Ger)
[Retinal metabolism and ionizing radiation. I. Modifications of protein synthesis in elements of centripetal conduction] Marzini G, et al. Ann Ottal 91:583-9, Jul 65 (It)
[Retinal metabolism and ionizing radiations. II. Modifications of protein synthesis in sensorial elements] Marzini G, et al. Ann Ottal 91:590-7, Jul 65 (It)

SURGERY

Transscleral freezing of the retina: an experimental study. Archambeau PL, et al. Invest Ophthal 4:885-93, Oct 65
[On some conditions for the use of lasers in photocoagulation of the retina] Blabla J, et al. Cesk Oftal 21:281-91, Jul 65 (Cz)

RETINAL DETACHMENT (C11)

Rhegmatogenous retinal detachment? What is the evidence? Potts AM. Amer J Ophthal 61:1264-71, May 66
The effects of detachment of the retina on the induced and resting ocular potentials in the rabbit. Foulds WS, et al. Invest Ophthal 5:93-100, Feb 66
Clinical study of lattice degeneration of the retina. Byer NE. Trans Amer Acad Ophthal Otolaryng 69:1065-81, Nov-Dec 65
An unusual form of glaucoma in aphakics. Roberts W. Trans Amer Acad Ophthal Otolaryng 69:1024-8, Nov-Dec 65
A clinical classification of retinoschisis with a preliminary report of three unusual fundus appearances. Crock GW. Trans Ophthal Soc New Zeal 17:18-24, 1965
[Bilateral annular detachment of the retina] Michiels J, et al. Bull Soc Belg Ophtal 141:581-90, 1965 (Fr)
[Aspect of the dysproteinemic fundus oculi (microaneurysms and retinal detachment) in a case of Waldenstrom's disease] Ardouin M, et al. Bull Soc Ophtal Franc 66:129-33, Jan 66 (Fr)
[Retinal detachment following psychic trauma?] Münchow W. Klin Mbl Augenheilk 147:580-7, Nov 65 (Ger)
[A case of retinal detachment occurring in flight] Terrana C, et al. Minerva Med 56:3963-4, 14 Nov 65 (It)
[Retinal detachment in Charlin's syndrome] Mazza C, et al. Riv Otoneurooftal 41:53-63, Jan-Feb 66 (It)
[Prurigo, cataract and retinal ablation—a rare oculo-cutaneous syndrome] Kotmińska A, et al. Przegl Derm 52:589-92, Nov-Dec 65 (Pol)
[Ophthalmologic observations following retinal coagulation by means of optic quantum generator] Puchovskaia NA, et al. Oftal Zh 20:428-31, 1965 (Rus)
[Retinoschisis] Pavia JJ, et al. Arch Oftal B Air 40:97-105, May 65 (Sp)

COMPLICATIONS

Intra-ocular pressure in retinal detachment. Linnér E. Acta Ophthal (Kobenhavn) Suppl 84:101-6, 1966
Retrolental membrane associated with Bloch-Sulzberger syndrome (incontinentia pigmenti). Jones ST. Amer J Ophthal 62:330-4, Aug 66
[Annular chorio-retinal detachment or exudative annular cyclitis. Reflections apropos of a further case] Paufique L, et al. Bull Soc Ophtal Franc 65:532-5, May 65 (Fr)
[Unrecognized intra-orbital foreign body and retinal detachment] Voisin J, et al. Bull Soc Ophtal Franc 65:864-6, Oct 65 (Fr)
[Observations on changes in the vitreous body and the extreme retinal periphery in normal elderly persons, in aphakic subjects and in patients with retinal detachment] Sanna G, et al. Ann Ottal 91:1031-8, Nov 65 (It)
[On a particular aspect of spontaneous resolution of retinal detachment: reattachment with amaurosis] Proto F, et al. Boll Oculist 44:725-33, Oct 65 (It)
[Uncommon postoperative complications in cases of retinal detachment] Hirose K, et al. Folia Ophthal Jap 16:740-2, Oct 65 (Jap)
[Lens opacities in cases of retinal detachment] Yoshioka H, et al. Folia Ophthal Jap 16:739, Oct 65 (Jap)

DIAGNOSIS

Visual field examination in retinal detachment. Enoksson P. Acta Ophthal (Kobenhavn) Suppl 84:93+, 1966
Intra-ocular pressure in retinal detachment. Linnér E. Acta Ophthal (Kobenhavn) Suppl 84:101-6, 1966
The electroretinogram in retinal detachment. Rendahl I. Acta Ophthal (Kobenhavn) Suppl 84:107-9, 1966
Choice of surgical technique. Rosengren B. Acta Ophthal (Kobenhavn) Suppl 84:163+, 1966
The search for retinal ruptures. Rosengren B. Acta Ophthal (Kobenhavn) Suppl 84:61-9, 1966
Some clinical types of retinal detachment. Törnquist R. Acta Ophthal (Kobenhavn) Suppl 84:87-91, 1966
Retinal detachment surgery. Diagnosis and treatment. Biomicroscopy of the fundus. Törnquist R. Acta Ophthal (Kobenhavn) Suppl 84:71-6, 1966
Coats' disease. Natural history and results of treatment. Gomez Morales A. Amer J Ophthal 60:855-65, Nov 65
Rhegmatogenous retinal detachment. Pilkerton R, et al. Med Ann DC 35:481-5 passim, Sep 66
Twin subretinal cysticerci simulating posttraumatic detachment of the retina. Radian AB, et al. Rum Med Rev 19:56-9, Oct-Dec 65
Recent developments in the management of retinal detachment. Schepens CL. Trans Amer Acad Ophthal Otolaryng 69:896-911, Sep-Oct 65
The clinical significance of the fundus periphery. Shanahan LF. Trans Ophthal Soc Aust 24:15-20, 1965
[Bilateral retinal pseudo-detachment caused by posterior uveitis during pregnancy] Hugonnier R, et al. Bull Soc Ophtal Franc 65:1103-5, Dec 65 (Fr)
[ERG and postoperative reapplication in retinal detachment] Jayle G, et al. Bull Soc Ophtal Franc 65:827-9, Sep 65 (Fr)
[Use of the suction cup in the diagnosis of idiopathic detachment of the retina] Tieri O, et al. Ann Ottal 91:875-8, Nov 65 (It)
[Prognostic value of some functional investigation methods in retinal detachment] Filatova ZA. Oftal Zh 20:496-500, 1965 (Rus)

X ETIOLOGY

Acute posterior vitreous detachment and its retinal complications. A clinical biomicroscopic study. Linder B. Acta Ophthal (Kobenhavn) Suppl 87:1-100, 1966
Chorioretinal lesions predisposing to retinal breaks. Dumas J, et al. Amer J Ophthal 61:620-30, Apr 66
Spontaneously reversible retinal detachment occurring during renal insufficiency. Lapco L, et al. Ann Intern Med 63:760-6, Nov 65
Experimental retinal detachment. Freilich DB, et al. Arch Ophthal (Chicago) 76:432-6, Sep 66
Retinal detachment in the retinopathy of prematurity. Tasman W, et al. Arch Ophthal (Chicago) 75:608-14, May 66
Retinal detachment in prosthetophakia. Tasman W, et al. Arch Ophthal (Chicago) 75:179-86, Feb 66
Retinal detachment with spontaneous regression in renal failure. Sharpstone P, et al. Brit Med J 5506:92-3, 9 Jul 66
Rhegmatogenous retinal detachment in Filipinos. I. Site and types of breaks and other associated findings. Espiritu RB, et al. Philipp J Surg 20:158-63, May-Jun 65
Retinal dialysis as the cause of a special type of retinal detachment. Hagler WS. Southern Med J 58:1475-82, Dec 65
New retinal tears following photocoagulation. Byer NE, et al. Trans Pacif Coast Otoophthal Soc 46:237-50, 1965
[Clinical aspects and treatment of retinal detachment] Seedorff HH. Maanedsskr Prakt Laegegern 43:261-9, Jun 65 (Dan)
[Ablatio retinae] Hagedoorn A. Nederl T Geneesk 109:1741-3, 11 Sep 65 (Dut)
[Apropos of traumatic retinal detachment in young subjects] Braun-Vallon S, et al. Bull Soc Ophtal Franc 65:171-7, Mar 65 (Fr)
[Bilateral detachment of the retina during eclampsia] Duhamel E, et al. Bull Soc Ophtal Franc 65:644-6, Jul-Aug 65 (Fr)
[Choroiditis in multiple sclerosis and so-called uveoencephalomeningitis] Bammer H, et al. Deutsch Z Nervenheilk 187:300-16, 2 Jul 65 (Ger)
[Retinal detachment, cataract, keratoconus as ocular symptom complex in endogenous eczema] Jütte A, et al. Klin Mbl Augenheilk 147:12-25, Sep 65 (Ger)
[Eye symptoms as first manifestations of bronchial

Fig. 3 Page from Cumulated Index Medicus, 1966, showing subject arrangement under "Retinal Detachment," and subheading "Etiology."

Subject	**Bibliog. for Dr.**		
Author			
Title			
Journal	**Vol.**	**Incl. Paging**	**Date**
Reference Obtained From:			

Fig. 4 Reference Slip. Note headings for each part of citation, and space for notes by reader. f citation, and space for notes by

you which headings are used in *Index Medicus* and under what heading you should look if the term you are using is not used as a separate subject. If you look at the appropriate page (Fig. 5) in the 1967 MeSH you see that "Retinal Detachment" is a separate subject, so that you don't need to look under any other subjects in this particular search. Looking higher up on the page you will see that if you wanted articles on "Angioid Streaks" you would want to look under both "Retina" and "Angioid Streaks." Further down in the same column you will see that if you were searching for articles on "Retrograde Degeneration" you should look under the heading "Nerve Degeneration," or moving further down, both literally and figuratively, if you wanted articles on "Retroperitoneal Fibrosis" you would also find articles dealing with "Ormond's Disease" under the same heading. A few minutes spent with MeSH before you start a search will enable you to cover the ground much more thoroughly and quickly than if you jumped right into *Index Medicus*.

The other major part of MeSH, the "Categorized Lists," gives you a broad picture of the arrangement of the headings themselves. The "C11" after "Retinal Detachment" (Fig. 1) refers you to the section of "Diseases" which covers specifically the "Sense Organ Diseases" (Fig. 6). Here you find part of the subject headings used in *Index Medicus* for these diseases. A glance over this may give you clues for other pertinent headings for your searching and it will also give you an indication of the thinking behind the choice of these headings.

Your searching of *Index Medicus* may have turned up several excellent references on your exact subject, but these references may have been to articles in Bulgarian, Portuguese, or some other language you do not read fluently. If this happened (and, since much of *Index Medicus* deals with foreign language material this is quite likely) your natural inclination might be to toss these references aside. Don't, at least not until you have taken several additional steps. First, if the reference is to a journal that is available in your library go and take a look at it. More and more foreign language journals are printing English summaries and such a summary may give you sufficient information. The summary sometimes appears at the beginning or end of the article, or sometimes they are all grouped together in one place near the front or back of the journal issue. If the article you are looking for does not fall into this category of journals, or if it is in a journal not immediately available, you still have another printed possibility. If you are searching for an English summary of an article on retinal detachment, you might turn to an English abstracting journal in the subject field. Bear in mind that it takes longer to produce an abstract than it does to index an article: there will often be a six to 12 months' lag before an English language abstract of a foreign language article appears.

The major English language abstracting journal is the series entitled *Excerpta Medica*. This is published in Amsterdam, in 33 subject sections. Each month an issue is produced in each of these subject areas: anatomy, ophthalmology, cancer, geriatrics, etc. *Excerpta Medica* covers several thousand journals from all over the world, and provides fairly detailed English abstracts for these articles.

In addition to *Excerpta Medica* many specialized abstracting journals exist and a few moments spent with the reference librarian in your library will acquaint you with the titles pertinent to your interests.

All of these abstracting journals serve several purposes. Not only will they furnish you with an

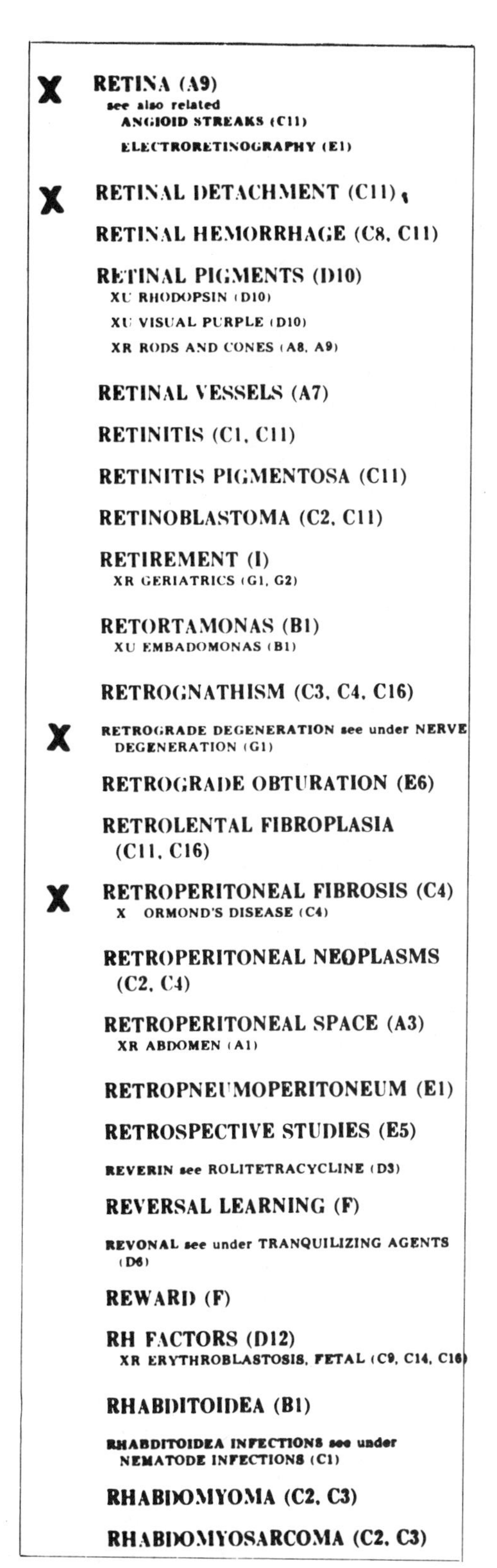

X **RETINA (A9)**
see also related
ANGIOID STREAKS (C11)
ELECTRORETINOGRAPHY (E1)

X **RETINAL DETACHMENT (C11)**

RETINAL HEMORRHAGE (C8, C11)

RETINAL PIGMENTS (D10)
XU RHODOPSIN (D10)
XU VISUAL PURPLE (D10)
XR RODS AND CONES (A8, A9)

RETINAL VESSELS (A7)

RETINITIS (C1, C11)

RETINITIS PIGMENTOSA (C11)

RETINOBLASTOMA (C2, C11)

RETIREMENT (I)
XR GERIATRICS (G1, G2)

RETORTAMONAS (B1)
XU EMBADOMONAS (B1)

RETROGNATHISM (C3, C4, C16)

X RETROGRADE DEGENERATION see under NERVE DEGENERATION (G1)

RETROGRADE OBTURATION (E6)

RETROLENTAL FIBROPLASIA (C11, C16)

X **RETROPERITONEAL FIBROSIS (C4)**
X ORMOND'S DISEASE (C4)

RETROPERITONEAL NEOPLASMS (C2, C4)

RETROPERITONEAL SPACE (A3)
XR ABDOMEN (A1)

RETROPNEUMOPERITONEUM (E1)

RETROSPECTIVE STUDIES (E5)

REVERIN see ROLITETRACYCLINE (D3)

REVERSAL LEARNING (F)

REVONAL see under TRANQUILIZING AGENTS (D6)

REWARD (F)

RH FACTORS (D12)
XR ERYTHROBLASTOSIS, FETAL (C9, C14, C16)

RHABDITOIDEA (B1)

RHABDITOIDEA INFECTIONS see under NEMATODE INFECTIONS (C1)

RHABDOMYOMA (C2, C3)

RHABDOMYOSARCOMA (C2, C3)

Fig. 5 Page from Medical Subject Headings (MeSH), 1967, showing that part of the Alphabetical List which contains "Retinal Detachment" and three other headings referred to in text.

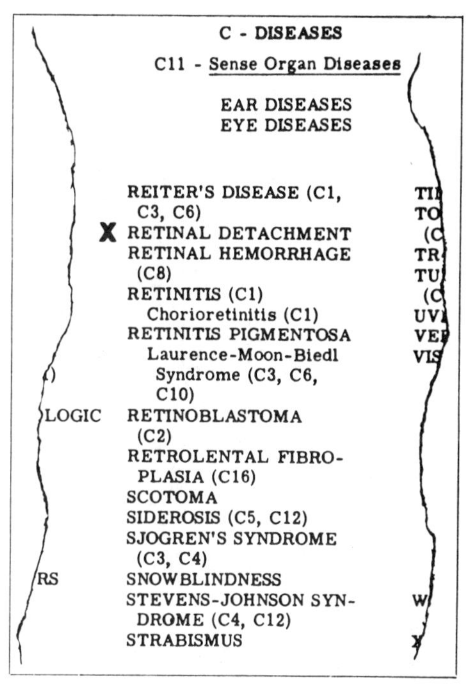

C - DISEASES

C11 - Sense Organ Diseases

EAR DISEASES
EYE DISEASES

REITER'S DISEASE (C1, C3, C6)
X RETINAL DETACHMENT
RETINAL HEMORRHAGE (C8)
RETINITIS (C1)
Chorioretinitis (C1)
RETINITIS PIGMENTOSA
Laurence-Moon-Biedl Syndrome (C3, C6, C10)
RETINOBLASTOMA (C2)
RETROLENTAL FIBROPLASIA (C16)
SCOTOMA
SIDEROSIS (C5, C12)
SJOGREN'S SYNDROME (C3, C4)
SNOWBLINDNESS
STEVENS-JOHNSON SYNDROME (C4, C12)
STRABISMUS

Fig. 6 Page showing C11, "Sense Organ Diseases," in "Categorized Lists" part of Medical Subject Headings, 1967.

English abstract of a specific article, but they are also useful for retrospective and "current awareness" searches.

A retrospective search is an extension in time of the original search you started out with, the one for "two or three good recent articles" on a specific subject. You can make a basic retrospective search by going back through several years of the *Cumulated Index Medicus* or you can expand this retrospective search both in number of journals covered and in immediately available information by using several years of one of the pertinent English-language abstracting journals. You will often be able to judge the pertinence of an article more readily from an abstract than from the index entry.

The "current awareness" search is one that keeps you up with the current articles in your field. If you want to know what is happening throughout the medical world in, for example, pediatrics, you would skim through each monthly issue of the section of *Excerpta Medica* on that subject as it comes in to your library. With a relatively small expenditure of time you will be able to keep up (taking into account the time-lag involved in writing and publishing abstracts) with the current work in your field.

After you have found some useful articles you will want to make notes on them. You can keep all of your information together by using your

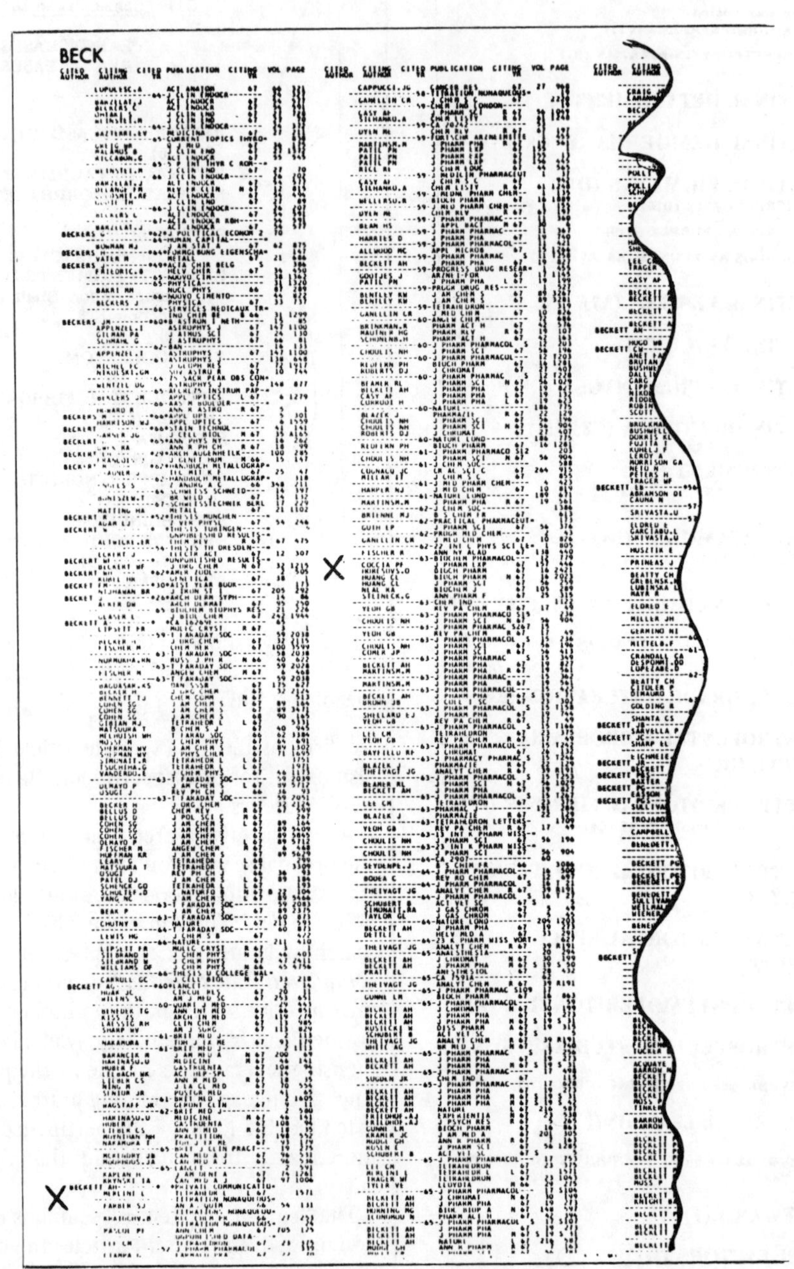
BECK

Fig. 7 Portion of page from Science Citation Index, 1967, showing arrangement. A. H. Beckett had a paper published in Biochemical Pharmacology in 1963, in volume 12 beginning on page 779 (second X). This article has been cited by Coccia (J Pharm Exp Ther 157:446, 1967), by Huang (Biochem Pharm 16: 2023, 1967), and by Neal (Biochem J 105:289, 1967).

reference slip (Fig. 4) for your notes as well. The references the author lists at the end of the article may be useful if you wish to pursue this subject further or if you want to check a specific point the author has mentioned. Most authors are careful to list only those references that proved helpful or directly pertinent. Occasionally, however, an author will just amass a list of references to make his paper look impressive. This is one of the cardinal sins of medical writing, and such authors soon become well-known for this "inflation."

Computers have made possible one of the most

intriguing indexing tools now available. The *Science Citation Index*, produced by the Institute for Scientific Information in Philadelphia, covers some 1,600 journals and indexes the references cited in them alphabetically and chronologically by author to show who has cited whom (Fig. 7). Such an index would simply not be possible without a computer to manipulate the millions of references involved. There are many potential uses for "SCI" and as you become acquainted with it you will find productive possibilities. Basically, you will be able to pursue a specific method, test, operative procedure, etc, and see who has referred to this same item.

If your search of the literature takes you back before the Second World War—and one or two important things did happen in medicine prior to 1940—you will find the *Index-Catalogue of the Library of the Surgeon-General's Office* useful. This monumental bibliography of 61 volumes was called by William Welch the greatest contribution to medicine by the United States after the development of surgical anesthesia. The *Index-Catalogue* lists books and journal articles by subject and books by author as well. It was issued in five alphabetical series which are gold-mines of references for the deep digger.

The front-line of medical science appears in the journals. However, books, reports, and other types of medical publications are also helpful, and if you need to cover these as well there are "keys" to this store of information. Currently, there is a branch of Medlars that presents a subject and author approach to recently published books and other nonjournal materials. The *Current Catalog* lists material recently catalogued by the National Library of Medicine. This comes out twice each month, and there are quarterly cumulations.

The best immediate source for available books on a particular subject is the card catalogue of your library. Here you will find books arranged by subject as well as by author. These cards will carry a "call number" derived from the subject classification system your library uses, and this will be helpful in locating the book on the library's shelves.

Medicine has a long and fascinating history, and if your interests are historically inclined you will find three "keys" that will be of special value. The first of these is a quarterly index produced in England, *Current Work in the History of Medicine*. This comprehensive index covers articles of medicohistorical interest that have appeared in both medical and nonmedical journals. The second, and newest, of these keys is an annual index to the history of medicine. Now in its third volume the *Bibliography of the History of Medicine*, another product of Medlars, will increase in usefulness as the years pass. The third key is a small book, *Garrison and Morton's Medical Bibliography: an Annotated Check-List of Texts Illustrating the History of Medicine*. The compilers have arranged the important books and journal articles chronologically within each subject. Many of the entries are annotated. *Garrison-Morton* will give you a panoramic view of how the knowledge of a particular medical subject has developed over the years and centuries, and will also acquaint you with the names of the important individuals in each field.

Computers have become useful tools in the bibliographic control of the medical literature. Types of indexes are now possible that could not have been produced by manual methods, and the production of most of the "old" indexes has been considerably speeded by automation. At the base of all of these "keys," however, are the qualified and experienced individuals who do the indexing and abstracting before the machine takes over for the mechanical processing. Keeping this in mind, and the immediately available assistance of the reference librarian in your own library, you should find that a search of the literature is not only a productive but a stimulating affair.

ANNOTATED LIST OF MAJOR INDEXING AND ABSTRACTING TOOLS

Index Medicus. New Series. Vol. 1- , 1960- . This is the major current medical index. It indexes 2,300 journals from 69 countries by subject and author. The *Cumulated Index Medicus* arranges the 12 monthly issues into one alphabet for subjects and one alphabet for authors each year.

Current List of Medical Literature. Vols. 1-36, 1941-1959. This predecessor of the "new" *Index Medicus* is especially useful for the period 1952-1959 when it was issued with semiannual cumulative indexes. Each issue lists articles alphabetically by journal title, and contains author and subject indexes.

Quarterly Cumulative Index Medicus. Vols. 1-60, 1927-1956. The "QCIM" is a useful index in "dictionary" form which should be used with *Current List of Medical Literature* since each of these indexed journals not covered by the other.

Index Medicus. Ser. I, Vols. 1-21, 1879-Apr., 1899; Ser. II, Vols. 1-18, 1903-1920; Ser. III, Vols. 1-6, 1921-June, 1927. Each issue gives an author and a subject approach, but the arrangement varies. This contains some material not found in the *Index-Catalogue*.

Quarterly Cumulative Index to Current Medical Literature. Vols. 1-12, 1916-1926. Should be used with the *Index Medicus* for this period.

Bibliographia Medica. Vols. 1-3, 1900-1902. A French publication, this attempted to fill part of the gap between the first and second series of *Index Medicus*.

Index-Catalogue of the Library of the Surgeon-General's Office. Ser. I, Vols. 1-16, 1880-1895; Ser. II, Vols. 1-21, 1896-1916; Ser. III, Vols. 1-10, 1918-1932; Ser. IV, Vols. 1-11, 1936-1955; Ser. V, Vols. 1-3, 1959-1961. This monumental work contains millions of references to books and articles. Anyone doing a comprehensive or historical search of the literature will find this an invaluable tool. Books are listed both under the author and the subject; journal articles are listed under the subject. The introduction to each series should be checked to find out what period is covered and what special material is contained in that series.

Bibliography of Medical Reviews. Vol. 1- , 1956- . Annual. This gives a subject and an author listing of recent review articles. Each entry gives full bibliographic citation and the number of references cited in the article. Beginning with 1968 BMR was published as a separate monthly journal as well as in the front of the monthly *Index Medicus*.

Excerpta Medica. Monthly. This is the major English-language abstracting journal. It is produced in 33 subject sections which cover the major preclinical and clinical fields. Fifteen of the sections began in 1947 or 1948. Each issue has author and subject indexes, and each volume has cumulated author and subject indexes.

Abstracts of World Medicine. Vol. 1- , 1947- . Monthly. This British publication provides "selective coverage of the important world literature" in all major subjects. Each issue has author and subject indexes, and each volume has cumulated author and subject indexes.

Science Citation Index. 1961, 1964- . The 1961 index was an annual; from 1964 on SCI has appeared quarterly with annual cumulations. This is an exhaustive index to references cited in some 1600 journals (many of them medical).

Biological Abstracts. Vol. 1- , 1926- . This major abstracting tool covers many fields related to medicine. It has a variety of up-to-date indexes.

Chemical Abstracts. Vol. 1- , 1907- . This is another major abstracting tool of considerable interest to those working in medicine. 10-year and 5-year cumulative indexes make searching quick and efficient.

Morton, Leslie T. Garrison and Morton's Medical Bibliography; An Annotated Check-List of Texts Illustrating the History of Medicine. 2nd ed., rev. London, Deutsch, 1965. "Garrison-Morton" is the basic handbook for the history of medicine.

Bibliography of the History of Medicine. No. 1- , 1965- . National Library of Medicine, Bethesda, Maryland. Annual. This indexes articles of medicohistorical interest, from medical and nonmedical journals, by subject and author.

Current Work in the History of Medicine. Quarterly. No. 1- , 1954- . The Wellcome Historical Medical Library produces this comprehensive index to articles in medical and nonmedical journals. It also gives the addresses of the authors, and lists new books and journals in the field.

Current Catalog, National Library of Medicine. Biweekly, with quarterly cumulations. Vol. 1- , 1966- . *Current Catalog* lists, by subject and author, monographs, new serial titles, and audiovisual materials catalogued by the National Library of Medicine. Information on prices and publishers is given when available.

ABOUT THE AUTHOR–William K. Beatty was educated at Harvard and Columbia, receiving a B.A. and an M.S.L.S. at the latter. He held positions at the College of Physicians of Philadelphia and the University of Missouri Medical Library before becoming Librarian and Professor of Medical Bibliography at Northwestern University Medical School.

In a sense, he has been the librarian's bibliographer. His "Winnowings" and "Journal Notes" in the *Bulletin of the Medical Library Association* have called his colleagues' attention to out-of-the-way publications of interest. He has edited *Vital Notes on Medical Periodicals* since 1955, and wrote the section of the *Handbook of Medical Library Practice*, third edition (Chicago, Medical Library Association, 1970) on "Selection, Acquisition, and Weeding." He has also been a bibliographer for the health scientist through "Winnowings" and other articles in *JAMA, The Journal of the American Medical Association* and editorship of the book review section in the *Journal of Medical Education*. He has explored the byroads of medicine through publication with Geoffrey Marks of *The Medical Garden* (Scribner's, 1971) and as a member of the Board of Advisors for the Medallic History of Medicine.

He has held many positions in the Special Libraries Association, the Medical Library Association, the American Library Association's Association of Hospital and Institutional Libraries, and the American Medical Writers Association.

Evaluating the Performance of a Large Computerized Information System

by Frederick W. Lancaster

This is the only full-scale, systematic evaluation of a large biomedical information retrieval system. The performance figures of 58% recall and 50% precision in the overall system are further examined for causes of failure.

The Medical Literature Analysis and Retrieval System (MEDLARS), in operation at the National Library of Medicine (NLM), is a multipurpose system, a prime purpose being the production of *Index Medicus* and other recurring bibliographies.[1] This two-year study concentrated on the evaluation of the demand search function of MEDLARS (ie, the conduct of retrospective literature searches in response to specific demands).[2]

The base of the retrospective search module consists of approximately 800,000 citations to biomedical journal articles input to the January 1964 and subsequent issues of the monthly *Index Medicus*. These articles have been indexed by means of a controlled vocabulary of *Medical Subject Headings* (*MeSH*). Over 3000 demand searches are now formulated annually at the NLM, additional searches being handled at regional MEDLARS centers in the United States, in the United Kingdom, and in Sweden.

Approximately 2,300 scientific journals are indexed regularly, one third exhaustively ("depth journals") at an average of ten terms per article, and the remainder less exhaustively ("nondepth journals") at an average of slightly less than four terms per article. The overall average is approximately 6.7 terms per article.

Medical Subject Headings consist of about 7,000 conventional subject headings in various broad subject categories. In January 1966, subheadings were introduced into the system. Subheadings, of which 53 were in use in 1966, are general concept terms (eg, "biosynthesis, complications") that can be affixed to main subject headings for greater specificity.

A demand search is currently conducted, by computer, through serial search of the index term profiles of the 800,000 citations on magnetic tape. This search is essentially a matching process: the index term profiles of journal articles are matched against a search formulation, which is a translation of a subject request into the controlled vocabulary of the system. Requests for demand searches are mainly received by mail at NLM, either in a letter or on a "demand search request form"; a higher proportion of the requests processed by regional MEDLARS centers are made by personal visit to the center. The search formulations are prepared, by search analysts, in the form of Boolean combinations (logical sums, logical products, and negations) of main subject headings and subheadings.

The final product of a MEDLARS search is a computer-printed demand search bibliography, the citations usually appearing in alphabetical order by author. Accompanying each citation is a complete set of tracings (ie, a record of all the index terms assigned to the article).

PURPOSE OF THE MEDLARS EVALUATION

Planning of the MEDLARS evaluation program began in December 1965, the principal objectives being to study the requirements of demand search users, to get an objective measure of a system performance in relation to these requirements, to disclose factors adversely affecting performance, and to determine ways of satisfying user needs more efficiently or more economically or both.

SOURCE: Reprinted from Frederick W. Lancaster, "Evaluating the Performance of a Large Computerized Information System," *JAMA, The Journal of the American Medical Association*, 207 (Jan. 6, 1969), pp. 114–120, by permission of the publisher and the author.

The prime requirements of demand search users were presumed to relate to the following factors:

1. The *coverage* of MEDLARS (ie, the proportion of the useful literature on a particular topic, within the time limits imposed, that is indexed into the system).
2. Its *recall* power (ie, its ability to retrieve "relevant" documents, which, within the context of this evaluation, means documents judged by a requester to be of value in relation to the information need that prompted his request to MEDLARS).
3. Its *precision power* (ie, its ability to hold back "non-relevant" documents).
4. The *response time* of the system (ie, the elapsed time between receipt of a request at a MEDLARS center and delivery of a printed bibliography).
5. The *format* in which search results are presented.
6. The amount of *effort* the user must personally expend to evoke a satisfactory response from the system.[3]

The two most critical problems faced in the design of the evaluation were: (1) ensuring that the body of test requests was, as far as possible, representative of the complete spectrum of "kinds" of requests processed; and (2) establishing methods for determining recall and precision figures.

THE TEST USER POPULATION

Through the detailed analysis of demand searches conducted at NLM in 1965, we established a list of 20 organizations that would form a suitable "test user group," ie, one representing a stratified sample of the complete MEDLARS population. It was representative of the principal types of organization using the system, the principal broad subject fields in which requests are made, and the various possible methods by which requests are put to the system. On formal invitation, the 20 major medical organizations thus selected agreed to participate. In addition, we included in the evaluation a number of requests made, within the test period, by private practitioners. While the organizations comprising the test user group agreed to cooperate in the evaluation program (eg, the dean of a medical school, or the director of a research institute, and their librarians), the individual requesters knew nothing of the evaluation program until they had submitted their requests. They were then asked to allow us to use their requests as "test requests." Thus, each test request quite definitely represented an actual information need.

ESTABLISHING THE PERFORMANCE FIGURES

For each of the test requests, a search was conducted and a computer printout of citations (demand search bibliography) was delivered to the requester. A second copy of this printout was used to extract a random sample of 25 to 30 of the retrieved citations. Photocopies of these sample articles were submitted to the requester for relevance assessment and a second copy was retained for analysis purposes. This figure of 25 to 30 represents an upper bound on the number of articles for which we felt we could reasonably expect to obtain careful assessments. A copy of a *Form for Document Evaluation* was attached to each article submitted for assessment.

A most important function of this form was to establish why certain articles were judged relevant and others not relevant (ie, of no value to the requester in relation to his information need).

The completed forms, when returned, were attached to the duplicate copies of the articles to which they related, and the precision ratio (ie, proportion of relevant articles retrieved to total retrieved) of the search was derived, as illustrated in Table 1. In this case, the requester was presented with a random sample of 25 articles, of which he assessed 20, judging ten to be of value ("relevant") and ten of no value. The precision ratio for this search is therefore 10/20 × 100, or 50%. While obtaining precision figures for a MEDLARS search presents no particular problem, it is extremely difficult to estimate the recall ratio (proportion of all the relevant articles within the data base that are

TABLE 1.

SEARCH RESULTS DERIVED ON THE BASIS OF RANDOM SAMPLING OF RETRIEVED CITATIONS

	Major	Minor	No Value	Not Assessed
Known in Advance	3	1	. . .	. . .
Not Known	1	5	10	5*

*These items could not be assessed because they are in languages unfamiliar to the requester.

retrieved by a search) for a "real-life" search in a file of 800,000 citations. The only way to obtain a true recall figure is to have the requester examine, and make assessments on, each and every document in the file. While this is feasible in certain experimental situations, it is obviously out of the question for a collection of the MEDLARS size.

We therefore estimated the MEDLARS recall figure on the basis of retrieval performance in relation to a number of documents, judged relevant by the requester, but found by means outside MEDLARS. For every test request, we attempted to obtain a record of any articles, within the time span of the system, that the requester already knew to be relevant to the subject of his request (recorded on a form, *Record of Known Relevant Documents*, after he had submitted his request but before he received the results of a MEDLARS search). In cases in which the requester was unable to name any relevant articles, or could name only one or two, an attempt was made to find additional potentially relevant articles by manual searching of conventional printed indexes at NLM (but not, of course, using any bibliographics generated from the MEDLARS data base). The additional documents found in this way were considered no more than "possibly relevant." They were not incorporated into the recall base until the requester had examined them and judged them relevant in relation to his information need. To achieve this, these additional items were interspersed with the precision set (ie, the articles selected by random sampling from the MEDLARS search printout). The requester then assessed the enlarged set at one time.

Table 2 illustrates the way in which this method of obtaining a recall estimate works. In this instance, the requester is able to name two relevant articles, and an additional seven potentially relevant items are produced by the manual search.

TABLE 2.

METHOD USED TO ESTABLISH A "RECALL BASE" AND A RECALL RATIO

Source	No. of Articles Supplied	No. of Relevant Articles*	No. Retrieved by MEDLARS
Requester	2	2	1
Manual Search	7	4	3
Totals	9	6	4

*Judged relevant by requester and found to be in MEDLARS base.

The user, asked to make assessments of these seven documents, judges four to be relevant. We now have six known relevant documents upon which we can base our recall figure. If all are in the MEDLARS data base, but only four are retrieved, we say that the recall ratio for this search is $4/6 \times 100$, or 66.7%. Recall and precision figures are merely yardsticks to measure the effect of making certain changes in our system or in ways of operating the system. Although the recall estimate obtained may be slightly inflated or deflated in relation to "true recall," since the method used to obtain the estimate was held constant throughout the evaluation program, the figures are still valid indicators of performance differences in various situations.

FORM FOR DOCUMENT EVALUATION

1. Were you previously aware of the existence of this article?

   Yes [ ] *How did you learn of its existence?*

   No [ ]

2. By checking the appropriate box, please evaluate this article in relation to the information need that prompted your request to MEDLARS.

   (*a*) Of major value to me in relation to my information need [ ] *Please explain why:*

   (*b*) Of minor value to me in relation to my information need [ ] *Please explain why:*

   (*c*) Of no value to me in relation to my information need [ ] *Please explain why:*

   Were you glad to learn of its existence because of some other need or project?

   Yes [ ] *Please explain why:*

   No [ ]

   (*d*) Unable to make an assessment because of language of the document [ ]

   Do you intend to take any steps to determine the contents of this foreign language document?

   Yes [ ] *Please specify what steps:*

   No [ ] *Please explain why:*

ANALYSIS OF SEARCH FAILURES

Having derived the performance figures for a test search, the next step was the detailed intellectual analysis of recall and precision failures. In the hypothetical search illustrated in Table 1 and Table 2, we are faced with the analysis of (1) two *recall failures* (two of the six "known relevant" articles were not retrieved), and (2) ten *precision failures* (ten of the 20 articles assessed by the requester were judged of no value).

These are not the only failures occurring in the search. They are the only ones that we know of, and as such they are accepted as exemplifying the complete recall and precision failures (ie, they are symptomatic of problems occurring in this search).

The "hindsight" analysis of each search failure involves an examination of the following: the full text of the document itself, the index terms assigned, the request statement, the search formulation upon which the search was conducted, the requester's completed assessment forms, and any other information supplied by the requester. On the basis of all these records, a decision is made regarding the prime cause or causes of the particular failure currently being reviewed.

THE MEDLARS TEST RESULTS

From August 1966 to July 1967, 410 test requests were processed to the point of submitting photocopies of sample articles to requesters. From these, 317 sets of relevance assessments were returned (ie, 77%) and 302 of these searches were completely analyzed. Figure 1 shows how these 302 requests break down by mode of interaction, by "kind" of organization, by subject field of request, and by the MEDLARS center processing the search.

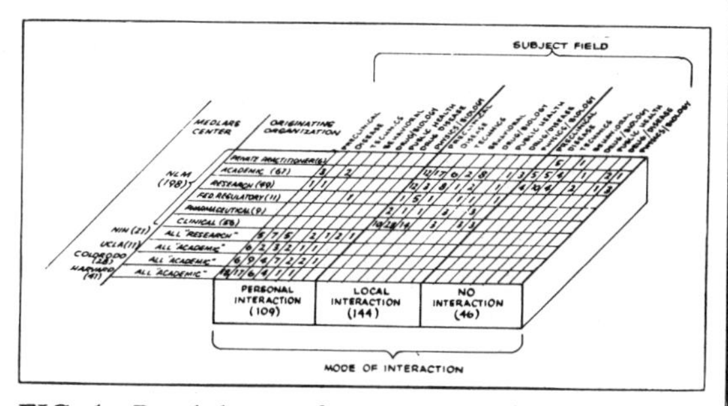

FIG. 1 Breakdown of 302 MEDLARS test requests by originating organization, subject field, mode of interaction, and MEDLARS processing center.

For three of the 302 searches, we were unable to obtain a recall base, but for the remaining 299 we have both precision and recall ratios. The average of the individual performance ratios for the 299 test searches gives the results in Table 3. Over a substantial representative sample of MEDLARS requests, the system was found to be operating, on the average, at 57.7% recall and 50.4% precision. That is, over the 299 test searches, MEDLARS retrieved an average of little less than 60% of the relevant literature within its base. At the same time, approximately 50% of the articles retrieved were, on the average, judged relevant by requesters. All failures were analyzed in detail. Table 4 attributes these recall and precision failures to the principal components of the complete system. Note that some failures could not be attributed to a single system component and were therefore jointly at-

TABLE 3.

AVERAGE RECALL AND PRECISION RATIOS FOR 299 SEARCHES*

Overall precision ratio†	50.4%
Precision ratio based on major value articles only	25.7%
Overall recall ratio (complete recall base)	57.7%
Recall ratio based on major value articles only (274 searches)	65.2%

*Omitting three that have no recall base.
†All figures in this table are calculated by averaging the individual ratios.

TABLE 4.

RECALL AND PRECISION FAILURES, OCCURRING IN 302 TEST SEARCHES, AS ATTRIBUTED TO MAJOR SYSTEM COMPONENTS

	Recall* Failures No. (%)	Precision† Failures No. (%)
Index Language	81 (10.2)	1,094 (36)
Indexing	298 (37.4)	393 (12.9)
Searching	279 (35.0)	983 (32.4)
Interaction	199 (25)	503 (16.6)
Other	11 (1.4)	78 (2.5)

*Based on an analysis of 797 separate failures.
†Based on an analysis of 3,038 separate failures.

tributed to two components (eg, indexing and searching, or indexing and index language).

FAILURES DUE TO THE INDEX LANGUAGE

Index-language failures are of two principal types: (1) failures due to lack of specificity in the terms, and (2) failures due to ambiguous or spurious relationships between terms.

Lack of specificity can cause either recall failures or precision failures. In this evaluation, it was responsible for 10.2% of all the recall failures.

To correct precision failures due to lack of specificity requires that terms or term combinations that uniquely define a notion not now covered specifically be added to the vocabulary. To correct recall failures, we do not need a unique designation, but we must include the notion in our entry vocabulary (ie, the vocabulary of natural-language biomedical terms that map onto the controlled terms of the system). The evaluation has shown that the MEDLARS entry vocabulary is somewhat weak. Recall failures could have been 10% less if a better entry vocabulary had been available. Lack of an adequate entry vocabulary can lead to indexer omissions, indexer inconsistencies, recall failures, and, in some cases, precision failures. Other index-language failures are due to ambiguous or spurious relationships between terms, either false coordinations or incorrect term relationships. Thus, a search for articles on the co-occurrence of leukemia and Down's syndrome (mongolism) will retrieve all articles assigned both indexing terms. However, in not all of these will the two terms be directly related. For example, we might retrieve a clinical study that discusses a number of different patients. Some of these have leukemia, others have Down's syndrome, but there is not coincidence of the two phenomena in the same patient. This is a false coordination (the two search terms are not directly related in the retrieved article). Another request, for articles on amenorrhea following discontinuance of oral contraceptive therapy, is searched on terms for oral contraceptives *and* amenorrhea. Not all the articles retrieved deal with amenorrhea following use of oral contraceptives. Some discuss the therapeutic use of contraceptive agents in the treatment of menstruation disorders (including amenorrhea). This is an incorrect term relationship. The two search terms are related in the retrieved articles but not in the way that the requester wants them related. False coordinations were responsible for 11.3% of the precision failures in the 302 searches, incorrect term relationships for 6.8%.

FAILURES DUE TO THE INDEXING SUBSYSTEM

Table 4 shows that the MEDLARS indexing contributed to 37.4% of the recall failures and 12.9% of the precision failures. These failures were due either to indexer error or to a policy decision governing the number of terms assigned to an article.

An indexer may either omit an important term or use a term that appears inappropriate to the subject matter of the article. Omissions will normally lead to recall failures, while an inappropriate term can cause either a precision failure or a recall failure. Use of inappropriate terms (ie, sheer mis-indexing) appears to be negligible in MEDLARS, contributing to about 1% of the precision failures and 1% of the recall failures. Indexer omissions, on the other hand, contribute to almost 10% of all the recall failures. These are fairly obvious errors (eg, terms omitted from titles) and cannot be blamed primarily on a policy decision governing the number of terms assigned. However, many of these cases derive from the fact that no *MeSH* term exists for the missed notion, and there is nothing in the entry vocabulary to say how the topic is to be indexed. Thus, the indexer is quite likely to omit the topic, rather than to translate it into a more general term. Indexer omissions of this type are likely to diminish as a more complete entry vocabulary is built up.

The most difficult problem relating to indexing policy, in any system, is the decision as to how many index terms to assign, on the average, to a document. If we index exhaustively (ie, use a large number of terms in an attempt to cover the complete extension of the contents of documents), we will tend to produce a system operating at high recall but low precision. Conversely, a low level of exhaustivity of indexing (ie, inclusion of "most important" concepts only) will tend to produce a high-precision, low-recall performance.

MEDLARS, predictably, shows failures of both types. Twenty percent of the recall failures are attributed to lack of indexing exhaustivity, while 11.5% of the precision failures are caused largely by exhaustive indexing. These results seem to suggest that the exhaustivity level should be increased, to improve the recall potential of the system, rather than reduced. It is better to err on the side of additional terms. Without a fairly high level of exhaustivity, it is difficult to achieve a high average recall performance at a tolerable precision level. On the other hand, we can usually improve the precision of a search by employing more precise search formulations.

However, there are two distinct exhaustivity levels in MEDLARS, "depth" indexing (approximately ten terms per article) and "nondepth" (about four terms per article). Because the nondepth articles are indexed with many fewer terms, they tend to be indexed not only less exhaustively than depth articles, but also less specifically. Consequently, both recall and precision failures result.

Experiments show that only a very much higher level of exhaustivity (say an increase from ten to 20 terms) would be likely to have any noticeable effect on the recall of depth articles. On the other hand, a 30% to 40% improvement in recall of the present nondepth articles would be likely if the average number of terms assigned to these items was raised to the "depth" level.

FAILURES DUE TO THE SEARCHING SUBSYSTEM

There are three types of searching failure:

1. The use of inappropriate terms or defective search logic. These are not particularly significant in MEDLARS (only 5% of the precision failures and less than 1% of the recall failures).
2. Failures due to the level of generality in a search strategy (a broad search will give high recall but low precision, a narrow search high precision, but low recall).
3. Those due to the searcher's failure to cover all reasonable approaches to the retrieval of relevant articles.

The last is by far the most important of the searching failures, being responsible for 21.5% of all the recall failures. In other words, 21.5% of the missed relevant articles could have been retrieved on terms or term combinations which, I feel, the searcher might reasonably have been expected to use in the search formulation. To quote one example, a search on potassium shifts in isolated cell preparations made no use of the term "cell membrane permeability," although, used in conjunction with "potassium" or "potassium chloride," this term would have retrieved several major relevance articles. This type of failure might be reduced if additional term displays, cutting across existing hierarchical structures (genus-species relations), were available to the search analysts.

Other searching failures are due simply to the level of generality adopted in a searching strategy. The central problem of searching is the decision as to the most appropriate level of generality to adopt for a particular request. The broader the strategy, the more documents will be retrieved, recall will tend to increase, and precision to decrease. The more narrow the strategy, the fewer documents will be retrieved, recall will tend to deteriorate, and precision to improve. About 11% of the recall failures were due to the use of somewhat narrow search strategies, while 27% of the precision failures were due to strategies that were rather general in relation to the requests made. It is obviously dangerous to generalize on the matter of searching strategy, and the correct level of generality to adopt for a particular request. Nevertheless, on the basis of the search analyses it has been possible to derive some general pointers as to where search generalization is justified, where not justified, and how it may best be accomplished.

FAILURES DUE TO DEFECTIVE INTERACTION BETWEEN THE REQUESTER AND THE SYSTEM

Defective user-system interaction contributed to 25% of the recall failures and 16.6% of the precision failures. Such a recall failure implies that the request put to the system is more specific than the actual area of information need. Relevant articles are not retrieved because the searcher adheres strictly to the request statement. A precision failure due to defective interaction implies that the stated request is more general than the actual information need. Irrelevant articles are retrieved. These match his stated request but are judged irrelevant because of some additional limitation or requirement that was not given in the request statement. In some searches there is a partial overlap between stated request and information need, and in these cases it is likely that both recall and precision failures will result from defective interaction.

In the design of the evaluation, we hypothesized that the most desirable mode of interaction would be that of personal interaction (the requester discusses his needs personally with a search analyst). The other modes (mailed request direct to the system, and the request transmitted through a local librarian) would be likely to be less successful on the whole. This hypothesis was not supported by the test results.

From these results, especially the detailed search analyses, it appears that the best request statements (ie, those that most closely reflect the actual area of information need) are those written down by the requester in his own natural-language narrative terms. When he discusses his need orally, with librarian or search analyst, a transformation takes place and, unfortunately, the request statement captured by the librarian or searcher is frequently a less perfect mirror of the information need than the one prepared by the requester himself in his own natural-language terms. When the user writes down his request, he is forced to think of what *exactly* he is looking for, without being particularly influenced by the logical and linguistic constraints of the system. When making a personal visit to a MEDLARS center, if he has not gone through the discipline of recording his request, he has a less well formed idea of what he is seeking. When he discusses this somewhat imprecise need with a search analyst, in terms of *Medical Subject Headings*, his request may become forced into the logic and language of the system.

COMMENT

The test results have shown that the system is operating, on the average, at about 58% recall (65% if we consider only the articles judged of major value by requesters) and 50% precision. Averages, however, are somewhat misleading. A scatter diagram shows that few of the individual search results fall in the area bounded by the average ratios ±5%. Some of the searches appear to have performed very well, with high recall accompanied by high precision. Others achieved completely unsatisfactory recall results. By a careful examination of a sample of searches at each end of the distribution, it has been possible to identify the most important factors governing the success or failure of a MEDLARS search.

We can plot as recall-precision points the average figures achieved in the test searches by each of the five MEDLARS processing centers. By extrapolation from these points, we can hypothesize a generalized MEDLARS performance curve somewhat

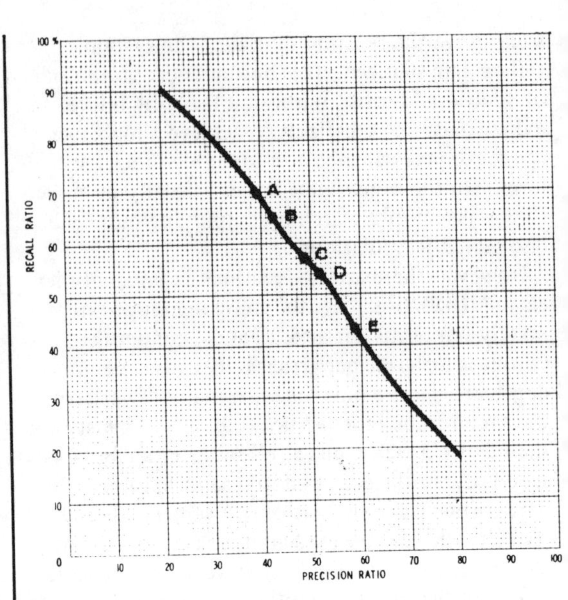

FIG. 2. Generalized MEDLARS performance curve extrapolated from performance figures of five search processing centers.

like that of Fig. 2. The fact that, on the average, MEDLARS is operating at 58% recall and 50% precision indicates that, consciously or unconsciously, the MEDLARS searchers choose to operate in this general area. It would be possible for MEDLARS to operate at a different performance point on the recall-precision curve of Fig. 2. By broadening of search strategies, the system could obtain a much higher average recall ratio, but this could only be achieved at a much lower average precision. From Fig. 2 it can be seen that there are differences in searching policies between the various centers, center E choosing to operate in a high precision mode, while center A appears to favor higher recall. The other centers use strategies that compromise more between recall and precision.

In operating at 58% recall and 50% precision, MEDLARS is retrieving an average of 175 citation per search. To operate at an average recall of 85% to 90%, and an average precision ratio in the region of 20% to 25%, implies that the system would need to retrieve an average perhaps of 500 to 600 citations per search. Are requesters willing to scan this many citations (75% of which are likely to be irrelevant) in order to obtain a much higher level of recall? Clearly, each individual has his own requirements in relation to the trade-off between recall and precision. It is obviously important that we establish for each request the recall requirements and precision tolerances of the requester, thus allowing the search analyst to prepare a strategy geared as required to high recall, high precision, or some compromise point in between.

The purpose of a comprehensive system evaluation, such as the one reported, is not simply to determine the present performance level but also to discover how to upgrade that performance. On the basis of the diagnostic search analyses, it has been possible to recommend improvements to the overall operating efficiency of the system. Some of the more important of these are as follows:

1. Direct attention should be devoted to the improvement of user request statements, because it is here that most immediate benefits in performance appear possible. The present search request form should be redesigned to elicit greater participation from the user in making his precise requirements known to the system. All requesters should be required to complete this form personally, even in situations in which the requester makes a personal visit to a MEDLARS center or to his local library.
2. The search request form should record the recall and precision requirements and tolerances of the individual user, and search analysts should make use of these data in the formulation of appropriate strategies
3. Consideration should be given to the possibility of establishing, and recording in machinable form, standard strategies for search elements likely to recur in a number of different searches.
4. The present distinction between "depth" and "nondepth" journals should be abandoned; each article should be treated on its own merit and sufficient terms assigned to index the extension and intension of its content. We estimate that the present overall level of indexing exhaustivity is adequate to meet the current type of demand.
5. The further development of the MEDLARS vocabulary should be based primarily on continuous inputs from the indexing and searching operations. The entry vocabulary should be expanded and made readily available to every indexer and searcher.
6. The use of subheadings should be extended to increase specificity of the vocabulary and to reduce the number of ambiguous and spurious term relationships.
7. Steps should be taken to effect greater integration between the activities of indexing, searching, and vocabulary control.

A large-scale study of this type exposes the greatest weaknesses of a system, but, no matter how comprehensive, it can discover only a small fraction of its specific (eg, terminological) inadequacies. This library is now investigating the feasibility of applying the evaluation procedures to the continuous monitoring of MEDLARS performance. By these quality-control measures we will (*a*) attempt to ensure that each search meets the performance needs of the individual MEDLARS user, and (*b*) collect necessary data to allow the continued improvement of indexing policies, searching strategies, vocabulary development, and modes of interaction with the user. Only by continuous self-appraisal and responsive modifications can this large information system remain responsive to the needs of the biomedical community.[4]

NOTES

[1] Karel, L.; Austin, C. J.; and Cummings, M. M.: Computerized Bibliographic Services for Biomedicine, *Science* **148**:766-772 (May 7) 1965.

[2] Lancaster, F. W.: Evaluation of the *MEDLARS Demand Search Service*, Bethesda, Md.: National Library of Medicine, 1968.

[3] Cleverdon, C. W.; Mills, J.; and Keen, M.: *Factors Determining the Performance of Indexing Systems*. Cranfield, England: ASLIB Cranfield Project, 1966, vol. 1.

[4] The author acknowledges the assistance and encouragement given by members of the MEDLARS Evaluation Advisory Committee: Charles J. Austin, Director of Computer Services and Assistant Professor, University of Colorado Medical Center, Denver; Julian H. Bigelow, PhD, Permanent Member, Institute for Advanced Study, Princeton, N. J.; Cyril W. Cleverdon, Librarian, College of Aeronautics, Cranfield, England; W. D. Climenson, Deputy Director of Computer Services, Central Intelligence Agency; Eugene K. Harris, PhD, Chief, Laboratory of Applied Studies, Division of Computer Research and Technology, National Institutes of Health; and Calvin N. Mooers, President, Rockford Research Institute Inc., Cambridge, Mass.

ABOUT THE AUTHOR—F. Wilfrid Lancaster is Associate Professor and Director of the Program in Biomedical Librarianship at the Graduate School of Library Science, University of Illinois. His first work in medical librarianship was at the National Library of Medicine where the study described in this paper was done. Prior to that, he had positions in public and special libraries here and in England. His basic research with indexing began as Senior Research Assistant at ASLIB in 1963 and continued through two years as Resident Consultant and Head Systems Evaluation Group at Herner and Company. After his work at the National Library of Medicine, he served at Westat Research, Inc., as Director of Information Retrieval Services for one year. He studied Library Science and English at The Newcastle upon Tyne School of Librarianship and is a Fellow (by thesis) of the Library Association of Great Britain.

Mr. Lancaster served on the Panel on Information Sciences Technology of the Committee on Scientific and Technical Information (COSATI) of The Federal Council for Science and Technology. The work on which this paper is based is more fully reported in *Evaluation of the MEDLARS Demand Search Service* (Bethesda, Md., National Library of Medicine, 1968). Mr. Lancaster received the award for the best *American Documentation* paper in 1969 and also the 1970 ASIS award for the best information science book, the latter for his *Information Retrieval Systems: Characteristics, Testing and Evaluation* (N. Y., John Wiley, 1968).

Evaluation of the Usage of a Custom Biological Literature Search Service: A Three Year Study

by Richard I. Rubinstein and Louise Schultz

Since the BIOSIS retrieval service was made available to a circumscribed group of users, it was possible to study the behavior of these users in terms of repeat questions to the system and intervals between repeat usage.

INTRODUCTION

This report attempts to determine the degree of satisfaction of requesters in a custom literature search service in the biological sciences from the patterns of system usage over a 33-month period. Studies of users and usage of an information system[1-3] commonly depend on questionnaires, interviews, and diaries through which the user reveals his information needs, use of the system, or degree of satisfaction with its performance. BioSciences Information Service (BIOSIS) has been operating and developing an information system[4] since May 1965, to the evaluation of which it could apply none of these measurement methods. This study suggests that performance evaluation can be inferred from empirical operations data gathered routinely and not influenced by user subjectivity (in the data-gathering phase).

THE SYSTEM, ITS ENVIRONMENT, AND ITS USERS

BioSciences Information Service of Biological Abstracts (BIOSIS) functions as both a secondary recorded-medium channel, in publishing *Biological Abstracts* and sister publications, and a type of information-center channel, in offering custom abstracts retrieval service.[5] Since its founding in 1927, *Biological Abstracts* has published approximately two million abstracts and citations of primary journal articles in the biological sciences.[6] Of these, indexes to nearly one million are available in machine form and the corresponding abstracts are on microfilm for duplication by a reader-printer.

To exploit this data base, an essentially manual retrieval service was initiated in May 1965 under the sponsorship of Walter Reed Army Institute of Research (WRAIR),[7] which has developed in the degree of computer support and has expanded to serve the research unit at Letterman General Hospital, San Francisco, and the U. S. Army Medical Corps Research and Development Command, Scientific and Technical Information Office (STINFO). The latter facility has not been included in this study because data are not available as to the identity of requesters, inasmuch as requests are entered by an intermediary in the 'name' of the facility.

The requester population at the using installations consists of both military and civilian personnel. There is a constant turnover of the former due to termination of duty tours. Individuals presently on staff at WRAIR were identified from a current directory, allowing comparisons to be made between those who still had access to the system at the end of the study period and those who had left WRAIR between the time of system usage and the end of the study period. This information was not available for requesters at Letterman General Hospital or U. S. Army Institute of Dental Research. Neither are precise data available on the maximum number of individuals having the

SOURCE: Reprinted from Richard I. Rubinstein and Louise Schultz, "Evaluation of the Usage of a Custom Biological Literature Search Service: a Three Year Study," *Proceedings of the American Society for Information Science*, 5 (1968), by permission of the publisher and the authors.

opportunity to use the system during the period, although we judge the number to be in the order of 1500, including all technical and administrative personnel. Work missions vary but include "bench research," evaluation of technical merit of proposals seeking funding support, and participation in or planning of special scientific short courses.

The interface between user and system consists of electrowriter-dataphone terminals located at the WRAIR library[8] and the Research and Development division of BIOSIS. An individual desiring to use the system obtains a dial-a-card from the librarian to establish communications with BIOSIS through telephone lines. He writes his inquiry message in natural language, in his own handwriting, on the electrowriter.

Receipt of the written message is usually monitored by experienced biologists at BIOSIS. When necessary, the BIOSIS 'search strategist' may negotiate with the requester, either in writing or by voice communication, to clarify ambiguities in the question or correct for electronic disturbances in the transmission. As discussed by Cavanaugh,[9] this type of dynamic interface, in which no constraints are imposed on dialogue between user and system operator is superior to one that offers only yes/no responses or one that requires the user to interpret the system responses. BIOSIS personnel are thus better able to formulate an effective search strategy.

This strategy is the plan by which BIOSIS personnel identify abstracts most likely to contain the information desired by the requester. It consists of

a. designation of files to be searched (keyword, subject, taxonomic and/or author indexes);
b. distribution of search tasks between computer and humans; and
c. assignment to appropriate search personnel (biologists and/or clerical).

Abstracts meeting search specifications are reproduced from microfilm on a reader-printer and screened by biologically trained personnel as to their pertinence to the query. Those selected are then mailed to the requester.

Data about each transmission and response are on punch cards for machine processing of operations reports. The information includes the user's name, department, date of transmission, transmission number, and number of abstracts sent. A "transmission" is defined as a communication from user to the system regardless of the number of questions (or "search tasks") encompassed.[10] Operations records, including for this report the calculation of intervals between transmissions, are based on number of working days per year rather than on calendar days; e.g., one year = approximately 251 days.

USAGE PATTERNS AND SATISFACTION IMPLICATIONS

This report considers the number of transmissions per user, the length of intervals (in working days) between an individual's transmissions, and number of abstracts sent per transmission. Information was correlated with the individual's department and/or installation, to examine implicit differences in user needs and satisfaction with the service based on his scientific discipline.

Between the inception of this information service and 31 January 1968, BIOSIS had processed more than 1000 transmissions from 416 different individuals from WRAIR, USAIDR and Letterman General Hospital Research Unit. Figure 1 plots the number of requests in quarterly intervals. The high initial activity can be accounted for by the novelty of the system and the fact that, by service contract definition, a correspondence existed between a "transmission" and a "search task." Subsequent to the first year, multiple requests per transmission were permitted. Excluding the first four quarters, the average is 85 transmissions per quarter with a standard deviation of 13 and a mean deviation of 11.

Completely without formal publicity or encouragement by WRAIR managers to use the system, first-time use has apparently increased steadily

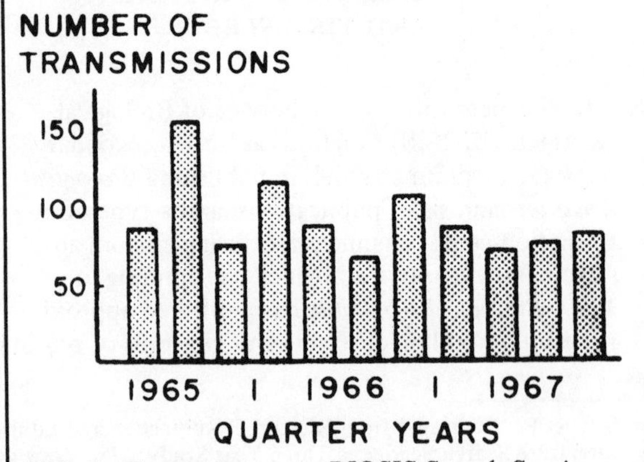

FIG. 1 Transmissions to BIOSIS Search Service by Calendar Quarter.

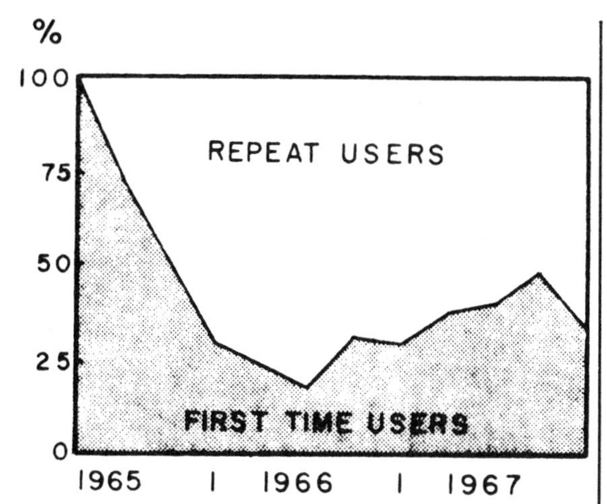

FIG. 2 Proportion of First-Time and Repeat Users of BIOSIS Search Service.

since the second quarter of 1966, as graphed in Figure 2. We can assume not only that total system usage levels are maintained in an environment of changing patrons (Figure 1) but also that "satisfied" users have mentioned this service to their colleagues, especially to new arrivals at the installation.

Another indication of user satisfaction might be his repeated use of the system. Of the total sample, 48 percent of the requesters initiated more than one transmission, the average being 2.5 transmissions per individual, 2.7 for WRAIR personnel. Figure 3 also illustrates the percentage of total users in each multiple-transmission group.

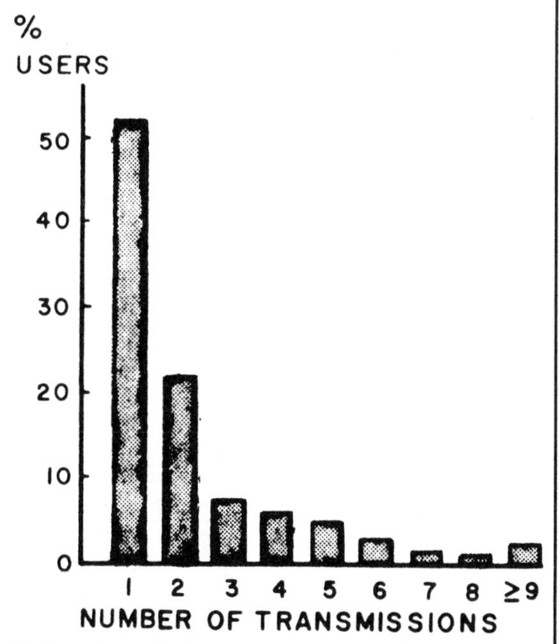

FIG. 3 Percentage of Users Transmitting One or More Inquiries.

In Figure 4, the pattern of access is plotted according to whether the individual is known to have been on the WRAIR staff at the end of the study period (labelled "WRAIR PRESENT"), apparently had left WRAIR (labelled "WRAIR NOT PRESENT"), or is from another installation and whose status is unknown (labelled "NON-WRAIR"). Notice that the pattern for both of the latter categories exhibits a definite cut-off trend. However, system drop-out for multiple-transmission users who are known to have been on the WRAIR staff at the close of the study period appears, in contrast, to approach a threshold, implying a measurement of satisfaction. That is, if the user re-enters the system once, the probabilities are 2 out of 3 that he will re-enter again and 1 out of 3 that he will re-enter four or more times. One out of seven users continuing to have access to the system develops a pattern of reuse averaging one transmission per quarter. Ten individuals at WRAIR used the sys-

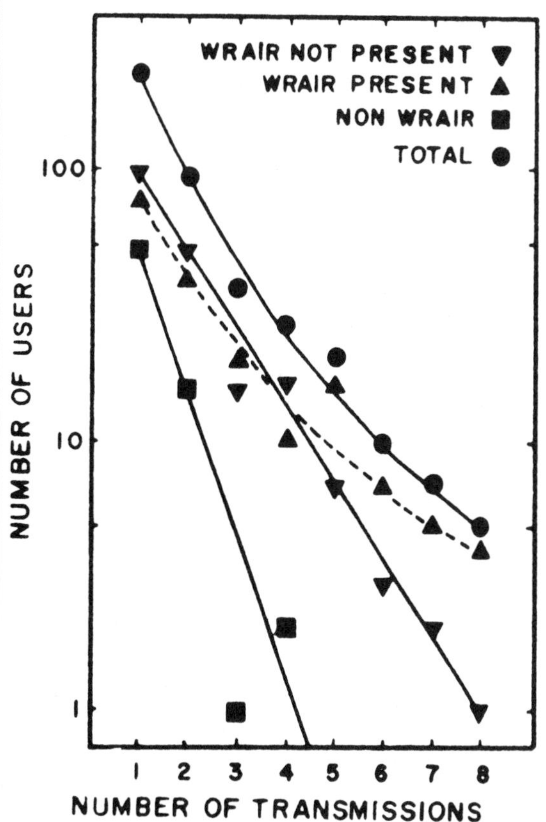

FIG. 4 Difference in Repeat Usage as a Function of Continued Access to the System.

TABLE 1

SYSTEM DROP-OUT DATA

			One-Time Requestors					
				Number			Percentage	
Yr. Qtr.	Total Trans.	First Trans.	P	G	N	P	G	N
65 2	88	64	6	15	1	6.8	17.1	1.3
3	155	85	8	27	2	5.2	17.4	1.3
4	75	28	5	5	0	6.7	6.7	0.0
66 1	117	27	3	4	2	2.6	3.4	1.7
2	88	16	3	3	1	3.4	3.4	1.1
3	69	23	4	6	0	5.8	8.7	0.0
4	107	36	4	12	5	3.7	11.2	4.7
67 1	98	37	10	9	8	13.1	9.2	8.2
2	71	28	9	6	6	12.7	8.5	8.5
3	77	35	10	2	8	13.0	2.6	11.3
4	81	29	5	5	14	6.2	6.2	17.3

P = WRAIR present G = WRAIR not present N = Non-WRAIR

tem nine or more times. Of these, four initiated more than 20 transmissions. Such behavior must be interpreted as satisfaction with system performance.

If multiple re-entry can be interpreted as a measure of satisfaction with system performance, single-entries–at least by any individual known to have been on the WRAIR staff at the end of the study period–must be examined as a measurement of dissatisfaction. Only 34 percent of the non-repeaters fall into the "WRAIR PRESENT" category (Figures 3 and 4). In Table 1, grouped by calendar quarter in which the inquiry was transmitted, are the number, and percentage of the total represented by that number, of one-time requesters.

For those known to have continuing access to the system, observe the minimum of about three percent drop-out per quarter and the maximum of 13 percent. Assuming the minimum to be the maximum tolerable, we may consider the higher initial drop-out as an 'adjustment' phase of operation upon which performance was improved during calendar 1966. Adjustment also encompasses the effects of the contract definition of a "search" mentioned earlier and discussed in detail in reference 10.

The unprecedented drop-out rate of the first three quarters of 1967 is influenced by (at least) the fact that re-entry occurs at some interval after first-time entry. That is, based on analysis of the interval between first and second entries for multiple-transmission users, we can correct the drop-out data. If the requester has not re-entered by the end of the same quarter, the probabilities are 1:3 that he will re-enter subsequently; by the end of the subsequent quarter, they drop to 1:6; by the end of the third quarter, to 1:10; by the end of the fourth quarter, to 1:14; by the end of the fifth quarter, to 1:20.

TABLE 2

LENGTH OF INTERVAL BETWEEN TRANSMISSIONS
FOR EACH ACCESS BY MULTIPLE-TRANSMISSION USERS.

	First			Second			Third			Fourth			Fifth			Sixth			All		
Trans.	S	Ave.	Max.	S	Ave.	Max.	S	Ave.	Max.	S	Ave.	Max.	S	Ave.	Max.	S	Ave.	Max.	S	Ave.	Max.
2	1	126	648																1	126	648
3	1	72	547	3	135	485													6	207	559
4	1	48	375	1	52	263	2	104	460										12	202	503
5	2	52	272	4	49	168	4	93	342	3	106	302							53	300	596
6	2	37	107	6	60	187	5	61	174	5	65	211	1	67	288				34	285	597
7	1	22	79	1	39	115	3	72	219	1	82	315	2	109	277	11	61	107	113	385	653
8	6	61	127	1	43	126	1	18	45	4	52	122	19	52	99	71	129	157	194	386	608

S = Shortest

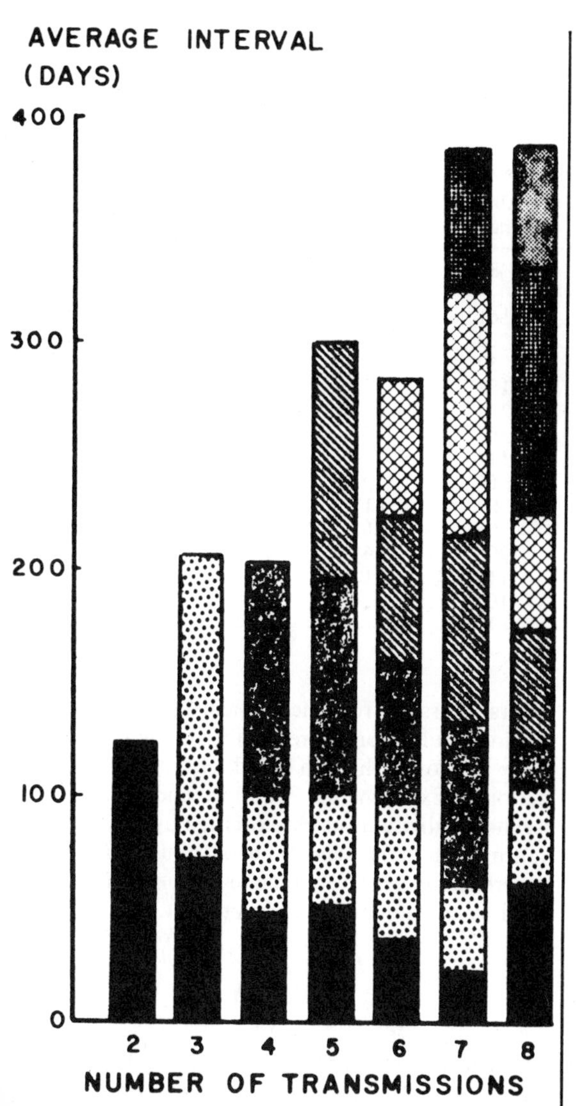

FIG. 5 Average interval between transmission for multiple-transmission users. (Intervals graphed in order of occurrence.)

Thus, one of the 10 drop-outs from the first quarter of 1967 may still be expected to re-enter (after the end of the study period), one of the nine from the second quarter, two of the ten from the third quarter, and two of the five from the fourth quarter. Although the resulting "corrected" drop-out rate for the fourth quarter is acceptable as an indication of improving system performance (which continues into 1968), the data for the first three quarters persist as a barometer of failure of the system to meet the needs of first-time requesters during that period. Jacobus[10] detects the same failure in data on inter-library loan requests by potential system users. The deadline date for submission of this paper precludes publication of data for 1968.

As implied above, the criterion for the performance is modified by the behavior of "satisfied" or multiple-entry users. Figure 5 illustrates the average intervals between transmissions, categorized on the basis of the total number of transmissions made by the user. These data, plus the shortest interval and longest interval between successive transmissions and between first and last entry, among those by individuals entering the system twice or more, are provided in Table 2.

In the graph of averages, we account for three factors:

1. for a fixed-length period, the length of interval between events perforce decreases as the number of events increases;
2. an information need, satisfaction of which requires exhaustive exploitation of a given data base (extremely large but growing only at about one percent per month), arises at some interval, called here a "nominal task interval" for any one individual; and
3. user confidence in system performance motivates re-entry at intervals shorter than the "nominal task interval" *perhaps*, at least in part, *because the task is accomplished or redirected more quickly with information service support*.

The comparative stability of interval-length for the six-transmission user leads us to consider these data the basis for a norm. That is, we define a "nominal task interval" as greater than 60 working days (approximately 3 calendar months) but less than the 126 working days between first and second entries by the two-transmission user. Further analysis is being made of comparable data for those users known to still have access to the system. However, the small number of individuals in the sample for six or more transmissions may be subject to too many variables of professional competence, sophistication in use of information services, work mission, etc., to justify drawing more incisive conclusions regarding differences in length of intervals between usage.

The final set of data presented here is given in Table 3, to examine the effects on user satisfaction (i.e., usage) of correspondence between his scientific discipline and BIOSIS file characteristics. For each research division of WRAIR are listed the total number of individuals who have transmitted at least one inquiry message, the number and percent of the total who are known to still have

TABLE 3

VARIATION IN USAGE BY DIVISION (SCIENTIFIC DISCIPLINE)

Division Name	Total Users From Div.	Users Present No.	Users Present %	Total Users Trans./User	Total Users Abs./Trans.	Users Present Trans./User	Users Present Abs./Trans.	Users Present Days in System Ave.	Users Present Days in System Med.
Biochemistry	8	3	38	4.9	87	1.0	8*	143	62
Comm. Dis. and Immunology	63	34	54	1.8	161	1.9	139*	404	524
Dentistry	29			1.4	30				
Exp. Pathology	14	10	72	4.4	59	4.7	51	438	379
Medicine	66	36	55	3.6	158	3.5	106	375	408
Med. Chemistry	25	15	60	4.3	222	5.5	195	367	323
Neuropsych.	32	14	44	3.4	67	5.3	50*	475	550
Nuclear Med.	25	13	52	2.6	111	2.7	62	407	579
Nursing	6	1	17	1.2	66	1.0	380	655	655
Prevent. Med.	17	6	35	2.0	97	3.1	142	356	420
Surgery	28	11	39	2.4	106	2.6	40	213	201
Veterin. Med.	20	8	40	1.9	204	2.4	140	335	373
Averages	28	13	47	2.9	114	3.1	119	379	
Median	25	11	44	2.5	102	2.7	106	375	

*=One or more 'Negative'. No abstracts sent

access to the system, and for each of these groups the average number of transmissions and average number of abstracts delivered per transmission. In general, the principal work mission of these individuals is laboratory research.

BIOSIS' policy for coverage of the biological literature emphasizes research aspects and de-emphasizes clinical and/or practice-oriented literature. The data indicate comparatively high continued usage by the divisions of Medicinal Chemistry, Neuropsychiatry, and Experimental Pathology. The Nursing division, as might be expected, exhibits the lowest usage. Data on the Biochemistry division apparently indicate recent separation of previously active users from the using installation (low median number of days those 'present' have been using the system).

The average number of abstracts delivered per transmission reflects the precision with which the inquiry was posed or else the effects of coverage policy. Excluding the single transmission by a Nursing division user, the high of 195 abstracts per transmission from the Medicinal Chemistry division results from a preference among this group to browse through broad responses. Satisfaction of Experimental Pathology and Neuropsychiatry divisions users, exhibited by the high transmission rates, may also be attributed to a preference for relatively precise responses indicated by the number of abstracts sent.

SUMMARY

Rather than measuring performance relative to percentages of "appropriate" and "inappropriate" items elicited from a file in response to designed inquiries, BIOSIS is gauging the performance of a developing retrieval system by the behavior of a significant number of users over a significantly long period and in a significant number of actual inquiry events. The prediction model is then the standard for evaluating the effect of operational changes to the system.[11]

NOTES

[1] Menzel, H., "Information Needs and Uses in Science and Technology," *Annual Review of Information Science and Technology* Vol. 1, Carlos A. Cuadra, ed., Interscience, N. Y., 1966, 41–69.

[2] Herner, S., and M. Herner, "Information Needs and Uses in Science and Technology," in *Annual Review of Information Science and Technology* Vol. 2, Carlos A. Cuadra, ed., Interscience, N. Y., 1967, 1–34.

[3]Rees, A. M., "Evaluation of Information Systems and Services," in *Annual Review of Information Science and Techonlogy* Vol. 2, Carlos A. Cuadra, ed., Interscience, N. Y., 1967, 63-86.

[4]Jacobus, D. P., R. R. Gulick, L. Schultz, and P. V. Parkins, "Direct User Access to the Biological Literature Through Abstracts: A Cooperative Experiment in Customized Service," *BioScience*, 16, 9, pp. 599-603 (1966).

[5]Murdock, J. W., and D. M. Liston, Jr., "A General Model of Information Transfer: Theme Paper 1968 Annual Convention," *American Documentation*, 18, 4, pp. 195-208 (1967).

[6]Parkins, P. V., "BioSciences Information Service of Biological Abstracts," *Science*, 152, 3724, pp. 889-894 (1966).

[7]Schultz, L., "Reestablishing the Direct Interface Between an Abstracting and Indexing Service and Individual Clients," in *Proceedings of the American Documentation Institute,* vol. 3, 1966 Annual Meeting, Oct. 3-7 1966, Santa Monica, Calif., Adrianne Press, 1966, 167-173.

[8]Terminals are also located at the other user installations mentioned.

[9]Cavanaugh, J. M. A., "Some Considerations Relating to User-System Interaction in Information Retrieval Systems," *Fourth Annual National Colloquium on Information Retrieval,* Albert B. Tonik, ed., International Information Inc., Philadelphia, 1967, 119-126.

[10]Jacobus, D. P., and E. Neuschatz; L. Schultz, W. C. Hoida, and A. I. Terrell, "Experience with a Mechanized Biological Information Service," presented at the meeting of the American Chemical Society, Chicago, Illinois, 13 September 1967 (to be published).

[11]The authors especially thank Mrs. Amie Rumsey of BioSciences Information Service for the illustrations in this report and Mrs. Evelyn Neuschatz, Librarian at WRAIR, for kindly supplying the directory of current personnel. They are also indebted to all other members of BIOSIS R&D staff and to Dr. Jacobus and the WRAIR staff for suggestions and data.

ABOUT THE AUTHORS–Richard Rubinstein is Senior Research Associate at BioSciences Information Service, having come there from positions in biochemical research at Smith Kline & French Laboratories and The Rockefeller Institute. He has an M.A. in Chemistry from Temple University and a B.S. in Zoology from Ohio State University. He is a member of the American Chemical Society.

Louise Schultz is Systems Development Director, BioSciences Information Service. She has a B.S. in Journalism and Latin American Affairs from the University of Illinois, and a Certificate in Electrical Engineering from Purdue University, and has pursued graduate and undergraduate studies in the philosophy of science, mathematics, physics, electrical engineering and electronic data processing at various universities. She had been Operations Research Scientist at Systems Development Corporation for eight years before going to BIOSIS. Prior to that she had held various engineering, writing and promotional positions.

As further indication of her versatility, her professional society memberships include the American Management Association, the Association for Computing Machinery and the Institute of Electrical and Electronics Engineers. She was Chairman of the Information Retrieval Colloquium in Philadelphia in 1969, and a Trustee for it in 1971.

Mechanization of Library Procedures in the Medium-sized Medical Library: XII. An Information Retrieval System: A Combination of a Manual Selective Dissemination of Information, and a Personal File Indexing System by Computer

by Miwa Ohta and Glyn T. Evans

Manual searching of incoming journals for materials of interest to a select group of scientists is supported by maintenance of a computer index to the individual participants' references. The cost of such personal services are summarized.

INTRODUCTION

The scientist's dilemma, caused by the desire and need to keep up to date and the difficulty of coping with a mass of publications within a limited time, is well known. Even though recent years have seen many advances in the bibliographic control of scientific information, the individual scientist must still wage a personal battle with publications. Many efforts have been made to relieve the scientist of some of the frustrating effort to keep up with the literature in his field, and thereby allow him to devote more time to the main purpose of his professional life, his patients, or his laboratory. The "Bibliographic Service" which was started in the 1940's at the Library of the Columbia University College of Physicians and Surgeons, for example, is one of the older services.

As the successful use of electronic data processing machines in business caught the attention of librarians and information specialists in the 1950's, the term, "Selective Dissemination of Information," or SDI, came into use. Although it is most often used to describe systems based on H. P. Luhn's idea of using computers to match profiles against document descriptors to select those documents which contain profile terms, it is also used to describe any procedure which attempts to provide a personalized current awareness service. It is in this latter context that the term SDI is used in this report. A by-product of the growth of SDI systems and one which is becoming increasingly important is the problem of keeping the references or reprints accumulated through SDI notification in an accessible form. This is an old problem, as shown by a study done by Jahoda, Hutchins, and Galford and reported in *American Documentation*,[1] which pointed out that 61 percent of the scientists interviewed at Florida State University graduate schools maintained reprint collections. All of the SDI users at the Washington University School of Medicine replied to a questionnaire that they had maintained reprint collections prior to our pilot study. Both of these problems (an SDI service and the handling of the resulting documents) are discussed in this report.

SDI is an alerting service, and the point of contact between the system and the user is the notification of new references of potential interest sent

---

SOURCE: Reprinted from Miwa Ohta and Glyn T. Evans, "Mechanization of Library Procedures in the Medium-Sized Library: XII. An Information Retrieval System: a Combination of a Manual Selective Dissemination of Information, and a Personal File Indexing System by Computer," *Bulletin of the Medical Library Association,* 58 (April, 1970), pp. 112–119, by permission of the publisher and the authors.
Article VIII appears on page 212 of this *Reader*. Earlier articles in this series appear in the *Bulletin* 51: 313–338, July 1963; *Ibid.*, 52: 370–385, Apr. 1964; *Ibid.*, 53: 99–101, 305–328, July 1965; *Ibid.*, 54: 259–260, July 1966; *Ibid.*, 56: 59–70, 71–79, Jan. 1968; *Ibid.*, 56: 123–131, Apr. 1968; *Ibid.*, 57: 260–263, 264–266, July 1969; *Ibid.*, 58: 120–125, Apr. 1970.

to the user. In other words, notices mark the end of the SDI process. An SDI system is expensive, especially a manual system, since the number of users such a system can accommodate is limited. The Library of Washington University School of Medicine therefore felt that by going one step further and providing an indexing system for relevant references, they could increase the utility of the system, and hence lower the unit cost. This is so because resultant lists can then be shared by several people.

DESIGN AND IMPLEMENTATION

The embryonic stage of the present SDI Section can be traced back to 1965 when a service, then called the "Current Awareness Service," was begun within the Reference Department. A fee was levied for this service. From 1966 to 1968 this manual alerting device functioned on a small scale. No attempt, however, was made to collect feedback data with which to evaluate the system.

In the fall of 1967 the decision was made to broaden the service by providing it free to a pilot group of users in various departments of the Medical Center, and by offering a computer-produced index to the references supplied. A separate budget, therefore, was proposed for a period of one year to implement and evaluate the system. The system objectives were:

1. To inform participants in the service as quickly as possible of newly published articles of potential interest.
2. To provide and maintain an index of relevant references for each user.
3. To obtain feedback from the users to be used in system evaluation as a guide to future planning.

In August 1968, a printed brochure describing the service was mailed to the Chairmen of the twenty departments at the Washington University School of Medicine. Within ten days twenty-one applications from faculty and research workers in the Center had been received. In order to have a fair representation of users, the number accepted from any one department was limited. The SDI department accepted twenty applicants, and further applicants were placed on a waiting list. Thirteen departments were represented on the list of participants.

Each applicant was interviewed. A profile was formulated after the interview and a copy sent to the applicant for his approval. Subsequent interviews and redrafting were arranged until the profile was approved. The profile is written in free statement form. The categorized lists in *MeSH* were found to be helpful in defining areas of interest. It later became apparent that scientists' profiles change constantly, necessitating updating on a regular basis. Some clues as to the status of a profile are afforded when the relevance ratio drops as the user's interests change.

This flowchart (Fig. 1) shows the procedures of the SDI department. The daily receipts of the approximately 1,870 journals subscribed to by the Washington University School of Medicine Library are scanned by the SDI Librarian. The monthly *Index Medicus* is used as a back-up service; that is, once a month, pages from the Index containing selected *MeSH* headings are sent to each user. When a user indicates interest in an article unobtainable at the Library, an interlibrary loan is arranged.

A citation coding form (Fig. 2) is typed for each reference. This form is designed in such a way as to be useful and intelligible to both SDI users and the keypuncher, thus eliminating an intermediate coding step. The typist cannot exceed in any box the permissible number of characters in the computer input cards. The form is in three parts, two of which are passed on to the user. These two copies, accompanied by a Xeroxed title page or summary of the reference, are batched and sent to the user once a week. The remaining copy is retained by the SDI Department. The user codes the relevancy of the reference and returns one copy of the form. If the citation is considered to be useful (that is, has been coded one or two), it is keypunched and added to the user's index.

Subject headings are assigned to each selected reference. A thesaurus has been compiled for the users, based on *MeSH*, with local expansion where necessary. *MeSH* was chosen for two reasons: firstly, because the users are familiar with both *Index Medicus* and the use of *MeSH* in the Library's computer-produced *Catalog of Books*, and, secondly, because of the relative ease of obtaining consolidating MEDLARS searches, if required.

The computer index system used in the Personal File Indexing System (PFIS) was originally designed by three of the Library's Trainees in Computer Librarianship in 1968 as their machine project, in conjunction with Mr. Bill Smith, a programmer from the Washington University Computational Facilities. At the start of the SDI Project the program had been written and indexes

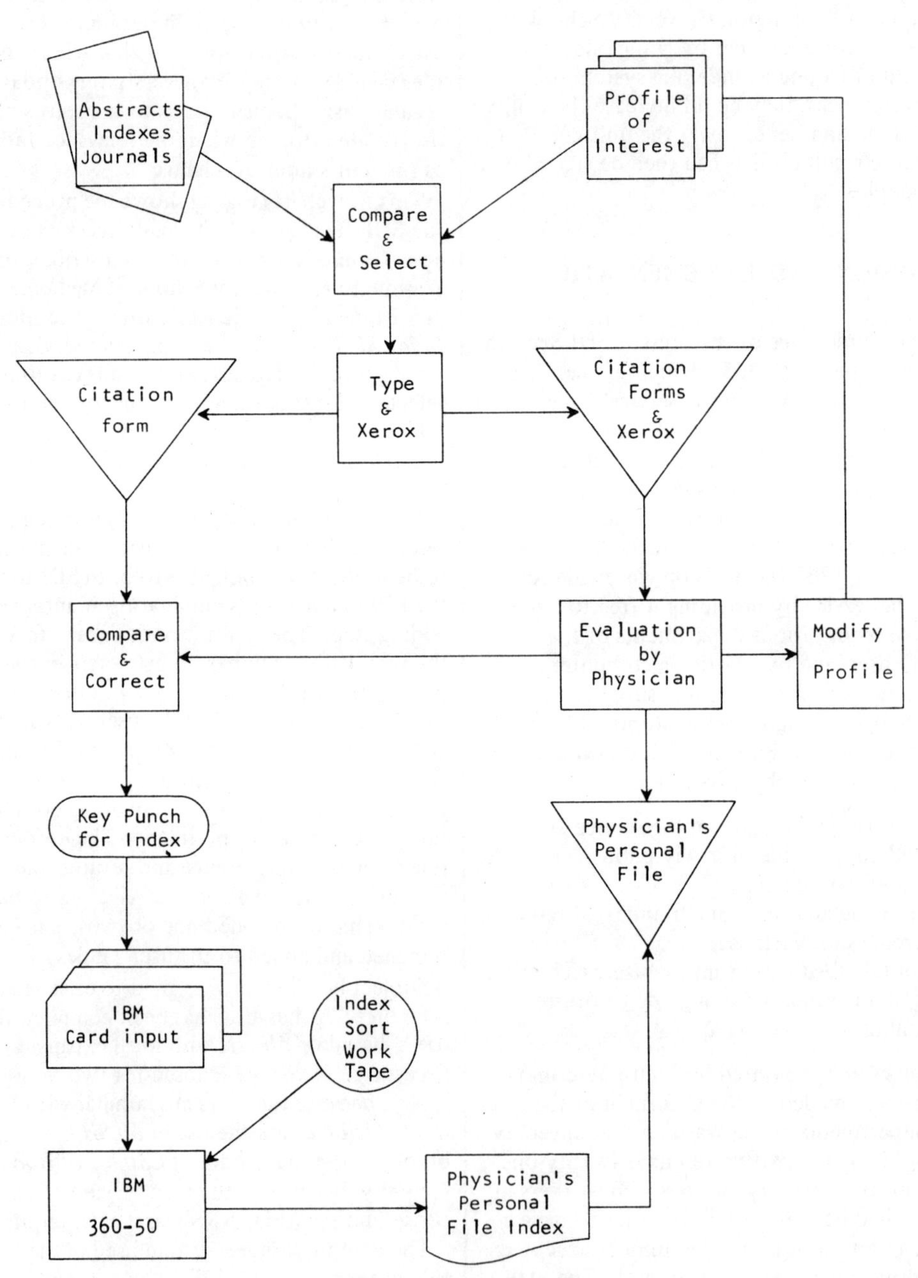

FIG. 1 SDI flow chart.

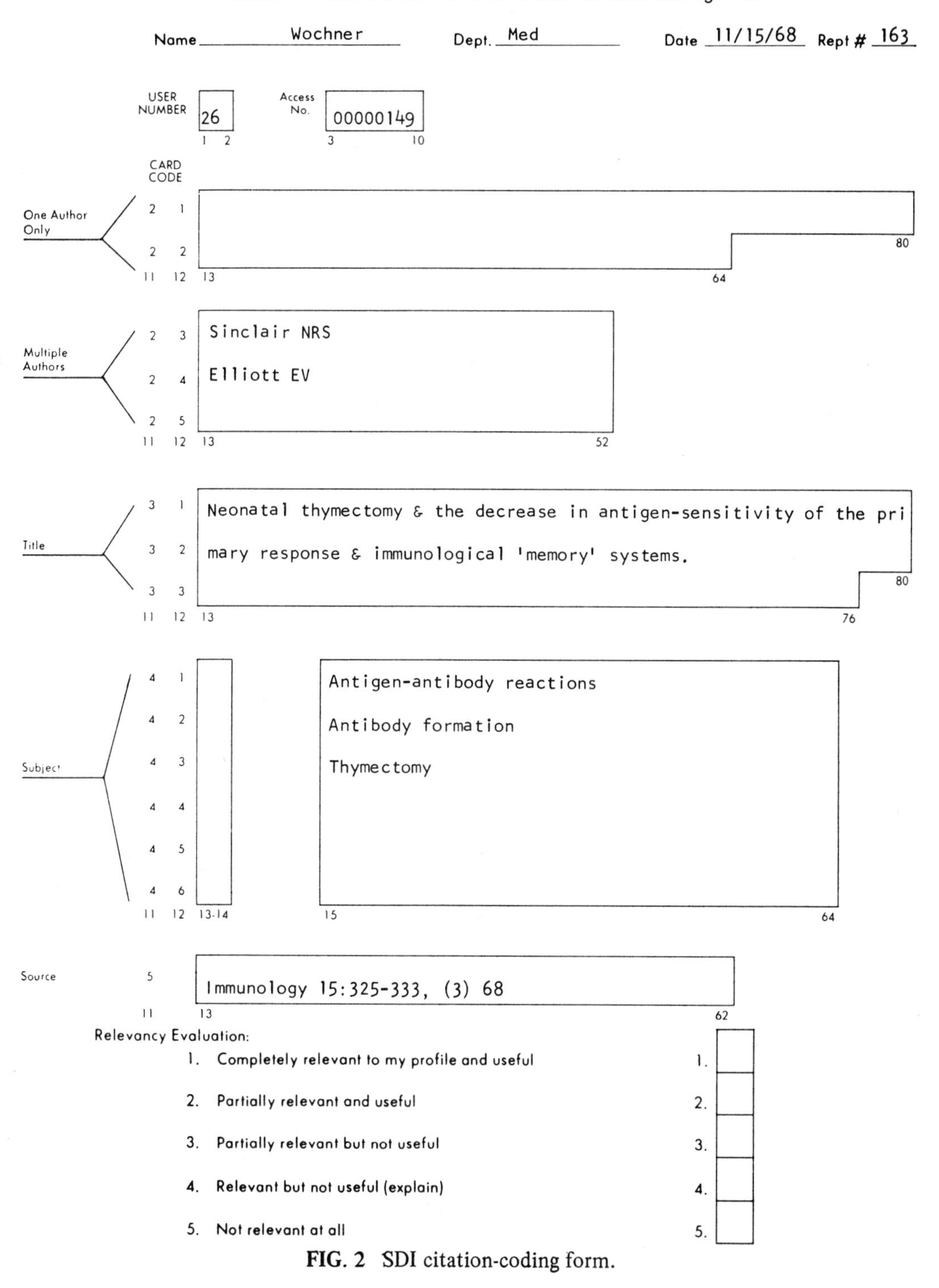

WASHINGTON UNIVERSITY SCHOOL OF MEDICINE LIBRARY
Selective Dissemination of Information Citation-Coding Form

Name Wochner Dept. Med Date 11/15/68 Rept # 163

USER NUMBER 26 (1 2)
Access No. 00000149 (3 10)

CARD CODE

One Author Only: 2 1; 2 2 (11 12 13 64 80)

Multiple Authors:
2 3 Sinclair NRS
2 4 Elliott EV
2 5
(11 12 13 52)

Title:
3 1 Neonatal thymectomy & the decrease in antigen-sensitivity of the pri
3 2 mary response & immunological 'memory' systems.
3 3
(11 12 13 76 80)

Subject:
4 1 Antigen-antibody reactions
4 2 Antibody formation
4 3 Thymectomy
4 4
4 5
4 6
(11 12 13-14 15 64)

Source: 5 Immunology 15:325-333, (3) 68
(11 13 62)

Relevancy Evaluation:

1. Completely relevant to my profile and useful 1. ☐
2. Partially relevant and useful 2. ☐
3. Partially relevant but not useful 3. ☐
4. Relevant but not useful (explain) 4. ☐
5. Not relevant at all 5. ☐

FIG. 2 SDI citation-coding form.

```
                        COMPOSITE COMPUTER PRINTOUT

                              ACCESSION LIST

00000149          SINCLAIR NRS
                  ELLIOTT EV
                    NEONATAL THYMECTOMY & THE DECREASE IN ANTIGEN-SENSITIVITY
                     OF THE PRIMARY RESPONSE & IMMUNOLGICAL 'MEMORY'
                     SYSTEMS.
                    IMMUNOLOGY 15:325-333, (3) 68

                              AUTHOR LIST

  FIRST AUTHOR

SINCLAIR NRS                                                         00000149
  NEONATAL THYMECTOMY & THE DECREASE IN ANTIGEN-SENSITIVITY
  OF THE PRIMARY RESPONSE & IMMUNOLGICAL 'MEMORY' SYSTEMS.
  IMMUNOLOGY 15:325-333, (3) 68

  SECOND AUTHOR

ELLIOTT EV                                                           00000149
  NEONATAL THYMECTOMY & THE DECREASE IN ANTIGEN-SENSITIVITY
  OF THE PRIMARY RESPONSE & IMMUNOLGICAL 'MEMORY' SYSTEMS.
  IMMUNOLOGY 15:325-333, (3) 68

  SUBJECT 1                   SUBJECT LIST

ANTIGEN-ANTIBODY REACTIONS

  SINCLAIR NRS                                                       00000149
  ELLIOTT EV
    NEONATAL THYMECTOMY & THE DECREASE IN ANTIGEN-SENSITIVITY
    OF THE PRIMARY RESPONSE & IMMUNOLGICAL 'MEMORY'
    SYSTEMS.
    IMMUNOLOGY 15:325-333, (3) 68

  SUBJECT 2

ANTIBODY FORMATION

  SINCLAIR NRS                                                       00000149
  ELLIOTT EV
    NEONATAL THYMECTOMY & THE DECREASE IN ANTIGEN-SENSITIVITY
    OF THE PRIMARY RESPONSE & IMMUNOLGICAL 'MEMORY'
    SYSTEMS.
    IMMUNOLOGY 15:325-333, (3) 68

  SUBJECT 3

THYMECTOMY

  SINCLAIR NRS                                                       00000149
  ELLIOTT EV
    NEONATAL THYMECTOMY & THE DECREASE IN ANTIGEN-SENSITIVITY
    OF THE PRIMARY RESPONSE & IMMUNOLGICAL 'MEMORY'
    SYSTEMS.
    IMMUNOLOGY 15:325-333, (3) 68

                              TITLE

NEONATAL THYMECTOMY & THE DECREASE IN ANTIGEN-SENSITIVITY           00000149
OF THE PRIMARY RESPONSE & IMMUNOLGICAL 'MEMORY' SYSTEMS.
  SINCLAIR NRS
  ELLIOTT EV
  IMMUNOLOGY 15:325-333, (3) 68

                              SOURCE

IMMUNOLOGY 15:325-333, (3) 68                                        00000149
  SINCLAIR NRS
  ELLIOTT EV
  NEONATAL THYMECTOMY & THE DECREASE IN ANTIGEN-SENSITIVITY
  OF THE PRIMARY RESPONSE & IMMUNOLGICAL 'MEMORY' SYSTEMS.
```

FIG. 3 SDI citations.

for three users had been prepared, but the program had not been tested in an operational environment. Nonetheless, it was decided to link the program to the SDI Project. A number of changes and refinements were made in the program to bring it to operational status. The program is written in COBOL for an IBM 360/50 computer with two tape drives and disc storage space.

The PFIS system maintains a magnetic tape file of bibliographic citations in serial (i.e., accession number) order for each user, and from this file produces on demand lists sorted by either author, title, subject headings, or source. Fig. 3 does not show an actual final printed list but is rather a composite from all available print formats, to demonstrate the way in which one citation is treated in all lists. Note that the citation appears under each named author. The subject headings are taken from the citations themselves and overprinted as headings to bring all like citations together. Within each user's file, the user has the option of specifying major subject interest areas which are maintained separately. For instance, a user may maintain one file labelled Neurochemistry, and another labelled Medical History.

Although it is possible for any user to go to his computer tape file when he wishes, the economy of the system demands that users batch their runs together. This procedure does not appear to inconvenience the users. As the user's tape file increases in size, it is possible to select the oldest items and store them on a second magnetic tape—a history tape. This allows them to be recalled for incorporation in the current file, if and when required. Thus the user is allowed to decide for himself how long he wishes to cumulate his 'current' items, yet he can reprint his entire file, should it be necessary. This procedure reduces the size of the current file, and hence keeps processing time and printing costs down.

The system allows access to any citation by accession number, each of the first three authors, title, source, or six subject headings: a total of twelve access points. In general, seven seems to be the average required. Some users, however, doubt the value of the title or source file and do not request them. Users' first preference seems to be about equally divided between author and subject files. We have done two computer runs during the fiscal year July 1968–June 1969, users with a large number of references being represented on both runs, and those with a small number on the second run only. The smallest file is of twenty-seven items, while the largest contains 1,185 citations, the average number of citations per file being 267. It has been found that the machine costs are about 2.5¢ per access point (that is, each time any citation appears on any list) or, say, 17¢ per citation per user per list. This figure would increase dramatically if the individual user were not to batch his run, since a significant proportion of the cost is due to getting on and off the computer. Keypunching costs are approximately 16¢ per item, and thus the total cost from input sheet to the first appearance of an item on a printout is 33¢. Of course, each time the same item appears on a cumulated list, the computer costs are repeated. The total cost for the first year of operation was $20,439.76, or $1,022.00 per scientist. This includes salaries, keypunching and computational costs, supplies, equipment, travel and telephone, as well as the cost for 13,137 pages of Xeroxing at 10¢ per exposure. Excluding Xeroxing, the cost of the selection and notification of any citation is $1.40. The goal of the system is to supply relevant and useful citations. Any expenditure within the system must be measured against the efficiency of the system. Thus the retrieval of a nonrelevant citation is an overhead which contributes to the cost of retrieving relevant citations. Considering this factor the cost of a relevant citation is $1.80. It will readily be seen that periodic profile monitoring is essential in maintaining the cost efficiency of the system.

RESULTS

At the end of the first year of operation a questionnaire sent to our users gave the following facts about the system, which is still continuing.

1. The present manual SDI service is well received and appreciated.
2. The PFIS index is used, both by participants and their colleagues.
3. The present format of PFIS is acceptable.
4. The use of *MeSH* Headings in PFIS is adequate.

In a ten-month period, a total of 9,763 citations was retrieved from approximately 12,070 issues of journals. Among those were seventy-one taken from the back-up monthly *Index Medicus*. As is true of most manual systems, the relevance ratio of the system was high. A total of 87.2 percent of the citations retrieved was evaluated as being either completely relevant (68.5 percent) or partially relevant and useful (18.7 percent).

A comparison of ASCA and the manual SDI service at Washington University School of Medicine Library was made for a six-week period by Miss Jean Miller, one of the 1969 trainees in Computer Librarianship, in collaboration with the SDI Department. Her findings indicated that during this period 84 percent of the total references retrieved in the study came from 664 core journals; that the overlap between the manual SDI and ASCA was only 16 percent; that the manual service was more timely but that, although it produced fewer citations, a higher proportion of these were relevant. She found that 346 useful citations were recovered from the manual service and 379 from the commercial service, of which only ninety-six citations were duplicates. These findings indicate that whenever complete coverage is desired, neither manual nor machine system can be used by itself.

Davidson and Matthews of the Scientific Documentation Centre in the United Kingdom,[2] which operates a manual SDI system commercially, conducted a study on the efficiency of various conventional and computer-produced indexes. Their results show that no single source located more than 40 percent of the references found after an exhaustive literature search. Why is this so? And how much complete coverage is desired by scientists, at what cost?

The answers for these questions necessarily depend upon the specific situation. However, we feel that in any information retrieval system, whether manual or mechanical, one of the crucial factors in determining the efficiency of the system is a close contact between indexers, searchers, and users in profile formulation and maintenance. Only when that is done, can one ask how complete a coverage is reasonable.

NOTES

1 Jahoda, G.; Hutchins, R. D.; and Galford, R. Characteristics and use of personal indexes maintained by scientists and engineers in one university. Amer. Doc. 17: 71–75, April 1966.

2 Davidson, P. S., and Matthews, D. A. R. Assessment of information services. Aslib Proc. 21: 280–283, July 1969.

ABOUT THE AUTHORS–Miwa Ohta graduated from the University of Akron and received an M.S. from the Case Western Reserve University School of Library Science. Prior to a recent move to Columbus, Ohio, with her husband, she was SDI Librarian and performed other reference and public services at the Washington University School of Medicine Library. She had also served on the staff of the St. Louis University School of Medicine Library and previously at Dayton & Montgomery County Public Library in Ohio.

Glyn Evans, is Coordinator of Library Systems to the Five Associated University Libraries. Previously, he was Research Associate in Machine Methods at the Washington University School of Medicine Library and Acting Deputy Librarian. He entered medical librarianship as Assistant at the Liverpool Medical Institution and became Librarian of the Institute of Neurology, London. Then he was appointed Leverhulme Research Associate to the Library of the Royal Society of Medicine. While at the Society, he was MEDLARS Liaison Officer for the Southeast England Region.

AIM-TWX Service at the University of Virginia: A Review and Evaluation

by Wilhelm Moll

One of the most exciting developments since the introduction of MEDLARS has been the availability of a portion of the MEDLARS data base at remote terminals for use on line. Here is described one group's experiment with the AIM-TWX data base.

On November 6, 1970, Mr. Davis B. McCarn, then Deputy Director of the Lister Hill National Center for Biomedical Communications, informed the Medical Librarian of the University of Virginia that the Library would have on-line access to the files of the AIM-TWX system for a two-week trial period from December 7 through December 18, 1970. Service was to be available for four hours daily from Mondays through Fridays. Thus began one of the most stimulating and exciting periods in the history of this library, whose major accomplishments form the basis of the following report.

AIM-TWX

As is probably well known, the AIM-TWX system, which utilizes a time-shared IBM 360/67 computer, was developed by the System Development Corporation at Santa Monica, California, for the Lister Hill Center. Its files are a subset of the *Index Medicus* data bank; namely, citations, including author, title, and source information, from 109 English language journals, beginning with 1966. The data can be retrieved on-line through a TWX (teletype) terminal which the Medical Library has had on its premises since early in 1966.[1]

As soon as formal approval for the two-week trial period was received, announcements were printed and disseminated to all Virginia hospitals and to the medical and nursing staffs of the Medical Center. Moreover, a press release was issued about one week after the beginning of the trial period which was featured in several media, including the Charlottesville *Daily Progress*. These announcements resulted in a rash of bibliographical search requests being submitted which kept the Library staff working overtime. The prospect of having rapid literature searches done free of charge may have been, in part, responsible for this tremendous demand. Although the "official" trial period was limited to the two weeks of December 7 through 18, actual use of the system began on November 19, as Mr. McCarn gave permission to "log in" for experimentation and demonstration purposes.

TRAINING OF OPERATORS

Inasmuch as the Medical Library does not have a regular Reader Services Department, it was decided to train four staff members in AIM-TWX methodology, including two professionals (Head Cataloger and Director of the Virginia Medical Information System–U. Va. Center) and two subprofessionals who had all been involved in interlibrary loan work and who knew how to operate the TWX machine.

At first the staff studied the various user manuals which were received about two weeks before the library had access to the computer. These manuals ("User's Manual for the ELHILL Program, Gamma Version, May 1970," "Introductory User Packet for the Experimental *AIM-TWX* System," and "Questions and Answers About AIM-TWX") were very helpful, but not quite understood at first reading. The staff kept refer-

SOURCE: Reprinted from Wilhelm Moll, "AIM-TWX Service at the University of Virginia: a Review and Evaluation," *Bulletin of the Medical Library Association*, 59 (July, 1971), pp. 458–462, by permission of the publisher and the author.

ring to the manuals throughout the trial period, and every one of the operators was under strict orders not to remove the booklets from a shelf near the teletype machine.

The second training experience was a face-to-face tutorial session conducted by Miss Kay Mayfield, a young, intelligent, and enthusiastic librarian who divides her time between work at the Lister Hill Center and at the National Library of Medicine. Miss Mayfield did a splendid job during the four-hour session, and no further formal training was necessary. This does not mean that "the system" was used to full effectiveness from the very beginning. Many small details had to be learned by working with the computer day by day, and frequent telephone calls had to be made to officials at the Lister Hill Center to iron out various problems which seemed to defy solution as they arose.[2]

OPERATING PROCEDURES

A detailed description of the various operating procedures of the information and retrieval system would go beyond the confines of this paper. In essence, the program manipulating the bibliographic files (called ELHILL) requires the issuance of certain commands and messages which must be properly understood by the operators. These communications are typed on the TWX keyboard and fed into the computer by striking the carriage return key. The program, in turn, searches the files for unit records that match the specifications that have been included in the search statement. It reports back on the number of citations which have or have not been retrieved, and print commands must then be issued in order that all or parts of the retrieved records may be printed out.

MeSH (MEDICAL SUBJECT HEADINGS)

Probably the most difficult, and at the same time interesting, aspect of the job of processing search requests for a variety of users was the search formulation. Like MEDLARS, the AIM-TWX system employs the network of *MeSH* descriptors and subheadings, and none of the staff was really well acquainted with the terminology and "trees" of *MeSH*. It became obvious from the beginning that the success or failure of a search depended heavily on the formulation of the search statements which were fed into the computer. Fortunately, the system is designed in such a way that even without access to the full printed *MeSH* vocabulary formulations can be made. Nevertheless, as any cataloger knows, the formulation of search statements came to be regarded as the most difficult, as well as challenging, aspect of the man-computer dialog.

It was also noted that much costly time could be spent developing search formulations while being "logged into" the machine, and every effort was made to prepare the searches on the day before they were actually "run." Two request forms were developed locally on which prospective patrons listed their search topics and parameters. Many search requests were called in on the telephone, however, or came by letter. Probably the very best results were achieved when the requestors couched their requests either in *MeSH* terminology which presumed a familiarity with *MeSH*, or when they were physically present when the search was run and could overview the citations as they came off the machine. In the latter case, they had an opportunity of advising the operators on means of either enlarging or narrowing the topics, or of introducing other subject terms and term combinations which would produce results.

RECORD KEEPING

A daily log was kept in a three-ring notebook on which the various searches were recorded. The log proved essential for any evaluation of the system because it not only provided detailed information for every search, but also data on the number of searches run each day, and on the length of time the machine was in actual contact with the computer.

WORKING THE SYSTEM: THE TEAM

Another decision made after some experimentation related to the staffing of the project. It was decided that a continuous four-hour stretch was too long for one person. A team effort evolved according to which two persons staffed the machine for the first two hours and another two for the second two. One of the two would always be working on the teletype; that is, doing the actual "input" or transmitting, while the other would record the findings on the log, keep the various

TABLE 1

AIM-TWX SERVICE AT U. VA. MEDICAL LIBRARY
NOVEMBER 19-DECEMBER 18, 1970

		Individual Searches			Citations Retrieved		
	Total Requestors	Total	Successful	Unsuccessful	Total	On Line	Off Line
Virginia Practitioners	50	103	83	20	2,013	381	1,632
U. Va. Medical Faculty	32	84	62	22	1,655	302	1,353
U. Va. Nursing Faculty	7	64	57	7	802	261	541
U. Va. House Staff & Students	17	39	36	3	756	250	506
MCV Faculty & House Staff	8	8	5	3	117	4	113
Totals	114	298	243	55	5,343	1,198	4,145

papers (search requests and results) in some order, and most important of all, being equipped with a copy of *MeSH*, would reformulate search statements as seemed necessary from time to time. The latter was an essential operation and became an important part of the work even if the initial search formulation had been carefully prepared the day before.

RESULTS

Although better results could have been obtained through greater familiarity with the system and, in particular, with *MeSH*, the overall results were most gratifying. AIM-TWX represents a unique, rapid method of retrieving bibliographical citations, especially for the clinically oriented user. Patrons who desired materials in the preclinical sciences or areas not specifically covered by the 109 journals in the system were disappointed, but the fact that the data base had been limited was pointed out in all presearch request discussions and in the publicity. Similarly, the limitations of *MeSH* had to be taken into account in evaluating the results of any particular search.

In the table above, statistical data are presented, regarding the type of user, the number of searches, and the number of citations retrieved or not retrieved.

USERS OF THE SYSTEM

A total of 114 individuals requested 298 searches during the nineteen-day trial period, and a total of 5,343 citations were retrieved.

The users ranged from practitioners in various communities of the state to medical and nursing school personnel, including teaching staff, specialists, house staff, and students. A few requests came from hospital administrators, nursing staff supervisors, and members of the paramedical professions.

Many of the requests originated in small communities such as Bloxom, Christiansburg, Galax, Radford, Wise, and Wray. Not all of the practitioners could be identified since some of the search requests were mailed or telephoned in by local secretaries or community hospital librarians, and time did not permit verifying the source of every request.

SEARCH AND CITATION FINDINGS

The survey indicates that fifty practitioners used the system, representing 44 percent of the total number of users. They requested 103 (or 35 percent) of all searches and obtained 2,013 (or 38 percent) of retrieved citations.

University of Virginia Medical School and Nursing School faculty comprised the second largest user group. There were thirty-nine requestors (or 34 percent) in that category. They asked for 148 (or 49 percent) searches and obtained a total of 2,457 (or 46 percent) retrieved citations.

The remaining users were University of Virginia house staff and students and a few Medical College of Virginia faculty whose requests were forwarded by the MCV reference staff.

"SUCCESSFUL" VERSUS "UNSUCCESSFUL" SEARCHES

The term "successful" is used here only in the sense that a search formulation produced citations. Accordingly, the vast majority of search requests (243, or 82 percent) resulted in citations being furnished. Only fifty-five searches (or 18 percent) out of the total of 298 produced no citations and were, therefore, termed "unsuccessful."

"ON-LINE" VERSUS "OFF-LINE" PRINTOUTS

According to ELHILL, citations may be printed on- or off-line. Our findings show that a substantial majority of searches (160) was done on-line, while seventy-three were printed off-line. In ten cases both on- and off-line citations were printed. However, the largest number (4,145) of all citations retrieved (5,343) was printed off-line, while only 1,198 were printed on-line.

In reviewing the findings, it should be considered that not *all* possible citations in the system were retrieved in *all* cases. The prime object of the searches was to produce quick and reasonable results which may explain the fact that many more on-line printouts were made.

The printing of large numbers of citations was only attempted in cases when the requestors desired "everything published." On such occasions, the "Print Off-Line" command was given, and the citations were printed in Santa Monica and mailed (air mail), arriving usually two to four days later.

On the whole, an attempt was made to keep the number of citations retrieved to a reasonable level, and it was found that the majority of requestors favored such a policy also. "Some of the latest papers" was a frequently heard request, especially on the part of the busy practitioner. In accordance with these policies, various qualifying elements were introduced whenever the computer reported an unduly large number of citations. They included time limitations (e.g., 1970 only), or subheadings which would bring the topic into sharper focus.

Another method designed to speeding up the compilation of citations was the practice of excluding authors' names from the printouts. It was found that the printing of many authors' names extended the printout time and did not add materially to the findings. Many users evaluated an item in a bibliography primarily on the basis of titles of articles rather than authors' names.

INTERRUPTIONS, CUT-OFFS, ETC.

Although the library had been promised a four-hour period daily from Monday through Friday, the periods of actual use were shorter due to many "cut-offs" which separated the user from the system either temporarily or permanently for that day. The causes cannot be explained entirely. They may have been due to machine, line, or computer malfunctioning, but the staff suspected that most of the difficulties originated with the computer in Santa Monica. Most of the interruptions were temporary, and it was possible to get back into the system, or "logged in," after a short break. Nevertheless, it should be stressed that interruptions were quite frustrating, especially when a physician had taken time off from patient care or other duties to be present in the library while the search was conducted. Hopefully, some of these problems will be ironed out in the not too distant future to guarantee an uninterrupted service.

TIME FACTORS

Inasmuch as time is money in a very real sense when one is hooked into a computer network, the following findings may be of special interest.

According to a review of the AIM-TWX log, the AIM-TWX system was in use during nineteen days —or less than three weeks. During that period, the average number of minutes of computer time on any given day was 200; the average number of searches, sixteen; and, the average number of searches per hour, 4.6.

It would be premature to make definitive statements on the basis of this very short experience. However, a tentative conclusion would be that given more expertise and know-how in terms of *MeSH* terminology and man-machine dialog, six searches could be carried out during one hour of uninterrupted service. Excluded from this estimate would be the time that it takes to dial into the system, to "call in" the program, and possible delays caused by accidental interruptions and "number of users exceeded" messages.

CONCLUSIONS

From November 19 to December 18, 1970, the Medical Library of the University of Virginia had on-line access to the AIM-TWX computer at Santa Monica, California. Although actual contact with the computer was to be had for four hours daily on five days a week, the average use per day was a little over three hours. During that time, the operators in the Library were able to run a total of 298 searches for 114 individual requestors which resulted in the printout of 5,343 citations from the current (1966 onwards) medical literature. Only fifty-five searches did not produce any citations, a fact which must not be regarded as a total failure, however, since some of these searches dealt with topics which may not have been reported on in the recent literature.

The fact that this mass of bibliographical output could be produced by an inexperienced staff–in terms of the vital *MeSH* terminology and in the use of on-line computers–with only minimal instruction speaks highly for the system. A few of the searches could have been handled in a manual way. The overwhelming majority of the searching, however, involved multi-concept requests which was greatly speeded up by the use of the machine. The experience indicated that AIM-TWX is a viable and productive system which, it is hoped, will soon be a permanent feature in most of the larger medical libraries serving a clinically-oriented clientele.

The Lister Hill Center staff and their California systems and development satellites must be congratulated on having produced a fully automated storage and retrieval system which should go far toward improving access to data in the vast biomedical literature of today.

NOTES

[1] The system can also be used with various acoustic-coupled terminals, including the teletype (TTY) and the wired IBM Selectric typewriter (2741).

[2] One of these calls, for example, concerned the input of the *MeSH* term CONDITIONING (PSYCHOLOGY) which was rejected by the computer. The staff was told that the proper way of entering this term is not to use parentheses but the character # instead.

ABOUT THE AUTHOR–Dr. Wilhelm Moll is Medical Librarian and Professor of Preventive Medicine at the University of Virginia Medical School. He was educated at Denison University, where he received a B.A. in History, and at the University of Chicago, where he received his J.D. in Law. He also received an M.S.L.S. from Catholic University. Prior to his present position, he served as Assistant Documents Librarian at Indiana University and Assistant Medical Librarian, University of Kentucky Medical Center. Immediately following World War II, he worked in Germany for the War and State Departments, and was subsequently a Research Associate on the War Documentation Project.

Dr. Moll is a member of the American Library Association and the American Association of the History of Medicine. He has served in various capacities in the Medical Library Association, being the Chairman of the Washington D.C. Regional Group in 1965-1966.

IV.

TYPES OF MEDICAL LIBRARY

Though the differences among medical libraries may not be as great as those between medical libraries and other kinds, there are very real distinctions. Primarily they relate to the kind of organization with which the libraries are associated. There are many variations on the major themes. For instance, most medical school libraries also serve hospitals, many hospital libraries are also involved with teaching functions, some medical school libraries are libraries for other health sciences, such as dentistry, pharmacy and nursing, and many medical society libraries are now associated with hospital or medical school libraries.

The libraries in industrial pharmaceutical organizations are sometimes considered to be medical libraries. They are not included here because their greater interest in chemistry and their industrial orientation make them atypical.

Health Sciences Libraries of Professional Societies, Voluntary Health Organizations, and Foundations

by Susan Crawford

Society libraries are among the oldest in the United States, but they and their associated voluntary health organization and foundation libraries have been overshadowed recently by the rapid growth of medical school and hospital libraries. The recent trend has been for local society libraries to join forces with other strong local medical libraries. Two of the most prominent, at the New York Academy of Medicine and the Philadelphia College of Physicians, have become Regional Medical Libraries.

In a recent study of the professions, Bucher and Stelling observed that it was "extremely difficult to draw sharp boundaries around the notion of a professional organization."[1] Characterization of the organizations which sponsor health sciences libraries in this paper is perhaps even more complex, as they include not only those of professional societies, but other social groups organized for diverse purposes.

In general, this paper covers three major types of organizations which are associated with or support health sciences libraries:

1. Professional societies or associations of colleagues in an occupational context, i.e., societies, colleges, academies or associations in medicine and the allied health sciences;
2. "Voluntary health organizations" composed of persons of heterogeneous background and orientation who organize to support special purposes related to the health field through voluntary contributions from the general public, i.e., International Planned Parenthood Federation, American Diabetes Association, Hay Fever Prevention Society;
3. Foundations, institutes and other organizations supported by private benefactors or through grants, and which do not fall within the first two categories, i.e., Salk Institute for Biological Studies, Germfree Life Research Center.

These organizations represent a variety of objectives and programs. The libraries assume a supportive role in fulfilling their objectives, and as such, they also exhibit great diversity in size, purpose and even life-span. They cannot be treated as a homogeneous group in our analysis, and our approach will be to first provide an overview and then to separate each subset for analysis.

Of the 3,155 health sciences libraries or collections identified in the 1969 survey,[2] 186 (6 percent) are libraries of professional societies, foundations and voluntary health organizations (SFO). These include libraries of national organizations and their branches, as well as local organizations. One hundred and five libraries are sponsored by professional societies,[3] 62 by foundations and 19 by voluntary health organizations.

The average annual expenditure of SFO libraries is around $36,500. This figure, however, is biased by six disproportionately large libraries: American Dental Association, American Hospital Association, American Medical Association, College of Physicians of Philadelphia, New York Academy of Medicine, and Los Angeles County Medical Society. As shown in Figure 1, 28 percent of SFO libraries have total expenditures of under $5,000 and 44 percent have expenditures between

SOURCE: Reprinted from Susan Crawford, "Health Sciences Libraries of Professional Societies, Voluntary Health Organizations, and Foundations," *Bulletin of the Medical Library Association*, 60 (April, 1972), Suppl., pp. 38–45, by permission of the publisher and the author. The research reported was supported in part by grant No. 5 Ro1 LM0064 from the National Library of Medicine, U.S. Department of Health, Education and Welfare.

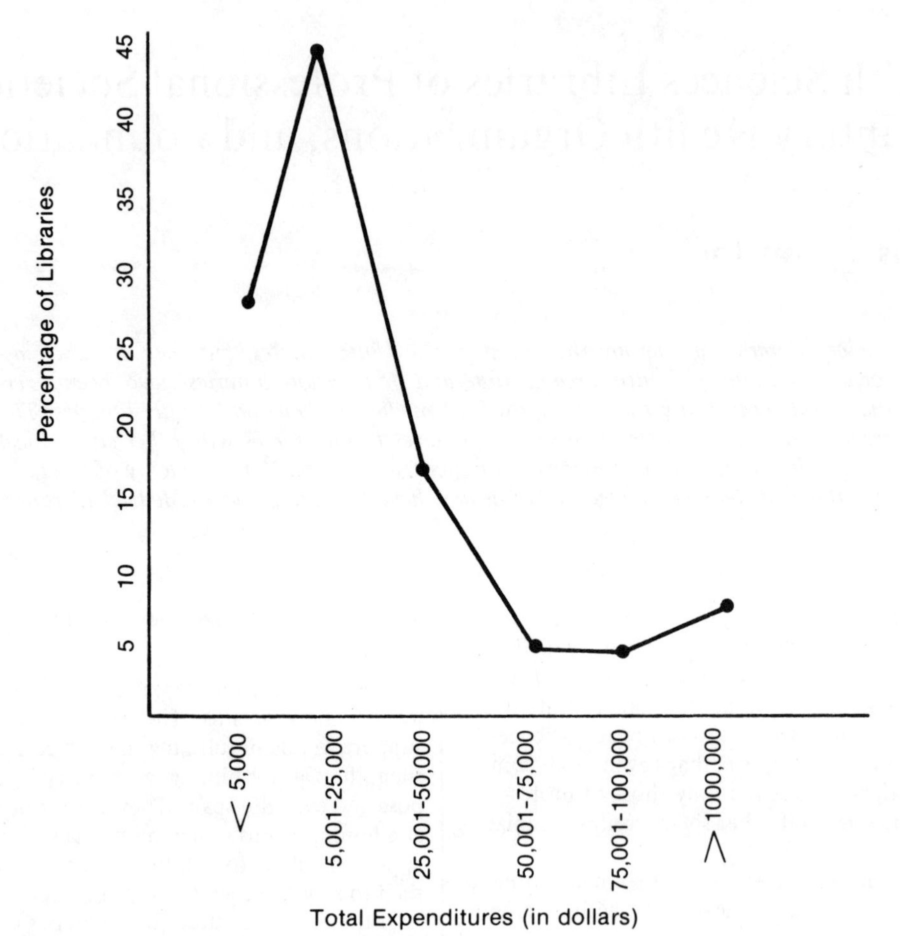

FIG. 1 Percentage of Health Sciences Libraries in Professional Societies, Foundations and Voluntary Health Organizations: By Amount of Total Expenditures (N=186)

$5,000 and $25,000. The data, therefore, indicate that almost three quarters (72 percent) of all SFO libraries have expenditures which are under $25,000. Over one-third of all SFO library funds were spent in the New York region, and most of this amount was spent in New York City.

SFO libraries contain around 2,700,000 bound volumes, or approximately 10 percent of the total volumes of all health sciences libraries in the country. As indicated earlier by the general expenditure indices, there are great individual differences among the libraries, ranging from a low of 50 bound volumes to a high of 543,760. A total of over a half million current serials are received by SFO libraries. Again, the number of current serials range from a low of two subscriptions through 5,320 subscriptions.

Salary information was provided by only 40 percent of the libraries. On the basis of this rather incomplete response, salary expenditures ranged from a low of $1,000 to a high of $384,600 (New York Academy of Medicine). The average salary expenditure for all SFO libraries was $30,191.

Table 1 illustrates the great variety of users served by SFO libraries. One hundred and one libraries (57 percent) provide services for physicians, making this the largest occupational group served. The next largest group served are those in biomedical research. SFO libraries, especially the state and county society libraries of the American Medical Association, often assume the role of community libraries in the health field. A total of 28 county or state society libraries (73 percent) indicated that, in addition to their membership, they provided services for anyone in the community who had a legitimate need for health science information. These include students, teachers, attorneys, pharmaceutical manufacturers, and the general public.

Based upon a 76 percent response, SFO libraries were found to employ a total of 589 staff mem-

TABLE 1

USERS SERVED BY HEALTH SCIENCES LIBRARIES IN PROFESSIONAL SOCIETIES, FOUNDATIONS AND VOLUNTARY HEALTH ORGANIZATIONS (N = 186)

User Class	Number of Libraries Serving Users
Medicine-Osteopathy	101
Dentistry	21
Nursing	43
Pharmacy	10
Veterinary Medicine	9
Other Health Professions	65
Biomedical Research	84
Non-Health Professions	28

TABLE 2

PERSONNEL OF HEALTH SCIENCES LIBRARIES IN PROFESSIONAL SOCIETIES, FOUNDATIONS AND VOLUNTARY HEALTH ORGANIZATIONS (N=186)

Personnel Class	Number of Staff
Professional	
Full-Time	170
Part-Time	41
Non-Professional	
Full-Time	197
Part-Time	126
Student Assistants	55
Total	589

*Based upon response rate of 76%.

bers, both professional and nonprofessional on a part or full-time basis (Table 2). Of this number, 170 were listed as full-time professionals and 197 were listed as full-time nonprofessionals. The libraries averaged two full-time staff members, but again, there were great individual differences, ranging from one part-time nonprofessional to fifty full-time staff (professional and nonprofessional). The number of one-man libraries (part or full-time) was found to be relatively low, accounting for only 19 percent of the libraries.

PROFESSIONAL SOCIETIES (NATIONAL AND LOCAL)

Vollmer and Mills[4] define "professional groups" as "associations of colleagues in an occupational context . . ." The purposes of professionalization, they add, are to "clothe a given area with standards of excellence, to establish rules of conduct, to develop a sense of responsibility, to set criteria for recruitment and training, to ensure a measure of protection for members, to establish collective control over the area, and to elevate it to a position of dignity and social standing in society."

There are degrees of professionalization, and some sociologists distinguish between the professions and semi-professions.[5] In our analysis, we have included all occupational groups in the health sciences regardless of specialty or judgement concerning degree of professionalization. "Professional societies" in our population, therefore, include such diverse groups as the American Pharmaceutical Association, American Society of Anesthesiologists, American School Health Association and American Hospital Association.

A total of 105 professional societies were identified which support health sciences libraries (Table 3). Of these, 37 are national societies; 39 are state or local constituents of the American Medical Association (AMA); 18 are psychoanalytic societies and training institutions; six are independent local societies; and five are constituents of the American Dental Association. The psychoanalytic societies and training institutes do not always fit into our model of professional societies and are difficult to classify. These libraries and the AMA libraries constitute special subsets, and will later be isolated for further analysis.

There are great differences among libraries of professional organizations in both size of collection and amount of support (Table 4). The average number of bound volumes is 28,892, and the average number of current serials is 215. While the population consists of both national and local

TABLE 3

TYPES OF PROFESSIONAL SOCIETIES SPONSORING HEALTH SCIENCES LIBRARIES (N = 105)

Type of Organization	Number of Libraries
National Professional Societies	37
American Medical Association State or County Societies	39
Psychoanalytic Societies and Training Institutes	18
Independent Local Societies	6
American Dental Association State or County Societies	5
Total	105

organizations, there is not always a correlation between size of library and size of professional society. Two of the largest libraries (by comparison with all health sciences libraries, including those of medical schools) are the New York Academy of Medicine and the College of Physicians of Philadelphia, but both had locally defined audiences at the time they were surveyed. Subsequently, both libraries have become regional medical libraries of the National Library of Medicine.

It should be noted that the usual indicators of size—number of bound volumes and current subscriptions—do not always apply in the case of professional society libraries. The latter often perform functions which are atypical of most medical libraries whose programs consist mainly of acquisition, processing, and circulation of materials and some level of literature search. National societies are often responsible for bibliographic control over a specified discipline or areas of interest to their membership. The American Hospital Association, for example, compiles and publishes the *Index to Hospital Literature*; the American Dental Association publishes the *Index to Dental Literature*; and the American Medical Association publishes *Medical Socioeconomic Research Sources*. They may also be responsible for writing, editing, and indexing reports, proceedings, and digests related to the history and policies of the societies. Some exercise great control over the society's computer facility, and are even called upon to devise systems for control of office records and for statistical surveys. Those societies which maintain archives are responsible for administering special collections as well as artifacts which require development of a museum.

THE AMERICAN MEDICAL ASSOCIATION: NATIONAL, STATE, AND COUNTY LIBRARIES

Libraries supported by state and county societies of the American Medical Association (AMA) comprise a large subgroup of the SFO libraries. In analyzing data on libraries supported by the AMA, the national library in Chicago was separated from the state and county society libraries. The national library functions primarily as the resource center for a large administrative staff which provides a diverse and vast number of services to both the membership and the community-at-large. These include support to scientific publications,

TABLE 4

RESOURCES, EXPENDITURES AND STAFF OF SFO LIBRARIES: BY TYPE OF ORGANIZATION (N=186)

Type of Organization	Number of Libraries	Number of Bound Volumes[1]			Number of Serials[2]			Total Expenditures[3]	Number of Full-Time Staff[4]	
		High	Low	Average	High	Low	Average	Average	Prof.	Non-Prof.
Professional Organizations (National and Local)	87	543,760	50	28,892	5,320	2	215	not computed	112	148
Foundations and Other Private Organizations	62	165,000	50	9,729	2,000	20	205	3,705	35	19
Voluntary Health Organizations	19	13,000	102	2,944	560	3	185	not computed	21	14
Psychoanalytic Societies and Training Institutions[5]	18	12,000	400	3,165	1,057	4	111	5,341	9	10

[1,2] Based upon return rate of 90%.
[3] Based upon a return rate of 60%.
[4] Based upon a return rate of 76%.
[5] Statistics do not include 3 libraries combined with general psychiatric collections.

TABLE 5

LIBRARY STATISTICS OF THE AMERICAN MEDICAL ASSOCIATION AND ITS STATE AND COUNTY SOCIETIES (N = 39)

Library Category	Number of Bound Volumes	Number of Current Serials	Total Expenditures	Number of Full-Time Staff Professional	Number of Full-Time Staff Non-Professional
AMA Headquarters Library*	50,000	2,600	$ 246,201	12	13
State and County Society Libraries					
1. Range					
High	106,000	1,450	146,145	4	5
Low	800	36	2,100	0	0
2. Average	26,020	363	28,298	0.95	0.89
Total for all AMA Society Libraries	936,735	15,310	1,123,465	48	49

*Statistics for the AMA headquarters library were separated from those of state and county society libraries, as we were interested in finding out more about the "typical" local society library. In calculating the *total* resources however, the headquarters library was included. These statistics are based upon response rates of ⩾ 95% for all variables tabulated.

health education, and communications programs of the Association.

What are the characteristics of the "typical" AMA state or county society library? As shown in Table 5, there is variation in both amount of resource and support among these libraries. Their budgets range from $2100 to $146,145. The average society library has a total of 26,020 bound volumes and receives 363 current journals. The societies spend an average of $28,298 on their library, and they are usually manned by two full-time staff members, one professional and one non-professional. The support of library activity by the American Medical Association and its constituents is a sizeable one, totalling over $1,123,465 during fiscal year 1969.

The typical state or county society library defines its primary user group by membership within a specified geographic area, i.e., members of a county or state society. However, the society library also serves an important function as information center for the adjacent community—73 percent indicated that they served the general public, students, attorneys, and allied health personnel. Services offered include literature searches, loan, and photocopying.

AMA society libraries were surveyed in 1964,[6] 1966,[7] and 1969.[8] When data were compared for these surveys, it was found that 14 libraries which appeared in the 1964 or 1966 surveys were no longer listed in the 1969 survey. In a subsurvey, we contacted these 14 societies which did not report libraries, and the results are indicated in Table 6. Typically, these were libraries which served physicians in local areas—county society libraries, which during the first half of this century, developed library service in response to needs of the membership, most of whom were practicing physicians.

In recent times, society libraries have found it increasingly difficult to maintain an adequate general medical library based upon the principle of serving all physicians within a given geographic area. Each of the societies contacted indicated that the membership had evaluated their library program and made the decision to enter into a cooperative program with a local institution—usually a hospital or a medical school. The cooperative or contractual arrangements vary among the libraries. Some libraries, although housed in cooperative facilities, remain autonomous. The San Diego County Medical Society Library, for example, is situated within the University of California (San Diego) complex, but provides the same general services with access to greater facilities and professional staff. In some smaller communities where the majority of physicians are affiliated with one or two hospitals, the society has moved its library to one of the major hospitals, continuing its support in a new setting. Through these and other arrangements, the society therefore continues to support or augment local library resources, but through a sharing of facilities, resources and operating costs. There is evidence that this trend toward local cooperation will continue.

TABLE 6

MEDICAL SOCIETY LIBRARIES WHICH HAVE DEVELOPED COOPERATIVE PROGRAMS WITH LOCAL INSTITUTIONS, 1964-1969 (N = 14)

Medical Society Library	Local Institution with which Library has Developed Cooperative Program
Academy of Medicine of Brooklyn, N.Y.	State University of New York, Brooklyn, N.Y.
Boston Medical Library, Boston, Mass.	Harvard University Medical School, Boston, Mass.
Broome County Medical Society, Binghamton, N.Y.	Binghamton General Hospital, Binghamton, N.Y.
Cleveland Medical Library Association, Cleveland, Ohio	Case Western Reserve University, Health Sciences Library, Cleveland, Ohio
Hall County Medical Society, Grand Island, Neb.	St. Francis Hospital, Grand Island, Neb.
Hillsborough County Medical Society, Tampa, Fla.	Tampa General Hospital, Tampa, Fla.
Jackson County Medical Society, Kansas City, Kans.	Kansas City General Hospital, Kansas City, Kans.
King County Medical Society, Seattle, Wash.	University of Washington, Health Sciences Library Seattle, Wash.
Mobile County Medical Society, Mobile, Ala.	Mobile General Hospital, Mobile, Ala.
Muscatine County Medical Society, Muscatine, Iowa	Muscatine General Hospital, Muscatine, Iowa
Pennsylvania Medical Society, LeMoyne, Penna.	Pennsylvania State University, Hershey, Penna.
Rowan-Davie County Medical Society, Salisbury, N.C.	Rowan Memorial Hospital, Salisbury, N.C.
San Diego County Medical Society, San Diego, Calif.	University of California, San Diego, La Jolla, Calif.
Shawnee County Medical Society, Topeka, Kans.	Stormont Medical Library, Topeka, Kans.

PSYCHOANALYTIC SOCIETIES AND TRAINING INSTITUTES

The American Psychoanalytic Association is made up of "affiliate" societies of psychoanalysts and training institutes, a flexible relationship which provides constituents a choice in degree of independence from the national organization.[9] There are a total of 29 affiliate societies. Psychoanalytic training is accomplished through the institutes which are approved by the Association. In general, these are organized according to one of three models: (1) they may be supported and controlled by the local society, and not affiliated with a university; (2) they may be university-based; or (3) they may be independent of both the local society or university. There are 29 training institutes, all of which have libraries to support their training programs.

Three of these have combined collections within a university, that is, the psychoanalytic publications are interfiled with the general psychiatric collection. Aside from these combined collections, the libraries are relatively small, having an average of 3,165 bound volumes. They receive an average of 111 current subscriptions and the average total annual expenditure is around $5,300.

In attempting to explain the small size of these collections, the librarian of one of the largest institutes[10] indicated that training institutes were not usually committed to maintaining comprehensive collections of general psychiatric materials. The core literature of psychoanalysis is not extensive in comparison with other sciences or specialties, either in number of monographs or in number of journals. In his experience, the library was rarely used by practicing analysts, who tended to maintain sizable private collections; however, analysts do request literature searches. It was his opinion that in-depth indexing of the literature to provide access to both private and society collections was one of the greatest current needs.

VOLUNTARY HEALTH ORGANIZATIONS

A voluntary health organization or agency has been defined by the American Medical Association and the Council on Voluntary Health Agencies as follows:[11]

> ". . . any nonprofit association organized on a national, state, or local level; composed of lay and professional persons; dedicated to the prevention, alleviation, and cure of a particular disease, disability, or group of diseases and disabilities. It is supported by voluntary contributions primarily from the general public and expends its resources for education, research, and service programs relevant to the disease and disabilities concerned."

The program of voluntary health organizations usually includes one or more of the following activities: (1) public education; (2) support of professional training; (3) support of services in diagnosis and treatment centers; (4) support of research; (5) publications for professional or general audiences. These activities may be undertaken in institutions developed by the voluntary organizations, or they may involve support to outside organizations and societies.

Nineteen voluntary health organizations have been identified which support health-related libraries (Table 4). Based upon a 95 percent response, these libraries averaged 2,944 bound volumes, ranging from a low of 102 volumes to a high of 13,000. They receive an average of 185 current subscriptions which range from a low of three journals to a high of 560. The American Cancer Society, American Heart Association, and the American Red Cross, three of the largest voluntary health organizations, also support the largest libraries.

Voluntary health organization libraries, in general, are small and specialized. With the exception of the few largest libraries, they are usually administered by a staff of one professional with some clerical assistance. Since the major function of voluntary health organizations is fundraising and distribution of support to outside organizations and programs, comprehensive libraries are not usually required to support their functions.

FOUNDATIONS AND OTHER PRIVATE ORGANIZATIONS

An analysis published by the Russell Sage Foundation[12] defines a foundation as a "nonprofit organization having a principal fund of its own, managed by its own trustees or directors, and established to maintain or aid social, charitable, religious or other activities serving the common welfare." By source of support, they may be divided into (1) family or personal foundations; (2) corporate foundations; (3) community trusts; (4) governmental foundations. The fourth category, of which the National Science Foundation is an example, is not included in this analysis.

Sixty-two foundations or other private organizations have been identified with programs which support health sciences libraries. These programs are usually based in an institution or facility for research, communication or patient care. Some examples are psychosomatic research, rehabilitation services, child study, and mental retardation. The libraries support these activities, usually providing special services for a limited set of users.

As indicated in Table 5, the average foundation library maintains a collection of 9,729 volumes and receives 215 serials. Total expenditures average $3,705 per year. Foundation libraries are, in general, private, special libraries which support the program of the institution in which they are situated, although the entire program may consist of supporting a unique library collection.

SUMMARY

This paper focused upon libraries supported by social groups which have organized for multipurposes related to the health sciences: research, health care, professional activities, and education. These include professional societies, voluntary health organizations and foundations. The 1969 survey identified 186 health sciences libraries sponsored by these groups, approximately 6 percent of the total number of health sciences libraries in the United States. Previous surveys of society libraries covered 51 institutions (1964) and 58 institutions (1966).

The contribution of SFO libraries to health sciences library resources of the United States is considerable—a projected $4,000,000 of support. The average society or foundation annually spends around $36,480 on its library. SFO libraries contain approximately 2,700,000 bound volumes and receive over a half million current serials.

Longitudinal data are not available for all SFO libraries, except those of professional societies. There is evidence that, during the past decade when health sciences libraries of academic institutions experienced great growth, there has been a decline in the number of local libraries independently supported by professional societies. This does not imply that professional societies no longer support library services, but the trend appears to be toward cooperation with local institutions to support the high cost of such services. On the other hand, there are national society libraries such as the American Medical Association Archive-Library which doubled its budget during the past ten years.

The 1960's were years of great growth and change for all the health sciences. We have seen new organizational forms emerge (regional medical libraries) and others strengthened (medical school libraries). By the end of the decade we also began to see evidence of severe financial, political and intellectual stress for universities. Now, the current focus appears to be upon the application of information and upon manpower production rather than the production of new information. These trends will undoubtedly have profound effects upon organization of library resources and institutions.

NOTES

[1] Bucher, R., and Stelling, J. Characteristics of Professional Organizations. J. Health and Social Behavior 10, March 1969, p. 14.

[2] Schick, F., and Crawford, S. Directory of Health Sciences Libraries, 1969. Chicago, American Medical Association, 1970.

[3] This figure includes psychoanalytic societies and training institutes (see Table 4 for breakdown).

[4] Vollmer, H. M., and Mills, D. L. Professionalization. New Jersey, Prentice-Hall, 1966.

[5] Etzioni, A., ed. The semi-professions and their organization. New York, Free Press, 1969.

[6] Crawford, S., Michel, C., Waligorski, C. The Contemporary Medical Society Library, Bull. Med. Lib. Ass. 53, April 1964, p. 178.

[7] Crawford, S. Libraries of National, State and Local Organizations. Bull. Med. Lib. Ass. 55, April 1967. p. 191.

[8] Schick, F., and Crawford, S. Directory, 1970.

[9] Mora, George. "Recent American Psychiatric Developments," in American Handbook of Psychiatry, ed. by S. Arieti. New York, Basic Books, Vol. 2, 1959: 18–57.

[10] Informal Communication with Glen Miller, Chicago Institute for Psychoanalysis.

[11] American Medical Association, Directory of National Voluntary Health Organizations. 6th rev. Chicago, the Association, 1968.

[12] Andrews, F. E. Philanthropic Foundations, New York, Russell Sage Foundation, 1961. Chap. 1.

ABOUT THE AUTHOR–Dr. Susan Crawford is Director of the Archive-Library Department of the American Medical Association. She holds a B.A. in Liberal Arts from the University of British Columbia and an M.A.L.S. from the University of Toronto. Her Ph.D. is in Library Science from the University of Chicago, where she also obtained an M.A. in Physiology and Psychology. Before she took her present position she was Chief Cataloger for the American Dental Association and then Assistant to the Executive Vice-President of the American Medical Association.

She is Chairman of the Committee on Surveys and Statistics of the Medical Library Association, and also holds membership in the American Library Association, Special Libraries Association and American Society for Information Science. Recently, she was appointed to the Board of Regents of the National Library of Medicine.

Examples of her wide range of interest are the fact that she edits the new A.M.A. publication, *Medical Socioeconomic Research Sources*, and that she has recently published on "Informal Communication Among Scientists in Sleep Research," (*Journal of the American Society for Information Science* 22: 301-310, Sept.-Oct. 1971). She wrote the chapter on "Audiovisual Materials" for the *Handbook of Medical Library Practice* (Chicago, Medical Library Association, 1970).

Hospital Libraries

Perhaps the most important trend initiated in the medical library system in recent years is the new role of hospital libraries. The increased emphasis on health care delivery requires that the health care team have literature available when and where they need it. The papers selected here are perhaps the most controversial in the book because of the stresses the hospital library is undergoing in adapting to change.

The final paper suggests a remedy which bypasses traditional library approaches in a manner reminiscent of the way Henry Ford disregarded customized production of cars when he created the model T.

The Hospital Library: the Patron's Statement

by Frances E. Noe

The local hospital library is examined by a patron and found satisfactory in its response to requests, but lacking in a dynamic approach to the real information needs of the staff. Suggestions for the active approach lead to a new role for hospital librarians.

My association with the various libraries at the many institutions with which I have been affiliated has been most fortunate. I rarely have asked for assistance which the library could not or would not give. Therefore it is difficult for me to come up with any criticism, constructive or otherwise. However, in preparing this paper, I found that there were a number of services available in the Sinai Hospital library of which I was completely unaware after five years of being in and out of the library at least a dozen times each week, and I suddenly realized the major disadvantage of just about every library I have dealt with.

The library is a passive service. I talked with other clinicians and inevitably got the same response, "Our library is wonderful; it always gets me what I want!" And that is the trouble; the library waits for us to come to it.

As the only source of medical information in most communities, the library should be a vital and active center for medical staff activities. It should not only function within its own area to draw busy clinicians but have an active program of participation in the hospital events and perhaps in appropriate community events. Supplying information to individuals for local professional or technical group meetings is a routine function of the library but one for which the library ordinarily gets no credit. Why not follow through with a librarian at the session with a small table of particularly pertinent or recent books on the subject of the meeting?

The same idea applies for routine hospital functions. Medical staff meetings usually have a preset program devoted to one or more clinical subjects. I will be the first to suggest that you had better chain the books to the table but I believe that you will find few clinicians who will ignore a display of five or six recent books in their field or books of general clinical application. Let me emphasize that word clinical; you may be avoided like the plague if the most prominent spot is taken by the latest edition of Guyton's text on physiology or West and Todd's biochemistry text.

Bring clinicians to the library for other reasons than their own need for information. If space allows one or more conference rooms as part of the library area, offer their use for clinical staff group conferences arranged with you beforehand so that there can just happen to be several recent acquisitions of interest to the group displayed in the room, and, if time and copy service allow, provide take-home copies of a list of these and any other new books of general interest to the group. Our Sinai Hospital library has a bulletin board in the doctors' lounge where jackets of books and such lists are displayed where every doctor entering or leaving the hospital can see them.

Our monthly medical staff publication, a dozen sheets of typed notices and news items, includes as part of every second or third issue a list of the latest acquisitions of the library, always on bright yellow sheets so that the habitual headline skimmer knows they are there if he is at all inclined to read them over.

Once the positive approach from the library is established, the next step might be a journal club program. Journal clubs are often considered a medium for educating the house staff of interns and residents, but the monthly meeting of our Sinai

SOURCE: Reprinted from Frances E. Noe, "The Hospital Library: the Patron's Statement," *Bulletin of the Medical Library Association*, 59 (April, 1971), pp. 335-336, by permission of the publisher and the author. Delivered as part of the General Session on Hospital Libraries at the Sixty-ninth Annual Meeting of the Medical Library Association at New Orleans, Louisiana, May 21, 1970.

Hospital anesthesiology department usually calls forth a full complement of the senior staff because the program is carefully planned to supplement the questions and problems that come up in our day's work. In suburban areas of large cities and especially near university centers, the demands on professional time are usually such that there are more visiting speakers and specialty group meetings than can be adequately attended, so purely local activities are not called for. However, in the average community the local hospital may offer the only avenue of intercommunication for physicians. The present emphasis on postgraduate education and the threatening rumbles advocating reevaluation examinations at intervals for physicians are making many of them more receptive to opportunities for catching up with recent advances in medical knowledge and techniques in their fields. Now neither you nor I are so naive as to think that you can make a grand announcement for such a program at the next medical staff meeting and be greeted by whistles and cheers. The plans must be made with and through a receptive physician or department office, and based on the library's offer of bibliography service for chosen topics, copying and distributing journal articles to a mailing list of participants and, if the library schedule allows it, the offer of the library as a meeting place. Try a meeting-to-meeting borrowing period for books and see if this will increase your lending rate. If this service calls for more office work than your staff can give, try the women's volunteer group or request volunteers through the local high school library for the more routine work.

What may be the easier though more expensive approach to a postgraduate educational program for the physicians of a community involves the use of Audiodigest tapes. In our hospital these are subscribed by the individual departments for use at weekly department meetings or individual use. They offer a wide range of subjects on the newest and more important developments in both general medicine and the various specialties. A group of physicians in an isolated community would do well to contribute to a joint subscription for suitable series of tapes which would be administered on a loan basis by the medical library. Monthly meetings might be arranged to allow the group to hear new tapes and then these would be added to the general collection for circulation to individuals for a reasonable period of time.

How does one initiate a working relationship between librarians and physicians in a specific institution? The problem is essentially one of communication, but it is nowhere near the problem it was ten or even five years ago. Physicians need the medical librarian and more and more of them are beginning to realize it. One would hope that the more impersonal projects such as bulletin board notices, book exhibits, and helpful notices in hospital publications would bring to the library the more receptive members of the medical staff if the librarian is not already aware of them. Then it is up to the librarian—a genuine and cheerfully given offer of practical help is usually not refused.

ABOUT THE AUTHOR—Dr. Frances E. Noe is Chairman, Section of Pulmonary Physiology and Research Associate, Division of Research at the Sinai Hospital of Detroit. She was formerly Assistant Professor in Anesthesiology, Wayne State University College of Medicine. She has a B.A. from Middlebury College, an M.N. from Yale University, and an M.D. from the University of Vermont College of Medicine. She was successively Intern at Mary Hitchcock Hospital at Dartmouth, Research Fellow of the Michigan Heart Association at the Harper Hospital in Detroit, Resident in Pulmonary Medicine at the Henry Ford Hospital, and Rands Fellow in Medicine, specializing in pulmonary physiology, at the Wayne State University College of Medicine.

Services in Hospital and Institution Libraries

by Margaret E. Monroe

The hospital librarian has an opportunity to affect patient care by supporting the physician actively and by providing bibliotherapy for the patient.

The walls between society and the hospital and correctional institutions are being lowered. On the one hand, hospitals and institutions are seeking to place their patients or inmates—soon we must have a new term here, perhaps clients—back into society for the therapy process. Milieu therapy and reality therapy are approaches based on the insight of professional therapists that there is an essential healing quality in normalcy and in the integration of the individual into his community.

On the other hand, many groups in society are now seeking to design various facets of the community to maintain physical, mental, and emotional health, and to offer specific programs of activity and guidance to those under special stress so that they may never lose contact with normalcy and their proper integration within the community. The concept of the welfare state may become more exactly expressed as the therapeutic society. The Economic Opportunity Act, Medicare, and the Kerner Commission Report offer three stunning illustrations of the concept of the therapeutic society; and an important ingredient in the national introspection following the tragic assassination of Robert Kennedy was the assumption that we have an obligation to maintain a minimum level of good mental health in our nation. The therapeutic society has become as fundamental a commitment as is our commitment to the scientific method in research; and it is in the process of creating as great a revolution.

This provides an important context in which to view the services of hospital and institution libraries. I am assuming the continuing need for institutions; no matter how effective the therapeutic society, the availability of intensive treatment and controlled environment can be assumed essential this side of Utopia. But as the walls between the institution and society are lowered, the special services of hospital and institution libraries take on a universal meaning in librarianship. What is pioneered in the institutional context will have broader application in public and school libraries; the educational and guidance services of school and public libraries will strengthen the approaches of institution and hospital librarianship. For this reason the opportunities for intensive development of the services program to clients in hospitals and institutions holds out significant hope for growth in services to readers generally.

We are fortunate, then, that hospital and institution libraries are so thoroughly oriented toward service to the user. The medical libraries, which are integral parts of the hospital and institution library complex, have developed highly sophisticated services to the professional staff. MEDLARS, as pace-setting as it is, is only an instance of one aspect of this service. Current awareness services demand the librarian's sensitivity to the concerns and activities of the professional staff; reference services, including MEDLARS, require the librarian's adaptation to crisis need for information; the more comprehensive literature searches and bibliographic services demand both thorough scholarly activity and evaluative skill in the various aspects of the medical field. This very competence in service to the professional staff becomes a major resource in the development of services to the patients and inmates, that "other half" of the clientele.

SOURCE: Reprinted from Margaret E. Monroe, "Services in Hospital and Institutional Libraries," *ALA Bulletin*, 63 (Oct., 1969), pp. 1280–1282, by permission of the publisher and the author. Part of a series, "Libraries in the Therapeutic Society," edited for the *ALA Bulletin* by Genevieve Casey, Associate Professor, Library Science, Wayne State University. This paper was presented by the author as the keynote address to the Workshop on Areas of Library Services of Concern to Hospital and Institutional Libraries in Kansas City, June 23, 1968.

In the therapeutic environment of the hospital or institution, all services must lead to the goal of therapy. The more exact the understanding of the librarian, the more focused and effective his services can become. Patients and inmates are people in crisis, people in need; and the professional librarian must provide service from a background of knowledge and understanding. The skill of the librarian is to bring a flawless knowledge of library resources together with a quick and precise understanding of the client's need, to create—efficiently and graciously—the service required. All that the librarian must know to serve the professional staff is mere background to the task of serving the patient.

Perhaps the best illustration of this point lies in the function of the librarian on the interdisciplinary team. When the librarian is privileged to serve on the interdisciplinary team, he has access to a depth understanding of his client in terms of the client's problems as understood by a variety of medical, psychiatric, and social work specialists, and he learns the kinds of experiences which his client is undergoing in the process of therapy. The librarian justifies his presence on the team by a readiness to use this knowledge wisely, bringing his knowledge of health and ill-health together with his particular art of librarianship into use for the client. The librarian becomes a full team member, however, as he contributes his observations from contact with the client, to increase the team understanding. To be sure, from his participation on the therapy team, the librarian increases his readiness to serve the professional staff, through increased understanding of the concerns and needs of their various fields.

The functions of the librarian on the interdisciplinary team offer a prototype for professional library service to readers in all types of libraries. The school librarian who functions with administrators, faculty, guidance officers, and other specialists has the same opportunities. The public librarian who functions in a great variety of milieus—the business community, government, education, social welfare—finds his interdisciplinary team for each separate function (typically a council or a coordinating agency), and he makes his contributions effectively both through them and with individuals, enriched by information gleaned in the team sessions. Rarely, however, does a librarian outside the hospital or institution setting have the opportunity for the team approach to individual service so beautifully available. The experience in this setting should contribute much to our professional understanding of services.

It takes a tough-minded librarian to survive the interdisciplinary team experience in any type of library and remain a librarian. As his sense of the total situation develops, he may be beguiled into "meeting imperative needs" rather than seeing the unique contributions which he as a librarian can make. Public librarians, exhilarated by the significance of problems revealed in the community council, have been so beguiled in the past; I surmise that we are becoming more sophisticated in this respect at this time. The hospital or institution librarian must grasp the essence of other forms of therapy being practiced and differentiate them from the library's therapy. A clear view of the contributions of the various library services and the conditions under which these contributions can be successfully made is essential to the librarian working on the team.

Is there an approved list of such activities? I know of none, and shudder at the thought that there might be one. Innovative services devised to meet individual circumstances is the essence of good library service. But the librarian must be able to recognize when a book service is or is not a library service. Book discussions for diagnostic purposes and dramatic play-reading for therapy may require the assistance of the librarian in the selection of materials, but the initiative and responsibility typically lie in other hands. Only when librarians are also physicians, psychiatrists, and social workers as well as professional librarians will prescription and analysis be the prerogative of the librarian.

I say these things to this group not because you do not know this both intellectually and instinctively, but because it is very important that this point be clear. If the concepts of hospital and institution library service are to have transfer value for librarians in the therapeutic society, all librarians must grasp the distinction.

The door is just beginning to open to the potential of bibliotherapy. The climate is right to undertake an elaboration of the field. Some fine insights and challenging concepts have come from psychiatrists and librarians. The Menningers' use of books for respite, for client insight, for understanding and information have been part of the pioneering effort.[1] A number of librarians have begun to identify the types of reading materials and types of reading experience useful for patients with particular types of problems. As we move further and further away from the primitive generalization that "reading is good" into a careful analysis of "for what" and "under what circumstances," we begin to make—if not a science—at least a practical art.

Once we have a skillfully evaluated summary of our pragmatic experience, we need to move into carefully controlled experiment and analysis. Leonard Berkowitz, professor of Psychology at the University of Wisconsin, has—in the process of studying aggression—been exploring the effect on viewers of film materials with varying degrees of aggression displayed.[2] These studies contain enough useful methodology and sound findings to encourage an expanded range of inquiry. And it is clear that this must be conducted as interdisciplinary research.

The excellent proposals of the Association of Hospital and Institution Libraries for such research should not gather dust. The St. Louis conference on bibliotherapy was a first small step to clearing the way to such serious inquiry. The National Institutes of Health seem the obvious source of support for such inquiry in our therapeutic society. The great potential of bibliotherapy will not be realized by heuristic experimentation alone; it requires carefully designed research that lays the foundation for a solid body of knowledge. We must begin to move in this direction, not only for the sake of hospital and institution library service but for the sake of our therapeutic society, its librarians, and its readers.

The Medical Library Assistance Act, with its provisions for education of health sciences librarians, and Title IV of the Library Services and Construction Act that enables state libraries to at last come to some realistic grip with the problems of hospital and institution libraries—both reflect the support which our society is giving this area of library service. This support has not been an unsolicited gift, but has been won by the health professions and the library profession. Grateful for this support, let us now move to justify it by increasing the sophistication of our service and the base of knowledge upon which it is founded.

NOTES

[1] Menninger, William C., *A Psychiatrist for a Troubled World*, Chap. 4 (1967).

[2] Berkowitz, Leonard, and Edna Rawlings, "Effect of Film Violence on Institutions Against Subsequent Aggression," *Journal of Abnormal and Social Psychology*, 66:405–12 (1961).

ABOUT THE AUTHOR—Dr. Margaret E. Monroe is Professor of Library Science at the University of Wisconsin Library School. She was Director of the School from 1963–1970. Previously she had been Associate Professor in Library Services at Rutgers University, Director of the American Heritage Project at the American Library Association, and Readers' Adviser at the New York Public Library. She holds a B.A. in English and a B.S.L.S. from N.Y. State College for Teachers, and an M.A. in English and a D.L.S. from Columbia.

She is a former President of the Adult Services Division of the American Library Association and a member of the ALA Council. She has also been a member of its Committee on Accreditation for a number of years. She was President of the Association of American Library Schools in 1971. In addition to journal publications, she has published *Library Adult Education* (N.Y., Scarecrow, 1963).

Services an Integrated Hospital Library Can and Cannot Provide

by Barbara Coe Johnson

The hospital is a complex organization and its library must perform many functions to satisfy the needs of its personnel. Service to laymen, whether they are patients or the hospital staff in their nonprofessional roles, should best be supplied by the public library. Thus Mrs. Johnson's and Miss Monroe's views contrast sharply.

All medical institutions are designed to fill four purposes: *research* to advance medical knowledge; *teaching specialized personnel* who can apply the knowledge produced by research; *public instruction* so that the population is prepared to apply general health principles and support those institutions contributing to better health; and *care* of those who are ill, so they may return to their productive role in the community, or at least be eased of suffering. A particular medical institution points out its primary purpose by giving priority to one or another of these goals, but *all* medical institutions share *all* these goals.

The primary concentration of a medical school is the teaching of specialized personnel; its secondary purpose, research, is so contiguous to teaching that some say it now comes first. Yet medical schools do not neglect their other purposes: they encourage their personnel to be members of national commissions concerned with the public's health, such as the President's Commission on Heart Disease, Cancer, and Stroke, and on a less exalted level, to address lay groups. And certainly medical schools are concerned with the care of the sick. Many university medical schools run hospitals, and every physician who is graduated from medical school has spent at least two of his four years of training in a hospital where he learned the art of his discipline through actual participation in patient treatment.

While hospital goals vary in position depending upon community role and means of support, in any hospital, patient care comes first. To say that this simple fact colors the whole character of hospitals is putting it mildly. Perhaps the easiest way to emphasize the pervasiveness of this concept is to look at the extra- and intramural organization of hospitals in the United States.

We are talking about a very big business when we are discussing hospitals. Overall, hospitals in this country rank fourth or fifth in terms of investment in plant, numbers of people employed, and gross income. One of the three top factors in the government's Cost of Living Index, immediately following costs for food and shelter, is the cost of medical care; and the largest part of the health dollar is spent on hospitals, either in the form of hospitalization insurance or in cash outlay. All other industries of this stature—government, steel, transportation, and utilities—are commonly recognized as "big," and each is characterized by central control exercised by a few decision-makers whose policies are followed industry-wide.

Hospitals do not follow this pattern. Even government-supported hospitals, like state hospitals or those operated under the Veterans Administration, despite the fact that they work within general guidelines set by the governmental unit, are in the last analysis managed by individual administrators who are given as one of their responsibilities the task of seeing that the specific hospital is sensitive to its community. And government-controlled

---

SOURCE: Reprinted from Barbara Coe Johnson, "Services an Integrated Hospital Library Can and Cannot Provide," *ALA Bulletin*, 63 (Dec., 1969), pp. 1554–1559, by permission of the publisher and the author. Part of a series, "Libraries in the Therapeutic Society," edited for the *ALA Bulletin* by Genevieve Casey, Associate Professor, Library Science, Wayne State University. This paper was presented at the Institutional Library Service Institute sponsored by the Wayne State University Department of Library Service on April 19, 1968.

hospitals with their modicum of central control comprise only a small proportion of hospitals in the United States.

The largest number of hospitals, as many as 90 per cent, operate under some kind of private control: church, proprietary, or voluntary. Church-controlled hospitals may seem to have a kind of central control exercised by the sponsoring religious body; but the number of church groups and the proliferation of individual orders within each requires that church-sponsored hospitals be classified as privately controlled. Proprietary hospitals, founded and run by physicians both to care for private patients and to produce a profit, certainly are private. The voluntary, nonprofit hospital, run in the community's interest and managed by the civic-minded citizens who comprise a board of trustees, obviously is private. Thus, except insofar as licensing regulations and voluntary acceptance of the standards of the Joint Commission for the Accreditation of Hospitals comprise central control, the bulk of hospitals in this country are privately run businesses dedicated to caring for a specific community's sick.

Now let us look at the intramural organization of hospitals. Again we find a unique situation. In every other "big" industry, and indeed in most small businesses, we find that the workers fall into two classes having different social status: the managerial and the production. I should not remind you of so obvious a fact that the managerial, or administrative, worker has higher status than the production worker except that I need to make the point that the situation is, while not entirely reversed in hospitals, at least different. The production worker, the one who controls the hospital's ultimate product—good patient care—is the physician. What the administrative staff of a hospital does is provide the physical conditions and atmosphere within which physicians can best give good patient care. I must say that I consider these two hospital functions to be of comparable importance, but while you conceivably could have a physician who lacked access to a hospital, you certainly could not have a hospital without physicians. Because of this incontrovertible fact hospitals are organized in a different way from other businesses. Were there not successful liaison, everyone on the hospital's payroll would have two lines of authority, and we all know that the usual result of that kind of organizational table is, at best, stalemate. Luckily most hospitals have resolved this difficulty by setting up and maintaining mechanisms which assure that physicians and administrators freely communicate with each other at the decision-making level. At the same time physicians in their day-to-day life deal only with decisions bearing directly on patient care, while other ordinary administrative tasks are left to the authority of the administrative staff. Human beings are, however, crotchety and irritable and above all, individual. Because of this, and because of the system's built-in instability, close attention must always be paid to making it work. It can fall apart with disastrous results, but by and large, I think it works as well as it does simply because it can never be neglected.

When I was discussing the overall organization of hospitals in this country, I in effect classified them by their pattern of financial support. Now I would like to interject four other elements which help classify hospitals: size; average length of stay per patient; whether or not the hospital carries on a formal teaching program; and whether or not the hospital primarily serves one segment of the population, like women, children, or the mentally ill. The confusing thing about all these classifications, and I have mentioned only a few, is that using one system does not preclude using another, and the variety of combinations is infinite. I don't know of one, but there's no reason a large, long-term, proprietary, non-teaching, children's psychiatric hospital could not exist. Hopefully, so few patients would need its services that it would soon go out of existence.

All these elements come into play in any hospital, and impose different sets of needs. As hospital libraries exist to fill the hospital's specific needs, any or all may be influential in determining what a specific library does, and I really doubt whether I know enough to anticipate here all the nuances which would influence a hospital library. What I do know something about, however, is the library of a large, short-term, general medical and surgical, teaching, nonprofit, voluntary hospital. Unlike my theoretical example above, such hospitals exist in every large city in this country, and I doubt that they will ever lack patients.

There is real confusion about the definition of the term "hospital library," even among the various medical and library associations who presumably know what they are talking about when they do such things as conceive and apply judgmental criteria—standards. To the Medical Library Association (MLA) the term means the collection and services offered to supply the informational needs of the hospital's medical staff. The American Library Association's Association of Hospital and Institution Libraries (ALA-AHIL) broadens the concept by adding to the hospital library's duties an obligation to give service to patients. The Special Libraries Association (SLA) classes the hospital library with special libraries in biomedical subject fields, assigning it membership to the Biological Sciences Division: by implication it seems to go along with MLA. The Joint Commission for the Accreditation of Hospitals (comprised of representatives of the American Medical Association, the American College of Surgeons, the American College of Physicians, and the American Hospital Association), accepts the standards endorsed in 1953 by the previously mentioned library associations, which in truth apply only to a physicians' library in a hospital. It really is no wonder that hospital librarians feel torn in all directions.

Fortunately we can hope for an early end to this situation, which has satisfied none of the interested organizations, much less the librarians of hospital libraries. After nearly five years of work, a Joint Committee of ALA-AHIL, CLA, SLA, and MLA hopes to be able to present for approval of its various members standards for hospital libraries. Implicit in these standards is a definition that embraces all the above variations on the theme. In addition, the standards are capable of separate application to the two segments of a hospital's library population, the professional or technical and the lay or "patients." These standards, when accepted by the library associations, will certainly be applied by the hospital accrediting body. One point is clear: the proposed standards clearly call for some form of consolidation of all elements found in libraries in hospitals, and that is an enormous step forward.

I certainly agree with the concept that some integrative approach is necessary, but I am inclined to think that lay and professional collections can only be coordinated—probably by sharing the same administrative librarian—while all service to technical and professional personnel can truly be integrated (combined, shared, consolidated, whatever word one wants to use). Thus my definition of the integrated library differs, if only in degree, from that now being proposed in the new standards.

Let us then define my concept of the integrated hospital library. I mean that department of the hospital invested with responsibility and authority to assure the hospital's educational, clinical, administrative, and research personnel of access to information which enables them to give the best patient care possible within the limitations of funds at hand. I have several reasons for omitting general services and collection from my definition. Before I go into them, however, let me tell you what produced the above definition, which allows the kind of library Harper Hospital Library exemplifies. Any special library exists only as an instrument which provides access to information otherwise not available. Further, the information must be demonstrably valuable for some specific social purpose, or else access to it is not necessary. Thus the special library's existence rests on the needs of those who use it and on society's recognition that *their* activities serve a useful purpose. A library is not an end in itself; it is a tool of its users.

Libraries in medical fields neatly demonstrate this principle. Medicine, together with all its ancillary disciplines, needs access to current information; society recognizes medicine's importance. Physicians' libraries in hospitals did not exist in great numbers until physicians found that their private collections did not supply them all the information they needed, where they needed it. We must not forget that libraries were not required, or rated, for accreditation until 1955 when the Joint Commission for Accreditation of Hospitals accepted the standards now in the process of revision. Nursing libraries followed the same pattern. Except for departmental collections, however, newer medical disciplines did not have libraries of their own. Technicians, chemists, administrators, nurses aids, and all the rest[1] had to rely on physicians' or nurses' libraries which might or might not be able to meet their needs. This pattern still persists where library needs of paramedical personnel are not obvious. The main stream of thought, however, is finding its way into the course of integrating service to medical and paramedical fields in the same library.

In large teaching hospitals, like Harper, one library serves the work-oriented needs of all hospital personnel. What accounts for this change and where will it lead? For one thing, the very nature of the fields served by biomedical libraries has altered, and therein lies a principle that forces action. Today's cross-fertilization among medical disciplines, with its concomitant blurring of previously defined boundaries, allows a biomedical library to meet the demands put upon it *only* if it cooperates with other such libraries. The basic principle involved here is that every biomedical library, large or small, has the responsibility to provide *all* the information requested of it; one cannot be satisfied with a respectable 85 per cent satisfaction level.

A second factor of great importance is our need for more technical personnel to serve our burgeoning population, and the nation's increased demand for the best attention to its health needs. Hospitals carry far and away the largest share of the burden of training practitioners of medical disciplines. Between 1951 and 1965 in Michigan, the number of physicians per 100,000 population shrank from 500 to 400, and our loss was mild compared to that of California or Colorado. There are not fewer physicians; there are just more people. With medical knowledge increasing, and physicians decreasing in proportion to demand, something has to fill the gap. The answer of course is technically trained personnel who take on tasks the physician used to perform himself; what results is a team of ancillary specialists. These people must be trained, and they are largely trained in hospitals which must have libraries to back up programs.

This problem, of providing access to information for *all* students and practitioners of *any* medical or paramedical discipline represented in the hospital, so consumes our interest that almost our whole attention is paid to integrating satisfaction of their informational needs into one hospital library, into an "integrated library." I doubt that I now really need enumerate the reasons I omitted lay services in my definition of the integrated library, but I would like to base my appeal for your real and present help to all hospital libraries on something more than an impassioned explanation of what I think hospital libraries should be doing.

The most important reason is the simplest: I do not believe you can add apples to oranges. Technical service to technical personnel is indirect service to the laity; therapeutic service to hospitalized patients, let alone recreational and educational service to the technical person in his lay capacity, is direct service. No librarian alive can put both first, and both direct and indirect service to the laity have their necessary place in hospitals. The two needs must be coordinated so that each section knows what the other is doing, and so that each is aware of the importance of the other's function. But the "line librarian" who is in direct contact with his separate public must be free to immerse himself in their needs. A hospital librarian can no more be expected to wear two hats than can any other person. The Veterans Administration and the Mayo Clinic, both leaders in hospital librarianship, recognize this fundamental fact, and I think it is time we all do.

The second reason is also relatively simple to to state. In a hospital, ethics demand that the technical and lay libraries be physically separated because patients use the lay library. It is as potentially dangerous to allow patients access to technical information which presumes the professional background necessary to place it in context as it is unethical for the pharmacist to dispense dangerous drugs without mediation by the physician.

The third reason is a little more complex, but it centers around "who's in charge here?" I believe that the hospitalized person is essentially the same as the non-hospitalized except for the need specifically generated by his illness. His needs would be met by a public library were he not confined to a hospital, but possibly they are more important when he is in the hospital. After all, public libraries have long accepted the responsibility of providing trained personnel versed not only in general service to the public, but also in specialized service to various segments of the population. Public librarians dealing with patients might need some special training in the psychology of illness, but obviously this kind of service can be performed well by public librarians as witness the experience of the Cleveland Public Library. I think public librarians feel a responsibility in this area, but I do not think they have been very aggressive about making their talents known; equally I think those in hospital libraries have not been very forward in asking for the help they need. Another factor enters here, too. The patient isn't the only one in a hospital who is in virtual captivity. Hospitals are twenty-four-hour-a-day propositions. A good many people who work in them, including students who need the humanistic broadening offered by a good general collection, cannot get to a local public library during the hours it is open. The potential for a good lay library in a hospital is large, and I really think the public library should be in charge. Besides, why should a hospital library attempt to do poorly what a public library can do well?

Right or wrong, my fourth reason rests on the federal government's interpretation of the function of a biomedical library. In this day of tight money—especially if like Harper Hospital one is thinking about a $26,000,000 building project—interpretations on the part of the party who provides the largest single share of your money are very important. The federal government recognizes both the library needs of the general public and of the biomedical libraries, but the twain do *not* meet. Separate acts, as all of you know, provide monies for the two different functions of libraries in hospitals, and hospitals may not apply for aid under the Library Services and Construction Act. They may apply for money under the

Medical Library Assistance Act, but those who meet to grant the money under this latter Act, try though they may, cannot justify the grant of public funds unless the cause of good *biomedical* communication is advanced, especially when public libraries have received and are receiving federal money to extend their services as needed.

Thus my appeal to you. These reasons explain why lay library service in most United States hospitals has been under-emphasized. I believe that as long as present patterns persist, and until our present problems of providing adequate technical information sources have been solved, general library service in private hospitals in this country will not be given much attention unless public libraries give it.

NOTE

[1] A recent American Hospital Association survey listed over sixty kinds of specialized hospital personnel who need access to a library.

ABOUT THE AUTHOR–Barbara Coe Johnson is Director of Libraries at Harper Hospital, Detroit. She has been Patients Librarian and Medical Librarian of the Veterans Administration Hospital in Palo Alto, California. She received her A.B. in Classical Archaeology from Bryn Mawr and studied Greek and Archaeology at Columbia. Her B.L.S. is from the University of California (Berkeley).

She has held various offices in the Special Libraries Association, the American Medical Writers Association and the Medical Library Association, most recently being a member of its Board of Directors. Her interest in standards is shown in her participation on the Hospital Library Standards Committee of the Association of Hospital and Institutional Libraries of the American Library Association.

An Investigation of the Education Needs of Health Sciences Library Manpower: Part V: Manpower for Hospital Libraries

by David A. Kronick, Alan M. Rees, and Lesliebeth Rothenberg

While hospitals represent "the single largest groups of outlets for information," "less than one-half of all the hospitals in the United States provide [library] service less than half the time."

Among the national goals we have set for ourselves is one of developing an information network which will provide equal access, on demand, to the constantly growing body of health-related information for everyone in the health care system. Our concept of networks is based principally on our well-established telephone system,[1] which is essentially a system based on switching centers, whose purpose is to channel information or services in any direction. Like any system it is generally as strong as its weakest link. The information network can also be defined in terms of its terminals, which in this case are the people in the health care system who need information to make decisions, and who in a sense, encompass almost everyone in the system. The ultimate terminals, in other words, are of course, people, or rather single individuals, because information is passive unless it is converted into some form of behavior through its interaction with a nervous system. The hospital is, therefore, not the ultimate terminal in the health sciences information network, but probably one of the most important links or switching stations, because there is where the network has the potential of reacting with the largest number of people involved in the health care system.

Furthermore, all the indications are that this role of the hospital will continue to grow in the future, as our population and our economy expand and as we channel more of our income into health care. In defining national goals the increase in expenditures for health has been projected from 34 billion dollars in 1962 to 89.9 billion in 1975.[2] Increases in employment in health care are expected to double in the same period (Table 1). The total increase in employment in the health service industry will increase, it is estimated, from 2,700,000 in 1965 to 3,600,000 in 1975.[3] Approximately 65 percent of this total in 1965 were employed in a hospital setting. It has also been estimated that the number of hospitals will increase from 6,100 in 1968 to 7,400 and the number of beds to 1.9 million in 1976,[4] which means that hospitals are growing not only in number but in size. Between 1963 and 1968 the number of community hospitals increased by 2 percent, while the number of beds in these institutions increased by 16 percent.[5] Another indication of the importance of the hospital in the health care system is pointed out by the differences in the increase for the period between 1955-1965 for physicians in private practice (12 percent) with the increase for physician-directed services (81 percent) and hospital services (65 percent) for the same period.[6]

It is axiomatic that good library services are essential where education is taking place. The hospital has provided one of the major teaching environments for the health professions, and while its role in training in the allied health sciences is changing, the indications are that the hospital's educational

SOURCE: Reprinted from David A. Kronick, Alan M. Rees, and Lesliebeth Rothenberg, "An Investigation of the Education Needs of Health Sciences Library Manpower: Part V. Manpower for Hospital Libraries," *Bulletin of the Medical Library Association,* 59 (July, 1971), pp. 392–403, by permission of the publisher and the authors. This work was supported by a National Library of Medicine PHS Grant, LM 00493, to the University of Texas Medical School at San Antonio. Previous papers in this series have appeared in the *Bulletin,* 58: 7-17, Jan. 1970; 58: 510-20 Oct. 1970; 59: 21-30, 31-40, Jan. 1971. Paper IV appears on page 136 of this *Reader.*

TABLE 1*
EMPLOYMENT IN HEALTH CARE SYSTEM

	1962	1975	Percent Increase
Nurses	591,000	1,091,000	85
Physicians.	238,000	402,000	69
Technicians.	171,000	352,000	106
Hospital Attendants.	458,000	1,229,000	168
Nurses, practical . . .	254,000	575,000	126

*Lecht, L. A.[3]

role will continue to expand. In 1945 the ratio of medical students to interns and residents was 2:1, by 1955 it was 1:1, and by 1966 it was 3:4; that is, there were four individuals in postgraduate medical education programs for every three medical students. An analysis of 4,396 health-related educational programs not including post-graduate medical programs, revealed that 2,623 or 59.6 percent of these were hospital based.[7] Most of these, it is true, were allied health programs, and changes are being made in this area with the development of schools of the allied health sciences, and allied health programs based in the junior and senior colleges, but the hospital will nevertheless continue to provide the basis for most of the clinical training in this field.

Good systems planning is essential in order that good information services can be provided to this expanding network. Since availability of necessary manpower to staff the network is a critical element of the system, a study was begun in the spring of 1968 with the following stated objectives: (1) to determine manpower needs in current and future health science and library information services, (2) to describe the work force that was currently staffing these health-related libraries, (3) to determine what the existing and anticipated vacancies and attrition rates were, (4) to determine what kind of educational programs were required, particularly in continuing education, and (5) to survey and evaluate current and past programs for the training of health science librarians and information specialists. This paper is the fifth in a series of reports on the results of these investigations and is concerned with the hospital component of the institutional-program base which formed the population used for the study. This research was a cooperative effort of The University of Texas Medical School at San Antonio and Bureau of Business Research at Austin, and Case Western Reserve University Center for Documentation and Communication Research in Cleveland.

Ideally, the population base for the study might have been all those individuals who make up the total personnel resources of the health care system since they constitute the ultimate terminals of the system. Since most of the individuals involved in the system, however, organize themselves around institutions and programs, and because this population was manageable and easier to identify, the decision was made to base the survey on an inventory of all health-related institutions and programs in the United States. Two other related surveys were found to be in progress when the project was started: (1) the American Hospital Association had already started a survey in depth of hospital libraries, and (2) the American Medical Association was in process of planning a survey of health science libraries.[8] The decision was made, therefore, to rely upon the AHA survey to provide the needed data about hospital library personnel, and to collaborate with the American Medical Association to develop the library base required to study nonhospital library personnel in the interest of the very worthy objective of avoiding duplication in questionnaires. The methodology and results of this later study have been reported in a series of articles preceding this one.[9,10] This article is based on an analysis of the data produced by the American Hospital Association survey and supplied by the American Hospital Association, which constitute an important element in the composite picture of health-related library personnel in the United States.[11] Of the total of some 14,000 institutions and programs which were identified in the inventory of health-related institutions and programs, approximately half were hospitals, and half nonhospitals. The inventory, to be sure, was not exhaustive, first because no comprehensive directories of, for example, local public health units existed, and second, because the anticipated yield of health-related library manpower in these segments of the population was too small to justify the effort. The institutional-program survey concentrated, therefore, on those nonhospital institutions and programs where organized information and library services were likely to exist, and was for that reason oriented primarily toward educational and research facilities. Two thousand nine hundred eighteen hospitals responded out of a total of 6,018 which were sent questionnaires by the American Hospital Association representing a response rate for all hospitals of only 48.5 percent (Table 2). On first inspection this response rate seems to be exceedingly low, but the lowest response rate is in the hospital size group under 100

TABLE 2

RESPONSE RATE U.S. HOSPITALS

Hospital Bed Size	Total in Category	Respondents	Percent Responding
Under 49	1,513	440	29.1
50–99	1,422	519	36.5
100–199	1,274	630	49.5
200–299	636	428	67.3
300–399	384	294	76.6
400 and over . .	789	607	76.9
Total	6,018	2,918	48.5

N = 6,018.

beds, where traditionally very few of the hospitals are known to have libraries. If all the hospitals below 100 beds are removed from the population, the response rate becomes 67.5 percent which makes it more comparable to the returns from the nonhospital institutions and programs. This is not to imply that hospitals below 100 beds in size do not need libraries, nor to indicate that they do not need trained personnel. If these questions are decided in the affirmative we have here an indication of a large manpower gap, in terms of need at least, because we have no means here of estimating the demand. The response rate did tend to increase with the size of the hospital, but the issue is clouded somewhat because much of the data is reported in terms of numbers of libraries reported, and the 2,918 hospitals reported a total of 4,315 libraries under the options that were provided, or about 1.5 libraries per reporting hospital (Table 3). This ratio, however, only holds true when measured against the reporting hospitals. If the assumption is made that all of the hospitals which did not report did not have libraries, which is not an entirely invalid assumption, the ratio of 1.5 holds true only for the largest hospitals, and the ratio for the entire population is .69 libraries per hospital (Table 4, Fig. 1). A great deal of this discussion, of course, also hinges on the definition of the word library, and respondents to the AHA questionnaire were asked simply to respond separately for each unit they themselves designated as a "library," which may have ranged anywhere from a few outdated texts to a comprehensive medical library collection.

The data from the AHA survey relating to bud get, collection size, etc. of hospital libraries will, hopefully, be reported elsewhere, but in order to provide some insight into the quality of the libraries included, some of the summary data may be helpful here. The mean number of volumes in the collections of the libraries reported ranged from 195 volumes for the smallest category to 5,542 for the largest category. Book titles added per year ranged from fifteen titles to 170 titles. More significant perhaps, particularly as it relates to manpower involvement, is the number of hours the library is staffed per week by at least one person. (Alan Rees and his group at Case Western Reserve University use this as a criterion for the definition of a library. Their definition of a "functional library" is based on a library supporting personnel actually performing library tasks, a significant distinction which will be discussed below.) Here the range was from a mean of twelve hours per week for the smallest category to a mean of forty-two hours per week for the largest category,

TABLE 3

LIBRARIES AND LIBRARIANS
REPORTED BY U.S. HOSPITALS

Hospital Bed Size	Total Hospitals	Total Libraries	Total Libraries Without Patient Libraries	Total Librarians
Under 25 . . .	297	74	67	23
25–49	1,255	429	383	183
50–99	1,532	713	605	344
100–199 . . .	1,335	854	723	502
200–299 . . .	637	688	561	510
300–399 . . .	383	457	368	375
400–499 . . .	217	312	245	266
500 and over .	520	788	540	669
Total . . .	6,176	4,315	3,211	2,872

N = 6,167.

TABLE 4

AVERAGE NUMBER OF
LIBRARIES PER HOSPITAL

Hospital Bed Size	Number of Hospitals	Libraries Reported	Average No. Libraries
Under 25	297	74	.25
25–49	1,255	429	.34
50–99	1,532	713	.46
100–199	1,335	854	.64
200–299	637	688	1.08
300–399	383	457	1.29
400–499	217	312	1.44
Over 500	520	788	1.52
Total	6,176	4,315	.70

N = 6,176

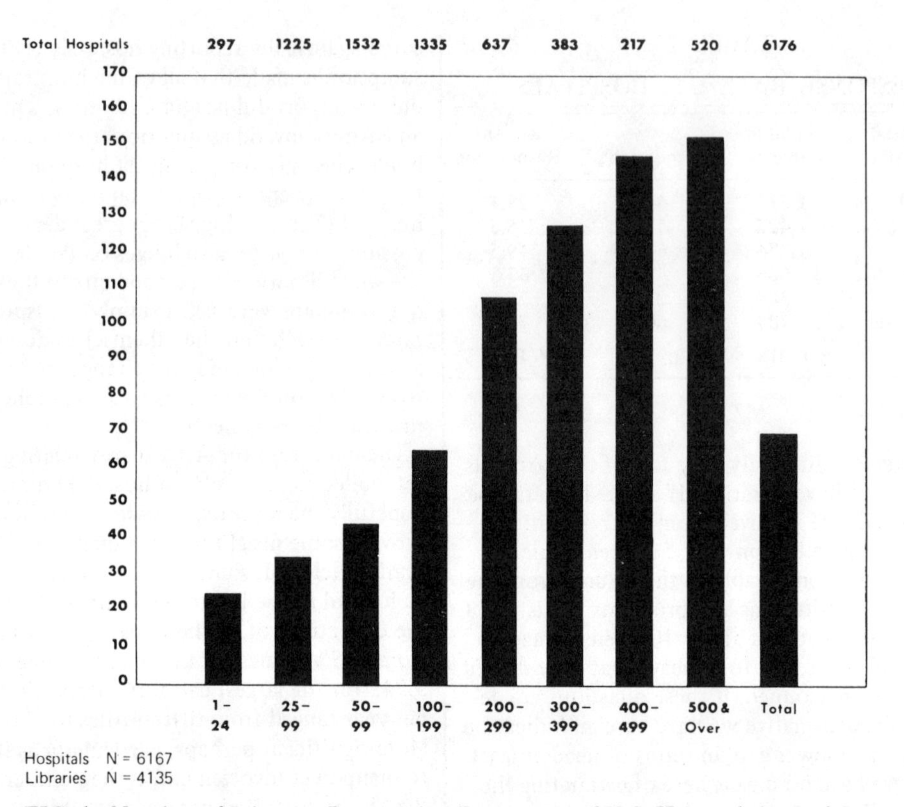

FIG. 1 Number of Libraries Reported as Percentage of U.S. Hospitals by Bed Size.

with a mean of twenty-five hours for the entire group. Theoretically, therefore, we could divide all the personnel reported in the survey by two, and come up with a fairly close approximation of the total number of full-time personnel involved in hospital libraries. Another complication that arises out of the survey is that patients' libraries were included in the survey; in fact, they constituted almost 20 percent of the number of libraries reported (Table 5). Strictly speaking, these libraries, important as they may be in terms of patients' welfare, are not really a part of the health science library population. Size of physical facilities is another criterion of quality of the libraries reported. Here the average square feet per library ranged from 167 sq. ft. for the smallest category to 2,389 sq. ft. for the largest category. One of the statistical anomalies in the survey occurred here, in that the average size of the library for the 100-199 bed category was reported as 2,173 sq. ft., while for the next highest category, 200-299 beds, it was reported as 985 sq. ft.

This is not the place to raise the question of standards for hospital libraries, or indeed the question of whether hospitals of certain bed capacity should have libraries at all, but it may be interesting to report some AHA data relative to this question from quite another source. As a part of its National Hospital Panel Survey for February 1969, which is based on a sampling of 5,872 community hospitals, the question was asked whether the hospital's library facilities were "presently inadequate," "adequate now but not in the future," or "adequate for only the next two to three years".[12] The response rate was projected to all the hospitals in the population, and varies somewhat over the various categories, but only 23 percent of the en-

TABLE 5

KINDS OF HOSPITAL LIBRARIES REPORTED

Kind	Number	Percent
Combined.	1,609	38
Physicians.	1,052	24
Nurses.	610	14
Patient-Medical.	57	7
Patient	823	19
Other	164	4
Total	4,315	100

N = 4,315.

tire population indicated that their facilities were presently inadequate (Table 6). The implications here are that over 75 percent of the hospitals regard their facilities as currently adequate. Considering what we know about the incidence of libraries in hospitals (58.6 percent of the hospitals had professional libraries in 1962),[13] we must infer that over 30 percent do not regard a library as a measure of hospital adequacy.

TABLE 6

PROJECTIONS FROM THE NATIONAL HOSPITAL PANEL SURVEY FEBRUARY
HOSPITALS REPORTING LIBRARY FACILITIES

No. of Hospitals	Presently Inadequate	Adequate Now, Not in Future	Adequate 2-3 Yrs.
5,872	23%	28%	49%
547	16%	18%	60%
1,439	21%	30%	49%
1,484	16%	28%	56%
1,139	26%	30%	44%
567	33%	23%	44%
302	40%	16%	44%
167	13%	41%	46%
240	35%	33%	32%

The AHA questionnaire asked for personnel to be reported under the following categories: librarian-in-charge, other librarians, clerical assistants, and other, and then to specify whether they were either full- or part-time salaried, or contributory or volunteered services. The 2,918 respondents reported 4,315 libraries which in turn reported 2,872 individuals under the rubrics for "librarians." Table 7 also shows data on the educational level for these librarians, because these data were elicited only under "librarian-in-charge" and "assistant librarian." This may be equated with the functional classification used in the second questionnaire for the nonhospital library population, but the comparison breaks down when we learn that only 26 percent of the "librarian" population of the hospital group have a master's degree or better (Figure 2) as against 42 percent of the entire population surveyed in the personnel survey of the nonhospital group. The 2,872 "librarians" reported, furthermore, represent only 51 percent of the total number of individuals reported as either full-time or part-time salaried personnel (Table 8). Of the total number of personnel reported by the respondent hospitals it can easily be seen (Figure 3) that about half of them pretty much across the board are non-

TABLE 8

SALARIED AND NONSALARIED PERSONNEL IN HOSPITAL LIBRARIES

	Salaried		Nonsalaried		Total	
Bed Size	No.	%	No.	%	No.	%
Under 25 . .	20	43	26	57	46	100
25–49	206	58	150	42	356	100
50–99	361	49	372	51	733	100
100–199. . .	620	50	605	50	1,225	100
200–299 . .	904	52	818	48	1,722	100
300–399 . .	819	52	752	48	1,571	100
400–499 . .	586	48	631	52	1,217	100
500 & Over .	2,143	59	1,503	41	3,646	100
Total . .	5,654	54	4,862	46	10,516	100

N = 10,516.

TABLE 7

EDUCATIONAL LEVEL OF LIBRARIANS

Hospital Bed Size	Libraries Reported	Librarians Reported	High School	Some College	B.A.	M.A.
Under 25	74	23	4	9	6	4
25–49	429	183	45	81	42	15
50–99	713	344	65	175	82	22
100–199	854	502	99	186	136	81
200–299	688	510	64	124	186	136
300–399	457	375	46	102	133	94
400–499	312	266	31	65	80	90
500 and Over.	788	669	64	135	186	284
Total	4,315	2,872	418	877	851	726

N = 4,315.

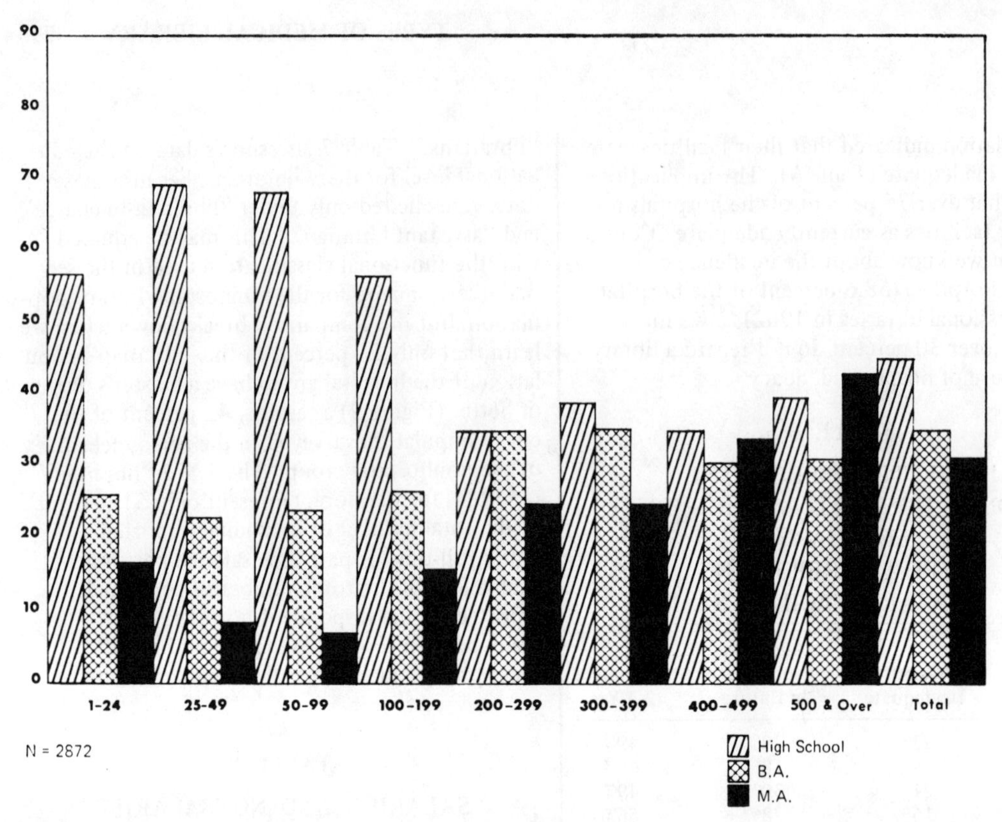

FIG. 2 Educational Attainment as Percentage of Librarians Reported by Hospital Bed Size.

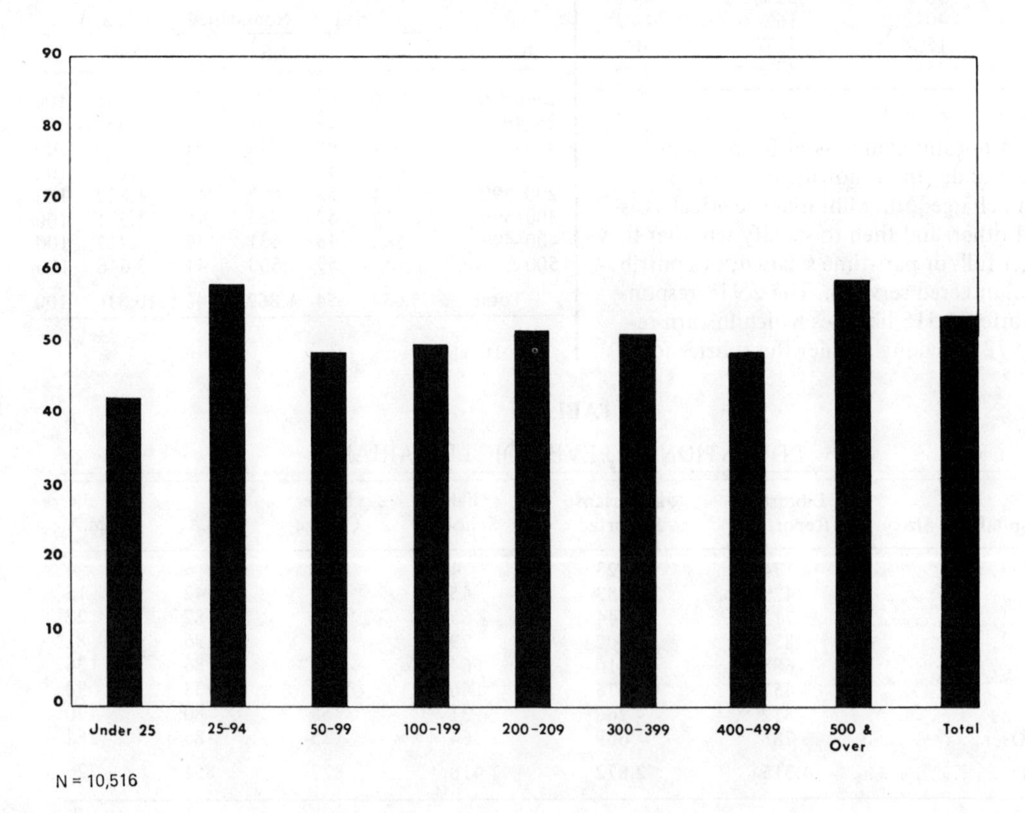

FIG. 3 Ratio of Salaried Personnel to Total Personnel by Hospital Bed Size.

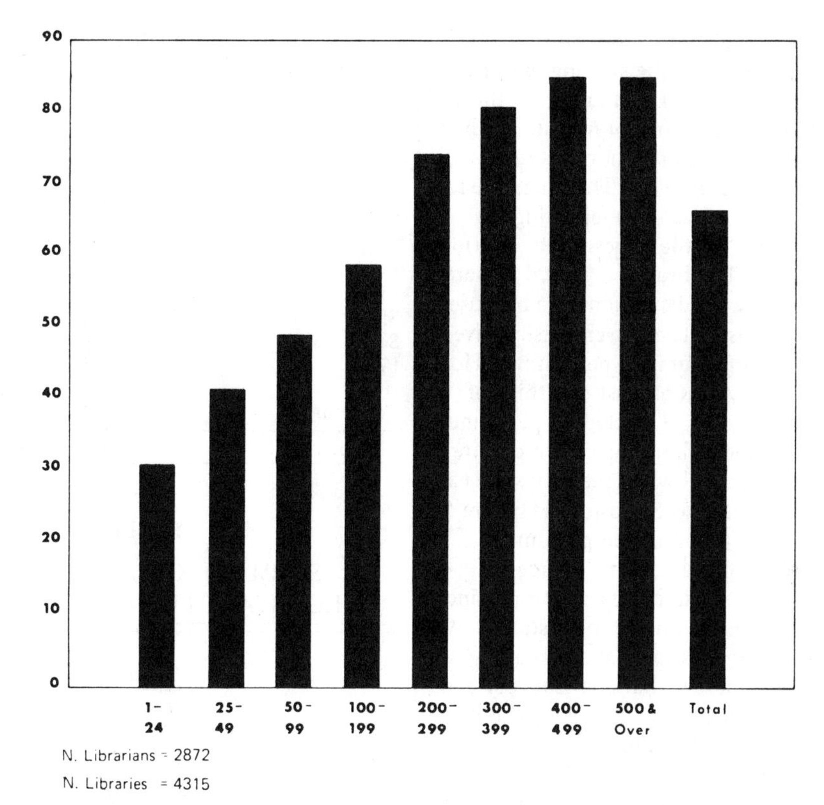

FIG. 4 Number of Librarians Reported as Percentage of Libraries Reported.

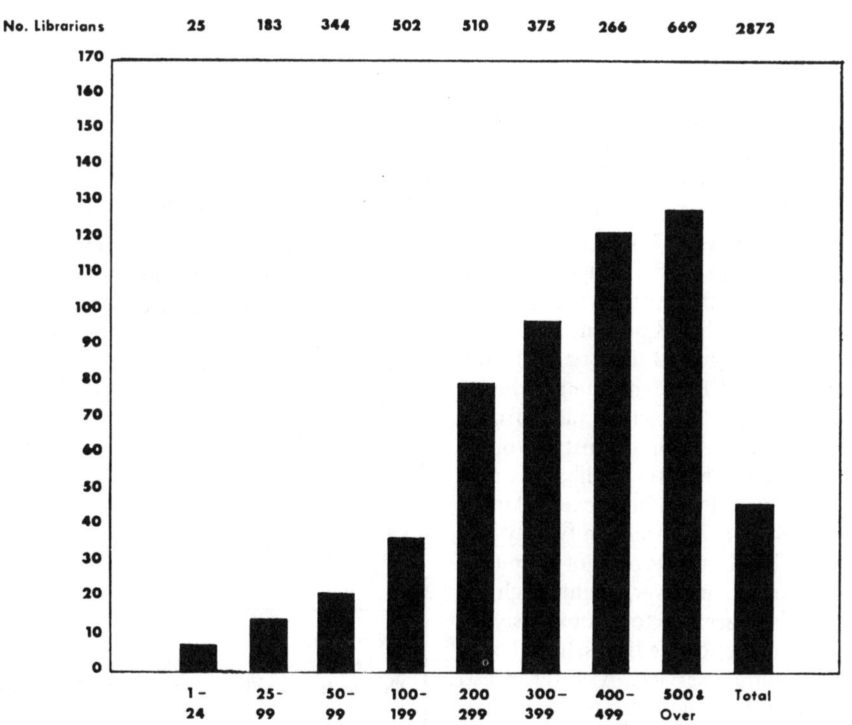

FIG. 5 Number of Librarians Reported as Percentage of U.S. Hospitals by Bed Size.

salaried, i.e. either contributory or voluntary. We can get another insight into the staffing patterns of these libraries, if we look at the number of "librarians" reported in each category of hospital by bed size, as a ratio of the number of libraries reported in the same category (Figure 4). The range is 31 percent for the smallest hospitals reporting libraries, to 85 percent for the largest, with a ratio of 67 percent for all the libraries reported. There is a good opportunity for distortion here because some of the larger hospitals may very easily have reported more than one librarian per library. However, we can easily say that at least one-third of the libraries reported are not staffed by personnel who could be reported as librarians. The picture becomes even more dismal when the ratios are calculated on the basis of all U.S. hospitals (Figure 5). The ratios of salaried to unsalaried personnel (Table 8) may be distorted to some degree by including patients' libraries in our calculations, since patients' libraries may tend more to be staffed by volunteer staff than professional staff libraries. However, it seems apparent that contributory and volunteer staff must also make up a significant part of the professional staff library personnel, since non-salaried personnel account for over 48 percent of the total number of personnel reported, whereas patient's libraries make up only 19 percent of all the libraries reported.

The research team at Case Western Reserve University had direct access to the AHA data on computer tapes and so were able to produce some analyses that were not available in the AHA-produced computer printouts. Their data on the staff size reported by each of the hospitals reporting, i.e. without respect to the number of libraries they reported, indicate that over 57 percent of the hospitals reported only one salaried individual staffing their library (Table 9), 80 percent as many as two staff members, and less than 8 percent five or more. These data also showed that for 3,211 hospitals reporting (Table 10) the median number of persons per hospital was two, with a range from one to ninety-four, and a mean of thirty-two, for the entire population. The fifty-six libraries reporting ten or more staff members, particularly since they averaged out to more than twenty-one, represented an affluence not typical of hospital libraries. On inspection, however, twenty-eight or over one-half of them seemed to be obviously reporting a medical center or medical school library as their source of library service. A closer investigation of the remainder might also reveal similar affiliations. When the volunteer personnel is elim-

TABLE 9

SIZE OF HOSPITAL LIBRARY STAFFS

Staff Size	No. of Hospitals	No. of Staff
One	1,507	1,507
Two	594	1,188
Three	225	675
Four	105	420
Five	64	320
Six	31	186
Seven	16	112
Eight	15	120
Nine	15	135
Ten or more	56	1,182
Total	2,628	5,845

TABLE 10

SUMMARY OF ALL REPORTED HOSPITAL* LIBRARY PERSONNEL

	Salaried		Contributory		
	FT	PT	FT	PT	Volunteers
Librarian-in-Charge	1,473	882	72	248	1,260
Other Librarians	555	255	23	71	518
Clerical Ass't.	841	744	22	110	426
All Others	167	772	39	278	1,811
Total	3,036	2,653	156	707	4,015

N = 10,567

*3,211 hospitals reported these personnel. The median number of persons per hospital library is two, the mean is thirty-two, and the range is one to ninety-four.

TABLE 11

SUMMARY OF HOSPITAL* LIBRARY PERSONNEL: SALARIED AND FULL-TIME CONTRIBUTORY PERSONNEL ONLY

	Salaried		Contributory
	FT	PT	FT only
Librarian-in-Charge	1,473	882	72
Other Librarians	555	255	22
Clerical Ass't.	841	744	39
All Others	167	772	39
Total	3,026	2,653	156

N = 5,845.

*2,628 hospitals reported personnel in these categories. The median number of persons per hospital library is one, the mean is twenty-two, and the range is one to ninety-four.

inated from the population the median drops to one, and the mean to twenty-two (Table 11).

Looking again at the educational qualifications reported by those individuals classified as librarians in the hospital survey (Figure 1), only 726 librarians were reported as having at least a master's degree. While we cannot equate the M.A. with the library degree in all cases (the question regarding subject major was asked but the data were not reported), nor can we say that all library degrees are indicated with the master's, we can say that almost 45 percent of the total number of individuals reported as librarians do not have any kind of a college degree.

COMPARATIVE STUDIES

It may be interesting to compare some of these data with earlier and with comparable studies. The research team at Case Western Reserve University conducted a survey of Ohio hospitals at about the same time that the AHA survey was taking place which does provide us with some results which can be compared with the Ohio data of the AHA survey.[14] In the AHA study, (Table 12), 123 Ohio hospitals out of a total of 232, reported 183 libraries, but only 123 "librarians," with a total of 259 for salaried personnel, while in the Case Western Reserve survey, for 220 hospitals surveyed, 148 libraries and at least 148 librarians were reported. The discrepancy is not nearly so great as appears, because Case Western Reserve counted only "functional" libraries, i.e. those that had personnel assigned to them.

TABLE 12

COMPARISON OF SURVEY DATA ON OHIO HOSPITALS

	Case-Western Reserve	A.H.A. Survey
Total Hospitals	220	232
Hospitals Reporting	220	123
Libraries Reported	148	183
Librarians Reported	148	125

It may also be informative to compare these results with the results obtained by AHA in their 1962 survey which attempted to gather similar information on the basis of a stratified sample and then projected their results to the entire hospital population.[13] The comparison shows remarkable similarities in some instances (Table 13) and just as remarkable differences in others. The growth in collection size may be rationalized to some degree on the basis of elapsed time, but it is extremely difficult to explain the differences in the total numbers of full-time staff reported.

There is one additional source of data about hospital library manpower which has not been previously reported. The data were collected for a survey of hospital manpower conducted in 1966 by the Bureau of Health Manpower, Public Health Service, and the American Hospital Association. They were not published in their *Summary Report*[15] because the numbers of medical librarians reported (2,347) represented what was considered too small a percentage of the total, so they were included with "All other professional and technical" personnel. It is nevertheless true that cytotechnologists (1,634) and social work assistants (1,467) were reported as separate categories. The unpublished data indicate that 5,342 hospitals responded out of 6,997 surveyed. They reported 2,347 librarians of whom 1,843 were full time and 504 were part time. A total of 602 of all the librarians reported held Medical Library Association certificates. The number of vacancies reported for 1966 was 602; of these, 449 of the positions called for trained medical librarians, i.e. with MLA certificates, a rather surprising number, because even taking the lower number of MLA certified librarians, it represents almost 20 percent of the reported work force. A projection of vacancies was also made for the following year of 1,210, of which 712 were for trained medical librarians.

SUMMARY AND CONCLUSIONS

Although the estimates of the existence of library service in hospitals resulting from this survey are complicated to some extent by the reporting of multiple libraries by many of the hospitals, there are still some generalizations that can be safely drawn. Despite the fact that the total number of hospital libraries reported in the 1968 AHA survey are equal to 70 percent of the total number of hospitals in the population, we can readily assume that the number of hospitals with libraries is considerably less, since the 70 percent figure includes more than one library reported by some hospitals. In the category below 100 beds, the total number of libraries reported is equal to only

TABLE 13

COMPARISON 1962 AND 1968,
AMERICAN HOSPITAL ASSOCIATION LIBRARY SURVEY

	Hospital Bed Size			
	1-99	100-399	400 & Over	Total
Number of Libraries				
1962	1,431	1,555	206	3,192
1968 (1)	1,116	1,874	737	3,827
Percentage of Hospitals				
1962	41.1	88.4	100.0	58.6
1968	36.2	80.0	100.0	61.8
Full-time Staff				
1962				863
1968 (2)				3,038
Part-time Staff				
1962				3,000
1968 (2)				2,616
Average Size of Collection				
1962				561
1968				1,939
Average Subscriptions				
1962				33
1968				76
Percent with College Degrees				
1962				54
1968				55
Total Personnel				
1962				3,904
1968				5,654

(1) Corrected for excess of libraries over hospitals in category.
(2) Salaried-only.

one-third of the total number of hospitals in that category. It is only when we go over 200 beds that we achieve some parity between numbers of hospitals and libraries, and yet almost three-fourths of U.S. hospitals fall into the category under 200 beds. Three thousand and one hundred hospitals or 51.5 percent of the total in the survey did not report the presence of a hospital library. While we cannot infer that all these do not have libraries, neither can we infer that all those institutions which did report libraries do indeed have library service which conforms to an acceptable definition of a library. Does a collection of books, no matter how large, constitute a library if no one is assigned to the responsibility for supervising it? The Case Western Reserve study defines the hospital library in terms of having individuals assigned to use it as a base for providing service. In this sense a library can exist with a minimum of books and journals and still provide excellent library service, as a switching center or channel to much wider resources than it could ever command itself.

A key element, therefore, in developing the hospital population as an adequately functioning part of the health sciences information network would be to develop an adequate staff of trained hospital library personnel. The question of how these personnel are to function and how they are to be trained is one that needs very much to be raised and answered. This analysis can only affirm that a very serious deficiency seems to exist. Fully one-third of the libraries reported in this study do not identify any member of their staff as a librarian. Although 4,315 libraries were reported, only 2,872 individuals were reported as librarians, and since some libraries reported more than one librarian per library, the percentage with qualified personnel is undoubtedly much lower. Furthermore, only about one-half of all the personnel is reported as being salaried. The deficiencies in library service are further reflected in the fact that the number of hours of service reported for all the hospital libraries averaged twenty-five hours per week. We have no firm data about the amount and kind of training that hospital library personnel enjoy, except that we can say that less than one third of all the personnel reported as librarians have a master's degree, which is tantamount to saying that less than that number are professionally trained librarians. Without too much insistence on the accuracy of the mathematics, the state of library service in hospitals in the United States could therefore be described as follows: less than one-half of all of the hospitals in the United States provide service less than half the time. Considering that hospitals represent the single largest group of outlets for information in our developing health sciences information network, this must be regarded as a serious systems deficiency.

NOTES

[1]Clapp, V. W. Public libraries and the network idea. Libr. J. Jan. 15, 1970:121–124.

[2]Lecht, L. A. Manpower Needs for National Goals in the 1970's. New York, Praeger, 1969. p. 23.

[3]*Ibid.* p. 74.

[4]McGibony, J. R. Principles of Hospital Administration. New York, Putnam's, 1969, p. 9.

[5]The national hospitals: a statistical profile. Hospitals. 43:463, Aug. 1, Pt. 2, 1969.

[6]National Advisory Commission on Health Manpower. Report. Washington, D.C., 1967. Vol. 1:7.

[7]Kronick, D. A.; Rees, A. M.; and Rothenberg, L. Educational Needs of Health Sciences Library Manpower. Report No. 1. Sources for Identifying Health Sciences Related Institutions and Supporting Data. Cleveland, Case Western Reserve University, Center for Documentation and Communication Research, 1969. p. 25.

[8]This project was also supported by the National Library of Medicine, PHS Grant LM 00493.

[9]Kronick, D. A.; Rees, A. M.; and Rothenberg, L. An investigation of the educational needs of health sciences library manpower. I. Definition of the manpower problem and research design. Bull. Med. Libr. Ass. 58:7–17, Jan. 1970.

[10]Rothenberg, L.; Rees, A. M.; and Kronick, D. A. An investigation of the educational needs of health sciences library manpower. Part 2. Health-related institutions and their library resources. Part 3. Manpower supply and demand in health sciences libraries. Bull. Med. Libr. Ass. 59:21–30, Jan. 1971.

[11]We would like to express our appreciation to the American Hospital Association and to Dr. Jon Miller, Director of their Division of Research, for making these data available to us.

[12]Unpublished data from the American Hospital Association.

[13]Giesler, R. H., and Yast, H. T. A survey of current hospital library resources. Hospitals 38:55-29, June 16, 1964.

[14]Rees, A. M., et al. Feasibility Study for Continuing Medical Education of Medical Librarians. Cleveland, Case Western Reserve University, Center for Documentation and Communication Research, 1968.

[15]Manpower Resources in Hospitals–1966, Summary Report of a Survey. Washington, Bureau of Health Manpower, 1966.

ABOUT THE AUTHORS–See pp. 145-146.

The Hospital Library

by Norman S. Stearns, Harold Bloomquist, and Wendy W. Ratcliff

Granted the difficult situation of libraries in hospitals described by Kronick et al. *(page 289), this paper is a "how to" description for librarians and hospital administrators, telling what can be done to build a dynamic hospital library with minimal resources.*

Early in 1968, the Postgraduate Medical Institute (PMI), a nonprofit educational corporation sponsored by the Massachusetts Medical Society, and the New England Regional Medical Library Service (NERMLS) joined forces to work toward an important common goal: the upgrading of health science libraries in community hospitals in New England. PMI had found that although these facilities generally were inadequate, there was enthusiasm for taking steps toward their improvement.

THE MEDICAL CORE LIBRARY

The earliest phase of the PMI-NERMLS program resulted in the creation of a medical core collection designed for use by physicians practicing in hospitals away from large medical centers.[1] Conceptually, the basic requirements of the core collection are that all major areas of medical practice be covered in the book collection, that a minimal number of high quality journals be included, that a carefully chosen collection of reference tools be acquired, and that all materials be readily accessible and logically arranged for use by health scientists. Along with the core collection, there are core requirements for space to house the library, for personnel, and for services. The "core," then, refers to the essential elements for a functional library.

The core library is viewed as a practical approach to stimulate interest in and to facilitate development of libraries in community hospitals as learning centers. The medical core library can serve as a primary tool both for patient care and for the continuing education of physicians and other health care personnel.

The feasibility of implementing the medical core library as part of an overall library development program that would include the training of library personnel was demonstrated in a study of 40 New England hospitals. The purpose of this article, therefore, is to provide guidelines for the development of total health science libraries in community hospitals, using the medical core collection as the basic stimulus. Special note should be made of the fact that separate core collections currently are being developed for nursing and for the allied health professions utilizing the same techniques of book and journal selection used for the creation of the medical core collection.[2] The concepts presented in this paper are applicable, therefore, to the development of the total health science library.

A NATIONAL NETWORK

Hospital educators should begin to view their own library facilities as part of an emerging network of biomedical information centers. Local facilities are not only the professional staff's pri-

---

SOURCE: Reprinted from Norman S. Stearns, Harold Bloomquist, and Wendy W. Ratcliff, "The Hospital Library–Parts 1 and 2," *Hospitals, Journal of the American Hospital Association*, 44 (Mar. 1 and 16, 1970), pp. 55–59 and 88–90, by permission of the publisher and the authors. The basic stimulus and the support for the PMI Library Development Program come from many sources including the National Library of Medicine through the New England Regional Medical Library Services at the Francis A. Countway Library of Medicine, the Tri-State Regional Medical Program (P.L. 89-239) and the Division of Physician Manpower, National Institutes of Health, U.S. Public Health Service.

mary reference resource but they also are a convenient mode of communication with the other, larger library services and collections available elsewhere. Indeed, the National Library of Medicine (NLM) has suggested the development of a national network of medical libraries using local hospital facilities as initial resources. This concept can be described as a pyramid of libraries with the libraries of community hospitals at the base and, proceeding upward, area libraries,[3] regional medical libraries, and the National Library of Medicine at the apex. Each level serves to back up and to supplement the resources of other levels.

The Medical Library Assistance Act of 1965 (P.L. 89-291) provided for the establishment of regional medical libraries[4] to bring the same level of library service to all health professionals regardless of their geographic location. The Francis A. Countway Library of Medicine in Boston and its New England Regional Medical Library Service was designated as the nation's first regional medical library. In its commitment to find the best ways to serve its region, NERMLS considers the development of libraries in community hospitals to be a primary component of its service. Until there are functional libraries in community hospitals, the regional library cannot function optimally.

To this end, a network of medical libraries is emerging in New England. Forty-four community hospitals are participating in the program along with area libraries that in turn relate to NERMLS at Francis A. Countway Library and ultimately to the National Library of Medicine. Library personnel in all of these institutions are endeavoring to provide and seek services in accordance with a reciprocal "network" concept.

THE HOSPITAL LIBRARY

Because they are the primary facilities for practitioners, community hospitals should no longer look at their libraries merely as collections of books and journals that must be maintained as one more requisite for accreditation. These libraries can and indeed should become vital centers within the hospital devoted to learning and to patient care. Professional health and medical associations have expressed the need for increased efforts in the continuing education of their members, and recent legislation calling for a more comprehensive and regional approach to patient care[5-7] emphasizes that the total body of available knowledge should be accessible to every health care practitioner.

These factors, plus the National Library of Medicine's Regional Medical Library Program, should provide strong incentive to community hospitals everywhere to survey their existing libraries and to undertake serious efforts to improve these facilities, or to consider the establishment of needed facilities. As patient care, teaching, and research programs increase, library needs also will increase.

The person who initiates support for library development might be a medical staff member, a director of medical education, a service chief, an administrator, a trustee, a nurse, or some other member of the hospital team. The following guidelines are offered to the individual or individuals who might be responsible for the library development program.

OBJECTIVES AND MORAL SUPPORT

Library development in community hospitals should be devoted to the establishment of a collection of books and introduction of services that will best serve the staff of the institution.

Both moral and financial support are basic to the development of a hospital library program, and both are necessary if the program is to be successful. Money that is not backed by interest and enthusiasm buys expensive dust collectors. The support of interested physicians on the staff should be secured by the director of medical education or by a physician with a special interest in books. The hospital administrator and trustees should view the library as a long-term investment and must be convinced of the importance of the library as a tool for continuing education.

A library committee should be appointed to work with the librarian and the administrator. The committee should include representatives of the major hospital divisions or services, such as medicine, pediatrics, surgery, and so on, and, because the library should develop into a facility to service the entire health care team, the committee should include nurses and other health professionals in its membership.

The library committee's function should be advisory; it should recommend to the librarian and to the administrator policies that will benefit the hospital's health team. Appointees to the library committee should be able and willing to meet frequently during the initial phases of the program and thereafter on a regular basis, perhaps four times a year.

FINANCIAL SUPPORT

The basic source of continuing financial support for a library program should be hospital operating funds. There are several sources of supplementary funding that also should be considered, however. For example, it is possible to obtain funds for library collections, personnel, and training from Medicare.[8] A current study indicates that not all hospital administrators are aware of these funding sources. The authors suggest that administrators check other third-party payers to determine whether library costs are reimbursable under certain of the major plans. Library programs sponsored by the various Regional Medical Programs (not to be confused with the Regional Medical Library Programs) also should be investigated. Resource grants from the National Library of Medicine have been awarded to some community hospitals. The possibility of financial support from the professional staff also should be considered. The core collection is a package that has appealed to local foundations as tangible evidence of support to the community's hospital. In any event, multiple funding sources are ideal because they promote and encourage the interest of many persons.

A budget for the library should be drafted annually by the librarian, reviewed by the library committee and the fiscal officer of the hospital, and submitted to the administrator as a proposal. The budget should provide for salaries, books, journal subscriptions, reference tools, binding, communications, supplies, travel, and physical maintenance.

CORE COLLECTION COST

The initial cost of the medical core collection including books, journals, and reference tools is approximately $2000. The primary cost of establishing this initial collection should be viewed as a capital expenditure and should not be budgeted as operating funds. Maintenance of the medical core collection, including book substitutions and annual journal subscriptions, will cost about $650 a year. Therefore, the library budget should include projected rather than current costs of salaries and materials and should take into account the rising prices of indexes, books, journals, and collection maintenance.

A library budget must be realistic in terms of providing sufficient library services to support the hospital's goals for continuing education and patient care. Hospital libraries, when viewed as health learning centers, should not be underrated as service facilities. Starting with a good book and journal collection, the library should grow into a total information center and should include the audio-visual devices and highly developed communications media that are now available. The potential for the shared use of these devices among several departments within a hospital, or even among several institutions in one community (not necessarily all health-oriented), might well bring them within financial reach.

PERSONNEL

A first priority in the development of a new or expanded library requires the hiring of a qualified person to supervise the library operation. The many questions and details of a library's function cannot be resolved without a skilled person who can devote at least several hours each day to library matters. A modern health science library is much less a repository for medical literature than it is a vital center for information services; such services can be mobilized only through the concentrated efforts of a properly trained individual.

There is not enough available manpower, nor is it necessary, to staff every community hospital library with a graduate librarian (an individual holding a baccalaureate degree plus a master's degree in library science). Intelligent, service-oriented, nongraduate personnel can be trained to service these facilities.[9] Valuable assistance also can be obtained from library consultants at area or regional libraries.

The properly trained nongraduate librarian's salary should be between $5000 and $6000 per year based on a full-time schedule. This range will vary depending upon local wage scales and cost-of-living indexes. Although the title "librarian" is most descriptive of the position, other titles might be used, especially in situations in which rigid personnel classifications place the position of "librarian" in a disadvantageous salary range. "Library supervisor" and "library service manager" are examples of titles that have been used with some frequency.

In many hospitals responsibility for the library is delegated to the medical record librarian. In spite of the terminology, medical record work does not always lend itself to integration with library work. Certainly the medical record department should not be physically merged with a health science library. If the medical record librarian acts as an assistant or works part time in the library, however, she should have special training in medical library work in order to stimulate her interest in the library and to prepare her for the functions of this new role.

It is possible that the position of librarian can be filled on a part-time basis until the library actually becomes a health learning center demanding the full-time services of the librarian. Two hours per day is the minimum amount of time that a part-time librarian should be on duty.

THE LIBRARIAN'S ROLE

It is possible and even desirable for the librarian to have other responsibilities in the hospital. For example, a most effective combination of responsibilities could be that of librarian and educational secretary to the director of medical education or to the medical staff. The services of the librarian could be used for preparing an inhouse newsletter, helping with annual reports and staff publications, maintaining and operating audio-visual equipment, and helping with the scheduling of rounds and conferences. Regardless of her responsibilities outside the library, she should be available when in the hospital to perform library services for the medical staff upon request. It is important that her hours in the library be specified and well publicized to the staff.

The possibility of two or more neighboring hospitals sharing one trained librarian should be considered.[10] In this way, a highly qualified librarian could be paid a much higher salary than any one institution could afford. This "shared" librarian also would be thoroughly familiar with the holdings of each library and would, therefore, be able to arrange loans of materials among the institutions. She could, in fact, act as a kind of information liaison as she familiarizes herself with the educational and scientific programs of each institution.

The hospital librarian should attend, if possible, the regional group meetings of the Medical Library Association as well as other regional or local library meetings. This will provide an additional opportunity for communication with peers. Information about such meetings can be obtained from area or regional libraries.

The amount of supportive personnel needed to operate the library will depend mainly upon the duties of the librarian and the number of hours the library is open. Some part-time clerical and monitoring help probably will be needed. Volunteers often are used successfully in hospital libraries.

DEVELOPING THE COLLECTION

At the very least there should be a core collection of books and journals that provides comprehensive coverage of all the major areas of medical practice, including essential materials in nursing and the allied health professions. A list of specific books and journals for the core collection is less important than adherence to the concept of comprehensive coverage with materials that are authoritative and current. Beyond the core collection, library materials should reflect the specific interests and needs of the hospital's professional staff including physicians, nurses, and others.

The following guidelines for developing the collection reflect the writers' experience in implementing the medical core as a practical beginning for developing a health science library. Hospital administrators have stated that the knowledge of such suggestions has increased their understanding of the problems involved in library development and also has heightened their desire to develop this facility as an education tool that will be highly useful to the entire health care team.

1. Modern library practice favors a single operation encompassing medical, nursing, and any other health science collections in the hospital. All scientific collections should be physically merged if possible or at least administered by the same librarian. It is also good practice to have the patients' library, if there is one, administered by the library supervisor. Patients should not be allowed to read or browse in the health science library.

2. In an already existing library, the book collection should be subjected to careful weeding with the help of professional staff and a graduate librarian. Resale or exchange value of outdated material should be determined.

TABLE 1

GENERAL CORE REFERENCE SUGGESTIONS

Abridged Index Medicus. Bethesda, Md.: National Library of Medicine, 1970. Monthly, $12 prepaid from U.S. Government Printing Office, Washington, D.C.

American Medical Dictionary, 24th ed. Chicago: American Medical Association, 1967. Parts I, II, III, $60.

Cumulated Index Medicus. Bethesda, Md.: National Library of Medicine, 1960. Annual, $72.25 prepaid from U.S. Government Printing Office, Washington, D.C.

Current Medical References, 6th ed. Chatton, M. J. and Sanazaro, P. J., editors. Los Altos, Calif.: Lange, 1969. $12.

Current Therapy. Conn, H. F., editor. Philadelphia: Saunders, 1969. Annual, $15.

Directory of Medical Specialists Holding Certification by American Specialty Boards, Vol. 13. Chicago: Marquis, 1968. $30.

Dorland's Illustrated Medical Dictionary, 24th ed. Philadelphia: Saunders, 1965. $13.

Hospitals, Journal of the American Hospital Association. Chicago: The Association. Semimonthly, $10, Guide Issue, Aug. 1, $7.50.

International Classification of Diseases Adapted for Use in the United States, PHS Publication No. 1693. Washington, D.C.: National Center for Health Statistics, 1968. Vol. 1 (tabular list), $3.25; Vol. 2 (alphabetical list), $4.50 prepaid. (Washington, D.C.: U.S. Government Printing Office.)

Journal of the American Medical Association. Chicago: The Association. Weekly, $23.

Webster's Seventh New Collegiate Dictionary. Springfield, Mass.: Merriam, 1965. $6.75.

World Almanac and Book of Facts, 1970. New York: Newspaper Enterprise Association, Inc., 1969. Annual, $1.95.

3. Files of medical journals should not exceed five years. A shorter cutoff date may be adopted if space is a problem. Existing bound volumes older than the agreed upon cutoff date should be offered for sale or exchange or disposed of annually. It should be noted here that binding reduces physical wear and loss as well as time needed to keep the collection in order. However, pamphlet boxes or other containers are less expensive alternatives to binding.

4. In the establishment of a new library, it is advisable to begin journal runs with the first issue of the current year. Materials needed from previous years may be obtained through interlibrary loan in original form or as photocopies.

5. The library should become an institutional member of the Medical Library Association (MLA). This membership makes available to the librarian the services of the MLA Exchange[11] to which she can send books and journals that are not useful. By the same token, she can select, from frequently published lists, books and journal issues that fill important gaps in the local library's collection.

6. Valuable tools in any library are complete back runs of indexes and abstracting journals—*Index Medicus* and the new *Abridged Index Medicus* being the most important. These and other reference tools (see Table 1) can be used to identify useful material that may be in the library collection or that can be obtained elsewhere. The reference collection also should include the local regional medical library's union list of periodicals.

Several lists[12-14] of suggested books and journals are available and should be consulted for relevant titles as backup collections are being developed.

7. It should be remembered that it is more economical to place all book or periodical orders with a single dealer (geographically located as close as possible) than it is to order directly from individual publishers.

8. Gifts, however well intentioned, should be added to the library only if they fall within the scope and the depth of the vital library collection. An established, publicized policy about accepting gifts can prevent embarrassing situations.

9. There is no necessity for original cataloging. Cataloging information may be obtained from area or regional libraries.

LOCATION IS IMPORTANT

Hospital libraries all too frequently have been cramped into out-of-the-way quarters—an annex to the record room or a converted boiler room in the basement.[15] If the hospital library is to assume its potential role as a health learning center, careful thought and planning must go into the housing of its services.

Top priority must be given to finding the best location for the health science library. Since its initial location may establish important utilization patterns, it should be located in an area that is easily accessible to most professional staff members. If there is a choice between locating the library in a small room that is centrally located and a large room away from the center of its user population, the library should be located in the smaller area. As professional staff members begin to rely on the services of the library, their use patterns will suggest the importance of the library as a service facility and will serve as an argument for expansion. If the collection is located in the larger, remote area, however, its use will be minimal, and the library's reputation as a seldom-used facility will be perpetuated.

While every attempt should be made to acquire adequate space for library functions, hospitals should not be deterred from developing library programs because of initial space limitations. Some hospitals have adapted storage areas for use as libraries. Such areas, which provide ample space to house the core collection and a few comfortable reading chairs and a desk, can be used satisfactorily until larger quarters can be found.

Any decision to locate or relocate a library should be preceded by a careful study of the library's role in the hospital. Planning should first involve the librarian, the administrator, the library committee, and a representative of the board of trustees. This group should then present a plan to an architect. Primary traffic patterns of physicians and other members of the health care team should be determined by the observation of traffic flow. Some technical matters should be explored, including a determination of the structural ability of the floor area to bear the weight of loaded book shelves.

The library deserves a room of its own. A room that is a multi-purpose facility used for luncheons, committee meetings, staff social gatherings, and classroom activities is not conducive to use as a library. A staff member who wants to consult a book quickly doesn't want to wait until the end of a class hour to get the item he needs.

PLAN FOR GROWTH

Two dimensions of library growth should be considered–first, the normal increase in materials, number of users, staff, and service programs; and, second, the new and expanded services necessitated by program changes and expansion. Minimum space needed to house the medical core collection, including five-year runs of journals, is 320 linear feet of shelving. Additional space will be required to house indepth medical collections and the core collection that has been developed for nursing[16] and the one that is being developed for the allied health professions.

The library should house all of its materials in one place. The storage of materials in inaccessible places is not satisfactory. Special collections located in hospital departments, though not necessarily cataloged as part of the library, should be known to the librarian. These collections, however, can be useful supplements to the primary library collection only if they can be made available to all members of the staff and if they can be controlled by the librarian.

Because users vary in their reading habits and requirements, reader accommodations should vary if possible. For example, individual study carrels in addition to traditional study tables could be made available. Planners should allow 25 to 30 square feet per reader. In order to provide for the future use of television or other audio-visual devices, some seating should be designed to accommodate special wiring, acoustical treatment, and lighting needs. The work space provided for the library staff ideally should be based on an allowance of 150 to 175 square feet per person.

Although the library should be functional and efficient, esthetic considerations should not be neglected. In addition to its prime function as a service center, the library can be a retreat where busy staff members can relax and use free moments for learning. Comfortable furniture, in addition to standard library tables and chairs, should be provided. The library should be imaginatively decorated, the room and its collections should be appealing, and the lighting and ventilation should be at comfortable levels.

LIBRARY SERVICES

Health scientists in community hospital settings frequently avoid the use of scientific literature available through the hospital library as a tool for their continuing education. This attitude may stem from a historical lack of available library services to aid them in their use of the literature. If, as suggested by Michael, the library can "abandon its traditional passive role of being a repository of information, guarded jealously by the librarian like a pack rat, and assume an aggressive, dynamic posture,"[15] the possibility of the library serving as an important tool for continuing education is within sight.

"Core" library services–the fundamental, essential services that a hospital library should perform, include: (1) ordering materials, making them available on the shelves, attending to the daily routines that make a library an efficient and pleasant facility to use; (2) lending materials to users; (3) arranging interlibrary loans; and (4) making available equipment for facsimile copying. Secondary services include (1) providing short answers to specific questions; (2) performing brief literature searches; and (3) verifying citations in the literature. Ideally, the busy health professional requiring a book, a journal article, or a specific fact should have only to make his need known to the librarian in order to obtain it. The librarian, without involving the user in behind-the-scenes machinery, should produce the necessary document or pieces of information in the form in which it is required and, if possible, at the place and the time when it is most useful to the user.

If the user is in the library, the core collection, properly arranged and clearly labeled, offers several advantages. Because the collection is small yet comprehensive, the practitioner can use it with ease and can quickly locate desired materials without consulting a card catalog or a librarian. The core materials then may lead him to seek further references, which the librarian should be prepared to provide.

Ideally, material in the core collection should not be borrowed from the library room except under special circumstances. A reserve or noncirculating collection is useful because a staff member is assured that the specific item he is looking for is on the shelves. Materials not in a reserve collection should be available for use outside the library.

The library should have available inexpensive and rapid photocopy service so that material can be copied and removed from the library. Coin-operated copy machines are available for such purposes at no cost to the library.

Accurate statistics should be kept to document objectively the library's use; these statistics also will establish the hours of heaviest use so that the library can be adequately staffed during those times.

The library should be available to its users *at all times*. "A physician who desires to use newer potent agents for a life threatening cardiac arrhythmia at 2 a.m. cannot wait until 8 a.m. to consult the latest journals on dose and techniques.[15] It is less expensive to replace a few books than to deny accessibility to the library; total library accessibility can be facilitated by making a key available in a well known and conveniently located place.

COMMUNICATION

The librarian should make every attempt to acquaint herself with the collections of scientific literature in her area, whether they are in hospital, public, university, medical school, or medical society libraries. There are materials in each of these collections that at some time will be useful to members of the health team at her hospital. She should, in turn, make efforts to acquaint other librarians with the collection at her institution. These important goals can be achieved by various methods, including the exchange of catalog cards, the exchange of shelf lists, a compilation of local union lists (composite lists of the holdings of local libraries), and most important, visits to other libraries and effective communication with other librarians.

An efficient interhospital loan service can be set up among hospitals when the librarians know each other and their respective collections. Some of the more formal procedures for obtaining materials from area or regional libraries can be avoided within this small subnetwork.

The coordination of purchases among several local hospitals for materials beyond the basic collection, or in special subject areas, also will be approached more realistically if the librarians involved are knowledgeable about the holdings of other libraries.

WATS (Wide Area Telephone Service) lines are being installed in a number of regional and area libraries. Hospital libraries within the region or area can telephone the larger library, using a special number, at the cost of a local call. Thus a hospital librarian who has a reference question that she cannot answer using materials in her own library, or who has an urgent interlibrary loan request, can use the telephone no matter what the distance without incurring a long-distance charge.

MEDLARS

Each regional medical library area contains a search center for MEDLARS (the National Library of Medicine's Medical Literature Analysis and Retrieval System). MEDLARS is a computer-based index to the international medical literature. A request for a search on a particular subject—generated, for example, by a physician in a health science library—can be telephoned or mailed by the hospital librarian to the search center, where it will be formulated logically into machine language and run on a computer. The resulting bibliography of articles on the specific subject then will be mailed to the requester within several weeks. There is no charge for MEDLARS searches.

MEDLARS II, now in its developmental stages, will permit the user to sit at a typewriter terminal directly connected with a computer for his own search, the results of which then would be typed out immediately at the terminal. A preview of this kind of service is in operation in the State University of New York's Biomedical Communications Network, which links several northeastern medical libraries. Searches can be formulated by the users themselves, using remote computer terminals, as described above. A regional and area library that is part of this network can use this system (called SYMBIOSIS) to produce bibliographies for library users in its region or area.

The librarian should know her particular library users; she should learn their special areas of practice; and she should take the initiative to call to their attention items of particular interest as they appear in the literature. One of the great advantages of a small library situation is the ability of the interested librarian to provide personalized service.

The librarian should keep the hospital staff informed about additions to the collection. Some services in this area are a regularly compiled list of recent acquisitions; personal notification of new titles to those who specifically requested them and to those whose area of practice would indicate special interest; and a display of new books or the dust jackets of new books.

The librarian should be able to do literature searches and verify bibliographic citations for her users who are publishing papers, or arrange to have these services performed elsewhere on her readers' behalf.

The librarian will need to provide interpretations of library policy so that users can be informed regarding services, hours of service, scope of the collection, and general principles of operation. A library guide or newsletter is an effective way to inform library users about library policy.

The librarian should consider her role as an educator–library users will look to her for guidance in the optimal use of library tools. She should be able to impart a basic understanding of the scope of the library and its place in the overall hospital educational program.

When the librarian has problems that appear insoluble, particularly those of a technical nature, she should not hesitate to call upon librarians in the area or regional libraries. In most cases these librarians will be delighted to help; in fact, in many cases such consultation services are part of the area or regional libraries' programs.

NOTES

[1]Stearns, N. S. and Ratcliff, W. W. A core medical library for practitioners in community hospitals. *New Engl. J. Med.* 280:474 Feb. 27, 1969.

[2]Bloomquist, H. The hospital's library. *New Engl. J. Med.* 280:503 Feb. 27, 1969.

[3]Area libraries are the large to medium-sized libraries that presently are providing services on a subregional basis to other libraries in their geographic area. They are neither designated nor funded by the NLM Regional Library Program, nor by their own regional library to perform these services, although in some cases they have received federal funds to aid in this work.

[4]Regional medical libraries are described in this volume in the final section.

[5]Regional Medical Programs. Public Law 89-239.

[6]Comprehensive Health Planning. Public Law 89-749.

[7]Veterans Hospitalization and Medical Services Modernization Amendments of 1966. Public Law 89-785.

[8]U. S. Department of Health, Education, and Welfare, Social Security Administration, *Provider Reimbursement Manual: Health Insurance for the Aged*, HIM-15, 1968.

[9]Two training institutes have been held at Francis A. Countway Library and courses are available in other regions of the country. Especially noteworthy is the library service institute sponsored by the American Hospital Association.

[10]Feltovic, H. F. Six coordinated medical libraries. *Bull. Med. Libr. Assn.* 52:670 Oct. 1964.

[11]MLA membership also brings the *Bulletin of the Medical Library Association* (quarterly) and the *MLA News* (quarterly), the two major publications dealing with health science librarianship. Such membership also places the librarian in a milieu in which she can benefit from the experiences of others. Institutional membership is $50 per year; information may be obtained from the Executive Secretary, MLA, 919 North Michigan Ave., Chicago, Ill. 60611.

[12]Blair, E. D. Basic reference aids for small medical libraries. *Bull. Med. Libr. Asso.* 55:160 April 1967.

[13]Brandon, A. N. Selected list of books and journals for a small medical library. *Bull. Med. Libr. Assn.* 57:130 April 1969.

[14]Yast, H. T. 90 recommended journals for the hospital's health science library. *Hospitals, J.A.H.A.* 41:59 July 1, 1967.
[15]Michael, M. The medical library's vital role in physicians' continuing education. *Hosp. Progr.* 49:92 Oct. 1968.
[16]Stearns, N. S., *et. al.* A core nursing library for practitioners. *Amer. J. Nurs.* 70: 818–823 April 1970.

ABOUT THE AUTHORS–Dr. Norman S. Stearns is Professor of Medicine, Tufts University Medical School. The accompanying paper was written while he was Executive Director of the Postgraduate Medical Institute, Boston, the education arm of the Massachusetts Medical Society, and Director of Medical Education at Newton-Wellesley (Mass.) Hospital and Waltham (Mass.) Hospital. Other positions he has held include Clinical Associate in Medicine at the Harvard Medical School and Postgraduate Research Fellow of the National Heart Institute at Boston University and at Harvard University. He received his bachelor's degree from Harvard College and an M.D. and M.A. in Pharmacology from Boston University.

Mr. Bloomquist's activities are described on page 184.

Mrs. Wendy Ratcliff Fink is currently Technical Associate, New England Regional Medical Library Service, and Planning Consultant, Office of Health Care Education of the New England Hospital Assembly, Inc., and the New England Center for Continuing Education. She was Director, Library Development Program, Postgraduate Medical Institute, at the time this article was written.

With Alan Rees and Helen Yast, Dr. Stearns and Mr. Bloomquist are editing a text, *Library Practice in Hospitals: A Basic Guide*, to which Mrs. Fink has contributed chapters.

Medical School Libraries

For many years, the medical school library was the typical medical library and it continues to have better facilities and resources than the hospital library. With increased funds for research in medical schools, an imbalance between library resources and those of the school became apparent. Scott Adams called the attention of educators to the libraries' plight in 1962. Subsequently the Association of American Medical Colleges established two committees to furnish guidelines and recommendations for the role of medical school libraries and their support which could be used by administrators. Introductions to the two Committee reports are included.

The last section of this *Reader* completes the story of the medical school libraries, since they are now beginning to function as nodes in the library networks described there.

Medical Libraries Are In Trouble

by Scott Adams

This paper is historical, telling of the depressed situation of medical school libraries in the early 1960's. This was before action by the Association of American Medical Colleges, the President's Commission on Heart Disease, Cancer and Stroke and the Congress. The paper suggests a program, many parts of which have subsequently been achieved.

Ten years ago the Survey of Medical Education in its report, *Medical Schools in the United States at Mid-Century,*[1] discussed the plight of the medical libraries. The Deitrick report noted that all was not well. In the ten years preceding the report, expenditures for research had increased eightfold, whereas the amounts spent on libraries by the 59 schools had but doubled. This lag had had a depressing effect on the supporting services which the libraries could provide. The report concluded that "little evidence was found by the Survey of attempts to meet the libraries' increased needs during a period of tremendous expansion in the research and other activities of the schools. Faculty members, research workers, and students," it continued, "will be severely handicapped unless the new demands placed upon the libraries are met by careful administrative and budgetary planning. In a nation dependent upon medical research to a greater degree than ever before, surprisingly little is being expended on the housing of the reports of that research and on making those reports available."

Today, ten year and some hundreds of millions of research dollars later, it is stated with increasing frequency that the medical libraries are worse off than ever before. In November 1961, the National Advisory Health Council submitted a resolution to the Surgeon General. "The medical library network," the resolution reads, "which has been designed to make the published record of medicine available, is in dire trouble. During a period of intensive development of research institutions, medical schools, and other medical facilities, their essential library support has been seriously neglected. In recent years, the needs for adequate library working and storage space, for more trained library personnel, and for new methods of handling and disseminating the growing scientific medical literature have become acute."

The National Advisory Health Council is but one of several groups which have described the medical library situation as critical. For years medical librarians have pointed out the deficiencies in their institutions, medical educators in many instances have joined with them, and research administrators are increasingly concerned.

Where does the school library in fact stand today in its efforts to service the twin requirements of medical education and research? Have the libraries kept pace or lagged? Are they, or are they not adequate for the purposes of modern biomedical research? In order to provide some current data from which an estimate of progress, or lack of it, over the past ten years could be made, the National Library of Medicine asked the Assistant Librarian of the Harvard University Schools of Medicine and Public Health, Harold Bloomquist, to collect data. His study collected information from 84 schools as compared to the 59 schools covered by Deitrick. Within the time limitation, it could not be an extensive inquiry; the selected data offered here must be considered preliminary.

LIBRARY SUPPORT

We might first look at the financial resources available for library development. The total

SOURCE: Reprinted from Scott Adams, "Medical Libraries Are in Trouble," *Library Journal*, 88 (July, 1963), pp. 2615–2621, by permission of the publisher and the author. Published by R. R. Bowker (a Xerox Company) copyright © 1963, R. R. Bowker Company. This paper, originally presented before the Association of American Medical Colleges in Los Angeles, October 1962, was originally reprinted with permission from the January 1963 issue of the *Journal of Medical Education.*

amount spent in 1961 by the schools on their medical libraries was $5,030,000. This compares to the $1,377,000 spent in 1951 by 59 schools. Over the same period, the *total* expenditures of the schools grew from $91,347,000 to $328,158,-000. The average library's share of the total expenditures has therefore remained constant at 1.5 per cent. One important school, however, reported a decrease from 1.9 to 1.2 per cent. Compared to the increase of funds spent for sponsored research, however, the average library share has declined. Research funds increased four-fold during the same period to a 1961 total of $135,000,-000. The percentage of library expenditures related to research funds decreased from 4.1 to 3.7 per cent.

Several points can and should be made. First, one and one-half percent of the total expenditures was not adequate in the opinion of the 1951 Survey to meet the current needs of 1951, much less to repair the then accumulated deficits. Second, this percentage is even less adequate today. The median spent by universities for their general research libraries is 3.3 per cent of the university budget. Third, the granting agencies have not yet found a mechanism to provide that an "adequate portion of the funds restricted to research is made available for the strengthening of the library," as recommended by the Survey group ten years ago.

COLLECTIONS

The next subject for attention is the book and journal collections. The largest collection held by a school library was 340,446 volumes, the smallest 12,000, and the median of 84 libraries, 54,779. The total book and journal resources represented by the school libraries represents a capital investment by society of approximately $270,000,000. The highest amount spent for books and journals in 1961 was $90,000, the lowest $4,000, with a median expenditure of $19,000. The median number of volumes added during the year was 2,647. Again, I should like to make a few points.

First, the median of 54,779 is about one-half the total collection generally agreed on as minimal for the support of a comprehensive biomedical research program. The target should be set at 100,-000 volumes now. Second, contemporary biomedical research requires a difference in kind of library materials collected, as well as a difference in amount. In general, the libraries are sadly lacking in the basic literature of scientific disciplines from which biomedicine derives its concepts, methodologies and data: the physical and chemical sciences, engineering, and the social sciences. We are in a multi-disciplinary revolution in medical research, and the libraries are not prepared to cope with the new types of demands.

LIBRARY BUILDINGS

Mr. Bloomquist next looked at plant facilities. Seventy per cent of the school libraries currently occupy buildings more than ten years old; 50 per cent of the buildings occupied are 30 years old or older.

In 1957, a survey[2] disclosed that over half of the libraries were either filled to capacity, or exceeded it. The warehousing of books and journals, with all the attendant problems of inaccessibility and inefficient service, is a common practice.

This same survey showed that 88 per cent of the libraries responding were in need of significant alterations; 31 per cent needed entirely new buildings.

Some general comments follow. First, too many of the facilities were planned years ago by architects and administrators with limited understanding of the organic functions and growth rates of libraries. In general, book stack areas, work space, reader space were all underplanned to accommodate *normal* library growth, much less the abnormal pressures of an increasing literature. This is not to be construed as a universal condemnation of architects. It is easy to understand these shortcomings in retrospect, but how many of us can visualize the impact of the trends toward miniaturization and computer installations on the planning of tomorrow's libraries?

Second, the space needs are both universal and critical, and except in isolated instances, local resources have not been found to satisfy them. Nor has the Federal Government yet made grants for the construction of medical library facilities. The last Congress considered two bills, both of which failed to be enacted. Both H.R. 4999 (the Health Professions Educational Assistance Act) and H.R. 8900 (the College Academic Facilities Act) included authorization for school library construction.

The Research Facilities Construction Program was, however, approved by the Congress for three more years. New administrative regulations have been written which define "research and related purposes" (the hitherto limiting feature of this Act) as "research and activities having related purposes (including research training and the use for medical libraries to the extent that they support research and research training)."

This change would appear to admit medical libraries to the competition for Federal research facility construction funds, insofar as they can demonstrate support for research and research training. The question which has concerned many of us lies in this competitive status. At the school level, how effectively will the libraries compete with new laboratory buildings? This question is yours to answer.

LIBRARY PERSONNEL

We might next look at the manpower resources available to the medical libraries. At present the medical schools employ a total of 324 professional librarians. The largest number employed in any one library is 11; the smallest, one. The median number of professional personnel for the 79 libraries is three.

The highest salary paid to a chief librarian is $14,500; the lowest, $4,500, with a median of $7,680. The median salary paid to professional librarians by the schools is $5,400.

The problem of manpower resources is simultaneously one of quantity and quality. It is difficult to believe that medical research conducted in this country at schools of medicine depends upon a pitifully small national pool of 324 persons for its library information services. Still more shocking is the median salary of $5,400 paid to a professional librarian presumably with a graduate degree, and hopefully with a background in the sciences.

All indications point to a critical national shortage of well qualified medical librarians. With job opportunities so restricted it is no wonder that there have been acute difficulties in attracting qualified personnel.

SERVICES

The Bloomquist study did not collect data on the services offered by the medical libraries. Invariably, however, the librarians expressed a desire to enlarge both the scope and the volume of their services to the school community. They have felt inhibited by lack of budget, lack of personnel, lack of journal and equipment resources in providing the following types of service to researchers, educators, and students: continuous bibliographical service to research groups, on-demand bibliographies, translation services, abstracting services, audio-visual services, loan and delivery services, rapid copying services, extension services to rural physicians and community health centers, provision of courses in medical bibliography, and the like. There is obviously a potential for developing the utilization of library resources which, because of the depressed state of affairs, has not been realized.

This recent survey of school medical library resources appears to confirm the earlier conclusions that the medical library network is in dire trouble. There were accumulated deficits in 1951. Like the Red Queen the libraries have been running like mad to stay in the same relative position they were in ten years ago. In the meantime the rapid growth of medical research has placed a new kind of load on the libraries with differences both of quantity and character. A basis of support related to increase of research funds has yet to be found.

Under these depressed circumstances, the libraries are being unfairly blamed for not accommodating themselves to the needs of research for information. Recognition that the library, as it has evolved through the centuries, is as efficient an institution for storing and retrieving information as society has yet evolved, is being challenged. The printed word, recorded and condensed between covers, organized for future retrieval, and economically stored, will be with us for many hundreds of years to come. I for one do not doubt the survival value of the library in our society.

On the other hand, a stereotype seems to be developing which describes the library as an institution which is antiquated, inefficient, and unworthy of survival. Libraries, as we know them, it is alleged, are a thing of the past. They should be replaced by some new institutional form made possible by modern technology.

NEW INSTITUTIONAL FORMS

In recent years, there has been much agitation for the establishment of two new types of information servicing institutions: the mechanized storage and retrieval system, and the science information center. The case for striking off the shackles of tradition and achieving a dramatic break-through commensurate with the capabilities and the requirements of an electronic age is strong. The technologies are well-developed, social concern with the problem of managing the outpourings of new research information is urgent, and large-scale funding is now available.

Since these proposed systems are advanced either to replace or to coexist with libraries under cooperative planning, and hence have their impact on the conventional medical library, it would be helpful to examine their possible roles.

MECHANIZED STORAGE AND RETRIEVAL

Several of the medical schools conduct research projects relating to the mechanized storage and retrieval of published information. Others have gone so far as to dream of the day when their computer facilities, already established, will "manage" the research literature for the benefit of local researchers.

Research and development in this area is uncoordinated, and is lacking in a common philosophical or sociological underpinning. We are still deficient in the fundamentals for the organization of knowledge (especially in the "soft science" areas of medicine), and in our understanding of the information needs of researchers. Technical feasibility makes possible, but does not guarantee acceptance of mechanized retrieval systems.

We believe at the National Library of Medicine (NLM) that we have a solution to the orderly development of this field, and that this solution does include both the perpetuation and the strengthening of medical libraries.

With the coming of MEDLARS the problem of machine retrieval of information at the level of citations to the published literature appears to us to be no longer a technical one. At this level, the computational and manipulative requirements of the computer are rudimentary. The purpose in employing the computer is to handle volume, not sophisticated calculations.

The computer, intelligently used, can be of great value in association with a medical library complex in solving the problem of access to the scientific literature. It is important, however, to understand what is involved in access.

There are two aspects of accessibility to the published medical literature: bibliographic and bibliothecal. Economics dictate that the former–indexing and abstracting–is best centralized; the latter–access to books and journals–decentralized.

Let's look more closely at bibliographic access. The NLM is currently indexing 145,000 papers from 2,000 journals at a cost of $2.20 per unit, or $373,500 per year. From this centralized operation, we produce the *Index Medicus* which is distributed to all the medical libraries. It does their indexing for them, and this and similar Library publications have done so for 80 years.

The same (or higher) unit costs will be involved in the intellectual preparation of input for a computer. Let us suppose there are 10 independent library centers, each engaged in preparing index copy for computer input at half this rate–1,000 journals, 90,000 entries. It would cost each $154,000 apiece each year, an amount in excess of the entire library budget of all but a handful of schools. Further, the manpower to do this indexing is in very short supply. And finally, the work of the 10 libraries would have a high degree of duplication with each other, and of course with the MEDLARS project at NLM.

The indexing which provides bibliographic access must remain a centralized function; the literature indexed must be strongly decentralized for local availability, or bibliothecal access.

The Library is applying this logic to the further development of the MEDLARS project.[3] MEDLARS (standing for Medical Literature Analysis and Retrieval System) is an effort to computerize the Library's indexing operations with the threefold objective: 1) of producing an enlarged *Index Medicus* directly from magnetic tape. Ultimately, this computer-compiled index would cover 2,500 journals, 250,000 citations, annually cumulating to a five-year store of 1,250,000 references, each with an average of 10 subject headings; 2) of providing 50 recurring specialized indexes for research fields; and 3) of providing a demand search and retrieval facility capable of handling 100 queries daily.

We are in midstream with this General Electric contract; operational status is scheduled next fall. MEDLARS will provide a primary centralized screening effort for a larger segment of the scientific literature than is covered by any other service in the world.

MEDLARS will provide bibliographic access to the literature of medicine on an unprecedented scale. But who is to provide physical access–not the power of retrieval, but the thing retrieved?

Local availability of the literature is absolutely essential if the national capabilities of MEDLARS are to be realized. The libraries of the schools in our 50 states must be built up, so that they can supply, without inordinate delays, the reading matter to which the new *Index Medicus* and the other MEDLARS products will guide them.

The foregoing suggests that it will be unnecessary for any one institution to conduct the expensive development work incidental to establishing an independent system; in addition, the previously described costs of input make the maintenance of separate, duplicative and incompatible systems undesirable.

This does not mean that further research and development should not be attempted. On the contrary, the MEDLARS product will provide a new base for future work. In many instances, in special fields and for special purposes, the need for more intensive machine exploitation of the information contained in scientific papers has economic justification. The relationship of MEDLARS to such projects is supportive, not competitive.

Among the possibilities for further development affecting other medical libraries is one in which the Library itself is interested. It is technically possible to duplicate MEDLARS tapes for searching in other university computer centers. A preliminary feasibility study suggests, however, that it would be more economical per unit search to expand the centralized facility. There are many unanswered questions, and we believe it advisable to conduct a controlled demonstration with some one institution to get firm data as a precondition to consideration of a national decentralized system.

SCIENCE INFORMATION CENTERS

The second new information service system which has been proposed is the science information center. This is a selective depository of published and unpublished information bearing on research problems.[4] Controlled by scientists, it functions to collect, evaluate, store and service data to the benefit of the categorical research area on a national scale. It operates a "current awareness" service, collects unpublished as well as published information, provides reference services, and prepares "state of the art" reports. It is, in effect, a specialized library with a scientific evaluation and review function added, and has become increasingly popular in some areas of science and technology.

Where it differs from a library is in its orientation to one research field. It is "mission" oriented, and as such is a child of the multidisciplinary revolution which is so dominant an influence in science today. It has a planned obsolescence; it lasts as long as the mission lasts, and may be disassembled in future time.

The essential operating differences between the science information center and the research library are:

1. The former collects selected data, published and unpublished, relating to the needs of a single research field; the latter collects broadly in many fields.
2. The former provides national service to a small decentralized group; the latter local services to a comprehensive central group.
3. The former has an active dissemination program of abstracts, review papers, news bulletins, etc. for its limited group, which the latter lacks.
4. The former is staffed by individuals trained in the sciences; the latter by librarian who may or may not have scientific backgrounds.

Both libraries and science information centers are concerned with the application of computers to information problems; both are concerned with lending, photo-duplication, and reference services. Both types of institutionalized information service have their strong points and their limitations.

The medical library, with its philosophic base in the universality of biomedical science, its "browsability," its collections in historic depth, has enduring values for free investigation. These must not be sacrificed for temporary advantage.

The effect of the information center concept on library evolution has not been carefully studied. Need there be competitive development, for example, or should we rather accelerate the pace of library development, so that one information processing organization can perform both functions? Certainly, where a library and an information center co-exist in the same academic environment, good management practice suggests that a close organizational relationship is highly desirable to hold possible duplication of functions to a minimum.

This, then, is the situation today. Support for the medical library has not kept pace with the growth of biomedical research. It would not be exaggerating to say that of all the school resources supporting research programs, the traditional library is the weakest.

The library's primary functions—those of acquiring, storing, and retrieving information—have overnight become a matter of deep social concern, so much so that society is inventing new instruments to perform these same functions.

The pace of library evolution, held back by inadequate funding for so many years, has in truth been too slow, but this circumstance does not call for revolution. There is too large a capital investment and proven values at stake, and the new mechanisms are untried, and have major elements of risk.

But this discussion does point up the critical position of medical library development today. Either the medical libraries undertake a major program of rehabilitation so that they can adapt their programs first, to the needs of contemporary biomedical research, and second, to the on-rushing new technologies, or they may not survive as functioning institutions.

The libraries are truly at a crossroads. If they continue, with inadequate support, inadequate housing, inadequate collections, and inadequately prepared personnel, they may wither and decay. If they are provided major reinforcement in each of these respects, they can then speed their evolution, become co-partners with mechanized retrieval systems and science information centers, both functioning to control and utilize the flood of new research information.

The latter alternative calls for a quantum jump from a depressed state to performance at a new level. How can this be accomplished?

A LIBRARY DEVELOPMENT PROGRAM

The foregoing suggests clearly the need for a large-scale national effort to rehabilitate the medical school libraries. New concepts of the importance of managed information supply to medical research call for new standards for personnel, for collections, and for performance. A temporary solution will not suffice; what we are here concerned with is the attainment in minimum time of a plateau well above the present depressed levels. Only then can the library begin to provide research support for the future.

No one agency can take the job on singlehanded. The medical schools cannot, the Federal Government cannot, nor can the state governments or private foundations. The job must be a cooperative one.

A program to revitalize the libraries must be developed in two stages. First, the libraries, as they now exist, must be strengthened; second, only after the foundations have been well-laid, must the library potential for supporting mechanized storage and retrieval systems and science information centers be exploited.

Within the Public Health Service, the NLM has proposed extramural programs to help develop the medical libraries. These programs have not received Congressional authorization, nor appropriations, and are still under advisement.

In an education and training program, the Library has proposed academic year support for students in medical librarianship and documentation, short-term institutes to update the skills of personnel on the job, support of the training institutions to enable them to do a better job, and an expanded intern program to give new graduates quality work experience.

Under a library resources development program, the Library has proposed a system of matching grants, calculated on a 50 per cent increase of the school library's annual operating budget, up to a maximum of five years. The Federal funds could be used for a variety of purposes: journal procurement, reduction of backlogs, personal services, and the like. Such funds would be conditioned on the maintenance or increase of the school budgets.

In connection with more adequate housing for medical libraries, we are as much interested as you in achieving a prompt solution to this continuing problem. We expect to work closely with the National Institutes of Health and other agencies in the Public Health Service to develop a support program commensurate with the needs.

In closing, I should like to make a practical suggestion. I submit that this matter of medical libraries, including measures for their support, minimal standards for their establishment and performance, and planning for their futures, is a topic of immediate concern to medical education and medical research. To the best of my knowledge, the Association of American Medical Colleges has never charged a committee with the continuing responsibility of planning, monitoring, and evaluating developments in this field.

I should like to suggest the establishment of such a committee. I should like to suggest further that this proposed committee establish liaison with the professional organization of medical librarians, the Medical Library Association, for technical consultation. There are very practical and immediate problems to be solved, as well as long-range planning to be done.

The librarians and the school administrators have a common cause. It will take the wisdom and experience of both groups to plan for the development of library resources, and to accommodate this development to the needs of medical research and education in the years to come.

NOTES

[1] Deitrick, J. E., and Berson, R. C. *Medical Schools in the United States at Mid-Century*. N.Y.: McGraw-Hill, 1953.

[2] Fry, A. and Adams, S. Medical Library Architecture in the Past Fifty Years. *Bulletin of the Medical Library Association*, 45: 471–79, 1957.

[3] General Electric Company, Defense Systems Division. *The MEDLARS Story*. Bethesda, Md: General Electric Company, 1962.

[4] Simpson, G. S., Jr. Scientific Information Centers in the United States. *American Documentation*, 13: 43–57, 1962.

ABOUT THE AUTHOR—See page 223.

The Challenge in Medical School Libraries

by Estelle Brodman

Dr. Brodman summarizes some of the findings, conclusions and implications of the Guidelines for Medical School Libraries *published by an Association of American Medical Colleges Committee established to construct them.*

This article presents some of the findings of the Committee on Guidelines for Medical School Libraries and some of the conclusions and implications which might be drawn from the Committee's year-long deliberations. In the Introduction to *Guidelines for Medical School Libraries*, an account is given of how the Committee was formed, the charge given it, and the methods by which the conclusions set forth in its report were arrived at. It is necessary to reiterate one point, however, because there seems to be some misunderstanding about it.

PURPOSE OF THE COMMITTEE

The Committee was specifically requested not to attempt to design a set of standards; instead, it was asked to consider guidelines. This the Committee cheerfully agreed to, since the members felt that the setting of standards implied too rigid a notion of what constituted excellence. In the medical school library there are too many variables to be considered before one can speak *ex cathedra* about such things as the optimal number of books and journals, the most productive ratio of staff to any one other factor, or even the future possibility of using computers to solve medical library problems. Each medical school library is a unique combination of the various factors involved. The Committee felt sure, also, that the deans and other administrative officers for whom it was making this report were too sophisticated intellectually to think that a series of definitive "right or wrong" answers could be given to the complicated problems facing the scientific community today in transmitting information from the producer to the consumer through all the intermediaries. If it were that simple, the problems would already have been solved and the AAMC would not have constituted our Committee in the first place.

ESTABLISHMENT OF FIRM STANDARDS

Yet many of the questions and comments the Committee received from its very start implied that some administrators hoped it would provide simple, concise, and exact formulas for determining everything measurable and several of the imponderables in a library. Would that were possible, but wishing it were so will not make it so. Indeed, this is the main point to the title of this article, "The Challenge in Medical School Libraries." Wishing for for certainty is negating reality, but studying a phenomenon and learning its characteristics may do much to clear away some of the nebulous, uncertain, "soft" data and perhaps bring the wished-for certainty and reality closer together. This is the challenge in medical school libraries today and can only be met by administrative officers and librarians working together, not by either group alone.

The two groups must unite in studying how to make the medical school library a responsive, integrated, and powerful force in medical education, research, and ultimately patient care. The President's Science Advisory Committee in its so-called "Weinberg Report" on the responsibilities

---

SOURCE: Reprinted from "The Challenge in Medical School Libraries," *Journal of Medical Education*, 40 (Jan., 1965, Part 1), pp. 1-4, by permission of the publisher and the author. Presented at 75th Annual Meeting, Association of American Medical Colleges, Denver, Colorado, October 19, 1964.

of the technical community and the government in the transfer of information[1] has stated, "Coping with the problems of communication...requires the help of all technical people, not only of the information specialists. . . The information process is an integral part of research and development. . . The technical community must recognize that handling of technical information is a worthy and integral part of science." That Committee defined libraries as "switching mechanisms," whereby information in one form or one place is transmitted in other forms to other places. Deans and library committees in medical schools must, it seems to the Guidelines Committee, think rigorously about three problems connected with the library. First, is it serving the role it should as the "switching mechanism" for information? Second, if not, is it the appropriate agency to do so, or is there another acceptable alternative? Third, whoever has this role, how will that agency be supported financially and intellectually? It is the feeling of the Committee that half-measures and temporizing here may be extremely bad for all the biomedical sciences.

If the Committee came to no other unanimous conclusion, it did decide that the single most important criterion of excellence in a medical school library was the caliber of the library staff. Given excellence in the chief librarian and his assistants, most other desirable ends followed, because in general a good staff obtained financial support for the library, as good quarters as outside school conditions permitted, and the acknowledgment of individual intellectual stature, making for understanding, equal consultation, and mutual appreciation. Good staffs got these things or left. Medical librarians today are in short supply. If they feel their usefulness is being hampered by poor financial and intellectual conditions in one institution, they tend to go to another one.

DEVELOPMENT OF SUPERIOR LIBRARY STAFFS

The second challenge to medical school libraries is where to obtain good medical librarians—men and women with backgrounds in and understanding of the biomedical sciences, scholarly abilities, administrative competence, and specialized knowledge of information technology. This list alone is a reminder that few such people exist in any field, not just medical librarianship. The challenge to deans and others in medical education or medical sciences is to help make scientific information. work become so stimulating intellectually that more of the better minds will be attracted to the field. If medical libraries are vital to the education of physicians, to medical research, and to the improvement of clinical medicine, then medical school faculties have a stake in attracting and keeping good thinkers in medical librarianship. This they can do by bringing the librarians into the scientific and educational stream of the medical school, by demanding as good a quality of thinking from their librarians as from their other faculty, and by encouraging and supporting experimentation in scientific communication in their library as much as experimentation in the subject areas of other departments of the school.

ELECTRONIC STORAGE AND RETRIEVAL OF INFORMATION

The third challenge to medical libraries concerns electronic means for storing and retrieving information, with interlocking questions of centralized libraries in Washington, semicentralized information centers in a geographic area-network around the country, and the fitting up of new library structures locally. The Committee understands and sympathizes with the desire of officials concerned with budgets to get clear answers to these problems. The future of medical librarianship is of primary concern both to administrators and librarians—indeed, it is literally a bread-and-butter question with the latter. The Committee wishes the answers were clearer, but it must admit to no certainty about the precise form the future medical school library will take. Three of the members of the Committee have worked intimately for some years in this field and their libraries are partially automated; many libraries have audio-visual materials, and the new teaching media do not cause any real concern. Certainly, some automation—and more than is now usual—will be present in medical school libraries in the coming years. As teaching methods change, medical school libraries will undoubtedly add teaching television, film strips, programmed learning machines, and the like. If arrangements have been made to inform the librarian of the kind of teaching proposed for the school (and this is most easily done automatically by having the librarian serve as a member of the faculty council or whatever body in the school discusses and passes on curriculum changes, general policies for the admission of students, new building programs, and the like) and if the necessary funds are provided, it is more than likely that the librarian will be able to handle the technical problems without too much difficulty.

It is imperative, however, that the medical school itself clarify its teaching program and settle its teaching methods so the librarian can proceed intelligently in presenting the devices needed to implement them. Here, as elsewhere, the library must be part of the total academic planning, not an appendage working in a vacuum.

The Committee would especially like to underscore this point. On its visits the Committee asked for statements on the schools' programs and frequently found either that one had not been formulated or it had not been transmitted to the librarian. If the medical school has no basic educational policy, whether because it believes each department should set its own policy as it sees fit or because it has not given the matter thought, or if the policy is unknown to the librarian, it cannot expect the library to deliver supporting services.

FUTURE OF THE MEDICAL LIBRARY

The crux of the dilemma of using electronic devices in libraries is the question of how long it will be before computers will be capable of transmitting scientific information needed for medical education and research at a price commensurate with the gains. On this point the Committee received conflicting—nearly diametrically opposed—advice from its consultants. Some felt the library as we know it today is obsolete (not obsolescent, but obsolete) and within a few years will be replaced by a TV-telephone arrangement on each research worker's desk for delivery of material from a central store in Washington. This system also would abolish publishing as it has developed to the present and substitute for it the deposit of typescripts and even raw record-data into the central pool. On the other hand, the Committee was advised by other consultants that technology has not worked out many of the problems inherent in such a system and that costs at present are still exorbitantly high.

Weighing all the evidence, the Committee could only conclude that the future is still difficult to see. It was forced to report that so far as it could tell, the medical school library of the next ten to fifteen years probably will be different from the present one only in an evolutionary way, not a revolutionary one. There will still be books, journals, indexes to the literature, stacks, reading areas, and staffs, all supplemented in a growing stream by centralized depositories and the use of newer technological devices. The Committee feels that the latter will start first with the simpler, background tasks required to make the literature available, such as journal control, circulation records, and the like, and only later will there be solutions to the more complicated problems of coding the literature for computer manipulation or of electronic transmission of hard copy at a distance.

The challenge to administrators of medical schools here is twofold. They must be willing to plan for and support traditional libraries for half a generation more, while still helping their library staffs to change over gradually to a different "switching mechanism." They must be willing to put into operation the many already well-established principles of library administration and function because, as the Committee quickly learned, many medical school libraries could be greatly improved and upgraded merely by using today's standard and traditional practices. (Perhaps this fact may turn out to be the most useful benefit to be derived from the Guidelines.)

CONCLUSION

To stop there, however, would be to back away from the greatest challenge in medical school libraries. A medical school library is a major educational resource, especially so today with the trend toward independent study in medical school as the preparation for independent study throughout life. It needs to be supported as such, just as much as it requires backing in its role as a tool of research. As was pointed out earlier, it must be developed as part of the total academic planning, not as an extraneous factor stuck on for academic respectability. Individually, regionally, and nationally, medical schools must work together toward better means of transmitting information to students as well as to research workers.

It is likely that in the future the medical school library will be different from present-day ones. It cannot, however, be a significant means by which the aims of the school are fulfilled unless the faculty and the administration work with it intellectually and support it financially.

The challenge in medical school libraries today is primarily the challenge to educators to work with their librarians as equals on a problem of vital concern to both.

NOTE

[1] President's Science Advisory Committee. *Science, Government and Information.* Washington, D.C.: U. S. Government Printing Office, 1963.

ABOUT THE AUTHOR–See page 214-215.

The Library as an Educational Instrument, The Problem

This paper is Chapter 1 of The Health Sciences Library: Its Role in Education for the Health Professions, a report to the National Library of Medicine by the Library Study Committee of the Association of American Medical Colleges, Merlin K. DuVal, Director and Seymour Alpert, Co-Director. The full report contains a number of specific recommendations about resources, practices and policies.

In slightly less than two decades the health industry has become one of the largest employers in the United States. It is exceeded only by agriculture, manufacturing, and the construction industry. The various personnel now working in the health field encompass a widening spectrum of activity. As the "team" concept of health care becomes more prevalent, it is reasonable to expect that even more people will find employment in the health field. These changes have stimulated the development of many new programs in education for the health sciences and also broadened those already in existence. It is necessary, then, to reexamine the resources available to these educational programs.

The principle influence on the health industry has been the federal government. In the twenty years since the end of World War II, it has invested more than 100 billion dollars for health and medical services. This exceeds the total funds that our nation had previously spent for these services throughout all the years of its history. The National Institutes of Health, which is only one of several agencies within the U.S. Public Health Service, is currently providing more than 16,000 research grants yearly, nearly 500 research contracts, and more than 8,000 training grants and fellowships.

Health scientists have responded to this nourishment by increasing the number of personnel who are actively engaged in research from 19,000 in 1954 to more than 50,000 in 1964. Unpublished data from the National Institutes of Health indicate that almost 90 per cent of all the scientists who have ever dedicated their lives to research are alive and in their laboratories today.

This investment has had a particularly big impact on the scholarly record. There are more than 75,000 scientific and technological journals available in 65 languages, and there are more than 3,500 journals that have as their only concern the abstracting of material published elsewhere. The problem is further compounded by the parallel investment that our government has made in the exploration of space. As a result, new knowledge is being generated at a rate that is straining our ability to synthesize, index, and store it. All of this has added a substantial burden to those charged with the responsibility for maintaining the scholarly record. And although academic institutions, industry, and government are fast becoming partners in an effort to manage this information explosion, much progress is still to be made.

Ultimately, the knowledge explosion has its greatest impact at the level of the individual scientist. An estimate in the U. S. National Library of Medicine annual report for 1963 indicated that the total volume of information available to the scientist has doubled over the last decade. For the health-oriented scientist there are more than 800 medical journals currently being published in the United States alone. The scientist is spared the assignment of reading all of them only because the great majority of the information has already been screened and selected for interest and pertinence by peer groups and editorial boards. This permits him to limit his current-awareness tools to areas of his personal

SOURCE: Reprinted from Association of American Medical Colleges Library Study Committee (Merlin K. DuVal, Director), "Chapter 1, The Library as an Educational Instrument, The Problem," *Journal of Medical Education*, 42 (Aug., 1967, Part 2), pp. 3–7, with the permission of the publisher and the Committee Director.

concern. Unfortunately, current research work is becoming so interdisciplinary and complex that it may be recorded in any of several journals. As a consequence, most of the old tools and devices on which the scientist has relied are rapidly losing their effectiveness.

In the field of patient care, fear has been expressed[1] that this situation has resulted in the appearance of a "knowledge gap." The essence of the argument is that the rate at which new information is accumulating in the laboratory and through clinical experience is so rapid that the individual physician cannot possibly be current in his awareness of it. This has led some to conclude[1] that the gap may have the effect of delaying—or even denying—the benefit of new discoveries to the patient who may be in need. Others take the position that it would be dangerous to have any existing gap closed completely, since it is preferable, and safer for the patient, for an interval to pass between the announcement of something new and its application in the field. Either way, there seems to be agreement that much of the new information is neither relevant nor useful in most clinical situations; and, therefore, the gap between the bench and the bedside may be less harmful than is feared.

SOLVING THE PROBLEM

It has been at least fifty years since H. G. Wells[2] suggested that the accumulation of scientific and technical knowledge would one day reach a point at which it would be necessary to set up a centralized storage system which could be tapped anywhere, at any time, by the working scientist. Wells referred to this centralized information bank as a "World Brain." The clarity and succinctness with which Wells described his solution to the information problem suggests that he would be dismayed, if not appalled, at some of the conditions under which we currently require our scientists to work. Fortunately, pressure is now developing within the scientific community to solve the problem of the information explosion; and national and local effort are being made to improve the situation.

Our society looks to the university as the instrument of primary responsibility for the creation of knowledge through research, its dissemination through teaching, and its application through service. Educational centers for the health professions have been developed as subdivisions of the universities to carry out this role with respect to knowledge in health-related matters. In this setting the health sciences library has become the focal point for housing and storing many of the resources that serve the several educational programs involved. However, changes in the techniques of information storage and retrieval are occurring so rapidly that this passive definition of a health sciences library will probably not be sufficient for the future.

Even if one concedes that some very impressive changes in the technology of information storage and retrieval are taking place, there are several cogent reasons to believe that the traditional library will continue to serve as an instrument in the educational process for a long time:

1. Certain documents are classic or original in their presentation. The traditional library makes the best housing for such documents.

2. Experience has shown[1] that the effectiveness of the presentation of information can be increased by involving more than one medium in its presentation. No matter how sophisticated the dissemination of new information becomes, there will probably always be a need for its presentation through the traditional methods of displaying the printed word.

3. Educational institutions have an obligation to support research. In a research-oriented environment the scientist must have access to as broad a portion of the scholarly record as is feasible. There is little likelihood that it will become economical or desirable to transfer the older portion of the record to other media for its retrieval when it is already available in an acceptable form.

4. In contrast with many other fields, medicine is an application of science rather than a science itself. Therefore, the thoughtful student of the clinical disciplines will wish to have access to the divergent views that have been faithfully recorded in the scholarly record.

5. Because new knowledge is accumulating so rapidly, the student who leaves the educational environment without an appreciation for both the traditional and the new methods for remaining up to date will always have difficulty. In his later years, one form or another of this same library will almost certainly serve as the principal instrument by which he can stay up to date. Therefore, he must become familiar with its use while he is in an educational setting.

It seems likely that the health sciences library will soon take on a new identity.[3] This will justify its existence in the health professions educational institution more than ever before. It has already been noted that there is a gap between discovery and use of information. There has been no suggestion that this gap will disappear by itself. Although the use of new devices—such as automated literature searches, cathode ray display tubes, light pens, and individual terminals—may increase the efficiency with which one may confront the scholarly record, it has been largely up to the individual scientist to determine how he can best remain as nearly up to date as possible. Now, however, there are reasons to believe that the health sciences library has much of the capability, and all of the potential, to solve this problem for the individual scientist.[3] If medical center administrators are willing to assign this new role to their libraries, then both the librarian and the administrator must accept certain responsibilities.

The Librarian

There are 3 activities which must be undertaken by those charged with the operation of the library of the future.

1. It will be necessary to begin a very active period of research into the most feasible modalities for disseminating the scholarly record to the scientist and the student. Generally, such dissemination will be primarily concerned with 2 things: (*a*) material that is of particular interest to the individual scientist and (*b*) material that is new. The opportunity for research of this type has never been greater—the Medical Library Assistance Act will support it; health sciences librarians want answers to some of the questions involved; and the scientist in the health field is eager to cooperate, since he knows that he will be the ultimate beneficiary of the research.

2. The health sciences librarian should be willing to accept an educational role that is much beyond anything he has been asked to accept up to this time. His educational programs will have 2 objectives: (*a*) to educate and familiarize the student of the health sciences with both the form in which the scholarly record is contained and the means by which one gains access to it; and (*b*) to identify, attract, and educate new talent for the increasingly specialized field of information management. The first of these objectives may require formal participation in the educational curriculum with the other academic departments. Such a step is readily justified when one considers that the knowledge imparted to the student regarding the best way to use the scholarly record can certainly be said to be as important as any other single educational experience. Further, it is likely that the student's success at remaining current in his thinking after he has left the educational institution will bear a direct relationship to the familiarity and ease with which he uses the library.

In anticipating educational programs for the new talent in the field of information management, it is probable that many of the librarians of the future will continue to come through the traditional route of the library school. On the other hand, there is increasing evidence[4] that some candidates for careers in this most interesting field will be coming from mathematics, biology, engineering, chemistry, and perhaps even merchandising. Consequently, it can be deduced that the librarian of the future, by assuming the role of "information specialist," will soon become the manager of a team of experts, each of whom may have particular competence in managing only 1 or 2 of the several media and carriers of information.

3. The health sciences library will probably have to adopt an entirely new philosophy in the area of service if the information gap is to be closed. It seems likely that such service will become active in character rather than passive as has been typical of the past. Indeed, one might look forward to an era in which health sciences information is actively disseminated in much the same manner that information is disseminated in the nonacademic sector. Specifically, the range of services which the library of the future might offer could include the provision of linkages between people with information as well as between people and documents. It could provide up-to-date directories of persons who are known to be doing certain types of research and where their latest results are published. It could maintain a continuous display of material relative to national meetings by organization or subject. It could also expand and develop current-awareness tools, introduce selective dissemination of information, circulate lists of new acquisitions, publish regular announcements or bulletins containing brief reviews of "what's new," and telecast graphic images of the tables of contents of newly arrived journals. The possibilities seem unlimited.

The Administration

If the administration of the health professions educational complex is willing to assign to the library a role such as that described above, then 3 other commitments will be necessary.

1. Since the library will be assuming intrinsic responsibility for research, education, and service, it will have fulfilled all of the usual and traditional requirements of an instructional department. As a result, the library should be accorded full academic partnership in the educational endeavor.

2. In order to meet some of the requirements imposed upon it as an educational instrument, it will have to be granted all the rights and privileges that other academic departments enjoy, including a voice in the structure of the curriculum and curriculum time for its own programs.

3. It should be allowed to compete, on equal terms, with other academic departments for its share of the instructional budget. In the past the library has generally occupied an anomalous position with regard to its budgeted support.

Since the role of the library and the librarian will have changed profoundly, administrative officials will have to be prepared to reorient their thinking with respect to this problem. They will also have to accept responsibility for the appointment of individuals who have the imagination and capacity to define the function of a library for the health science schools.

NOTES

[1] U. S. President's Commission on Heart Disease, Cancer and Stroke. Report to the President. *A National Program to Conquer Heart Disease, Cancer and Stroke*. (Volume II.) Washington, D.C.: U. S. Government Printing Office, 1965.

[2] Wells, H. G. *World Brain.* London: Methuen & Co., 1938.

[3] Miller, J. G. Design of a University Health Sciences Information Center. J. Med. Educ. 42: 404–429, 1967.

[4] *Bricks and Mortarboards: A Report on College Planning and Building*. New York: Educational Facilities Laboratories, Inc., May, 1964, P. 83.

ABOUT THE AUTHOR–Dr. Merlin K. DuVal is Assistant Secretary for Health and Scientific Affairs of the Department of Health, Education and Welfare. From 1964 until 1971 he was Dean of the new College of Medicine at the University of Arizona. Before that he had held positions in surgery at the Veterans Administration Hospital in the Bronx, the State University of New York, Brooklyn, and the University of Oklahoma Medical Center, where he was Professor of Surgery and Vice Chairman of the Department of Surgery. His A. B. is from Dartmouth College and his M.D. from Cornell University Medical College.

Dr. DuVal is a Fellow of the American College of Surgeons and also serves on the College's Committee on Undergraduate Education. He is a Diplomate of the American Board of Surgery and the National Board of Medical Examiners. Besides being Director of the Library Study Committee of the Association of American Medical Colleges, he serves on the editorial board of its *Journal of Medical Education.* He was also Director of the Arizona Regional Medical Programs and Chairman of the Commission on Education for the Health Professions of the National Association of State Universities and Land Grant Colleges.

V.

MEDICAL LIBRARY NETWORKS

Insofar as a library network is a formal extension of library resources by cooperation with other libraries in a geographic area, library networks have existed for years and there have been a number of medical library networks, for example in the Detroit area[1] and within the State University of New York.[2] One description, that of The Medical Library Center of New York, has been chosen to represent all such cooperative efforts, even though each is different in its organization and functions.

Since the Report of the President's Commission on Heart Disease, Cancer and Stroke, funds have been available to strengthen medical libraries and biomedical communications in general and to enable development of a national medical library network. These funds come from two separate pieces of legislation—the Medical Library Assistance Act and that providing funds for Regional Medical Programs. Activities under both programs are described.

[1]Chesier, Robert G. *et al.* "Metropolitan Detroit's Network," *Bulletin of the Medical Library Association*, 56 (July, 1968), pp. 268-291.

[2]Pizer, Irwin H. "A Regional Medical Library Network," *Bulletin of the Medical Library Association*, 57 (Apr., 1969), pp. 101-115.

The Medical Library Center of New York: A Progress Report

by Jacqueline W. Felter

The cooperative project described here antedates the era of government support in medical library cooperation. It is interesting because of its existence separate from any of the participating libraries and the gradually more sophisticated services it has provided its users. The Union Catalog of Medical Periodicals *has gained wider use since the publication of this paper.*

At the Medical Library Center we have a saying that, if one were to cross the Center for Research Libraries in Chicago with the Philadelphia Union Catalog, the Medical Library Center of New York would be the result. Certainly the objectives of MLC are similar to both of these prototypes, but the narrowly defined area MLC serves and the needs of the community make implementation of the objectives unique. In 1962 Eric Meyerhoff wrote an article which tells the history of the Medical Library Center and outlines its proposed program.[1] This paper was an architect's rendering, so to speak; now it is possible to view the actual structure. After four years of successful operation it can no longer be called an "experiment."

THE BUILDING

Even though the Medical Library Center purchased its building toward the end of 1961, the staff was not able to occupy its permanent quarters until January 1964. It is obvious that actual operation did not start with lightning speed. The building, designed as a garage, but with two floors suitable also for light industry, was not suited to library use without extensive renovation. Financial help was needed to make the alterations possible. Caution urged that final architectural plans should be drawn and remodeling begun only after funds for the purpose were assured. Matching grants from the Alfred P. Sloan Foundation and the Rockefeller Foundation, together with a grant received previously from the Department of Health of the City of New York through its Health Research Council, finally made it possible to start construction. Even then the increase in building costs over the earlier estimate made it necessary to defer renovation of the sixth floor and convert only the seventh floor to offices for the staff and book stacks capable of housing approximately 200,000 items.

A building designed for another purpose offers both disadvantages and advantages to its new occupant. Contrary to expectation the floor load capacity—120 pounds per square foot—prevented us from using book stacks especially constructed for compact storage. Therefore, to make storage as compact as possible with standard library book stacks, textbooks and monographs are shelved by size in fixed locations. This arrangement is possible because MLC is not open to the reader, except by special arrangement; it circulates its material as interlibrary loans. It is not a browsing library. Journals and other materials, however, are shelved in the conventional ways. On the other hand, the unusually high ceilings made it possible to accommodate ventilator ducts and electrical conduits and, in the office area, conceal them with hung ceilings. The resulting quarters are well-lighted, air-conditioned, and, except for the stack area which is more functional than decorative, brightly painted.

SOURCE: Reprinted from Jacqueline W. Felter, "The Medical Library Center of New York: a Progress Report," *Bulletin of the Medical Library Association*, 56 (Jan., 1968), pp. 15–20, by permission of the publisher and the author.

The seven floors not occupied by the Medical Library Center are rented to other organizations. Half of the space is occupied by a garage, sorely needed in a neighborhood characterized by expanding medical institutions with large numbers of personnel and visitors. The remaining space was formerly occupied by other commercial enterprises, but, as the leases have expired, the space has been taken by the New York Medical College and Mount Sinai School of Medicine. Thus, the building has become, in part, an educational and professional center; the property and neighborhood have been improved, and the taxes have been reduced by the tenancy of our tax-free neighbors.

MEMBERSHIP

Though the original Sponsoring Institutions have some of the largest and strongest libraries, it was not intended that the Center should serve only to relieve their growing pains. It was conceivable that a center which could house the overflow of large libraries could also serve as a back-up facility for institutions that might well maintain the smaller working literature collections. We welcome and have acquired a number of hospital libraries as participating members. Serving both large and small libraries does not result in a dichotomy, because both are doing the same work on a difficult scale, but the different types of libraries do make different demands on the Center.

To the nine original Sponsoring Institutions have been added two medical schools: New Jersey College of Medicine and Dentistry, and the newly incorporated Mount Sinai School of Medicine. There are now also twelve Participating Institutions, of which eleven are hospitals, making a total of twenty-three member institutions.

The annual membership fees are: Sponsoring Institutions, $10,000, Participating Institutions, $2,000, and Commercial Firms, $5,000. As yet, no commercial firms have become members. Nonmembers in the New York Area may borrow items, but they must pay a unit transaction fee.

ADMINISTRATION

Operation of The Medical Library Center is guided by the Director. Professional librarians head the Technical Services Division and the Union Catalog of Medical Periodicals. Building maintenance and services are supervised by a part-time engineer. The Assistant Treasurer, or business manager, is also a part-time employee.

In the normal operating staff, excluding the part-time engineer and business manager, the ratio of professional to nonprofessional employees is 1:4. During the period of compilation of the Union Catalog, however, while there is need for considerable cataloging expertise and grant funds provide an augmented budget, the UCMP staff includes three additional librarians. Similarly, the Technical Services Division had as an additional cataloger for six months, Mrs. Elfrida Ureta of the Biblioteca Escuela de Medicina Universidad de Chile, Santiago, Chile, who was in New York while her husband was on a medical fellowship here. During this time the ratio of professional to nonprofessional employees was 1:2.

The Board of Trustees consists of one administrator from each Sponsoring Institution and is concerned mainly with financial affairs. The Board meets three times a year to vote on the budget and consider any facets of fiscal policy that are brought to its attention by the Director and Business Manager.

The librarians of the member institutions form the Advisory Committee of Librarians. This committee meets several times a year, usually at the request of the Director. Its function is to give the Director the members' views on the existing services, suggest changes or additional services, and act on those the Director proposes. The chairman is one of the librarians, elected by the membership; the Director of the Center serves as secretary. *Ad hoc* committees wrestle with special problems and procedures. Because the membership in the Center has increased, the Advisory Committee has become too large to function efficiently as a steering committee, and recently a Planning Committee was appointed to study current conditions and recommend future programs of service and acquisitions.

FINANCES

The Medical Library Center is a nonprofit organization. It was anticipated at first that surplus income from rentals would pay more than half of the operating expenses of the Medical Library Center, thereby enabling us to reduce the amount of the members' fees. In practice, thus far, this hope has not been realized. The building had not been well maintained by the previous owner, and most of the rental income has been reinvested in expensive repairs and replacement of equipment. The operating expenses of MLC, therefore, are still paid by the members' fees. In time, however, the original plan should become fact.

The income was augmented by an extension of the John A. Hartford Foundation grant which supported the Union Catalog of Medical Periodicals entirely through October 31, 1965. From November 1, 1965 through May 31, 1968, grant funds, first from the Department of Health of the City of New York (Grant No. U-1653 of the Health Research Council) and then from the National Library of Medicine (Grant No. LM00042-01 and 02), have partially supported the Union Catalog. The grant funds are applied to the expense of completing the conversion of the original records to machine-readable form. Operating expenses of the Union Catalog are included in the MLC budget.

SERVICES

The first service to be initiated was the delivery service; it continues to be the most popular of the various services. Driving a Hertz rented truck, our driver makes daily trips to the member libraries in Manhattan, the Bronx, and Brooklyn; on three days a week he includes New Jersey in his rounds, and on the remaining two days he stops at libraries in Nassau County on Long Island. The speedometer clocks 450 miles a week. The messenger not only delivers and picks up for return the items borrowed from MLC, but also delivers the interlibrary loans the member libraries exchange with each other. One librarian of a Sponsoring Institution has said that the delivery service saves her library the salaries of two messengers. The truck service is possible, of course, because MLC serves a compact geographic area. Such an arrangement would not be possible for an organization such as the Center for Research Libraries, whose service area includes many states.

A Xerox copy reimbursement service, begun in 1966, is also generally satisfactory. This service was designed to speed interlibrary loan transactions and reduce paper work. It speeds loans by eliminating the negotiations necessary for advance payment when the borrowing library requests an article in a journal that is restricted from circulation by the lending library. The lending library simply fills the request with a photocopy and sends to MLC a statement of the amount due at ten cents per page. The Center does the paper work, reimbursing each library once a month for the Xerox copies it has made for other members. Actually the Center is paying the members with their own money because it comes out of their dues, but it saves them nuisance and labor.

A TWX network was inaugurated on May 1, 1967. While it may be argued that TWX is not necessary in a restricted geographic area where telephone service is as fast and possibly cheaper, it was the consensus of the librarians of the member institutions that the written record TWX provides would improve the accuracy of interlibrary loan requests. A written record is made, of course, if the ALA interlibrary loan form is used; but, sent by mail or even picked up and delivered by the MLC messenger, the ALA form cannot be transmitted as rapidly as the TWX message. The Medical Library Center pays the cost of installation and monthly rental of the equipment; the member libraries pay for their messages. Thus far, TWX has been installed only in the libraries of Sponsoring Institutions. This policy does not reflect discrimination against the smaller Participating Institutions, for there certainly is as much justification for facilitating the interlibrary loan transaction in the library that is mainly a borrower as in the one that is mainly a lender. It is not discrimination; it is simply a matter of money. Here again, when MLC pays the equipment rental charge, it is only spending the member library's dues, and it cannot include TWX in the services to a Participating Institution that pays $2,000 a year and still make ends meet. If the participating libraries can manage an increase in membership fees, MLC can manage to include TWX.

THE DEPOSITORY COLLECTION

The depository collection, which initially seemed to hold great promise, has perhaps, not completely fulfilled our expectations. There are two basic categories of deposit: deposit without expectation of return, and rental storage. Rental storage was intended to be of limited duration, an expedient for a library in the process of moving, temporarily in need of extra space, or awaiting completion of a larger stack area. For this, the member library pays a small fee to cover service, for books to and from rental storage are charged out and delivered by messenger, as are items from the permanent depository collection. Some rental storage collections do fit the initial specifications. Other collections, however, consist of long runs of common journals that might well be on permanent deposit (and often duplicate permanent deposits). They come from libraries where, as much as can be judged, there is little hope of larger book stacks to house them or little evidence of need, so long as the volumes are available for loan from MLC's permanent collection. Rarely would a volume be unavailable, because generally Xerox copies of the articles requested are supplied. This use of rental storage implies a lack of commitment to the idea of the central depository collection. It also reflects an outmoded belief on the part of institution administrators rather than librarians that the size of a library is a status symbol, even though a large proportion of the volumes are too old or unsuitable to earn their keep. Reluctance of large libraries to commit to the Center back files of common journals also does not enable MLC to fulfill as readily as we wish the objective of using the resources of the large libraries to back up the working collections of small ones.

Nevertheless, a considerable depository collection has been acquired. MLC has accepted what the member libraries have chosen to separate from their collections. In other words, the term "less-used" in the original policy statement has, in reality, meant that the donor library determines what is less-used and expendable in its collection. Thus, from one library we may have received a collection of institutional annual reports, while from another we have a large number of runs of journals including quite recent volumes. The term "less-used" is, of course, subject to different interpretations. Take state medical journals, for instance; they lend themselves to deposit because, though less-used in a research library, they may be much used in a library serving mostly clinicians.

Textbooks and monographs are noncurrent editions, less-used by everyone. The Center is the one place in the area where one copy of each edition of long-lived, frequently revised publications should be retained for historical reference and comparison. It is the logical resting place for the aforementioned administrative annual reports of medical institutions, organizations, and government agencies. The medical and paramedical dissertations from foreign universities, formerly held by the New York libraries, have been collected in MLC.

At the end of 1966 the holdings of the Medical Library Center included:

Journals	108,744
Textbooks and monographs	20,830
Government documents and institutional reports	20,665
Medical dissertations	209,000

The journals are a mixed lot of bound and unbound pieces; the figure 108,744 is items, not volumes.

ACQUISITIONS

While it is evident that the periodical holdings of the Medical Library Center duplicate those of some of its members, and the duplication is justified by the aforementioned use to fill requests of small libraries, in general the policy of MLC is to complement, rather than duplicate, the libraries of its members. For this reason, MLC does not acquire current textbooks and monographs. In a region as richly endowed with medical libraries as New York, complementary materials are likely to be the less-used types that fit comfortably into the MLC acquisitions policy. Current journals is an example. At present, subscriptions are maintained only for medical journals indexed in *Index Medicus* that are not received currently by any library in the New York area. The Center has entered subscriptions also for thirty-six uncommon veterinary journals, a scarce commodity in this urban area. Current journals in other subject areas, such as nursing and dentistry, should be added to the subscription list in the future. The Center not only houses the dissertations of foreign medical faculties but has assumed responsibility for keeping the collection up to date. Gaps in journal holdings are filled from exchange lists, and there is a long-range plan to assemble from member libraries their fragments of foreign journals to make stronger sets in MLC, using the Union Catalog as a guide.

A modest reference collection is maintained. Back volumes of indexing services are usually gifts, but current issues are obtained by subscription. An extensive collection of union lists has been acquired for reference by the staff of the Union Catalog of Medical Periodicals.

The cooperative acquisition of expensive and/or infrequently used reference works, outlined in the original policy statement, has only just begun. The first such purchase was a subscription to the costly periodical, *Adverse Reactions Titles*, with the multiple copies distributed to the member libraries that wish to have them.

CATALOGING AND PHYSICAL CARE

Cataloging procedures are simple. Journals, as is customary, are shelflisted by title, with holdings given in detail. They are, of course, included in the Union Catalog of Medical Periodicals. Inasmuch as MLC is not a browsing library, subject control of monographs and textbooks is unnecessary. Being shelved by size in fixed location, the books are identified by a location mark rather than a classification number. An author catalog only is maintained because all loans are interlibrary loans, and the items are requested by main entry, presumably verified in advance. Nevertheless the reference collection is useful for the checking of occasional puzzling requests.

Dissertations published during the last five years are shelved alphabetically by author. As they are retired from the current shelves, the older dissertations are arranged by university and year. To make author cards for over 200,000 dissertations would be a considerable undertaking and will be done only if experience shows that the present system is unworkable or if a bonanza and sufficient demand should justify publication of a dissertations catalog.

Annual reports are shelved in the conventional way, grouped by corporate body. A catalog of these is also a project for the distant future if the need is apparent.

Even though many of the periodicals are unbound, MLC has no binding program. Xerox copies are supplied in lieu of hard copy whenever it is possible. Therefore, we can preserve unbound issues, and it is often easier to copy pages in them. The Center owns a microfilm camera and will eventually film deteriorating journals, especially medical newspapers.

UNION CATALOG OF MEDICAL PERIODICALS

The computer-based Union Catalog of Medical Periodicals has been described elsewhere.[2,3] The articles referred to, however, do not describe its service policy.

The Union Catalog publishes volumes of selected periodical titles with library holdings and provides by telephone holdings information for the journals not included in these works. The policy, at present, is not to publish lists of journals that ceased publication before 1929, because such older material will not be sought frequently. The Union Catalog is, therefore, a service rather than a product.

The service and published volumes are included in membership in the Medical Library Center. Within MLC's service area—the New York Metropolitan Area—the service and publications are available also to nonmembers for a graduated annual subscription fee that is determined by the subscribing library's budget. In addition, libraries outside the New York Metropolitan Area may purchase the published volumes at cost and, presumably, they would not be interested in the telephone service at long distance rates. The installation of TWX, however, might result in a contradiction of this supposition.

Now that the conversion of the retrospective records to machine-readable form is nearly finished, it is possible to contemplate the addition of more contributing libraries. The first additions are about twenty libraries in Nassau County that had formerly compiled their own local union list. In the spring of 1966, when this list was in need of revision, the Medical Librarians of Long Island entered into an agreement with the Union Catalog for the preparation of a new Long Island Union List. The Union Catalog is absorbing the Long Island Union List but, at the same time, preserving its integrity on a separate computer tape so that a separate printout can be produced. The Union Catalog has assumed responsibility for updating its own and the Long Island lists as the librarians send in current information. The Medical Librarians of Long Island reimburse the Union Catalog for computer time and pay the cost of making multiple copies of the printout for local distribution. The Long Island Union List is not in competition with the Union Catalog; it enables the Long Island libraries to help one another with a compact local union list that is easy to use.

The new and revised computer programs of the Union Catalog of Medical Periodicals and the role that the Union Catalog is playing in helping other regional union lists develop should be the subjects of a separate article.

THE FUTURE

After only four years of operation, the present stack area of MLC is filled to capacity, and shelving has been installed on another floor. The additional stack area has 10,000 square feet and should hold another 100,000 items.

In the future, the strength of the Medical Library Center may be in rendering services rather than in warehousing books. That is the reason why, with the aid of a Resource Grant from the National Library of Medicine, a study of the feasibility of centralized and automated record keeping for circulation and serials control for our member libraries is in progress. The study is being made by Nelson Associates in collaboration with the Theodore Stein Company. They have been commissioned to determine how much each library should benefit by centralized record keeping; whether each library should delegate to MLC both functions, or one, or none; to recommend equipment to be used if the routines are automated; and to estimate the costs of the service. At the Jacobi Library, Mount Sinai School of Medicine, a current periodicals control system is being designed that makes use of data prepared for the Union Catalog of Medical Periodicals and may well be a prototype for serials control systems for other members.

The progress that has been reported is the result of the foresight, imagination, and energy of Erich Meyerhoff, the first Director of the Medical Library Center; the support of the member institutions; and the cooperation of the librarians of the member institutions. While new projects will undoubtedly pass through trial periods, the Medical Library Center as a whole appears to have survived the era of experimentation.

NOTES

[1] Meyerhoff, E. The Medical Library Center of New York: An experiment in cooperative acquisition and storage of medical library materials. Bulletin 51:501–506, Oct. 1963.

[2] Felter, J. W., and Tjoeng, D. S. A computer system for a union catalog: Theme and variations. Bulletin 53:163–177, Apr. 1965.

[3] Felter, J. W. The Union Catalog of Medical Periodicals of New York. In: Information Retrieval with Special Reference to the Biological Sciences. Minneapolis, University of Minnesota, Nolte Center for Continuing Education, 1966, p. 117–131.

ABOUT THE AUTHOR—Jacqueline W. Felter joined the staff of The Medical Library Center of New York in 1961 as Director of one of its programs, *The Union Catalog of Medical Periodicals*. She became Director of the Center in 1967. She received her B.S.L.S. from Western University, and after work in public and high school libraries, went to the New York Postgraduate Medical School and Hospital, where she later became Librarian. She was also for a number of years Librarian of the Memorial Sloan-Kettering Cancer Center.

Mrs. Felter has served on the editorial staff of the *Bulletin of the Medical Library Association*, was co-editor of the *Handbook of Medical Library Practice*, third edition (Chicago, Medical Library Association, 1970), and is a Past President of the Medical Library Association.

National Library of Medicine Support and Regional Medical Libraries

Support of the Regional Medical Libraries is only one aspect of the National Library of Medicine's contributions to a national biomedical communications network. Through its Lister Hill National Center for Biomedical Communications, the Library has studied the engineering and systems aspects of networks. Through various parts of the Medical Library Assistance Act, the Library has strengthened such elements of the system as publications and individual libraries and librarians.

The functions of the Lister Hill Center are suggested in the first paper and the total operation of the Medical Library Assistance Act is described in the second. The other two papers discuss two possible patterns for management of a Regional Medical Library, one highly centralized and the other decentralized.

The Lister Hill National Center for Biomedical Communications

by E. Grey Dimond

A single individual experience in medical libraries of the Washington, D.C., area contrasts the electronic conveniences of everyday life with the lack of new techniques in biomedical communication. It is hoped that the Lister Hill National Center for Biomedical Communications will relieve the situation.

To introduce my remarks, I will describe a recent experience of mine. I was in Washington temporarily and consequently away from my own library and from the library amenities which come with a position with a medical institution. I needed to have in my hands a copy of Paul Wood's book, The Heart and Circulation, published in 1956. I needed to document a statement in a manuscript I was preparing. Specifically, I wanted to be certain that in this particular edition of Paul Wood's book he had not indicated awareness of the altered heart movements in angina pectoris.

On this given day I therefore called the National Library of Medicine and asked if this particular book was available. Upon being assured that it was, I drove through 45 minutes of traffic to the Library and went immediately to the index file. There I found the catalog number, filled out the proper form and took it to the reference desk. I presented the card number and was asked to wait "a few minutes" while the book was brought to the desk from the stacks. At the end of some 30 minutes, during which time I interrupted the busy librarian three times to ask for progress reports, I learned that the book was indeed correctly cataloged and *should* be at the Library but that it was missing and presumed stolen. The librarian was concerned and helpful. She volunterred to obtain a loan copy but indicated it would take one or two days and I would need to return. I therefore drove to Georgetown University Medical School and went directly to the office of Dr. Proctor Harvey. I knew he had a copy of this particular book on his own shelf. I found his office locked and, upon inquiry, learned that both Dr. Harvey and his secretary were ill with Hong Kong flu and a key to his private office was not in the building.

Next I took myself to the nearby Medical School Main Library. There the librarian advised me that since I was "unknown" I would need to have some identification from a faculty member. We then called a Georgetown faculty member, who assured the librarian by telephone that it was appropriate for me to have access to the Library. Finally, the librarian placed before me a copy of Paul Wood's book, with the admonition that it could not be removed from the Library. I inquired about the possibility of Xeroxing certain pages and learned that this service was not available. I therefore copied in longhand for more than 30 minutes the specific paragraphs and references I needed. A total of some four hours had now passed since I set out to get my reference, and my enthusiasm received its final blow when I returned to my automobile and found a parking ticket on the windshield. Therefore, the human variables of traffic, theft of books, the absence of universal identification, Hong Kong flu, lack of copying equipment and a parking ticket were hardly evidence that this famed electronic era had influenced an ordinary physician and his relation to a medical library.

By contrast, I would like to review the life of most of us in this room over the past 72 hours. There would be variations, but for most of us the following experiences would qualify.

SOURCE: Reprinted from E. Grey Dimond, "The Lister Hill National Center for Biomedical Communications," an editorial in *American Journal of Cardiology*, 23 (May, 1969), pp. 629–632, by permission of the publisher and the author. Presented at the First Conference of the Lister Hill National Center for Biomedical Communications, National Library of Medicine, December 17, 1968.

1. You left your home and, upon presenting yourself at the check-in counter of the airline, the attendant glanced at your ticket, tapped the keyboard to a computer and in perhaps 15 seconds identified you, your class of travel, your location, your connecting planes and your destination. Remember the library where it took 30 minutes to identify a lost book?

2. Stepping out into the corridor you glanced up at the television screens which kept a constant record of every plane's coming and going, date and time. Remember the library where I waited 30 minutes, repeatedly interrupting the librarian while trying to understand the delay?

3. With 20 minutes to spend, you stopped at the bar and watched, live, the playing of the international golf tourney originating in St. Andrews, Scotland. Why cannot major medical events be seen routinely, privately, conveniently by physicians?

4. Aboard the plane you were able to watch a video film, hear classical or popular music, at your discretion. A printed program told you the sequence of the music, and you could switch from channel to channel as it suited you. Why cannot similar scheduling and programming, with a TV Medical Guide, be offered routinely, privately, conveniently to physicians?

5. The plane remained in constant radio and radar contact with the ground and, in addition, the captain reported to you the half-time score of a big game which was then being played on the ground thousands of miles away.

6. Unusual scenery passing below the plane was quietly called to your attention by intercom.

7. Upon your arrival you stepped up to a counter, greeted by a young lady who had never seen you before. You handed her a credit card; she did not glance at it but put it in a small press, moved her hand back and forth and handed you the keys to a $4,000 automobile. Remember that $15 book that was "on reserve" and could not be taken from the medical library?

8. At your hotel, you used the same magic carpet card and, next month, statements that literally no one has seen will come to your office. From signals put in motion by the credit card, the computer will compute the bill, address the envelope, stamp it and mail it. Can a patient routinely do this in your office? Clinic? Pharmacy? Hospital?

9. Just before going to bed, you picked up the hotel telephone, punched a sequence of perhaps 11 numbers and 10 seconds later the phone rang in your home and you were able to speak to your wife and children. From the beginning of the dialing until next month when the statement arrives, your conversation involved just you and your family and a computer. Computers, banked with medical facts, diagnostic analyses and clinical histories, could be reached equally rapidly and displayed on your personal television viewer.

10. You glanced at your watch, wondered about the correct time, picked up the telephone and a recorded voice told you precisely the local time. Your curiosity got the best of you and you decided to look at the phone book and see what else you could learn by quizzing the telephone. You were overwhelmed to learn that in Washington, D.C., you could:

Dial -A- Devotion
Dial -A- Dietician
Dial -A- Movie
Dial -A- Prayer
Dial -A- Saint
Dial -A- Satellite
Dial -A- Sermonette
Dial Family Bible

You could receive taped information on Alcoholics Anonymous, suicide prevention, poison prevention and the John Birch Society, also by telephone.

11. In addition, in this 72 hours, you undoubtedly read at least one newspaper each day, a current copy of *Time* or *Life Magazine* and a hardcover book, enjoyed seeing and hearing the live performance of Meet the Press on television, and fell asleep after watching a video tape of a good movie.

I could add to this list, but my intent is already clear to you. Specifically, the technology for a biomedical network is all about us and in use. We do not need to labor over its availability. Instead, we labor within our complex profession without the expedition that we consider ordinary in our nonprofessional lives.

However, there are other varieties of significance in these comments. First, not one thing that I have described was *necessary*. In 1820 we could equally well have assembled here in Washington, D.C. A handwritten letter of invitation would have been sent you in 1819, and you would have left your home some weeks ago and by horse, carriage and barge arrived safely. Good food and amenities have not changed and, even more thought-provoking, the capability of cerebration has not altered in these 148 years.

Today, as in 1820, the ultimate objective would be a meeting of men and women, an interplay of human brains, all with the same intellectual capacities and the same gamut of emotions, securities and ambitions.

You perceive my cumbersome point: all the remarkable devices I have listed are but *to facilitate* us. Our innate abilities have not changed, but our capacities for the endeavors which are a human being's specialty are extended. Human beings think, plan, create, cry, anticipate, care. . .and, especially, human beings are preferred by other human beings for their medical care. Machines but extend the time we have for these human specialties.

Another objective in defining the ways we are facilitated is to remind of the obvious: the newer method does not necessarily replace the old. Things will persist or disappear on merit. The jet is here, the barge is gone. Television is here, yet the book, magazine, newspaper and radio remain.

Still another point needs expression: the gamut of things used in our travels needed both *regional* and *national* contribution. The local news offered by radio and television is essential coverage, yet how impractical it would be for every television and radio station to insist upon providing its own national news program. The regional personalities have ready access to the press, radio and television, but it is accepted that some things are done better nationally. Some things can be afforded only if costs are shared. Some things done regionally (St. Andrew's golf tourney) need to be shared nationally.

Another obvious fact: some of the learning process or communication is best done totally alone, as with a journal or a book. Some of it requires a physical movement of people to a common meeting place where communication takes place by printed word, visual image, organized lectures, informal conversations and by technics that have no scientifically proved rationale—coffee breaks, liquor and food, corridor chats.

Still another obvious fact; just as we have noted that some programs are best done locally and some nationally, some can be well done with video tape replay but, equally, there is a place for the sense of involvement and anticipation and the excitement of sharing an unpredictable moment. Specifically, there is a need for live television. The fact that television makes it possible not only to hear but to see, guides us too often into utilizing unnecessary props, animation and motion. Yet some of the finest use of television—panel discussions, news presentations—requires only simple dialog, no props, slides, or personal involvement of the listener.

I dwell at some length on this point because many of us in medical education find ourselves restricting our understanding of how television has involved us. We find ourselves excessive in our use of props and animation and forgetful that voices, faces and content, *not the vehicle*, still are the message.

DEVELOPMENT OF A BIOMEDICAL COMMUNICATIONS NETWORK

We know that technology is available, that many media will continue to be needed and that there will be no violation of regional priorities with national imposition of programs. What, then, are some of the general or even new truths that must be considered in developing the Lister Hill National Center for Biomedical Communications Network?

I suggest that the following facts are pertinent:

1. Today's student is differently conditioned from yesterday's student. He arrives at college age having already watched 15,000 hours of television. He is comfortable with computers and programmed learning.

2. Although we usually think of educational categories—premedical student, medical student, intern, resident and practicing physician—in reality we are speaking of a continuum. From premedical to medical student, to house staff, to physician, we are speaking of the same human being at different stages of his life. Those technics of learning with which he becomes comfortable as a premedical student and medical student will stay with him throughout his lifetime. If our capacity for instruction during these formative years is limited to the patterns of the 1930's, how can we expect the mature practicing physician to be comfortable with the potential of his own computer console?

3. Medical care and medical education will increasingly share the same facilities and bring the medical school, community hospitals and the university campus all into a common endeavor.

4. The network potential is limited if we confine ourselves to thinking in terms of books and retrieval of book information. We must also think of universal medical records, universal insurance forms and universal data retrieval.

5. By a *national program* in which we define the

design and the numbers of communication units needed, we can hurry along with standardization and the advantages of lowered costs. We can then move on to placing the peripheral units in the home and office of every physician, medical student, resident and house officer. What is the usefulness of a national network unless there is absolutely universal ability to receive? How can we have universal ability to receive until we have standardized design and have lowered the cost of production and installation by defining the maximal number of recipients? How can we have the maximal number of recipients unless we get on with the training of individuals during their formative years in the concepts and technics of utilizating such a network? How can we separate any one part from the whole? The proliferation of "micro-networks" on a regional basis requires careful coordination if all are to be compatible with the national facility.

THE LISTER HILL NATIONAL CENTER

The Lister Hill Center will provide a national focus for developing the needed medical communications network of television, electronics and computers. There is now the realistic promise of two or three channels of television, received on the physician's personal set at his home, office and hospital, all keyed to a printed "TV Medical Guide" informing him of the channel and time for the variety of information needed:

1. Live transmission of any major medical meeting, from any place in the world.
2. Regularly scheduled repeat showings of such meetings, which he can see at a time convenient to him.
3. Formal, planned and sequential courses offered by medical school facilities, or a nationally representative faculty brought together under the sponsorship of the Lister Hill Center; programs which can be keyed to hospital staff conferences because of prior long-range scheduling.
4. A medical journal of the air, again regularly scheduled through the weekly TV Medical Guide, with articles presented in abstract, medical news, editorial comment, product information and the like.
5. Medical films stored regionally, requested by dial phone by the physician and seen at his own convenience on his own set.
6. Stored information, as vast and familiar as today's library, available at the physician's desk, either seen visually on the television screen or printed by his own copying device. All available by dial phone to computer-stored data banks; differential diagnosis, drug advice, consulting advice and bibliographic references, among others.
7. Self-examination televised quizzes; skillfully developed programmed learning.

One suggests that the time is right, the need great and the technics ready for this new legislation of August 3, 1968 (Public Law 90-456), formally establishing The Lister Hill National Center for Biomedical Communications, and a benevolent giant in medical education has been launched.

ABOUT THE AUTHOR–Dr. E. Grey Dimond is Distinguished Professor of Medicine and Provost for the Health Sciences, University of Missouri-Kansas City. Before that he was a Member of the Scripps Institute of Oceanography, La Jolla, California, serving as Research Associate, Physiology Research Laboratory, and Director, Institute for Cardiopulmonary Diseases. During the 1950's he was Professor of Medicine and Chairman, Department of Medicine, and Director of the Cardiovascular Laboratory, University of Kansas Medical School. He has a B.S. and M.D. from Indiana University, and was House Officer at the Indiana University Medical Center. He was also a Fellow at the Massachusetts General Hospital and Lecturer at the School of Aviation Medicine, San Antonio, Texas.

He is certified by the American Board of Internal Medicine and by the Sub-board in Cardiology. He has served on the Board of Trustees of the American College of Cardiology and was its President. He was a Member of the White House Conference on Health in 1965 and in 1971 served on the Committee on Automation Opportunities in Service Areas of the Federal Council for Science and Technology. He is a Consultant to the Lister Hill Center for Biomedical Communications and Special Consultant to the Assistant Secretary for Health and Scientific Affairs, Department of Health, Education and Welfare. He was a Scholar-In-Residence at the Library in 1967. Among several books he has written is *Electrocardiography*, now in its fourth edition; he is Editor-in-Chief of ACCESS, the American College of Cardiology's audio tape journal.

The Medical Library Assistance Act: An Analysis of the NLM Extramural Programs, 1965–1970

by Martin M. Cummings, and Mary E. Corning

The five-year experience in administration of the Medical Library Assistance Act is summarized. Of $40.8 million expended, the largest amounts were spent for resources and construction. Activities to date provide a reasonable base for improved services, but leave the medical library community with a number of challenges for innovative use of funds in planning for the future.

INTRODUCTION

The Medical Library Assistance Act, PL 89-291, (MLAA), was enacted by the U.S. Congress in October 1965. In the five fiscal years (FY 1966-1970) which have elapsed, 40.8 million dollars have been made available to the medical library community from the National Library of Medicine under a competitive grant and contract mechanism. The length of time and the amount of money expended justify an assessment of

1. The fundamental concepts embodied in the Act
2. The allocation of resources to fulfill the expectations of the Act
3. The impact on the National Library of Medicine
4. The performance and level of accomplishment by the medical library community which received these funds, and
5. The impact on users.

STATUS OF THE MEDICAL LIBRARY COMMUNITY PRIOR TO THE MLAA

The concepts developed and embodied in the MLAA reflected both the strengths and weaknesses of the U.S. medical library community.

In 1964, the National Library of Medicine (NLM) was serving as a national resource; it had a budget of $4 million, a staff of 350, provided services nationwide, and was an innovator in the use of technology to develop a computer-based information storage and retrieval system (MEDLARS) which had just become operational.

The weak status of the medical libraries in this country had been described by Deitrick and Berson[1] and Bloomquist.[2] In 1962, the Surgeon General held a Conference on Health Communications.[3] The recommendations related to the need for improved communications research, training, and the use of libraries as communications centers and resources.

The National Academy of Sciences–National Research Council (NAS-NRC) studied "Communication Problems in Biomedical Research"[4] in 1963. The NAS-NRC conclusions and recommendations emphasized the responsibilities of the biomedical community for facilities and services, research and development, training and coordination of the biomedical information complex. The U.S. President's Commission on Heart Disease, Cancer and Stroke[5] assessed communications problems within the context of three specific diseases; and its communications recommendations were specifically addressed to the need for better facilities, resources, and legislation. Thus, significant studies and evaluations from professional user

SOURCE: Reprinted from Martin M. Cummings and Mary E. Corning, "The Medical Library Assistance Act: An Analysis of the NLM Extramural Programs, 1965-1970," *Bulletin of the Medical Library Association,* 59 (July, 1971), pp. 375-391, by permission of the publisher and the authors. Presented at the Seventieth Annual Meeting of the Medical Library Association, New York, New York, June 3, 1971, as part of the General Session.

groups highlighted the need for improved biomedical communication.

Activity in the medical library world was reflected in the substantive articles of the 1964 issues of the *Bulletin of the Medical Library Association*[6] which reviewed the National Library of Medicine's new computer-based system, MEDLARS, *Medical Subject Headings (MeSH)*, and the NLM bibliographic services. The relative service roles of both the NLM and individual libraries in interlibrary lending and photocopying, and the establishment of an MLA Committee on the NLM were treated in Editorials and News Notes.[7]

Other articles in the *Bulletin* described an International Congress on Medical Librarianship; operating aspects of individual medical libraries; mechanization; library statistics; the growth of the literature in specialized areas of health. A special section was devoted to "Regional Plans for Medical Library Service" with representatives from six states assessing independently their current and potential scope of services. There was a recurring theme: librarians were interested in responding to more than their immediate local clientele; but they were hampered by lack of facilities, equipment, staff, and money.

This can be expressed as the imbalance between library resources and users' demands for services. This imbalance can be traced to the greatly increased funding of medical research and education with no attendant increase for library resources. During 1964, NLM examined the great disparity between the present and potential roles of a medical library. Problems existed in meeting the needs of the professional user, whether he worked in health research, education or practice. These problems were traceable to the fundamental issues of the nature, availability and utilization of resources—both human and materiel. Some physicians and scientists, geographically distant from modern library facilities, were found to be isolated from current information sources. Some libraries could be characterized not only by inadequate funding but by a low level of performance. The NLM commissioned studies to be done by the Association of American Medical Colleges[8,9,10] on needs of medical school libraries, and requested assistance from the Medical Library Association to crystalize data and statistics on problems facing medical libraries.[11]

NLM also reexamined the NLM mandate from the U.S. Congress to serve as a national resource and "to assist the advancement of medical and related sciences and to aid the dissemination and exchange of scientific and other information important to the progress of medicine and to the public health." As a result of these examinations, Cummings recommended that the future role of the National Library of Medicine should include programs to upgrade the nation's medical libraries and recommended regional and local interrelationships in which the constituent elements would have clearly defined roles and responsibilities. The totality would then be a strong entity which would encompass a sharing of talent and resources to achieve the primary objective of responding more effectively to the information needs of the health professional.

Specifications were then developed for legislation which would create new programs directed at both the individual and the institution, and at local, regional and national levels. Cummings[12] described NLM's proposed supporting functions and activities at the dedication of the Countway Library in 1965. He presented the philosophy underlying the pending legislation, which was subsequently enacted by the U.S. Congress in October 1965, as the Medical Library Assistance Act (PL 89-291):

> It is my view that the time has come for rapid expansion of library resources locally. Continued dependency of the more than 6,000 medical libraries upon the services of the National Library of Medicine would lead ultimately to the evolution of a monolithic medical library resource in this nation. For the convenience of the user, for the inspiration which the presence of the local library gives to its own community, for the serendipity which accompanies browsing and search, strong medical libraries must exist wherever there are strong biomedical interests.
>
> In my view, our country requires the development of a complex of regional medical libraries with adequate facilities, resources, and personnel to serve those sections of the nation with underdeveloped library facilities. NLM has submitted legislative specifications to Congress and the Administration requesting authority and funds to provide assistance to local and regional libraries for (1) library construction, (2) training of librarians, (3) research in the field of information sciences, (4) library resources, (5) development of regional libraries, (6) publications and translations support. I am encouraged by the favorable reaction of librarians, physicians, and scientists to these proposals.

During this same year (1965), articles published in the *Bulletin* showed a continued preoccupation with MEDLARS activities; and the Medical Library Assistance Act occupied the Editorial and News Notes Sections.

By contrast, in 1970, 25 percent of the papers published in the MLA *Bulletin* described activities funded by the Medical Library Assistance Act. Subjects included educational needs of health sciences library manpower; information needs of specialty groups; mechanization of library procedures; automated serials accession systems; library management data; and regional medical libraries—their services and functions.

INTERRELATIONSHIP OF NLM AND THE MEDICAL LIBRARY COMMUNITY (FY 1966–1970)

During the period of the MLAA (July 1965–June 1970), the total five-year cumulative budget of the NLM was approximately $87.6 million. Of this, NLM provided 49 percent or $43 million to the U.S. medical library community: 40.8 million under the MLAA and 2.2 million through contracts for MEDLARS Centers and other library-based activities. This sum is relatively large when viewed against a prior base of no federal support for medical libraries, It is small in comparison with the total national expenditures for health care, medical research, and communications. The total (extramural and intramural) efforts of the National Library of Medicine in 1969 represented only 0.03 percent of the overall national funding for health activities (Fig.1). However, the very existence of these funds is significant because they are unique and are the principal existing mechanism for the exclusive improvement of the resources and services of U.S. medical libraries.

In any federal grant program, the funding institution cannot dictate the usage of these funds. It can only present the philosophy, the objectives, the criteria, and then respond to the submitted proposals which are evaluated by an external review group for technical merit and priority. Accordingly, the usage of the NLM funds essentially reflects the perspective and priorities of the medical library community.

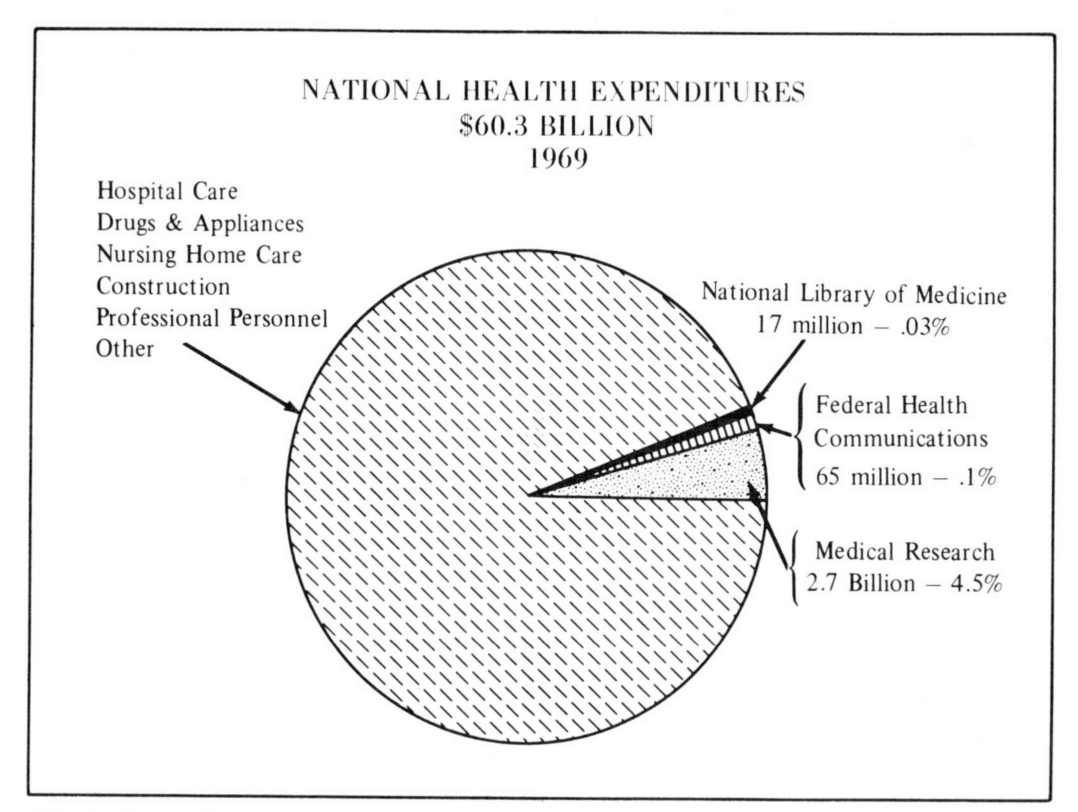

FIG. 1 National health expenditures in 1969 for health care, medical research and communications.

PROGRAMS EXECUTED UNDER THE MLAA

The underlying purpose of the MLAA is to improve biomedical information services. This assumes a conversion from traditional attitudes and mechanisms to emphasize that (1) the modern medical library is part of the communication process, and (2) improved communication is necessary for advances in medical research, education and practice.

The MLAA (1965) authorized the following programs:

1. Construction of facilities
2. Training in medical library sciences
3. Special scientific projects
4. Research and development in medical library science and related fields
5. Improvement and expansion of the basic resources of medical libraries and related instrumentalities
6. Establishment of regional medical libraries
7. Biomedical publications, and
8. Regional branches of the National Library of Medicine.

The NLM has acted to implement all of these programs with the exception of establishing our own Regional Branches. We decided, instead, to try to improve existing resources rather than to create competitive federal entities.

Comparison of the level of funding authorized by Congress under the MLAA and the funds actually appropriated (Table 1A) indicates that only 39 percent of the total authorization was made available to the NLM. The distribution of authorized and appropriated funds by program illustrates two program areas received 50 percent or more of funds authorized; Training Grants and Resource Grants.

The NLM has maintained records of those projects which have been approved but could not be

TABLE 1

COMPARISON OF NLM AUTHORIZATION, APPROPRIATIONS, AND UNFUNDED PROJECTS UNDER THE MEDICAL LIBRARY ASSISTANCE ACT OF 1965 FOR FY 1966-1970 (JULY 1, 1965–JUNE 30, 1970)
(Million $)

(A)

Program	Funds Authorized	Funds Appropriated and Awarded	Percentage of Authorized Funds Appropriated	Number of Projects
Resources	$15	$11.8	79%	402
Construction	40	11.3	28	11
Research and Development	15	6.0	40	103
Regional Medical Libraries	12.5	4.7	38	10
Training	5	4.5	90	28
Publications	5	2.3	46	43
Special Scientific Projects	2.5	.2	8	7
NLM Regional Branches	10	0	0	0
Totals	$105	$40.8	39%	604

(B)

Program	Difference Between Authorized and Appropriated Funds	Project Funds Requested but Unavailable
Resources	$ 3.2	$ .9
Construction	28.7	34.8
Research and Development	9.0	.5
Regional Medical Libraries	7.8	.9
Training	.5	.3
Publications	2.7	.2
Special Scientific Projects	2.3	0
NLM Regional Branches	10	0
Totals	$64.2	$37.6

supported due to inadequate funding. The amount of monies represented by these unfunded projects (Table 1B) are identified by program areas. Only in the construction program does the sum of the funded and unfunded projects total more than the original estimate of needs as reflected in the basic Congressional authorization. In all other program areas, the level of unfunded projects does not equal, and oftentimes is a small percentage of what had been originally estimated as needed by the medical library community. There are three interpretations for this: (1) the original estimate in the Act was not realistic, (2) the scarcity of funding tempered the number of requests received by the NLM, or (3) the medical library community was unable to convince those who authorized appropriations of its needs. We believe the interpretations (2) and (3) are the primary reasons for the failure to achieve more adequate funding.

The total number of grants awarded through the MLAA was 604, and the distribution by programs and funds is shown in Table 1A. Figure 2 gives the percentage distribution of MLAA funds by program areas. Resource Grants utilized 29 percent; Construction 28 percent; Research and Development 15 percent; Regional Medical Libraries 12 percent; Training/Fellowships 11 percent; Publications 6 percent; and Special Scientific Projects 0.5 percent.

We have tried to estimate how the MLAA funds have been utilized in terms of personnel, materiel, services and techniques. These figures are shown in Figure 3. Although there needs to be some refinement of the data, the gross picture is clear. Assistance for materiel has been provided within the Construction, Resource, Publications, and Regional Medical Library (RML) Grants. The Training Program emphasis has been on people, and salaries have been provided for medical library staff through both the Resource and Regional Medical Library Programs. Techniques (development and utilization of technologies) are made possible through both the Resource and the Research and Development Programs. The service function is primarily reflected within the RML program. Overall, it is clear that emphasis has been overwhelmingly on materiel (55 percent),

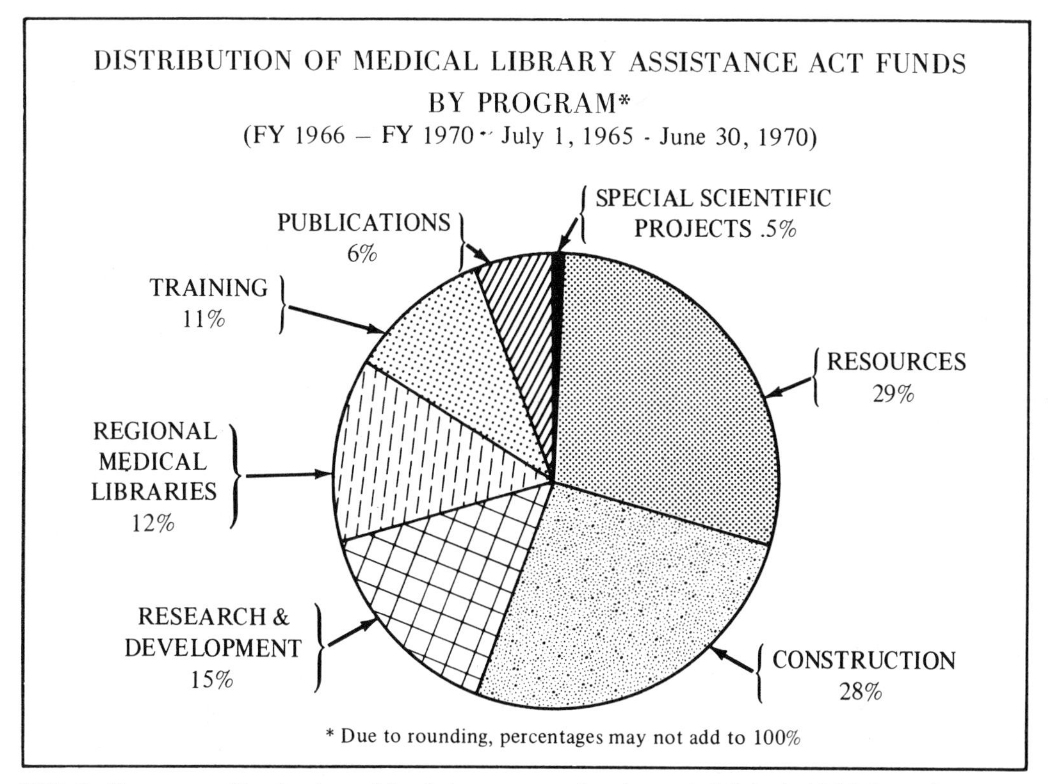

FIG. 2 Percentage distribution of funds by program for the period July 1, 1965 through June 30, 1970.

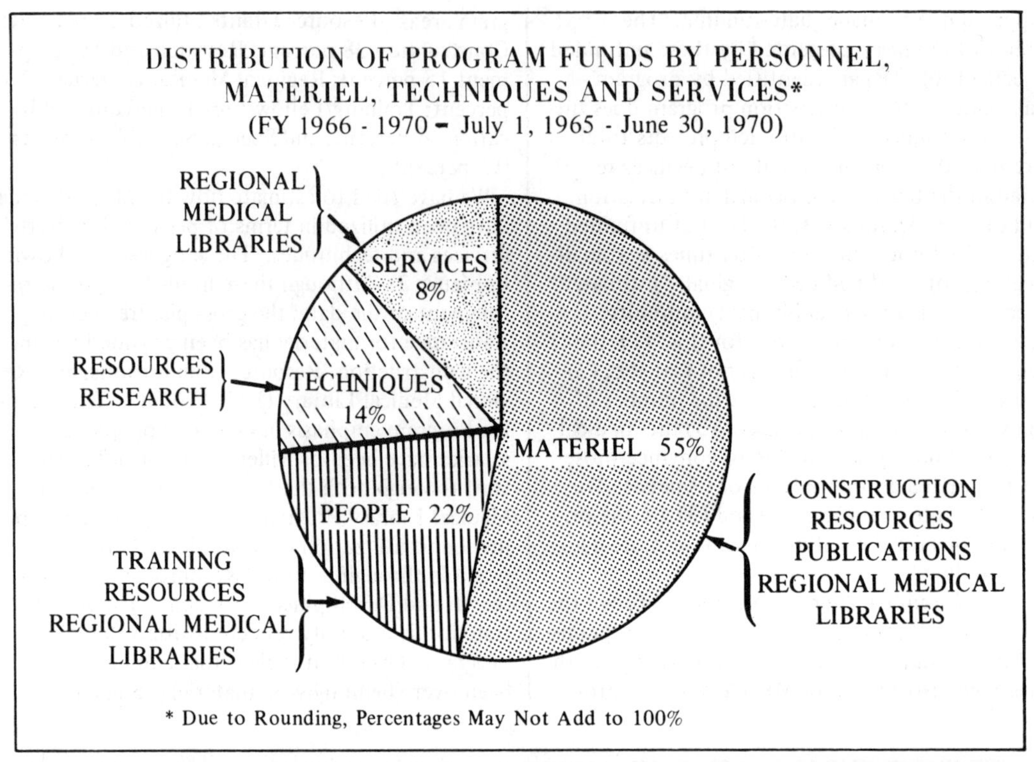

FIG. 3 Percentage distribution of program funds by personnel, materiel, techniques and services for the period July 1, 1965 through June 30, 1970.

with relatively little emphasis on new services (8 percent).

Some specific details on the individual programs follow.

RESEARCH AND DEVELOPMENT

The Research and Development Program was intended to encourage research in medical library science and the development of new techniques, systems and equipment for information storage and retrieval. The projects have been grouped in three categories.

1. Library Services, Operations and Manpower—projects concerning development and evaluation of information activities in libraries, and studies of manpower needs and training to provide these services
2. Biomedical Communications Usage and Tools—projects, studies, publications in the broad field of biomedical communications
3. History of Medicine and the Life Sciences—historical studies of matters related to health and medicine

The distribution of the number of grants and contracts and funds among the three program categories is given in Table 2. Library services accounted for 13 percent of the projects and 35 percent of the funds; biomedical communications 42 percent of the projects and 49 percent of the funds; and history of medicine 45 percent of the projects and 16 percent of the funds.

Projects supported have included surveys on health library manpower, an on-line computer serials control system, studies of communication patterns among medical researchers, development of standard nomenclatures, evaluation of self-instruction materials, and language analysis for information retrieval. There has been heavy emphasis within the program on history of medicine projects. New research methodology was not a prominent feature of grant applications by librarians and information specialists. Thus, few research projects to date have led to the application and implementation of new modes of biomedical communications.

TABLE 2

NLM RESEARCH AND DEVELOPMENT PROGRAM GRANTS AND CONTRACTS AWARDED, FY 1966-70 (JULY 1, 1965–JUNE 30, 1970)

Category	Number of Projects	Amount (Million $)
Library Services, Operations and Manpower	14	2.1
Biomedical Communications Usage and Tools	43	3.0
History of Medicine	46	1.0
Total	103	6.1

TRAINING

The Training Program included both training grants and fellowships as follows:

(1) Traineeships and fellowships for advanced academic degrees in library or information science
(2) Retraining or special training for health science librarians or information specialists
(3) Institutional programs for training in library science and communication
(4) Establishment of internship programs in medical libraries.

A summary of the training grants and fellowships is shown in Table 3. The training funds made available by the NLM for FY 1966-70 will have provided for the training of approximately 350 individuals. The average cost per trainee is $8,100, of which 57 percent covers stipend and trainee expenses, and 43 percent is nontrainee expenditures. Insufficient emphasis was placed on retraining existing librarians in modern information-handling methods, and there were no grants to train library assistants.

PUBLICATIONS

Forty-three scientific health publications, critical reviews, atlases, compendia, and abstracting and indexing tools were supported, with an expenditure of $2.3 million under this program. Many secondary literature services and specialized subjects series have resulted and these would not have been supported by commercial ventures (Table 4).

TABLE 3

NLM TRAINING PROGRAMS, FY 1966-70 (JULY 1, 1965–JUNE 30, 1970)

	Projects Funded	Individuals Supported[1]
A. Training Grants:		
Non-Degree Programs	6	77
Degree Programs		
Masters	9	143
Ph.D.	5	33
Total	20	253*
B. Fellowships:		
Postdoctoral Research		
History	6	6
Biomedical Communications.	2	2
Total	8	8

*Training programs funded during 1966-70 will have provided training for approximately 350 individuals, some of whom will actually receive this training in FY 1971. Funds awarded totaled $4.46 million.

[1] During 1966-70; some for more than one year.

TABLE 4

NLM PUBLICATION PROGRAM GRANTS AND CONTRACTS, FY 1966-70 (JULY 1, 1965–JUNE 30, 1970)

Category	No. of Projects
Abstracts	8
Atlases	6
Bibliographies	6
Critical Reviews	1
Handbooks and Catalogs	8
Monographs	3
Translation Projects	6
Other Media	5
Total	43
Total $ Awarded	2.3 Million

SPECIAL SCIENTIFIC PROJECTS

This program provided ten special fellowships for preparing scholarly studies on topics such as discovery, regulation and use of drugs, and interorganizational aspects of urban community health. Approximately $200,000 was expended for this program. Although the quality of work seems uniformly good, the small number of participants who applied has been disappointing.

It is evident that few scholars accepted this

TABLE 5

LIST OF INSTITUTIONS RECEIVING NLM CONSTRUCTION GRANTS (FISCAL YEARS 1967-1970)*

	RML Region	Type of Institution	Award	Net S.F. Area	Volume Capacity
Boston University Boston, Massachusetts	I	Medical School	$ 1,017,891	29,900	100,000
Brown University Providence, Rhode Island	I	Medical School	536,331	14,119	100,000
Rutgers, The State University New Brunswick, New Jersey	II	Medical School	541,293	12,498	100,000
Jefferson University Philadelphia, Pennsylvania	III	Medical School	1,765,636	44,465	145,000
George Washington University Washington, D. C.	IV	Medical School	1,295,595	29,271	80,000
Wayne State University Detroit, Michigan	V	Medical School	1,459,567	50,107	130,000
Auburn University Auburn, Alabama	VI	Vet. Med. School	101,229	4,000	17,000
Southern College of Optometry Memphis, Tennessee	VI	Optometry School	176,525	5,924	20,000
University of Nebraska Omaha, Nebraska	VIII	Medical School	1,636,077	59,629	273,000
University of Utah Salt Lake City, Utah	VIII	Medical School	1,121,450	35,425	190,000
University of Texas (Medical Branch) Galveston, Texas	IX	Medical School	1,598,406	48,783	150,000
Totals			$11,250,000	334,121	1,305,000

*Congressional appropriations were not made for Construction until FY 1967.

opportunity to do creative writing and study. The deficiency rests with the U. S. medical community and not with librarians.

CONSTRUCTION

Construction grants were made to eleven institutions: nine Medical Schools; one School of Optometry; and one School of Veterinary Medicine. The specifics are given in Table 5. It is clear that this program will have a profound impact on improving library resources in those areas where they are being constructed. There is a great need to expand this program to other needy institutions (approximately twenty-five to forty).

RESOURCES

Under the Resource Grant Program 401 grants have been made, totaling 11.8 million dollars. The distribution and utilization of these grants provides us with an interesting commentary on medical library operations. Approximately 50 percent of the number of resource grants went to hospital libraries, whereas 63 percent of the funds went to medical libraries within academic institutions (Figures 4 and 5). Over 50 percent of the funds expended under the resource grants were used to acquire journals, books, and informational materials. Approximately 24 percent of the monies enabled the medical libraries to increase the number of their staff, and 16 percent was for the purchase of equipment.

Thus, this program has had a major impact on the enlargement of collections. More than 400 local libraries have been assisted, but most did not use the funds to improve the nature and scope of services through increased manpower or by the application of new technology.

REGIONAL MEDICAL LIBRARIES

As noted earlier, the NLM decided not to establish its own Regional Branches but chose to sup-

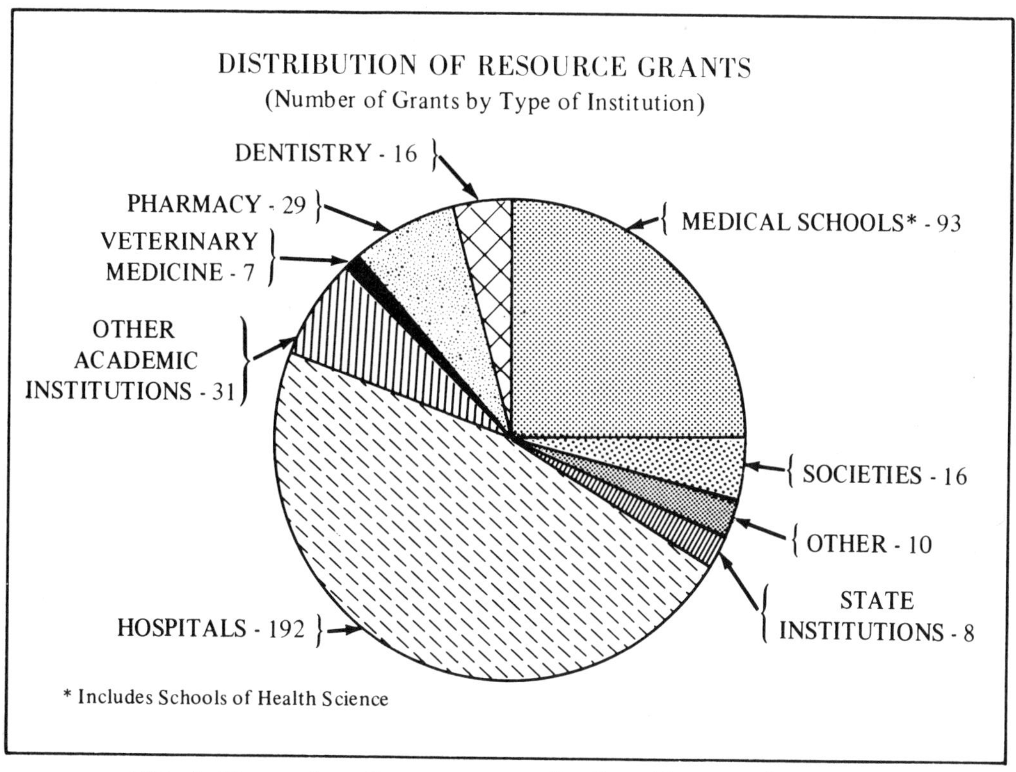

FIG. 4 The number of resource grants distributed by type of institution.

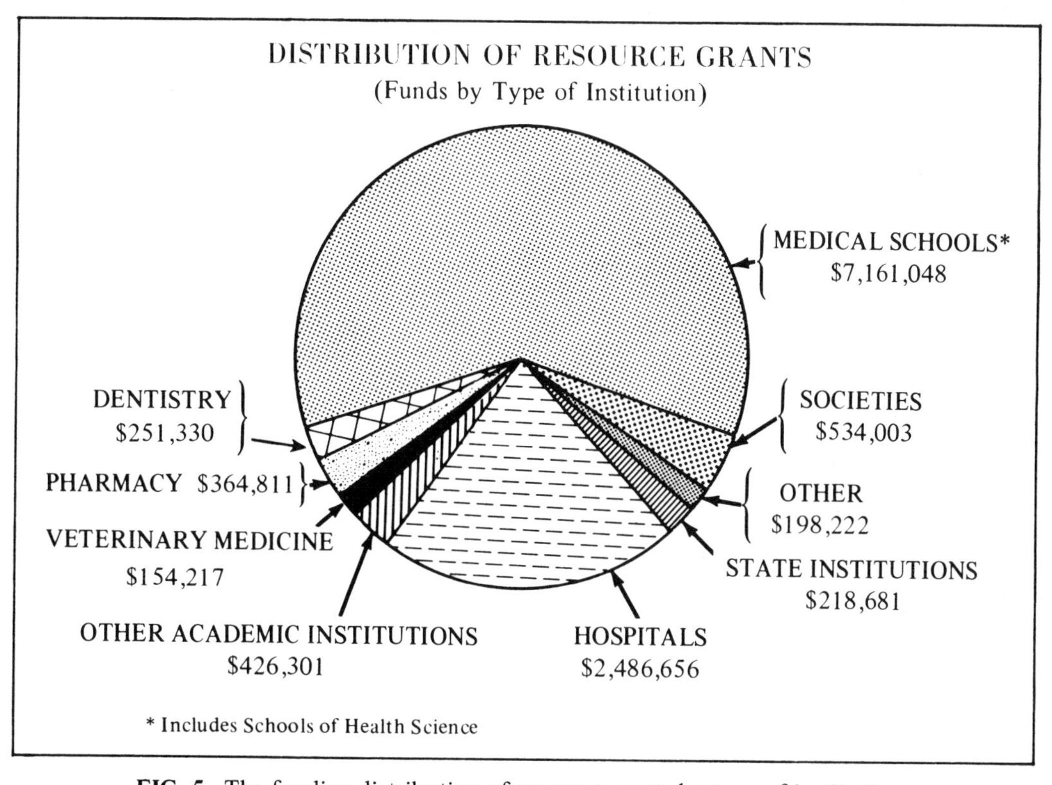

FIG. 5 The funding distribution of resource grants by type of institution.

port regional services through existing libraries of excellence or those with potential. We tried to develop a "network" to achieve the goal of responding more effectively to the needs of the health professionals. We did not define the "network" as a rigid unchanging snare of interconnections; we visualized a planned sharing of resources systematically so that improved services could be provided with maximum efficient utilization of available resources—manpower, fiscal, and technological. Thus, the underlying principle was "cooperative service."

In order to assist the local institutions in a systematic and constructive manner, we established a regional link to interrelate the national and local institutional levels. This link was the Regional Medical Library. Regional Medical Libraries were principally university-based, were selected competitively from libraries with strong collections, well-trained staffs, and a good record of providing medical library services. The first Regional Medical Library was established at Harvard in 1967. Today there are eleven such Regional Medical Libraries, with the National Library of Medicine, itself, designated as a Regional Library for a geographic area in the mid-Atlantic United States (Table 6).

The hierarchical concept for the Medical Library Network (Figure 6) is as follows:

1. The NLM is the comprehensive national resource which can assist other medical libraries in terms of material not in their collection, as well as serving as the medical indexing and cataloging center for the nation.
2. The Regional Libraries are to improve and expand their reference and interlibrary loan services to medical and hospital libraries in a broad geographic area, and
3. The local libraries are to assist individual health professionals as the closest point for library service.

Designation as a Regional Medical Library required the recipient institution to increase its scope and nature of services to health professional users in a broader geographic area. Since the operation of the first Regional Medical Library in 1967, 4.7 million dollars have been expended and all eleven of the Regional Medical Libraries are in various stages of operational activity. If one examines the last year of operations for seven Regional Medical Libraries (with four of them operational for less than one year), the distribution of 1.65 million dollars in grant funds in terms of service is:

42% for Interlibrary Loan Services
17% MEDLARS Demand Search Services
9% Education and Consultation primarily for local hospital libraries
7% Preparation of Union Lists
6% Orientation and Information Programs
4% Reference Services
15% Other (Management and Overhead)

Prior to the establishment of the Regional Medical Libraries in 1967, the National Library of Medicine was receiving on a national basis approximately 175,000 interlibrary loan requests annually (Figure 7). In the subsequent three years, with the Regional Medical Libraries in various stages of operational capability, the total national interlibrary loan activity for both the National Library of Medicine and the Regional Medical Libraries has more than doubled. This is a real measurement of successful performance. If one excludes interlibrary loan requests which NLM receives in its role as a Regional Medical Library, and from foreign sources, then the level of interlibrary loan requests NLM receives in its capacity as a national resource has dropped to approximately 48,000. Although fewer in number, these requests are for the most inaccessible and rare items in the medical literature. Overall, however, we still provide more than 100,000 loans annually.

The establishment, in 1964, of the NLM's computer-based bibliographic storage and retrieval system, MEDLARS, generated considerable demand for MEDLARS demand searches throughout the U. S. and abroad. Accordingly, decentralized MEDLARS Centers were established in the United States. Some of these centers are part of the Regional Medical Libraries; others are located in different institutions in the same region and they work cooperatively with the Regional Medical Library. In the last year, there were 22,000 MEDLARS demand searches released. Of these, approximately 16 percent were performed by NLM, 48 percent by U. S. Centers, and 36 percent by Foreign Centers. The interlibrary loan and the demand search services are thus two functions of the National Library of Medicine which have been decentralized successfully in an effort to make these services available more efficiently to the professional health user. We are now planning to decentralize AIM-TWX, our successful on-line bibliographic service in a similar way.

An analysis of distribution of funds by program,

TABLE 6

LIBRARIES RECEIVING NLM GRANTS TO SERVE AS REGIONAL MEDICAL LIBRARIES IN ELEVEN GEOGRAPHIC REGIONS

	States	Funds (Million $)	Operational
#1–New England New England Regional Medical Library The Francis A. Countway Library of Medicine Boston, Massachusetts	Connecticut Maine Massachusetts New Hampshire Rhode Island Vermont	1.020	10/1/67
#2–New York New York & Northern New Jersey Regional Medical Library New York Academy of Medicine New York, N. Y.	New Jersey (Northern Counties: Bergen, Essex, Hudson, Hunterdon, Middlesex, Morris, Passaic, Somerset, Sussex, Union, & Warren) New York	.336	2/16/70
#3–Mid-Eastern Mid-Eastern Regional Medical Library College of Physicians of Philadelphia Philadelphia, Pennsylvania	Delaware New Jersey (Southern Counties: Atlantic, Burlington, Camden, Cape May, Cumberland, Gloucester, Mercer, Monmouth, Ocean, & Salem)	.715	7/1/68
#4–Mid-Atlantic Mid-Atlantic Regional Medical Library P. O. Box 30260 Bethesda, Maryland–(NLM)	Maryland North Carolina Virginia Washington, D. C. West Virginia		
#5–East Central Kentucky-Ohio-Michigan Regional Medical Library Wayne State University Detroit, Michigan	Kentucky Michigan Ohio	.256	4/1/69
#6–Southeastern Southeastern Regional Medical Library A. W. Calhoun Medical Library Woodruff Research Building Emory University Atlanta, Georgia	Alabama Florida Georgia Mississippi Puerto Rico South Carolina Tennessee	.470	1/2/70
#7–Midwest Midwest Regional Medical Library The John Crerar Library Chicago, Illinois	Illinois Indiana Iowa Minnesota North Dakota Wisconsin	.325	11/18/68
#8–Midcontinental Mid-Continental Regional Medical Library University of Nebraska Medical Center Omaha, Nebraska	Colorado Kansas Missouri Nebraska South Dakota Utah Wyoming	.228	7/1/70
#9–South Central University of Texas Southwestern Medical School at Dallas Dallas, Texas	Arkansas Louisiana New Mexico Oklahoma Texas	.178	2/1/70

TABLE 6—*Continued*

	States	Funds (Million $)	Operational
#10–Pacific Northwest Pacific Northwest Regional Health Sciences Library University of Washington Seattle, Washington	Alaska Idaho Montana Oregon Washington	.639	10/1/68
#11–Pacific Southwest Pacific Southwest Regional Medical Library, Center for Health Science University of California Los Angeles, California	Arizona California Hawaii Nevada	.512	9/1/69

according to regions presently defined for the Regional Libraries (Figure 8), indicates that each of the regions was funded in the 3.4–4.4 million dollar range, with two exceptions, Region VI (Southeastern) and Region X (Pacific Northwest). Although the funding would appear to have a fairly consistent distribution overall, the constituent elements vary considerably from region to region.

Construction funds increase the level of funding for each region. However, Regions VII (Midwest) and XI (Pacific Southwest) which had no construction monies still maintain a high overall figure because of emphasis on research and training. In these two areas only, the research and training funds totaled more than resource funds. By contrast, in Regions I (New England), II (New York), and VI (Southeast) the sum spent for both research and training was less than one-half that spent for resources.

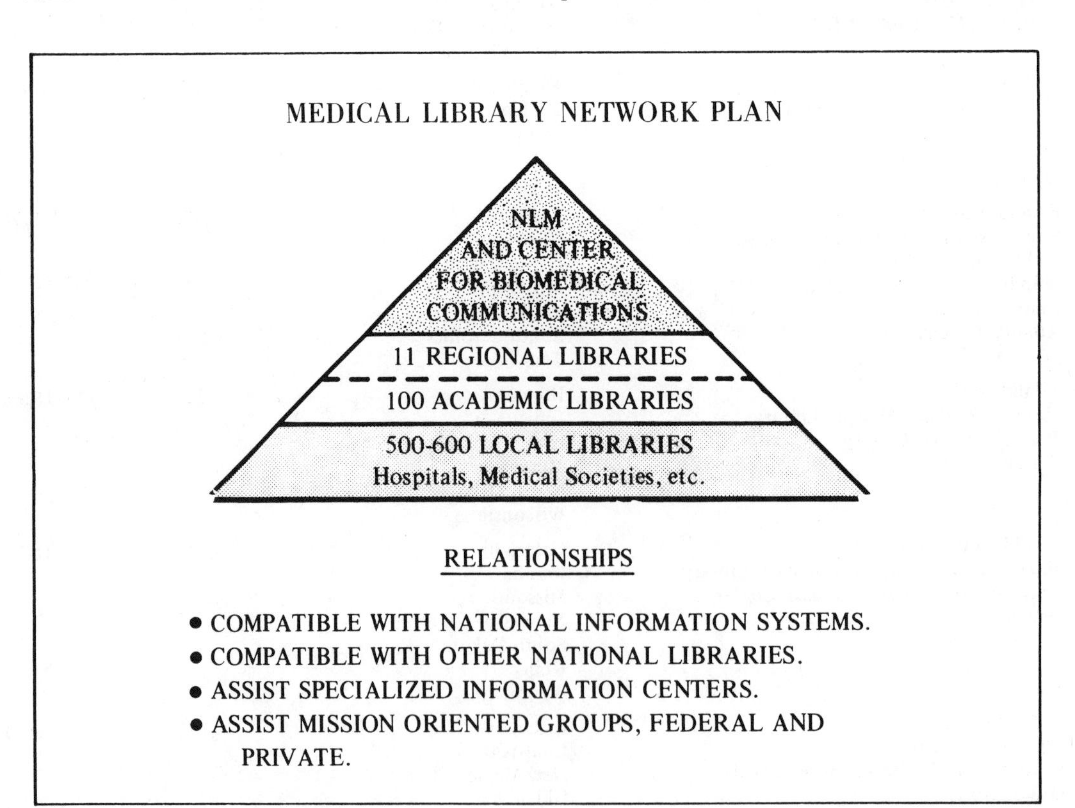

FIG. 6. Hierarchical structure of Medical Library Network Plan.

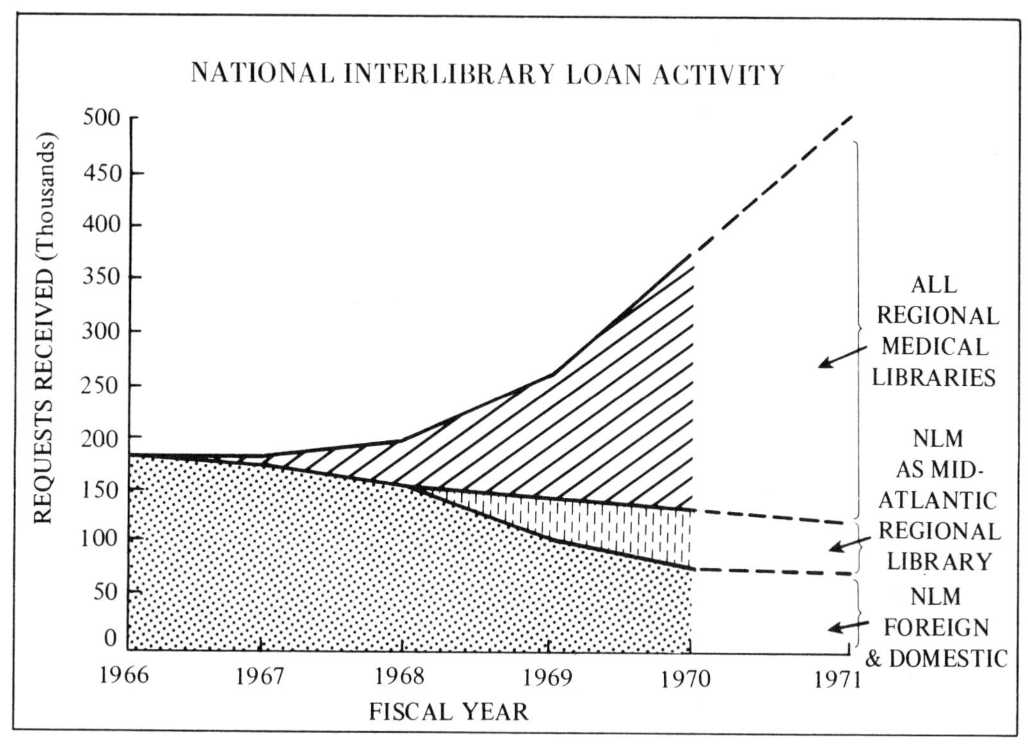

FIG. 7 A comparison of the distribution of national interlibrary loan activity before and after the establishment of Regional Medical Libraries.

ASSESSMENT OF THE MEDICAL LIBRARY ASSISTANCE ACT

Fundamental Concepts Embodied in the Act

The fundamental concept of the Medical Library Assistance Act is to develop a cooperative sharing of resources in order to improve library and information services to the health community. The Act provides the mechanism and the authorization for funding to achieve this goal. We continue to believe that this is a firm and constructive basis for developing a national medical library network with clearly delineated responsibilities at the national, regional, and local levels.

Allocation of Resources

The appropriation of resources to fulfill the expectations of the Act has been 39 percent of what had been authorized. Accordingly, we have fallen short of goals which we had originally identified. For example, we had hoped to reach 600–700 medical libraries through our resource program; instead, we were able to assist only 400. We were informed in 1964 of immediate construction needs for eighty-six health sciences libraries, but we have been able to assist only eleven. Our training program has served to stimulate and encourage specialization in medical librarianship, but it cannot begin to fulfill overall manpower requirements. Thus, in both the specific and overall programs we have made a beginning, but the limited availability of funds has prevented more substantial accomplishments.

Impact on the National Library of Medicine

The MLAA has affected NLM both organizationally and functionally:

1. NLM has become part of a national medical library network instead of serving as every institution's library.

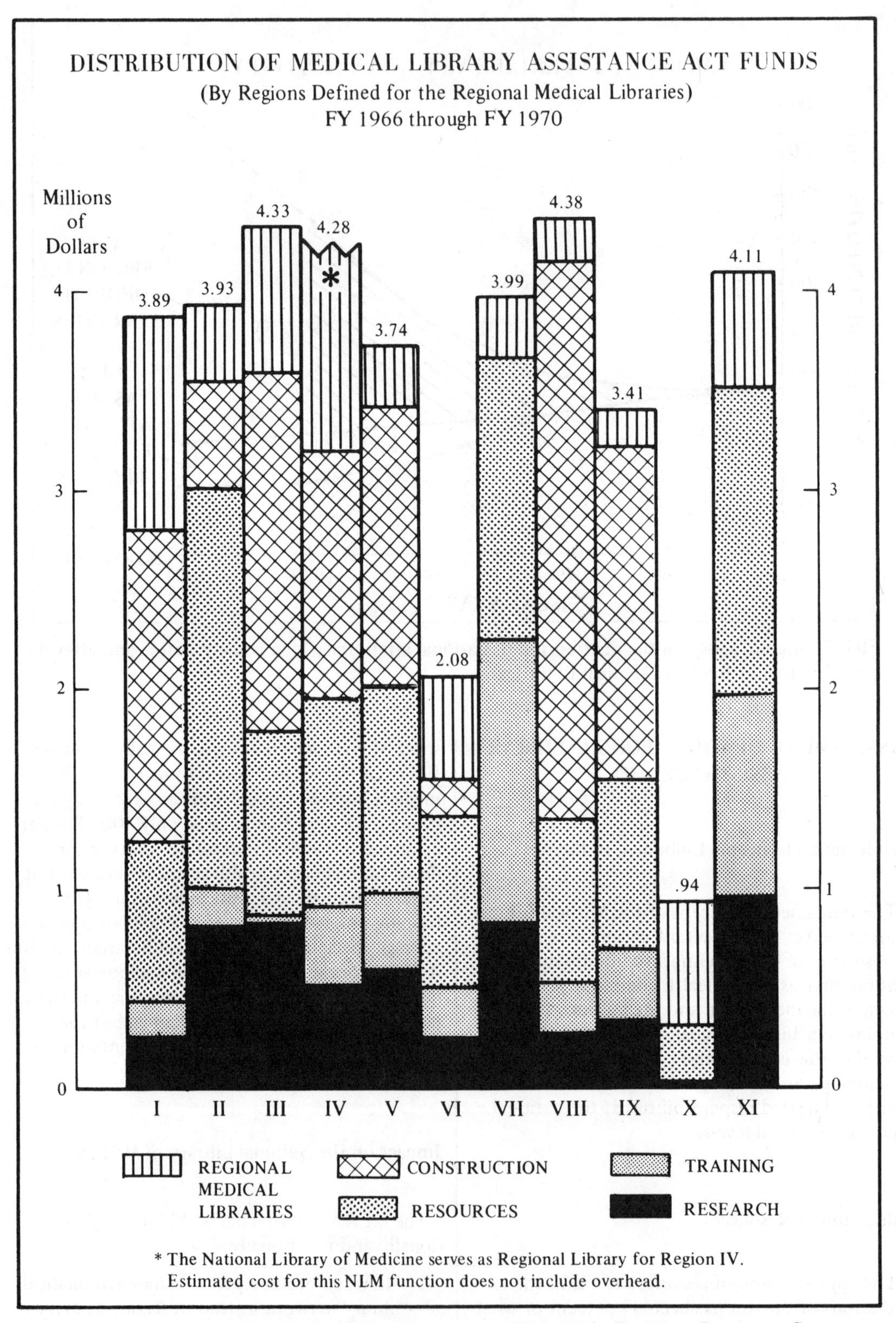

FIG. 8 Regional distribution of MLAA funds in terms of Research, Training, Resource, Construction and Regional Medical Library Programs of the NLM.

TABLE 7
COMPARISON OF SCOPE AND LEVEL OF NLM'S SERVICES
FY 1964, 1967, 1970

	1964	1967	1970
Interlibrary Loans	130,555	175,000	100,611
Reference Requests	20,154	25,514	21,702
Technical Services			
Items Catalogued	14,157	14,529	17,767
Publications Added	91,105	112,301	121,942
History of Medicine Services			
Reference	281	1,338	1,461
Index Medicus			
Articles Indexed	144,057	168,310	210,000*
Subscriptions	7,600	4,757	5,151
Abridged Index Medicus			1,924
MEDLARS Searches	586	4,733	22,000†
Recurring Bibliographies		10	18
Literature Searches Distributed		19,177	23,351
Audiovisuals Distributed			72,865**

*Includes NLM and U.S. and foreign sources under contract.
†NLM: 3,520; U.S. Centers: 10,560; Foreign Centers: 7,920.
**National Medical Audiovisual Center.

2. NLM has decentralized, to date, two information service functions (Interlibrary Loans and MEDLARS) to regional centers, with an accompanying provision of funds to these regions for increased resources.
3. NLM has expanded its efforts to identify not only the needs of the professional health user, but also of the medical library community and to seek appropriate solutions.
4. Considerable NLM staff time and resources are devoted not solely to the NLM daily operations but to the administrative support of programs directly relating to the medical library community.

It was anticipated that the development of a national medical library network would indeed shift workloads so that maximum efficiency would be achieved. This in fact has occurred, with NLM assuming greater workloads in some technical areas and lesser ones in others. NLM's service level in 1964 is compared with 1967 and 1970 in Table 7. The MLAA programs have reduced interlibrary loan and MEDLARS demand services from NLM, but they have altered significantly the kind and scope of other services provided by NLM. This is reflected in new products such as *Current Catalog*, *Abridged Index Medicus (AIM)*, the on-line time-sharing system of AIM-TWX, and audiovisual services.

Impact on the U. S. Medical Library Community

It is true that the period of our experience with "regionalism" is short. However, definitive trends are becoming evident. Medical libraries seem to have been most interested in improving their collections or physical resources before improving medical library services. This appears logical if one has clearly in mind the level and scope of the services to be performed. However, the time has come for primary emphasis on providing improved service.

We are not convinced that there is a sharp delineation of functions at the national, regional, and local levels (as portrayed in Figure 6) nor does there seem to be a clear understanding of this division of responsibilities. In some cases we find a "local" library with "regional" aspirations and a "regional" library with "national" inclinations. With limited resources, every library cannot be of equal size and status.

The National Library of Medicine has unique national responsibilities not only to serve as a resource library but to acquire, index, and catalog comprehensively. It should also encourage the establishment of library standards, union serial lists, and cooperative cataloging. Some of these tools and procedures are best developed cooperatively on an overall basis with subsequent availability to all. Otherwise, uncorrelated independent efforts will consume the limited available resources and produce few overall advances.

Impact on the User

Our experience with the Regional Library Network has convinced us that a medical library network is no longer a concept but a reality. This is particularly important now when the workloads continue to increase at national, regional, and local levels without a corresponding increase in fiscal and personnel resources. Conceptually, we believe that the value of the network is clearly demonstrated by the rising number of service requests made to local and regional libraries and by the increasing number of responses made by these libraries. We do not have, however, a quantitative measure of user reaction.

Practically, the linkage aspect of the network should permit a more effective redistribution of functions and workloads at all levels and an overall increase in both the number and kinds of services to users. The most tangible evidence we have noted is in the shift from the national level to the regional level in the provision of interlibrary loan and MEDLARS demand services to the individual. The NLM's role, particularly with regard to interlibrary loan service, is now primarily to respond to those interlibrary loan requests which the Regional Medical Libraries cannot fill.

We are disappointed, however, that there have not been adequate funds for an increase in reference services, for emphasis on consultation and educational programs, and the inclusion of multimedia informational services. The consultation and educational role of the Regional Medical Libraries should be developed so that they become demonstration and training centers. This does not mean that Regional Medical Libraries will vie with academic institutions for formal training programs, but they can be a unique resource for internships and specialized work experiences.

We are convinced that audiovisual materials as well as the printed word are important media to convey medical information. It must be determined whether the Regional Medical Library can become a multi-media information center to serve as a depository for the collection and dissemination of audiovisual materials.

CONCLUSIONS

We believe that, in the aggregate, the Medical Library Assistance Act and the extramural programs of the National Library of Medicine have had a significant beneficial effect on the improvement of library and information services to physicians, scientists, and other related health personnel. The impact of these programs obviously would be more profound had the appropriations been larger. This is particularly true with respect to medical library construction, where the funds made available were only sufficient to support the building of eleven new medical libraries. Funds invested in support of research were probably the least rewarding for several reasons: (1) Most medical librarians were not trained in the scientific method nor had they had a previous experience with research, (2) the so-called "information scientist" competed most successfully for the lion's share of these funds and thus made contributions which were only peripherally relevant to the improvement of library services. Funds appropriated for training of medical librarians have been well spent. Graduates from these programs may well be our library leaders of the future. More emphasis on retraining of existing librarians seems indicated. Resource grants have expanded the collection of many small libraries but there remains a need to use these funds for improved services. Historical studies and special publications have enriched the literature of medicine. Eleven Regional Medical Libraries (including NLM) are now operational as the first step toward a medical library network.

In summary, the MLAA has done much to upgrade medical library services to the nation's health community. However, we have not done well enough. There is a need for financial resources to reach all medical libraries who lack personnel to serve adequately health personnel requiring medical information. We believe that through creative resource sharing we can improve our collective performance. As the NLM now enters the period of administering extramural programs under a three-year extension of this Act, we shall be in a better position to allocate resources which are more realistically attuned to library performance and user needs.

NOTES

[1] Deitrick, J. E., and Berson, R. C. Medical Schools in the United States at Mid Century. New York, McGraw-Hill, 1953.
[2] Bloomquist, Harold. The status and needs of medical school libraries in the United States. J. Med. Educ. 38: 145-163, March 1963.
[3] Surgeon General's Conference on Health Communications, November 1962. Washington, D. C., U. S. Department of Health, Education, and Welfare, Public Health Service, Feb. 1963.
[4] National Academy of Sciences–National Research Council. Division of Medical Sciences. Communication Problems in Biomedical Research: Report of a Study. Washington, D. C., Oct. 1963; Supplement, Washington, D. C., March 1964.
[5] President's Commission on Heart Disease, Cancer and Stroke. A National Program to Conquer Heart Disease, Cancer and Stroke. Volume I, Dec. 1964; Volume II, Feb. 1965. Washington, D. C., U. S. Government Printing Office.
[6] Bull. Med. Libr. Ass. 52: 148-180, 414, 545, 645, 1964.
[7] Bull. Med. Libr. Ass. 52: 442, 795, 1964.
[8] Datagram. Medical library needs. J. Med. Educ. 40: 396-397, April 1965.
[9] Guidelines for Medical School Libraries (Special Issue) J. Med. Educ. 40: 5-64, 1965.
[10] Library Study Committee of the Association of American Medical Colleges. Merlin K. DuVal, M.D., Director, and Seymour Alpert, M.D., Co-Director. The health sciences library: its role in education for the health professions. J. Med. Educ. Part 2, Aug. 1967.
[11] Committee on Surveys and Statistics of the Medical Library Association. Library statistics of schools in the health sciences: Part I. Bull. Med. Libr. Ass. 54: 206-229, July 1966; Part II. Bull. Med. Libr. Ass. 55: 178-206, Apr. 1967.
[12] Cummings, Martin M. The Edge of Husbandry: The Role of the National Library of Medicine. Biblioteca Medica: Physician for Tomorrow, Ed. by David McCord. Boston, Harvard Medical School, 1966.

ABOUT THE AUTHORS–Dr. Martin M. Cummings has been Director of the National Library of Medicine since 1964, and thus has been responsible for the expansion of MEDLARS and the impact of the Medical Library Assistance Act on medical librarianship. Before coming to the Library, he was Chief, Office of International Research and Associate Director for Research Grants at the National Heart Institute. He has a B.S. from Bucknell University and an M.D. from Duke University School of Medicine. Other positions he has held are: Director of the Tuberculosis Evaluation Laboratory, Communicable Disease Center; Associate Professor of Bacteriology and Medicine at Emory University School of Medicine; Chief, Tuberculosis Research Laboratory, Veterans Administration Hospital, Atlanta; Director, Research Services, Veterans Administration Central Office, Washington, D.C.; Special Lecturer in Microbiology, George Washington University School of Medicine; and Chairman and Professor, Department of Microbiology, University of Oklahoma School of Medicine.

Dr. Cummings is a member of the American Academy of Microbiology, Inc., the American Board of Microbiology, the American Association for the History of Medicine, and many other groups. He has served on the Board of Directors of the Association of Research Libraries, of the Gorgas Memorial Foundation, and of the Medical Library Association. He has received the VA Exceptional Service Medal, the DHEW Superior Service Award, the DHEW Distinguished Service Award, the Distinguished Alumnus Award from Duke University, and honorary degrees from Bucknell, University of Nebraska, Georgetown University and Emory University.

Miss Mary Corning is Special Assistant to the Director of the National Library of Medicine for International Programs. Prior to that, she was Chief of the Publications and Translations Division of the Library's Extramural Program. After a tour of duty as a Physical Chemist and Technical Assistant to the Associate Director for Chemistry of the National Bureau of Standards, she was Special Assistant to the Science Advisor to the Secretary of State. She served the National Science Foundation as a member of its Planning Group and in the Office of International Science Activities as Special Assistant to the Head and as Associate Program Director for Cooperative International Science Activities. She received a B.A. from Connecticut College for Women and an M.A. in physical chemistry from Mount Holyoke College.

Special assignments have included U.S. National Liaison Officer to the Organization for Economic Cooperation and Development (OECD), Executive Secretary for the Public Health Service Advisory Committee for Scientific Publications, and membership on the National Academy of Sciences-National Research Council U.S. National Committee for the International Commission for Optics, the U.S. National Committee for the International Federation for Documentation, and the International Panel of the Committee on Scientific and Technical Information (COSATI). From 1950-1960, Miss Corning was Assistant Editor of the *Journal of the Optical Society* and Editor-in-Chief of the forty-volume *Analytical Subject Index* for the *Journal*. In 1971, she received the DHEW Superior Service Award.

The Pacific Northwest Regional Health Sciences Library: A Centralized Operation

by Gerald Oppenheimer

The scarcity of medical library resources in the Pacific Northwest has led to development of a centralized Regional Medical Library service. Because of the great distances involved and central responsibility, an automated reporting system provides knowledge of the operation. The public relations effort is particularly important in the kind of region described.

In spite of apparent similarities of Regional Medical Library Programs, the differences caused by geography, population size and distribution, health care activity and health manpower ratios, and bibliographic resources are far more significant in the eventual determination of the program, in setting priorities, in the pace of development, and the cost of projects. These factors will also influence the particular type of structure in which the Regional Medical Library is imbedded and the amount of formal or informal cooperation which develops. In a subtler vein, perhaps, it guides the attitudes of the Regional Library towards its own admittedly experimental policies, rules and regulations and the degree of acceptance which may be expected from individuals and institutions served.

Region X, the Pacific Northwest, covers five states–Alaska, Idaho, Montana, Oregon, and Washington. The program of its Regional Library was indeed influenced considerably by the geographic and demographic character of this part of the country. Its most noticeable feature is its size. The total area of Region X is 1,000,000 square miles or almost 30 percent of the total land mass of the United States. Perhaps even more startling are the distances of this region which covers five time zones.

Seattle itself has a fairly central location: 200 air miles to Spokane, 120 to Portland, 500 to Pocatello, 625 to Billings, 1450 to Anchorage. Yet the distance between Seattle and Attu is about the same as that between Seattle and Havana, and from Seattle to Point Barrow is about as far as between Seattle and New Orleans. In view of such distances travel is mostly by air, particularly since the Region is also poor in roads. Consider, for example, the difference between Alaska's 6,500 miles of paved roads and Texas, the state nearest in size, with 240,000. The total population of the Region is approximately 7 million or about 3.5 percent of the population of the United States.

Consider also the distribution of this population. Over half of Alaska's people live in the vicinity of Anchorage, and the rest in widely scattered and isolated towns and villages. Idaho has one city with a population exceeding 50,000, Montana two, Oregon and Washington three each.

As regards health resources of the Region there are about 350 nonfederal hospitals ranging from 150 in Washington to thirty in Alaska. The number of physicians ranges from 4,500 in Washington to 175 in Alaska, with a total of almost 8,800, or approximately one physician for 800 persons compared to the national average of 1 to 700. In Alaska there are only two communities with more than ten physicians, and out of a total of 434 towns, 412 have no local physician at all. Its active nurses live in fifty-eight different communities, leaving 376 localities bereft of even such elementary health care. In the total Region, health-related personnel, including public health

---

SOURCE: Reprinted from Gerald Oppenheimer, "The Pacific Northwest Regional Health Sciences Library: a Centralized Operation," *Bulletin of the Medical Library Association*, 59 (April, 1971), pp. 237–241, by permission of the publisher and the author. Delivered as part of the General Session on "Contrast in Patterns of Regional Medical Library Service" at the Sixty-ninth Annual Meeting of the Medical Library Association in New Orleans, Louisiana, May 20, 1970.

officials, technicians, hospital administrators, and pharmacists amounts to 45,000, or about 3 percent of the health manpower of the Nation.

Among the institutional health resources of the Region there are only two medical schools, two dental schools, five schools of pharmacy, and three postbasic and postgraduate schools of nursing plus thirty-three NLN approved basic schools and only one firm as far as we have been able to discover which is a member of the American Pharmaceutical Manufacturers Association.

An appreciation of the Region must take into account bibliographic resources as well, and, specifically, health-related ones.

The 1968/1969 *American Library Directory* lists only three health-related libraries in Alaska, one for Idaho, eight for Montana, thirteen for Oregon and twenty-four for Washington. There are only seven of all of these libraries which exceed the 10,000 volume mark.

The question whether this area constitutes a natural region in some sense must, I believe, be answered affirmatively. On the whole there has always existed some cohesiveness, particularly in the area of health and library affairs. Both Portland and Seattle are referral centers of long standing, the latter particularly in relation to Alaska, and both medical schools have mounted continuing medical and paramedical education efforts for neighboring states, much accelerated recently, of course, by the Regional Medical Program.

Bibliographically the region has had a long history of cooperation. The five states and in some cases also the Province of British Columbia are those which are covered by the Pacific Northwest Library Association, the first regional library association in the country, by the Pacific Northwest Chapter of SLA, by the Pacific Northwest Regional Group of MLA and by the Pacific Northwest Bibliographic Center housed at the University of Washington.

Full operation of PNRHSL began on October 1, 1968. The cordial and uncomplicated relationship with the University of Oregon and the absence of any other library with which cooperative arrangements were to be made allowed the PNRHSL to concentrate on developing its service program.

Among these services there was first of all document delivery service. Next in importance we felt was the counterbalance to the "central resource" role, the stimulation of local self-reliance through resource development. We did not take resource development, however, as being synonymous with collection building. Major emphasis in this part of the program was placed on consultation in the field with library supervisors, hospital administrators, and chairmen of library committees, on training library personnel, primarily through workshops, at various locations in the region, on bringing the existence of the Library to the attention of potential users, and on gathering information about available resources. Other activities which had priority were a fully responsive reference service strengthened by MEDLARS search capability, and finally the production of a distributable Union List of Serials.

Since the responsibility for the Program in our centralized operation was not formally shared, our immediate attention had to be directed towards discovering ways and means of acquiring knowledge about the region and our users.

This requirement led us very early to the use of an automated reporting system developed by our systems analyst which would allow us to obtain the necessary data on all document delivery transactions. This system also produces as a subset of its total reporting capability the data required by the National Library of Medicine.

Each month the computer prepares a list of borrowers who have been active since the beginning of the report year. For each the tally will show the monthly figure and cumulative total for number of requests received, the number of requests not accepted, the number filled, the performance ratio, the number of photocopy sheets, and the number filled by loan and by photocopy.

These monthly reports are studied carefully, especially with an eye toward trends and changes in performance. Variations which are of particular interest to us are activity levels by state and for localities contacted by our field team. Another item which is scrutinized carefully is our performance ratio. In the original grant application we expressed confidence that the Health Sciences Library of the University of Washington would be a 90 percent library. Whatever criticism may be levelled against this concept, we would regard a decline from this figure as a cause of concern because this would demonstrate that for over 10 percent of requests regional resources are inadequate, delays would be inevitable, and the cost of operation would increase. The latest cumulative figures indicate an overall performance ratio of 91 percent for the second year. It might be true of course that as local libraries come into existence and others build up their holdings, users will no longer approach us for the same high percentage of the mundane, and as the proportion of more exotic requests increases our performance ratio will drop. Should such a drop occur, our reporting system will allow us to test this hypothesis. This information and my regular inspection of unfilled transaction records and of those transaction records not filled through Health Sciences Library holdings are used as guides for acquisition of monographs or journals on a selective basis. This is done because here also we have in mind our role as regional resource library. It should be noted that these additions are not charged to the Regional Library budget, which is only tapped for duplication made necessary by regional demands.

Most of the data on journal titles requested is derived from another portion of the computer output which on a quarterly basis lists journal titles by CODEN, year, and requester. An annual printout arranged by requester, title, and frequency allows us without additional effort to determine the request patterns of any of our institutional borrowers. This listing has enabled us, for example, to assert that the frequency of requests per title has not exceeded for any user the degree which could reasonably suggest that placing a subscription rather than borrowing would be advisable. This device, of course, is not only helpful to us but also to the requester, who may obtain a copy of the printout from us for his own purposes.

Another data element in this monitoring system should be described. Flowthrough time is determined for filled and unfilled requests and reasons for delay are specified when processing time exceeds three days. The latest cumulation shows that 77.6 percent of filled requests are processed within two days, but that 5 percent take more than ten days and that 80 percent of unfilled requests required more than three days before their fate is determined. The last two figures require some explanation. Neither should simply be ascribed to the proverbial reluctance of librarians to give up. Our willingness to fill requests after ten days, and sometimes considerably longer, and to try to fill other requests (unsuccessfully as it may turn out) stems from the relative absence of other easily available sources and the fact that bibliographic searching is best conducted at PNRHSL short of sending the request on to the referral library, NLM, for example. There are several factors which tend to lengthen the processing time. The first has to do with the fact that we treat the whole University of Washington Library system rather than just the Health Sciences Library as our base of operation. This means that a PNRHSL searcher consults the bibliographic apparatus of the Main Library and, if the item is located, retrieves the material for loan or copying. I should add that the University has become the willing partner in our service in line with long established attitudes about its obligation to the Pacific Northwest.

Secondly, we occasionally also rely on the cooperative spirit exhibited by such a library as that of the King County Medical Society. Thirdly, we will in many cases hold requests for material not immediately available. It is our experience that claims for the universality of the need for urgency have been exaggerated. To be certain, however, we have developed a notification procedure which allows requesters to indicate their choice of courses of action for us to take. Our following up and responding definitively, even if late, has increased the feeling of confidence and reliability for the regional operation on the part of the user.

The centralized position of PNRHSL and the dearth of bibliographic tools in the Region led us to adopt a policy which is as free of restrictions as is compatible with efficient functioning in-house. We reject, for example, requests for reasons of lack of verification only when absolutely necessary and when our own efforts of identification have been fruitless.

As mentioned earlier and in contrast with other regional libraries operating in a different milieu we honor requests for any journal title and do not anticipate that we will be issuing a list of forbidden titles in the forseeable future.

Within our particular configuration it is obvious that much care must be given to the development of avenues of communication. Our efforts in this direction have so far been mainly confined to attempts to stimulate the establishment of TWX units, to find means of connecting to the Advanced Record System employed by the General Services Administration which would allow direct contact with the Veterans Administration installations, and even establish contact in similar fashion to the state most in need of such a link, Alaska.

In addition to this method of communication, PNRHSL is engaged in an effort to contact in person, through field representatives, each of the hospitals and hospital libraries in the Region. The frequency with which this needs to take place has still to be determined.

What are the impressions that we have gained after a year and a half of operating this program?

One should take a look first of all at the user of PNRHSL. The first progress report showed that out of 12,000 ILL requests received, approximately 25 percent were from federal hospitals, 30 percent from other public and private hospitals, 10 percent from academic institutions, less than 5 percent from commercial enterprises including pharmaceutical companies, and 5 percent from individuals. It remains to be determined whether the surprisingly low figure of 4.3 percent direct requests from practitioners is due to the fact that more health professionals than expected do have access to an institution or whether a substantial number of this group are unaware of our existence or other means to satisfy their informational needs.

Another unanticipated result was the distribution of requests from the various states. While the pattern for Montana, Idaho, and even Washington is fairly straightforward, i.e., percentage of requests and percentage of health manpower running parallel, Oregon with 31 percent of all practitioners accounted for only 7.4 percent of requests, and Alaska with 2 percent of physicians was responsible for 11 percent of requests. The following hypotheses are offered in explanation of these apparent discrepancies.

First, the relatively high number of physicians in Oregon combined with a relatively low number of requests tends to show that where there is a good medical library like that of the University of Oregon Medical School with a well-established service pattern, the existence of the Regional Library appears not to disrupt this service, but to furnish a readily approachable resource whose response time, as acknowledged by the requesting library, is indeed satisfactory.

Second, the relatively low number of physicians combined with the relatively high number of requests from Alaska, particularly via the Alaska Health Sciences Library, seems to point up the effect of a small library with only a basic collection but with an aggressive and responsive service program.

This phenomenon provoked the question whether our obviously centralized pattern was not already on the road, in a natural and informal manner, toward decentralization by way of subregionalization. If this were true, the PNRHSL would still be the resource library but would relate differently not only to Idaho and Montana as compared to Oregon and Alaska but it could be expected that its service to Oregon would take on a different form from its assistance to the Alaska Health Sciences Library. Without going into details at this time, it may perhaps be summarized by saying that in the case of our neighbor to the south we shall continue to act as last regional resource library and to plan for cooperative service, using as partners the excellent staff of the University of Oregon Medical School Library. For our neighbor to the north it is perhaps more important that the Regional Library find ways and means of making the Alaska Library more self-sufficient in terms of its own well thought out program. The problems there center around increasing its staff and its collection, and supporting and augmenting services already under way on a minimal scale but with highly effective results, and those yet to be offered.

A look at the trip reports of our field librarians may provide partial answers to two further questions about the experiences gained during the operation of PNRHSL: first, the question of the effectiveness of the publicity effort undertaken to draw attention to PNRHSL services, and second, the question of whether or not, particularly in a strongly centralized set-up, the avowed intent of stimulating local initiative is not thwarted by the very existence of the Regional Medical Library. To answer the first, let me give you a very typical quote from the report of a trip in Washington State.

> This hospital library did not know of us and they were glad to hear of the PNRHSL. Since the Library is just getting under way, many questions arose. There is much interest and they want the Library to succeed and to be used.

Our publicity effort consisted of several mailings, one of which in particular we regarded as well designed and attractive. This literature was sent to every physician in the region, every hospital administrator, every state health department, all health-related and major other libraries, and all members of the Pacific Northwest Group of the Medical Library Association. It consisted of editorials and articles in local medical journals and newspapers, of appearances before annual conventions of state medical associations and other professional groups. We occupied booths at some of these meetings. The yield of this effort, we must conclude, has been low. Perhaps not lower than any other such publicity campaign, but low enough to convince us that field contact is absolutely indispensable.

Has the existence of the Regional Library

harmed local development? Because the elapsed time is still relatively short and conditions are still fluid it may perhaps be too sanguine to assume that all the buds our field librarians saw will turn into flowers, yet far from encountering the discontinuance of local service, which was sporadic at best, we find ourselves cast in the role of catalyst. Particularly in Idaho and Montana efforts are under way to build resources, to establish communication links, and to upgrade the quality of personnel and services, relying of course heavily on the backstopping function of PNRHSL.

In trying to anticipate what trends may establish themselves as far as features of the program are concerned, I believe that PNRHSL may become even less of a first-contact library and that reliance will be placed on the small hospital library which should gradually become more adequate. In a larger sense this process will of course be accelerated should subregionalization occur which would, in effect, create a middle layer of service. Even then I do not expect the number of interlibrary loans to diminish. We all know very well that as library service grows, it outpaces resources and we look forward to increased demands on us from this direction.

I see a continuing need for field visits to hospital libraries on a rotating basis. Not only is this a conviction based on the needs as observed by our field librarians but on the excellent results which can be demonstrated by a similar operation of the neighboring British Columbia Medical Library Service.

Workshops and continuing education opportunities for library supervisors will be prominent in the years ahead. We see possibilities however even in our region for a sharing of this burden and the feasibility that in some cases our participation will be minimal.

We also expect an extension of the TWX network which may reach Alaska in 1970 or 1971.

When I try to speculate what the Regional Medical Library Program might be some years from now, I encounter questions rather than visions.

Let me briefly indicate what some of these questions are. The National Library of Medicine in pursuing the objectives of the Medical Library Assistance Act has quite properly assumed responsibility for the Regional Medical Library Program, including plans for the development of a biomedical communications network. Yet at the same time, perhaps, equally properly, it is asserted that by this is not meant total responsibility. This is sometimes defended on philosophic grounds as when it is said that this attitude is necessary so that none of the interests of the other sectors will be compromised. More frequently however it is limitations of funding which, it is asserted, require multiple sources rather than a single source of revenue for full regional medical library service. The question then arises: How can the development of the subunits of the great network be secured? Even where enthusiasm runs high, are local resources sufficient to provide the links? When demonstration and persuasion have failed, is there another way in which priorities of other potential funding organizations can be altered in favor of library development? If local support is meager or nonexistent does this mean that the need is nonexistent? It will be of great interest to all of us how future goals are to be realized.

The whole staff of PNRHSL are extremely gratified in being part of an enterprise which one of our grateful users claimed to be the "single most effective piece of health legislation yet." We ourselves can from our corner of the country only think of the Regional Medical Library Program as a permanent federal obligation towards increasing the spread of knowledge which hopefully will lead to better health care. Whatever evidence we have been able to gather at least points in this direction.

ABOUT THE AUTHOR—Gerald J. Oppenheimer is Assistant Director of Libraries for Health Sciences at the University of Washington. Prior to that he was Head Librarian of the Health Sciences Library. His previous positions include: Manager of Information Services at the Boeing Science Research Laboratories, Librarian at the Fisheries-Oceanography Library of the University of Washington Library and Junior Librarian at the Seattle Public Library. He has studied at Whitman College, the University of Washington (B.A. and M.A.), Harvard University, and Columbia University (M.S.L.S.).

He is editor of *Regional Medical Library Service in the Pacific Northwest* (1967). He holds membership in Special Libraries Association, Medical Library Association, American Association for Information Science and the Association for Symbolic Logic.

The Midcontinental Regional Medical Library: A Decentralized Service

by Bernice M. Hetzner

In contrast with the Pacific Northwest region, the Midcontinental Regional Medical Library has a number of approximately equivalent resource libraries in its geographic area. Hence, a decentralized regional library was established, with different areas of responsibility assigned to specific libraries. Possible advantages and disadvantages of a decentralized system are discussed.

I cannot tell you how a totally decentralized system operates. Since we really are not operational as yet, I am limited to a description of an idea. To do that, I want to take you back to 1968 and tell you about the situation as it was at that time.

The area based at Nebraska was one of the last two regions to be identified. The Midcontinental Regional Medical Library area came into being by a process of elimination. The great blank spot on the map (Fig. 1) represents the area that was left over after forty-one contiguous states had chosen sides, you might say, and decided to cast their individual lot with one of the ten areas surrounding that spot. Of the over three million square miles in continental United States (excluding Alaska), this area represents 19.6 percent or 593,300 square miles. Geographically, this region is a large share of the total continental area to be served by a network. By population, however, it represents only about 6.5 percent of the total population with only 19.5 people per square mile. Figure 2 shows the eight states that comprised the area just recently alluded to as the "blank spot."

This is the area and the resources we had to work with in 1968. There has been a change but that is immaterial to our discussion; North Dakota participated in the original discussions but has since elected to join the Midwest Regional Medical Library group. The intention is to take you back in time, look at the situation as it was then and to try to explain the rationale behind the decision to become a decentralized system.

This area contained thirteen institutions with biomedical collections participating in the initial effort. On the map they are represented by triangles. Later others joined but, again, that is another story.

The density of medical manpower in the region follows the density of the population (Table 1). In some professions the region has somewhat more than its standard share. It is not surprising to find that the area has the services of 11.8 percent of all veterinarians in the country. We also have more than our share of medical technologists; we have 13.44 percent of these professionals in the area. The area is also rich in health profession schools, again having more than its share, on a population basis (Table 2).

Turning our attention to the biomedical collections which provide health-related information in the area, we find that at that time the size of the collections ranged from approximately 19,000 volumes to 110,000 volumes with four libraries of comparable size at the upper level (Fig. 3). The number of serials currently received is frequently used as a measure of a library's capability to meet needs; current serials received ranged from 2,199 titles to 425 titles (Fig. 4).

The St. Louis medical librarians were the first ones to get together and do something definite

SOURCE: Reprinted from Bernice M. Hetzner, "The Midcontinental Regional Medical Library: a Decentralized Service," *Bulletin of the Medical Library Association*, 59 (April, 1971), pp. 247-253, by permission of the publisher and the author. Delivered at The General Session on "Contrast in Patterns of Regional Medical Library Service" at the Sixty-ninth Annual Meeting of the Medical Library Association in New Orleans, Louisiana, on May 20, 1970.

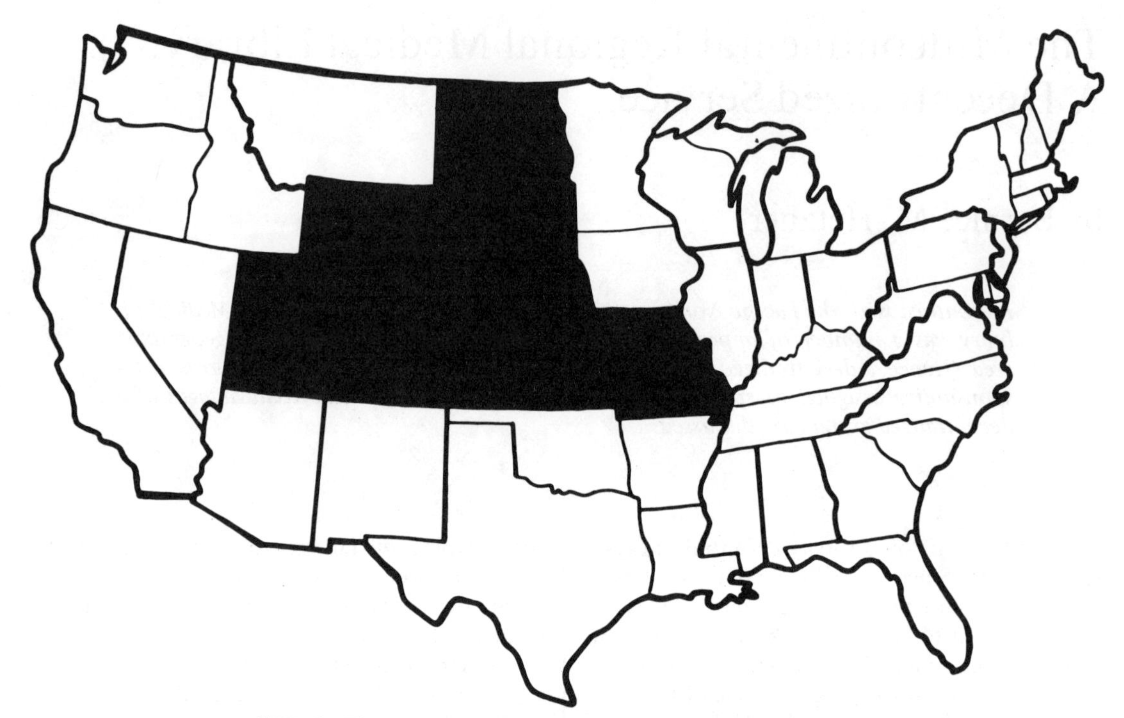

FIG. 1 The Midcontinental Regional Medical Library Area

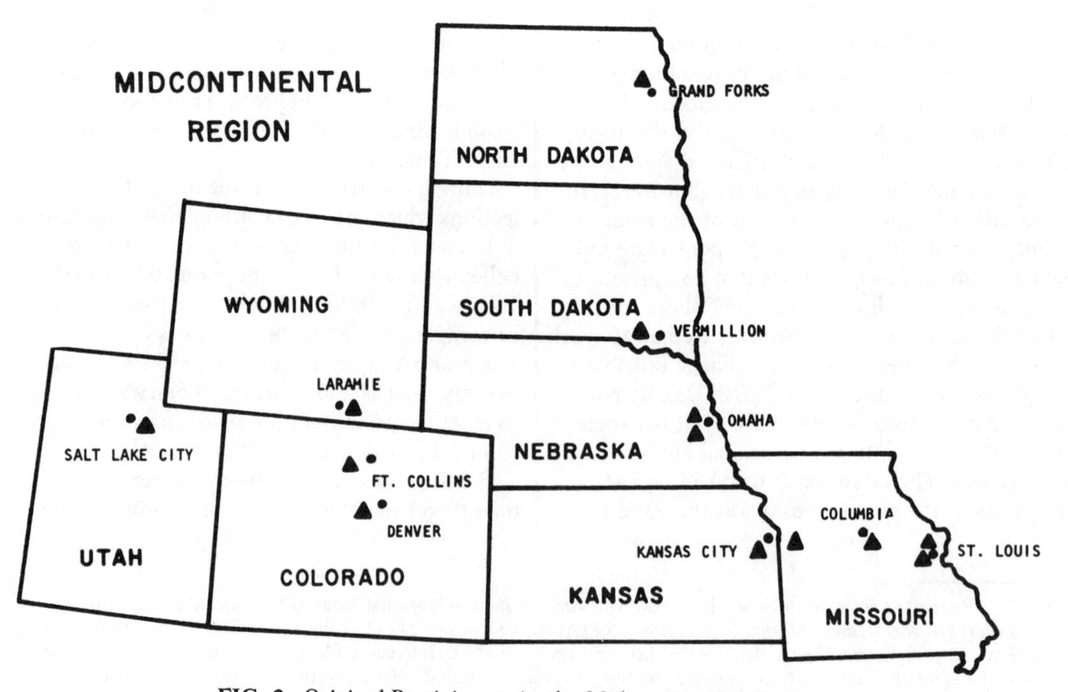

FIG. 2 Original Participants in the Midcontinental Region

TABLE 1

PERCENTAGE OF HEALTH-RELATED MANPOWER IN THE AREA

	Percent in Area
Medical technologists	13.44
Veterinarians	11.8
Speech pathologists	8.96
Medical record librarians	8.76
Physical therapists	8.71
Radiologic technologists	7.88
Clinical psychologists	7.6
Practical nurses	7.31
Occupational therapists	7.23
Pharmacists	7.06
Optometrists	6.84
Dentists	6.5
Dietitians & nutritionists	6.31
Physicians (M.D. & D.O.)	6.11
Professional nurses	5.97
Hospital administrators	5.76

TABLE 2

DISTRIBUTION OF HEALTH-RELATED PROFESSIONAL SCHOOLS IN MIDCONTINENTAL REGION

	U.S. Totals	Area Total
Medical	94	10
Dental	50	5
Professional Nursing	1,247	107
Pharmacy	75	10
Veterinary medicine	18	3
Food & nutrition	660	13
Practical nursing	1,116	60
Occupational therapy	32	5
Physical therapy	45	4
Radiologic technology	964	97
Speech pathology	271	37
Optometry	10	0
Medical technology	786	73
Medical record librarianship	27	4
Hospital administration	24	3
Total	5,419	431

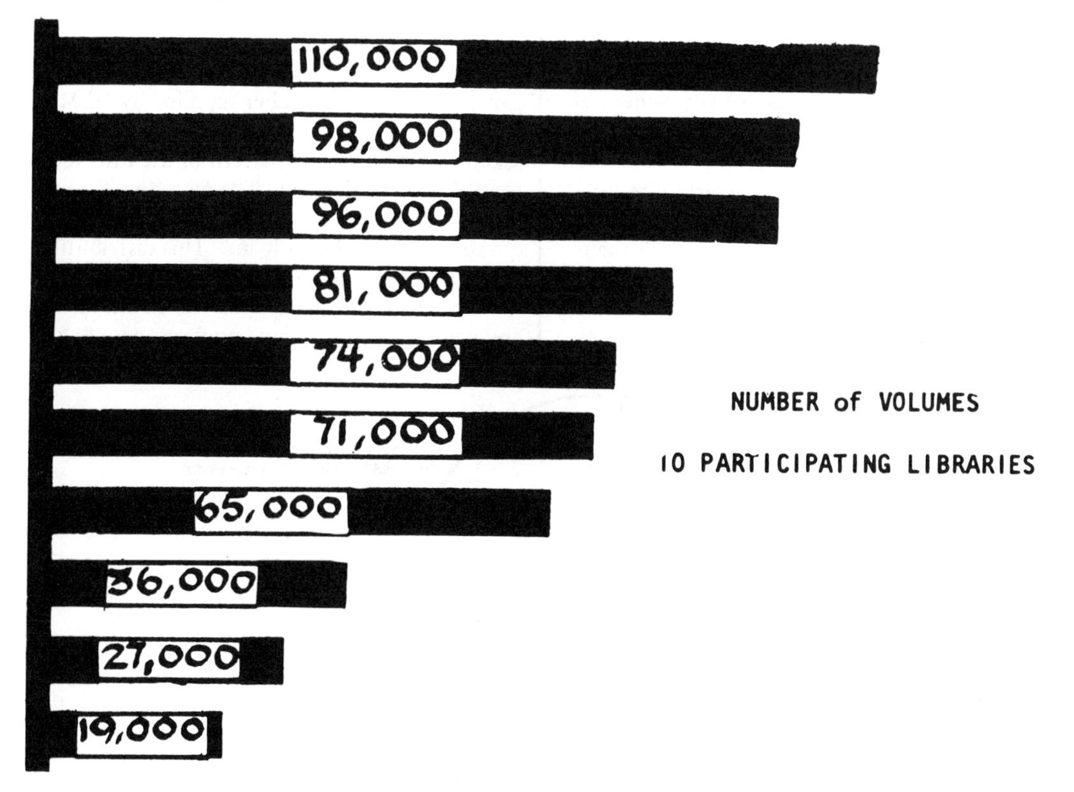

FIG. 3 Number of Volumes in Ten Participating Libraries.

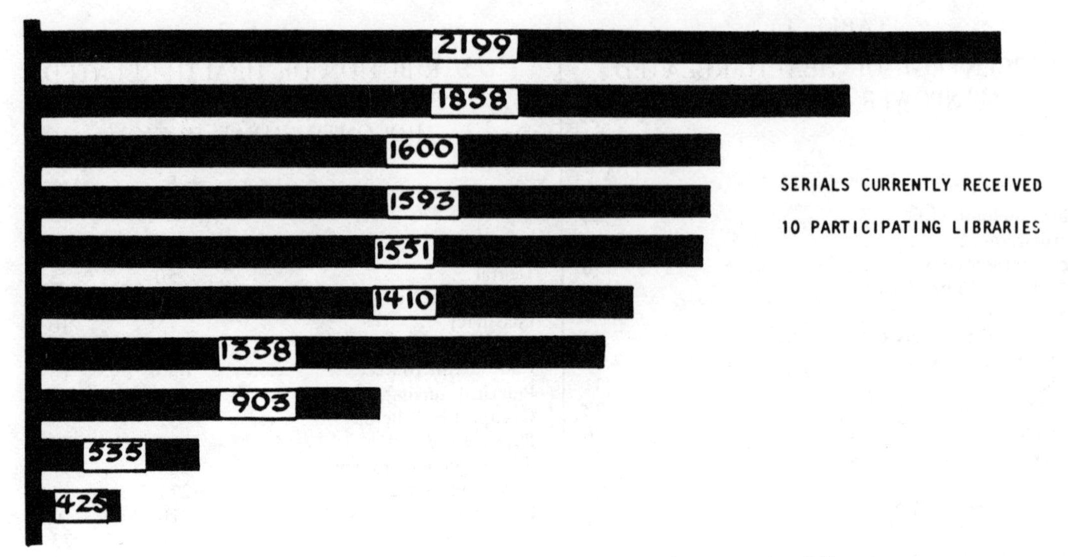

FIG. 4 Serials Currently Received in Ten Participating Libraries

about organizing some regional activity, although there had been a history of cooperation and communication over the years and some negotiations as early as June 1965. A meeting was called in St. Louis for March 1968. Prior to that meeting, much pertinent data was put together by Mrs. Nina Matheson, Instructor and Librarian, Missouri Institute of Psychiatry and Linda Van Wagoner, formerly on the Washington University School of Medicine Library staff, with the help of many people.

In a two-month survey in 1968, certain reporting libraries loaned 3,084 items and they were distributed in this manner: 66.8 percent of them were filled by three libraries and 33.2 percent were distributed by the other eight libraries reporting (Fig. 5). The material borrowed followed about the same pattern also: 966 items were borrowed in this two-month period; 80 percent of the items borrowed were requested by four libraries (Fig. 6).

The survey then considered sources this group used when there was a need to borrow. Fig. 7 shows the number borrowed within the state, out of the state, within the region, and out of the region, as well as the number supplied by NLM. The diverse manner in which libraries of the area asked for help shows a pattern of use directed toward the east (Fig. 8). The map, Fig. 9, shows how libraries in this area distributed materials requested on interlibrary loans. This distribution appears to have a western trend.

These facts faced us in St. Louis in March 1968 and we formulated a plan based on these facts.

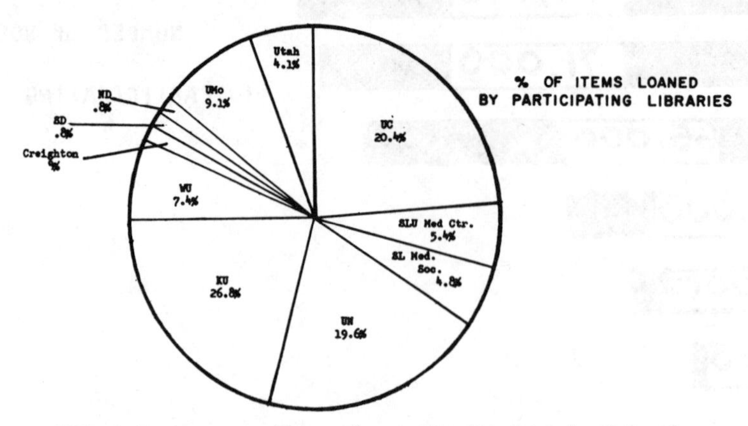

FIG. 5 Percentage of Items Loaned by Participating Libraries

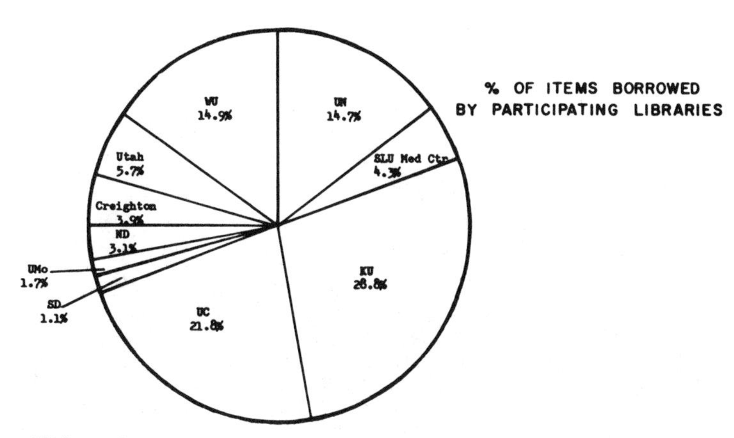

FIG. 6 Percentage of Items Borrowed by Participating Libraries

As we examined the resources and services needed to meet the purposes set forth in the policy statement, we concluded that the area did not have an establishment which was of outstanding stature sufficient to perform, by itself, the functions of the Regional Medical Library as set out in the Guidelines and a consortium of libraries was proposed. There was another reason for this suggestion. This area is dominated by state supported schools. Each of six states has such a medical school. Each of these state medical schools felt then and still feels somewhat compelled to supply biomedical services including information services within the boundary of its own state.

The MEDLARS station at the University of Colorado had been in operation since February 1965, and the responsibility for serving this particular eight-state region was assigned in January 1969. It was concluded that the MEDLARS operation would continue as it had been operating in the past. Since Washington University School of Medicine Library had long maintained a high reputation for mechanized library services, it was decided to place the responsibility for Union List of Serials with that Library.

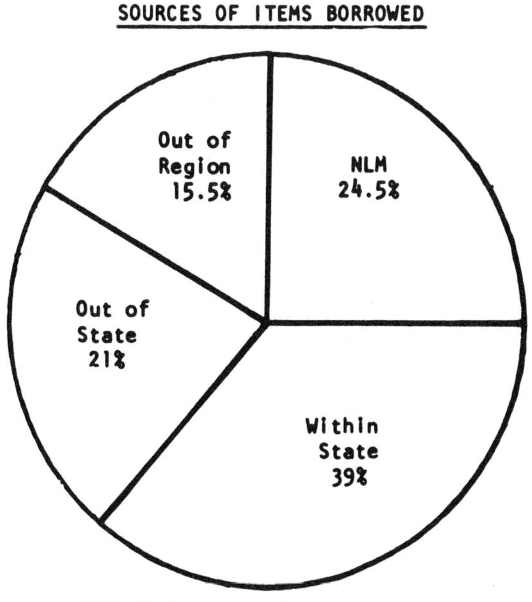

FIG. 7 Sources of Items Borrowed

It might be pointed out that people in this region are activists. It was realized that drawing up a formal application asking for financial assistance, its presentation, its review, and the hoped-for approval with subsequent funding, would take some time. It was felt that the need for library service was urgent and that we could use a Union List of Serials immediately. The representatives of four universities decided to contribute $1,500 each to underwrite a contract with the Medical Library Center of New York to prepare a Union List of Serials to include holdings in the four medical libraries. The University of Nebraska was named fiscal agent. Subsequently, additional libraries joined the Union List of Serials, each parent institution contributing a sum of $1,500 towards this project. It was clearly demonstrated that the group to be known as the Midcontinental Regional Medical Library was a group of people who could meet their responsibilities. Following funding of the Midcontinental Regional Medical Library program, the Union List of Serials is now being expanded to include nine more medical libraries in order to take full advantage of resources in the area and particularly to tap the resources of special collections in the area. This expanded Union List is expected to be available approximately September 1, 1970. With the expanded

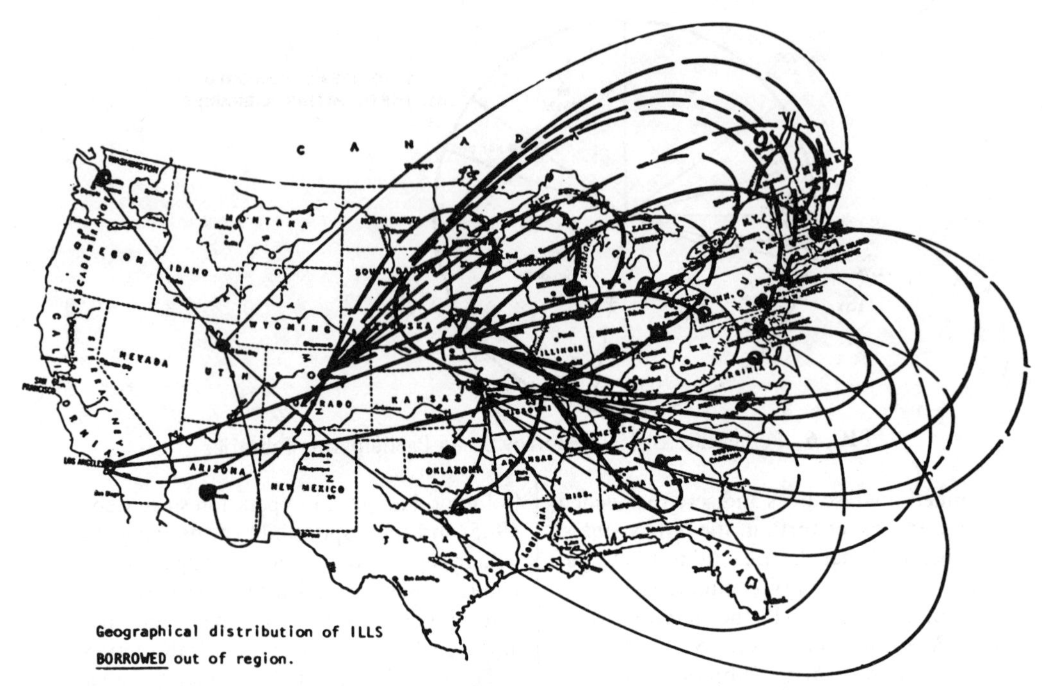

FIG. 8 Geographical Distribution of ILLs Borrowed out of Region

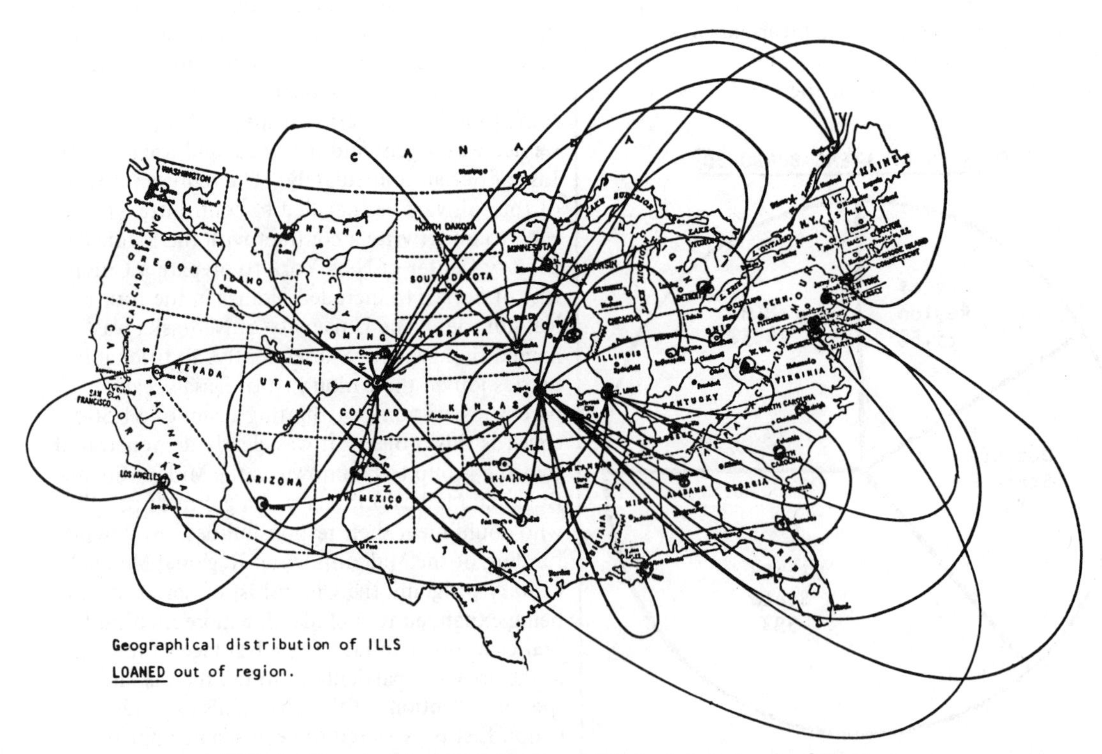

FIG. 9 Geographical Distribution of ILLs Loaned out of Region

Union List of Serials, it is now proposed that resource libraries in the area be named and that all requests for information in the Midcontinental area will be satisfied by tapping the collections in the area before turning to out-of-region sources. Such a program requires each participating library to face those facts that were mentioned earlier. We are now undergoing a period of self-examination within each participating institution. Agreements will be written with each participating library that will require detailed reporting of their activities and a willingness to serve in the capacity of a resource library even though it seems quite apparent, under present funding, that money to compensate for increased document delivery cost is not available. If it is true that some libraries organized within institutional boundaries are not fulfilling information needs, then a new organization is required.

We in the Midcontinental area are not sure that we have the answer, but at least we feel there are some advantages to this approach to the problem. One of the early criticisms of the Regional Medical Library Program was that it tended to bypass the smaller libraries and to undermine local support and therefore might be a threat to the local library. The decentralized regional library system calls upon each participating library in the region and challenges those who are not participating to extend their resources and services beyond their own institutional or geographic boundary. Second, the decentralized regional library takes advantage of the expertise of the various individuals in the region and, by assigning the separate tasks to different organizations, it eliminates the requirement of a large central staff. As future plans are developed, communications will be improved and training will be in the hands of all individuals in the area that wish to participate.

There are also certain disadvantages in a decentralized system for a large region such as under discussion here. In order to give equal representation to all the institutions involved, all the health professions in the area, and the various users of the biomedical information system, committees become large and require subcommittees and delegation of authority as well as responsibilities. I need not labor the point that the larger the committee, the more difficult it is to accomplish the objectives for which the committee was organized.

While we have no figures to date since we are not operational, it is strongly suspected that a decentralized system might be more expensive to manage and operate. Cost accounting will be set up to determine whether or not this belief can be sustained. To date, our experiences have shown that the communications necessary to establish this system required a great deal of time on long line, both TWX and telephone.

However, the national goal of equal access must take precedence over local administrative rigidity. If the decentralized system provides faster and better use of local resources, then it will have made a contribution to better health care.

ABOUT THE AUTHOR–Bernice M. Hetzner is Librarian and Professor of Library Science at the University of Nebraska College of Medicine. She is also Acting Director, Midcontinental Regional Medical Library Program. Before coming to the University of Nebraska, she had held a number of positions in school and public libraries as well as a brief position as Cataloger in the School of Nursing Library, St. Elizabeth Hospital, Lincoln, Nebraska, and one as Film Librarian and Demonstrator of Audio Visual Aids at the University of Omaha. She studied at Creighton University and received an A.B.L.S. from the University of Denver. She has an M.A. in Education from Colorado State College of Education.

She is author of the chapter on "The Medical Librarian" in the *Handbook of Medical Library Practice*, third edition (Chicago, Medical Library Association, 1970). She received the Medical Library Association's Murray Gottlieb Prize Essay Award in 1958. She has been active in Medical Library Association committee and Board work and was a member of the "Weighting Task Force" to evaluate users services in medical school libraries (See page 152). She was also a member of the Committee on Guidelines for Medical School Libraries of the Association of American Medical Colleges (See page 318). She was President of the Medical Library Association in 1971-1972 and has recently been appointed to the Board of Regents of the National Library of Medicine.

Regional Medical Programs

Regional Medical Programs stress continuing education and the need for supporting information, so that medical libraries inevitably participate. The first paper describes coordination between Regional Medical Program library activities and those of the Medical Library Assistance Act, and the second gives an example of one library operation within a Regional Medical Program.

Coordination of Regional Libraries with Regional Medical Program Projects

by David F. Kefauver

The background of the two programs and the necessity for and examples of coordination are described. With smaller regional focus under the Regional Medical Programs, local initiative is felt. Grass-roots projects can be linked with those of the Regional Medical Library Network.

How do the Regional Medical Library Program of the National Library of Medicine and the library projects of the Regional Medical Program mesh, can they cooperate effectively, and how can they provide the most efficient health library services for institutions and individuals alike? There are many individual health-related information activities which contribute toward the objectives of both programs.

As a representative of the National Library of Medicine it would be inappropriate for me to attempt to speak on behalf of the Regional Medical Program and I shall not attempt to do so. I can speak for the interests of the Library and the Regional Medical Library Program and I think I can usefully describe the developing regional library program and its relationship to the Regional Medical Program-supported information projects from this one point of view.

The historical perspective on the development of these programs can serve to illuminate the goals and concepts, similarities and dissimilarities, of these two federal agencies and their programs. National recognition of need and the impetus for both programs came from the report of the President's Commission on Heart Disease, Cancer, and Stroke issued in December 1964. Recommendations of the Commission, chaired by Dr. Michael E. DeBakey, led to the passage of the enabling legislation for the Regional Medical Program. The Commission also recommended that "a legislative proposal should be developed and enacted providing for the support and stimulation of a National Medical Libraries Network . . . including a limited number of regional libraries; regional library facility construction; training for medical librarians; and a program of research designed to improve systems and methods of handling medical literature." The Heart Disease, Cancer, and Stroke Amendments of 1965 (Public Law 89-239) were passed on October 6, 1965. They authorize the establishment and maintenance of Regional Medical Programs to assist the nation's health resources in making available the best possible patient care for heart disease, cancer, stroke, and related diseases. The Medical Library Assistance Act of 1965 was signed into law on October 22, 1965.

The Medical Library Assistance Act of 1965 authorizes the Regional Medical Library Program and six other programs. The objectives of these programs are those defined in that legislation. Briefly, their primary objective is to help expand and improve information services in health fields. These programs were created to attempt to deal with the problem of a rapidly expanding volume of health information in the United States at a time when health libraries had serious deficits of facilities and resources, manpower, and the technology necessary to process information rapidly and efficiently. The National Library of Medicine is now implementing these seven programs, three of which are specifically oriented toward assistance to health libraries. These programs for libraries are (1) to support health library construction, (2) to provide

SOURCE: Reprinted from David F. Kefauver, "Coordination of Regional Libraries with Regional Medical Program Projects," *Bulletin of the Medical Library Association*, 58 (July, 1970), pp. 325–329, by permission of the publisher and the author. Presented at the Sixty-eighth Annual Meeting of the Medical Library Association, Louisville, Kentucky, October 30, 1969, as part of the General Session on the Regional Medical Program and the Regional Medical Library Program.

funds for library resources to permit health libraries to improve their service capabilities through the purchase of resource materials, and (3) the Regional Medical Library Program. The ultimate beneficiary of these programs is the health worker, whether involved in health education, the provision of health services, or health-related research. These programs are not intended to set priorities among the various categories of health information use.

The specific objective of the Regional Medical Library Program as stated in the law is to "assist in the development of a national system of regional medical libraries, each of which would have facilities of sufficient depth and scope to supplement the services of other medical libraries within the region served by it."

The Regional Medical Library Program shares with the programs of the Division of Regional Medical Programs the concept of "regionalization": cooperative arrangements can enhance the effectiveness of, and access to, services and resources. The regional library program is intended to equalize access to high quality health information services throughout each designated region, particularly for users who are remote from centers for such services, without costly duplication of extensive or specialized collections. Toward this goal, regional library planners are urged to identify, study, and work to coordinate all interested institutions and individuals in the regional health community, including health libraries and other institutional resources for regional information services and the potential regional clientele. The policy guide for this program states: "Of importance will be the planning to coordinate programs of the proposed regional medical library with existing or proposed Regional Medical Programs (for heart disease, cancer, stroke, and related diseases), Title IX of the Public Health Services Act, Public Law 89-239." I am pleased to report that the advisory committees for all but two of the library regions funded or planned for grant support include representation of the local Regional Medical Programs.

The Regional Medical Library Program is a new program of Federal assistance. The first regional library grant was awarded in June 1967, for the six-state New England Region; this program has been operational for two years. Three programs have received support for less than eighteen months, and four for less than one year. Two of the eleven regions have not yet been funded.

Regional Medical Libraries must provide the following services:

- Free loan service to qualified users within the region, and, when appropriate, free photocopy service in lieu of loan of the original;
- MEDLARS search formulation services, and training for personnel to provide such services (through arrangement with the NLM);
- assistance to local libraries and qualified individuals in providing reference services;
- orientation and training of personnel from major user facilities in medical library services to assure effective use of the regional resources;
- evaluation of information needs and resources of the region on a continuing basis;
- announcement of regional acquisitions and services;
- support for continuing educational programs for the health professions when such support is realistic and within program objectives.

Before we can understand the relationship of Regional Medical Program information programs to the Regional Medical Library Program, we must understand the role of regional libraries in the context of the health information objectives which they share with other programs under the Medical Library Assistance Act. As the program develops and regional libraries can expand into the full provision of services, this role can and should be much broader than simply the provision of conventional library services to health libraries and geographically isolated individual users. The regional library will serve as a locator backup within the region; an innovator with regard to health communication services, training, and the design and distribution of resources within the region; and a coordinator and organizer for cooperative library efforts in the region. The regional library should carry the combined functions of the helping hand and the inquiring mind.

Regional Medical Programs projects reveal an emphasis on continuing education of physicians and allied health professional personnel and the need to encourage rapid and effective transmission of vital health information to these groups. Regional Medical Program legislation has no library-specific program authorizations. It is inevitable, however, that libraries will be involved in projects to expedite the processing and distribution of health information toward improved health care. The Extramural Programs of the National Library of Medicine emphasize expansion and improvement of all health information services, through aid for academic, research, and health care institutions specifically for health information projects and resources.

The National Library of Medicine places great emphasis on inter-regional cooperation and compatibility with a centrally determined information network. The Regional Medical Library Program has designated eleven regions, which for the present divide the U.S. into large geographical areas with large and varied health professional populations and programs. The Regional Medical Program has, at the present time, fifty-five regions. It is entirely appropriate that Regional Medical Program library-based projects support a concentration of services and resources at the local level (subregional to the larger National Library of Medicine library regions) which it is not possible for the regional library program to provide both in terms of the larger regional focus of this program and also in consideration of the limited financial resources available to it. Of equal importance, projects within smaller geographical areas can most effectively discover and react to the differing needs of local communities.

The Extramural Program, which includes the regional library program, is only one of many activities of the National Library of Medicine, which also has a large intramural program. Extramural support for all grant-supported activities for fiscal year 1969 totalled $9.17 million. Of this amount, $2.088 million was obligated for the Regional Medical Library Program. To date, I am informed by Division of Regional Medical Program staff, the Regional Medical Program has supported information ("audio-visual") projects in thirty-seven regions, including fourteen regions in which there are sixteen specific library projects. Libraries are also involved in other information activities of Regional Medical Programs. Support for all information projects to date totals over $25 million.

With this as background, I will describe briefly how the Division of Regional Medical Programs and the National Library of Medicine work to coordinate their information-related activities. Coordination at the national level between the granting agencies is accomplished through formal and informal exchange of information on the programs and on individual information projects; participation by staff of one agency in the review activities of the other agency, or attendance as an observer at such review sessions; and the provision of technical advice and consultation on specific projects or policies.

Coordination at the regional level is something with which I am sure you are all familiar. Individuals engaged in local planning for Regional Medical Program projects also participate in the planning for regional library programs. As I noted earlier, we urge and encourage such cooperative planning, through Regional Medical Program representation on regional library advisory committees, for example, and hope that it will continue and increase. Exchange of information on program objectives and activities occurs both formally (through brochures, or fact sheets) and informally through personal exchange. At the regional level, coordination is achieved through joint support of selected projects. Finally, at the local level, the same librarians and other individual information specialists are frequently involved in projects under both programs.

The Library's support for projects of mutual interest has not been restricted to the Regional Medical Library Program. Neither has joint support always been simultaneous. For example, the Library has supported the development of information tools through research grants and contracts to investigators. Further development, testing, and installation in the hospital setting of such information aids have later been accomplished under projects of the Regional Medical Programs. The reverse order of involvement should also be possible, and I hope that this will occur, that the experience of Regional Medical Program project personnel will suggest health information research and development projects of the kind which the National Library of Medicine is authorized to support and wishes to encourage, to develop new or improved techniques and devices for health information processing and use.

A few examples of such coordination of library services and library-oriented projects may be of interest. In several Regional Medical Library Program regions, the regional library staff advises or is involved in information projects generated by one or another of the Regional Medical Program regional programs. For New England, the Regional Medical Library Program has designated a single region which includes all of the New England states. Within this Library region, there are four Regional Medical Program regions. These four New England Regional Medical Programs at the present time support two active library projects, one in Maine and one in Connecticut, and four nonlibrary information projects. The Division of Regional Medical Programs has provided over $260,000 for these six information projects. Members of the staff of the Countway Library at Harvard, which is the National Library of Medicine regional library for the large Regional Medical Library Program region, encouraged and helped to advance joint Regional Medical Program–Regional Medical Library Program supported projects such as the project of Dr. Norman S. Stearns, Executive Director, Postgraduate Medical Institute, Boston, Massachusetts, to develop an experimental core medical collection for hospitals. Dr. Stearns has reported on the progress of this project to the Advisory Committee of the New England Regional Medical Library. He has also discussed his project directly with National Library of Medicine staff and has thoughtfully provided us with a report and illustrations about the core collection project.

The National Library of Medicine itself serves as the regional library for a designated "Mid-Atlantic Region" which includes the District of Columbia, Maryland, North Carolina, Virginia, and West Virginia. There are five Regional Medical Program Regions in this one medical library region. In two of these regions, library-based information projects are supported currently. Three final examples kindly supplied by the Division of Regional Medical Programs will serve to illustrate the library activities supported within other regional library regions.

In the Regional Medical Library Program Pacific Northwest Region, which serves Alaska, Washington, Oregon, Idaho, and Montana, the following Regional Medical Program project is being supported. Alaska has never had an adequate medical library, so the Washington-Alaska Region is establishing a community medical library at Anchorage. The Alaska Native Medical Center, which is a Federal Government facility, has made space available. In addition to building and cataloging a collection it is planned that the library will provide reference service, compile bibliographies, disseminate current information, and develop a union catalog of medical holdings of all medical establishments served.

In the Regional Medical Library Program Southeastern Region, under Regional Medical Program auspices, Emory Medical College and the Medical College of Georgia are cooperating to provide interlibrary loan and copying services to medical students, residents, and practicing physicians in the Georgia Region. Both colleges will loan publications and provide 3,000 pages of free photocopy to each hospital annually. Information and publications will be furnished to physicians contacting the libraries directly.

In the Mid-Eastern Region of the regional library program, (Pennsylvania, Delaware, and southern New Jersey) a project has received three years of support under a Regional Medical Program grant to develop a cooperative library service program linking the University of Pittsburgh and 100 hospital medical libraries in western Pennsylvania. The participants in this project will develop a union list of serials for western Pennsylvania, and will share resources in order to provide cooperative photocopy and loan service, MEDLARS search formulation service, reference service, and consultant visits to hospitals in the area to encourage participation in the program and to learn about local needs. This group will develop plans to evaluate the project and will conduct research on the provision of health information services within the Regional Medical Program region.

To summarize, information or audiovisual projects have been supported in thirty-seven Regional Medical Program regions. Such projects include radio, television, telephone, computer, film, tapes, and document (library) activities such as those described here. Support for such projects has totalled over $25 million.

With proper coordination and cooperation, the availability of Regional Medical Program support for appropriate information projects which include libraries permits the regional library program to concentrate on regional and national network operation and the provision of health information resources and services in areas where locally financed support is minimal. Regional libraries are also freed to exercise broad responsibilities for planning and development, the coordination of programs and the development of consistent policies and technical compatibility among emerging services and projects.

In this review I have attempted to demonstrate that, while the grant programs of the National Library of Medicine seek to improve and expand information services for health and to provide assistance for health libraries, and whereas the Regional Medical Programs have a different primary objective, there are many areas of mutual interest in health information fields. These areas of mutual interest can be expected to continue and expand. I have indicated how coordination mechanisms have developed and are implemented between the two agencies. Such coordination will continue to be an important responsibility of both agencies.

In the information field, these programs have complemented one another in the past, do so at the present time, and may be expected each to enhance the effectiveness of the others in the future. Services of regional medical libraries are, of course, available for Regional Medical Program supported projects and activities, so long as the users are eligible under the broad definition of regional library clientele. To the extent that funds for its information and library programs will permit, the Library is very pleased to be able to contribute services through these programs to the Regional Medical Program projects as well as to other Federal and local health programs.

What will happen in the future? First, I think we will undoubtedly see a strong effort to satisfy as nearly as possible the nation's need for traditional library services in the most efficient manner possible. Here again, this will be a first objective of the Regional Medical Library Program and an indirect effect of support toward the more global objectives of the Regional Medical Program. Secondly, I think we will see both programs continuing to strive in appropriate ways toward the ultimate objective of improvements in the public health. Thirdly, I think that it is quite possible that we will see expanded local Regional Medical Program activities with the dual objectives of strengthening the potential for regional health services and of responding to the challenge of coordination and assurance of compatibility.

ABOUT THE AUTHOR—David F. Kefauver is Acting Assistant Director for Extramural Programs of the National Institute of Mental Health, Health Services and Mental Health Administration. He was formerly Associate Director of the National Library of Medicine for Extramural Programs, after being Operations Officer and Chief of the Research & Training Division and Acting Chief of the Publications and Translations Division. He had also served as Training Grants Officer in the National Institute of Arthritis & Metabolic Diseases, and was Chief of the Bacteriology Division of Norwich Pharmaceutical Company. He has a B.S. and M.S. in Microbiology from the University of Maryland and did postgraduate study in Public Administration at American University.

Besides publications on medical library activities and resources, he has a number of publications in microbiology. He is a member of the New York Academy of Science, American Society for Microbiology, and International Federation for Documentation.

Kansas Regional Medical Program Library Services

by Desi Bravo Schaffer

A concrete example of the use of Regional Medical Program funds for the development of a statewide library system began with the establishment of library support for the Kansas Regional Medical Program. Subsequently a Kansas Medical Library System grew out of the demonstration of what could be done. The availability of increased resources has made possible more complete services to health professionals throughout the state.

The state of Kansas, like most areas in the nation, has problems which are associated with the communication of new medical knowledge, both to researchers who must use the knowledge to explore further and to practitioners who must have access to it to improve the nation's health. The medical library system is particularly essential to the transmission of medical information across time and space. To achieve ready access to a comprehensive store of recorded knowledge is an ideal towards which many have worked. Libraries have, as their primary functions, the acquisition of recorded scientific knowledge, the indexing, cataloging, classification, storage for use in the present and the future, and the dissemination of such information. The library and its functions are so woven into the basic fabric of research, teaching, and practice that they are indispensable to progress in these pursuits. The medical library plays the central role in the interchange of published biomedical information.

However, medical libraries have been unable to keep up with the pace of medical education and medical care. The medical research program can be hampered by the inability to gain efficient access to the biomedical literature needed. Teachers and students often cannot make gains in educational pursuits. The medical practitioners do not always have ready access to the growing body of new medical information. Inefficiency within the medical library network results in unnecessary duplication of research efforts and postpones the application of new knowledge to aid human suffering. An inadequate medical library system hampers any health program.

Kansas is 208 miles in length, 410 miles in breadth and it encompasses an area of 82,264 square miles. The estimated 1968 population is 2,303,000. There are approximately 21,800 health related personnel including 2,680 medical doctors and doctors of osteopathy. There are an estimated twenty specialized health-related libraries in the state. The six located in Wichita include the Veterans Administration Hospital Library, the Sedgwick County Medical Library located at the Wichita State University Library, the Wichita Clinic Library and hospital medical libraries at St. Francis Hospital, St. Joseph Hospital and Rehabilitation Center, and Wesley Medical Center. The six Topeka medical libraries include the Veterans Administration Hospital Library, City County Health Department Library, Kansas Neurological Institute Library, Topeka State Hospital Library, Menninger Foundation Clinic Library, and the Stormont Medical Library. The two libraries in Kansas City are the Providence Hospital Medical Library and the Clendening Medical Library at the University of Kansas Medical Center. The other six libraries in Kansas include the Veterans Administration Hospital Library in Wadsworth, Hertzler Clinic Library at Halstead,

SOURCE: Reprinted from Desi Bravo Schaffer, "Kansas Regional Medical Program Library Services," *Bulletin of the Medical Library Association*, 58 (July, 1970), pp. 311–315, by permission of the publisher and the author. Presented at the Sixty-eighth Annual Meeting of the Medical Library Association, Louisville, Kentucky, October 30, 1969, as part of the General Session on the Regional Medical Program and the Regional Medical Library Program. This project is funded by Public Health Service grant 5 G03 RM-00002-03.

and the medical libraries located at the state hospitals at Osawatomie, Parsons, Winfield, and Larned. These libraries vary in specialization, function, size, and quality of resources. The Clendening Medical Library at the University of Kansas Medical Center has the largest and most comprehensive collection in the state. Eight of the libraries have collections which are composed primarily of psychiatric works. One of these is the Menninger Foundation Clinic Library which has one of the finest psychiatric collections in the United States.

Besides these twenty Kansas medical libraries, there are collections located at every hospital in the state accredited by the Joint Commission on Hospital Accreditation. These collections are usually taken care of by the medical records librarian, or by a secretary or clerk. The books are generally old and the journal holdings few and incomplete. There usually is no provision in the hospital budget for the upkeep of the collection. In some cases the county medical society pays for what books and journals are purchased. In general the hospital medical libraries, other than the ones already mentioned, are inadequate and, therefore, seldom used. The medical and health related personnel engaged in the state's health programs are hampered to a great degree by inadequate access to the biomedical literature.

The Kansas Regional Medical Program has realized the difficulties of the Kansas medical libraries and the consequences of their difficulties. Therefore, to help alleviate these difficulties a library project was included in the initial grant request to the Division of Regional Medical Programs. The primary objective of the project was to link the medical library resources in the state so that they effectively become a single library and are readily available to and used by the health-related personnel in Kansas. Soon after receiving the operational grant award in June 1967, an office for Library Services was opened to plan a medical library system to meet the aforementioned objective. The University of Kansas Medical Center is the fiscal agent for the Kansas Regional Medical Program, and therefore most of the KRMP staff is located at the Medical Center. The Office for Library Services is housed at the Clendening Medical Library at the University of Kansas Medical Center. There the staff has access to the largest and most comprehensive medical library collection in the state. KRMP does not have a medical library collection of its own. KRMP uses and augments the collection of the Clendening Medical Library. Another important resource library accessible to the KRMP staff is the Linda Hall Library located in Kansas City, Missouri. The Linda Hall Library has one of the most outstanding basic science collections in the United States.

In conjunction with the opening of the KRMP Office for Library Services in Kansas City, a librarian was placed at the Central Kansas Medical Center, Great Bend, to build a medical library collection and to provide medical library services to the health-related professionals in Great Bend and the surrounding area. There was a small and very inadequate collection at the hospital. The KRMP librarian was given a room in the hospital to house a collection. The physicians provided journals from their own collections, and KRMP and Clendening Medical Library provided journals from an excess collection. KRMP also provided funds to buy a basic reference collection and begin journal subscriptions.

The library offers twenty-four-hour telephone answering service, reference and bibliographic services, and photocopying of articles. Daily contact is kept between the Central Kansas Medical Center and the KRMP Library Services in Kansas City by telephone. Books or photocopies of journal articles not available in Great Bend are sent on the same day as requested by first class United States Mail. Usually the packet arrives in Great Bend the next morning. The mail service has proved very satisfactory for sending items throughout the state.

The KRMP library staff provides medical library services to all the KRMP staff located at the University of Kansas Medical Center. Early in the program, this was one of our major duties. We set up a selective dissemination of information system for the senior staff, provided technical reports from the Clearinghouse for Scientific Technical Information, compiled bibliographies, provided reference services, and photocopied articles. As our services were offered to more and more health professionals in the state, our services to our own staff have decreased as we feel medical library services to the state health professionals our most important job.

Expansion of our services to the state included offering services to the Topeka area. Most of the Topeka medical libraries are primarily psychiatric collections. Therefore, the greatest need was for literature in fields of general medicine and surgery. The only general medical library collection is located at the Stormont Vail Hospital. It was taking ten days to two weeks for interlibrary loans between the Clendening Medical Library and Topeka. An informal agreement was made with the Topeka medical librarians to provide materials to them through the Stormont Medical Library. Daily contact is kept with the librarian at Stormont Medical Library to get requests for books and journals needed by the other medical libraries as well as Stormont. Services KRMP offered include free photocopies of journal articles, lending of books, and reference services. Materials are sent back and forth by a library courier service. On Monday, Wednesday, and Friday the courier runs between Kansas State University in Manhattan to the University of Kansas Medical Center and Linda Hall Library in Kansas City with intermediate stops at the Topeka Public Library and Kansas Historical Society Library, Topeka, and the University of Kansas Libraries, Lawrence. On Tuesday and Thursday this same courier runs between Kansas State University and Wichita State University with an intermediate stop at Kansas State Teachers College at Emporia. This courier service has greatly decreased the interlibrary loan time between the major libraries in the state. Library materials can be transferred between institutions within a few hours.

All materials for the Topeka Medical libraries have to be ready by noon for the return trip of the courier. The packages are left at the Topeka Public Library which is across the street from Stormont Vail Hospital. The local courier from the hospital picks up the material and delivers them to the local medical libraries. This system has greatly facilitated the sending of medical literature between the Clendening Medical Library and the Topeka medical libraries.

Interlibrary loan forms are not necessary for requesting journal articles. All transmission of requests is done by telephone. Although many feel that errors can be made, we have found the errors to be negligible in comparison with the time saved from filling out the forms. Further, verification of the articles is not necessary. If the article is not readily found, which is seldom, the citation is verified by one of the KRMP librarians. If it cannot be verified, the citation is returned to the requesting library to be confirmed with the requester. If the particular journal requested is not available, for instance, lost, checked out, or at the bindery, the requesting library is informed within hours of the request and, if possible, given a few suggestions of where it can be borrowed. This service is provided since many small libraries do not have access to the *Union List of Serials* or *New Serial Titles*.

In requesting books, the requesting library does not need to provide a specific title. The request may be for a book in a subject field and we will send one available from the Clendening collection. If a specific title is requested, one of the KRMP librarians will fill out the interlibrary loan forms and send the book. If the book is not available, the library is informed immediately, sometimes with a suggestion of where it can be borrowed. If the book is in the collection but not available immediately, the library is informed and if the requester can wait, the book is sent later when available. This immediate response about the accessibility of the journal or book has facilitated the interlibrary lending. The borrowing library no longer has to wait for a week to ten days just to find out that the lending library does not have the book. In finding out within minutes, the borrowing library can try elsewhere immediately, thus saving time.

Besides Great Bend and Topeka, services were offered to groups and individuals throughout the state who showed interest or requested services. Collect calls were accepted from individual health practitioners. A few towns were served through the public library but in only one circumstance did this work. In this case, the librarian had had some training in medicine and is familiar with the terminology. In fact, he has a small medical literature collection in the public library for the use of health-related personnel in the town. The other public librarians have an inadequate knowledge of the terminology and the requests that reach us are usually imcomplete. Requests have also been sent by teletype. This method also proved unsuccessful except in the case of requests for specific books and journal articles. But the majority of requests relate to a patient problem, a paper, or a speech. The health practitioner wants a bibliography, current articles, or both. We have found personal contact over the telephone to be much more satisfactory than any other communication media. In most cases the requester is not altogether certain of what he wants, or he is not aware of what is available. On the telephone we can query him directly, and, therefore, send him only material which is pertinent to his request. This direct interaction between the health professional and the medical librarian facilitates answering the request.

In the spring of 1968 a proposal for a Kansas Medical Library System was submitted to the Kansas Regional Advisory Group, passed by that group, and sent to Washington for review by the Regional Medical Program National Advisory Council. It was approved and funded in June 1969. The objectives of the project are as follows: (1) to provide an adequate network so that health personnel would know where they can obtain medical library service and to inform these health personnel about current medical literature available, (2) to help hospital administrators in building or improving medical library collections in the Kansas hospitals, and (3) to inform the medical librarian of what is available in library collections in the state and to receive help in obtaining materials not in the local areas. The proposal included an INWATS (Inward Wide Area Telephone Service) line to the office in Kansas City. (The University of Kansas Medical Center already has two outbound WATS lines which are available for use.) Also part of the proposal was the establishment of field offices in Topeka and Wichita staffed by professional librarians. The responsibilities of these librarians include:

(1) compiling and maintaining a union list of medical serials in those areas,
(2) coordinating an interlibrary network for lending and borrowing material within the area,
(3) coordinating medical library acquisitions in order to maintain a goal of filling 90 percent of the local requests within the area,
(4) aiding health professionals in the area who do not have access to established medical library services,
(5) publicizing the availability of rapid and expanded medical library services,
(6) advising hospitals and clinics on building appropriate medical library collections,
(7) organizing and maintaining a storage collection of less frequently requested medical library materials, and
(8) cooperating with the KRMP library services staff in implementing the objectives of the project.

The Clendening Medical Library has always offered extension services to the health professionals in Kansas but has never had the staff or funds to publicize the service or to offer it widely. KRMP has taken over this extension service and has expanded it. Since the Clendening Medical Library is the major medical resource in the state, the collection is used as a backup for requests that cannot be filled in the local area. The collection will be built up to meet the increased use by the health personnel in the state. All books and journals purchased for the Clendening Medical Library will be fully cataloged and integrated into the collection.

Approximately 60 percent of the Kansas health professionals are located in Topeka, Wichita, Kansas City, and Great Bend where KRMP has staffed and built a medical library collection. The 40 percent of the health personnel not located within a telephone toll-free area of these four cities have available to them the free INWATS line and the services of the KRMP library staff at the Clendening Medical Library. This staff provides free medical library services to any member of the health profession who does not have ready access to such a service. The services include (1) compiling bibliographies on biomedical topics, (2) aiding in submitting requests to MEDLARS, (3) obtaining published bibliographies, (4) obtaining scientific and technical reports, (5) answering reference questions, (6) providing free hard copy of requested articles, (7) lending requested books, and (8) borrowing material not in the area from other libraries.

A trained medical librarian is available Monday through Friday from 8:00 A.M. to 4:30 P.M. to discuss any requests for literature the health professional may have. The INWATS line has a Code-a-Phone attachment which records requests when the office is closed at night, weekends, and holidays. Requests for specific journal articles and books are completed the same day and usually sent to the requester by the next day. Requests for bibliographies or those that require extensive research are completed within two to three days. Another service provided is aid in building or upgrading hospital medical library collections. KRMP does not provide funds, but does provide the expertise of a medical librarian to help any hospital.

Before the Kansas Medical Library System was funded in June 1969, and because of the limited funds of the KRMP library budget, we could not offer medical library services to all the health professionals in the state. Pending approval of the project, we continued to expand and extend services to the state according to the guidelines of the project. By June 1968, we had provided services to health professionals in nineteen towns and by January 1969, to thirty-eight towns. In March 1969, an INWATS line and Code-a-Phone were installed in the Kansas City office and medical library services were offered to the health professionals in twenty Kansas towns.

In June 1969, the project for the Kansas Medical Library System was funded and medical library services were offered to all the health professionals in the state. The Biomedical Library Information Center staffed with a professional librarian and a clerk was set up at the Wichita State University. A similar office is being set up in Topeka. By June 1969, fifty-seven towns were served, and by September, ninety-six. Brochures announcing the offices and the services were sent to health professionals in Kansas. Press releases were sent to the news media. Telephone stickers with our INWATS number were sent to many of the health professions. The illustrations are based on a slide show which was made to show how to use our services and how requests are processed. We hope to meet with the professional staffs of the Kansas hospitals to show the slides and explain our services. Further publicity including television spots is being planned.

The library services staff in Kansas City presently consists of three professional librarians, one semiprofessional, one secretary, and one clerk. We hope to add another librarian and more clerical help as our services expand.

We feel that with this system we have provided a service that is much needed in Kansas. The whole concept has been well received by the health professionals in the state and those people who have used the service have been very appreciative. We hope that in the next year we will be able to inform and educate many more of the health professionals in Kansas about the medical library services of KRMP available to them. The Kansas Medical Library System is not the complete solution to all the problems of the dissemination of biomedical information but it does fill a pressing need of the Kansas health professional. We are continually searching for new technology and new communications media in order to improve our transmission of medical information.

ABOUT THE AUTHOR–Desi Bravo Schaffer is Executive Director, Officer for Library Services, and Project Director, Kansas Medical Library System, Kansas Regional Medical Program, University of Kansas Medical Center. After attending Goucher College and obtaining a B.S. in Chemistry from the University of Kansas, Mrs. Schaffer received her M.L.S. from the University of Pittsburgh. She was a Library Associate at the National Library of Medicine.

Her Medical Library Association activities include membership on its Committee on Regional Medical Programs and Regional Medical Library Programs, and Committee on Internship.

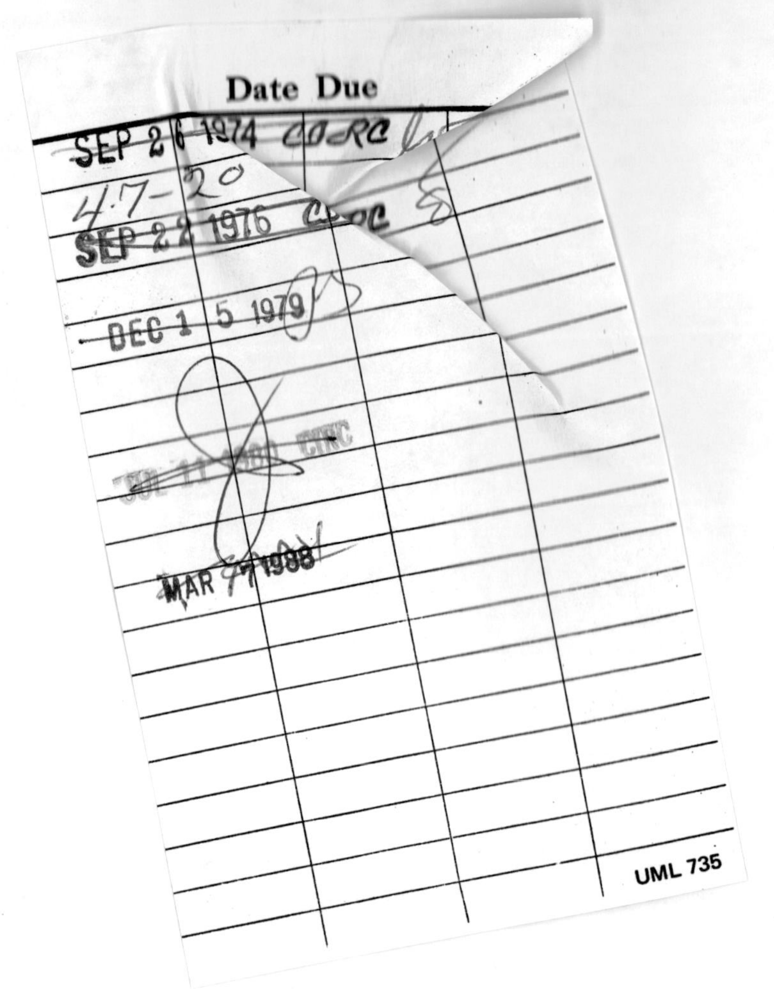